Biotechnology in the Feed Industry

Biotechnology in the Feed Industry

Proceedings of
Alltech's Sixteenth Annual Symposium

Edited by TP Lyons and KA Jacques

NOTTINGHAM
University Press

Nottingham University Press
Manor Farm, Main Street, Thrumpton
Nottingham, NG11 0AX, United Kingdom

NOTTINGHAM

First published 2000

Editor's note: The opinions expressed herein are those of the authors
and do not imply endorsement of any product by the author or any
policy or claim on the part of the Symposium sponsor.

ISBN   1-897676-751

Typeset by Nottingham University Press, Nottingham
Printed and bound by Redwood Books, Trowbridge, Wiltshire, England

Table of Contents

Contents

Section 2: An update on phytase production methods and new applications for the non-GMO phytase

Contents

Section 5: Reducing mycotoxin impact with a low inclusion biological binder

Section 6: Silage science in 2000: improving animal performance

Contents

K.K. Bolsen[1], Mike Wilkinson[2] and C.J. Lin[3]
[1]*Kansas State University, Manhattan, Kansas, USA*
[2]*University of Leeds, Leeds, UK*
[3]*Roanoke City Mills, Roanoke, Virginia, USA*

Section 7: Focus on forage digestion: yeast culture mode of action, rumen-protected enzymes

Karl A. Dawson
North American Biosciences Center, Alltech Inc., Nicholasville Kentucky

J.D. Johnston
Ritchie Feed & Seed, Gloucester, Ontario, Canada

The globalization of the animal feed industry: are we marketing animal feed or human food?

PEARSE LYONS

Alltech Inc., Nicholasville, Kentucky, USA

While the rest of the world rejoiced in millennium–induced fervor, the feed industry took a more serious view of the challenges that lay ahead. This industry—specifically the livestock production and feed milling sectors—has been battered by successive food scares. Consequently, consumers have lost confidence in the animal food industry's ability to provide products that are free of contaminants, pathogenic microorganisms, residues, toxins, and other harmful compounds. Even in countries such as the US that have well-established industry and regulatory agencies, people have become skeptical of food companies. They are being perceived less as benevolent providers of sustenance and more as faceless multinational conglomerates. Therefore, the primary focus of the industry in the new millennium is two-fold: restore consumer confidence and stem media hostilities while positioning itself firmly in the food chain. The good news is that it has the tools to accomplish these important objectives.

The year in review: a continuous challenge

For the past several years, the livestock rearing and feed manufacturing sectors of the food chain have faced major challenges. Many have involved food safety crises in Europe that have reverberated throughout the rest of the world. Many of the problems that occurred in the past are still being addressed today (Table 1). For example, the discovery of bovine spongiform encephalopathy (BSE) in beef cattle during the late 1980s resulted in a ban on the export of beef from the United Kingdom. Now, more than a decade later, Germany and France are maintaining their embargo on UK beef in defiance of the European Union, which lifted its ban on UK beef exports in August of last year. Both countries defended their stance, claiming that UK beef continued to pose a threat to consumer health. In the US, a growing number of cases of antibiotic-resistant pathogens have prompted the Food and Drug Administration to establish a task force to investigate the contribution of the growth-enhancing antibiotics in animal agriculture to the problem.

1

Table 1. A review of 1999.

January
- FDA demands human health impact study for antimicrobials.
- Australia and New Zealand announce strict GMO labeling.
- Switzerland bans antimicrobial growth promoters.
- High concentrations of mycotoxins found in grain in seven southern US states.
- Pollen from Bt corn kills Monarch butterfly larva.
- Pfizer files suit to reverse EU virginiamycin ban.

February
- Canada rejects BST for dairy cows for animal health reasons.
- EU calls for livestock extensification and GMO certification.
- The Netherlands finds *Salmonella enteriditis* in 12% of layer units.
- EU abandons plan to ban use of fish meal in animal feed.
- US proposes labeling for beef exports to EU.
- WVA, IFAP and COMISA: prudent antibiotic use principles.

March
- Swiss expand BSE monitoring with Prionics BSE test.
- US swine integrators Smithfield and Carroll's combine to become the world's largest pork producer.
- UK sets out date-based scheme for EU beef exports.

April
- Virulent Newcastle disease hits NSW, Australia.
- Vietnam stiffens meat inspection.
- Korean cooperatives market selenium-enriched pork.

May
- France opens food safety agency, AFSSA.
- Belgium starts new epidemiological surveillance of cattle.
- EP calls for feed ingredient labeling to aid BSE control.
- Stefane André reports hormones in 12% of hormone-free US beef.

June
- Substantial DNA differences found in resistant *Enterococcus faecium* from chickens and humans.
- Dioxins in Belgium – bans on EU animal produce.
- EU signs up for battery cage ban for 2013.
- EU antimicrobial growth promoter ban in force.

July
- France calls for ban on animal meal in feed.
- US feed giants Cargill and Continental Grain merge,
- AAFCO in US forms a 'nutraceutical/functional foods' task force
- Germany extends pig hygiene law to all producers.

August
- US and EU recognize equivalence in sanitary measures.
- EU lifts ban on UK beef exports.
- Swiss find hormones in hormone-free US beef.
- US FDA proposes Veterinary Feed Directive.
- FDA amends new animal drug regulations.

September
- Germany sets up centralized cattle database for 2000.
- Malaysia levies heavy fines for use of banned antibiotics.
- China regulates feed ingredients.
- EU issues regulation on organic livestock production.
- UK's main poultry producer rejects antibiotic growth promoters.
- EU's FVO notes deficiencies in Brazil's residue controls.

Table 1 (contd.).

October
- Swiss animal movement databank opens for cattle.
- FDA finds detectable levels of dioxin in a majority of clay samples.
- Citizens' group ask US Congress to enact GM foods labeling law.
- FDA issues draft medicated feeds policy for minor species.
- EU postpones beef labeling and proposes food safety agency.

November/December
- France and Germany maintain beef ban.
- Three US cooperatives merge into mega-feed company.
- Canadian food processor refuses GM potatoes.
- Brazil proposes establishing GM-free crop zones.
- US poultry industry commits to eliminating pathogens.
- UK lifts beef-on-the-bone ban in time for Christmas.
- EU lifts dioxin testing for Belgian pork and poultry.

Adapted from Animal Pharm, December, 1999.

Food safety problems have done considerable damage to the international feed industry. In most cases, perception overrode reality. The absence of evidence did not necessarily constitute evidence of absence.

In another interesting shift, food retailers in some countries have taken a proactive role. Supermarkets in the UK and a few other markets have assumed the role of custodians of food safety. They believe that they are in the best position to guarantee the wholesomeness of food. These companies also have a global influence, dictating to meat producers as far away as Brazil and Thailand how animal products they purchase must be fed and reared. Others urge adoption of the organic approach as a marketing strategy. Successful retailers have always achieved their success based on placing the consumer at the heart of their marketing strategies; and agribusiness can be no different.

> **"If a butterfly dies in Iowa, does Wallstreet mourn?**
> **Welcome to the new era of bioagriculture"**
>
> *Kiplingers Investing, January 2000*

Even the stock market responds to consumer concerns. The death of a monarch butterfly from ingesting pollen from a genetically modified corn variety had a disastrous effect on share prices for the seed company. Farm-to-folk-to-finances appears to be the order of the day.

A new food safety furor has erupted over the use of genetically-modified (GM) crops—mainly corn and soybeans—in the production of food. Europeans have been the most vocal in their opposition to GM foods (Figure 1). Several retailers in the UK have prohibited GM ingredients from being

3

Figure 1. New choices for the millennium.

included in their own-label products—including food produced from livestock fed GM grains. This was in spite of the fact that the scientific evidence surrounding GM crop varieties is sound. However, consumers in many parts of the world are expressing their own concerns about the impact that GM foods might have on human health and the environment. For example, in the US, consumer activists petitioned the FDA to create a labeling program for foods that contain GM products. As recently as March of 2000 President Clinton announced that meat from animals fed on GM crops would not be considered organic. Brazil has enacted a moratorium on the approval of GM crops. Japan has approved the importation of a small number of varieties of several GM crops. However, government regulators promised Japanese consumer groups that it would not approve any others.

One reason that consumers are hesitant to accept GM crops is because they do not see the benefits. Most of the traits—herbicide tolerance and insect resistance—are economic advantages to the farmer. These are 'production genes' with no direct advantage for the consumer. However, the consumer must assume a risk, although it may be small. The main argument then is: Why shouldn't the food industry offer consumers a choice when deciding whether to purchase GM foods?

This past year also ushered in the ban of four antibiotic growth promoters in Europe. As the end of the year approached, European Commissioner

David Byrne, on advice from the Scientific Steering Committee, announced that he was considering banning the growth promoter avilamycin. Avilamycin, among others, escaped the original ban because it did not "contribute to the development of resistance to human medicines [or] belong to the antibiotic families authorized in human medicines". Mired in a seemingly relentless series of food crises and facing on-going erosion of consumer confidence, the Commissioner sought to err on the side of political and/or scientific caution.

The feed chain – now the food chain

"Safety is the number 1 ingredient in food"

D. Byrne
EU Commissioner for Public Health
and Consumer Protection

It is not difficult to see which way the wind is blowing in the global market for animal feed. Due to changing regulations, we as an industry are fast moving closer to the food industry in production standards. Feed mills of the future may start to resemble food production plants; biosecure facilities that can guarantee feed is free from contaminants, manufactured from raw materials that meet the highest standards of nutrition and hygiene. Further consolidation of the retail sector promises to usher in a new era of price and margin pressures for suppliers.

The implications for the agribusiness sector are clear. The feed chain is firmly affixed as part of the food chain (Figure 2). The challenge facing us is to accept that the consumer will define what products are acceptable in the food chain and that we must become proactive in our approach to these demands.

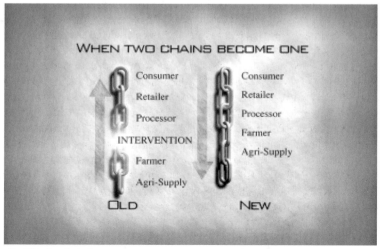

Figure 2. The food chain

Alltech in 2000: scientifically proven solutions

Since its foundation in 1980, Alltech's product development strategy has been guided by the ACE principle, i.e. producing products that are:

*   *Animal*-friendly: scientifically proven to respect livestock welfare and enhance physiological condition through nutrition.

*   *Consumer*-friendly: 100% natural, traceable, non-GM products.

*   *Environmentally*-friendly – products that actively reduce the environmental impact of intensive livestock production through the reduction of both atmospheric emissions and effluents.

For 20 years, Alltech, in partnership with the feed industry, has investigated the major issues facing our industry. Through the forum of Lecture Tours and the annual Alltech Symposium, we have collectively developed new and innovative ideas to respond to both the needs for increased health and productivity in the livestock sector and the growing expectations of the consumer . The following pages summarize progress and describe the goals for six key projects within Alltech.

Scientific projects produce natural solutions: Sel-Plex: organic selenium

Despite routine supplementation with sodium selenite, selenium-deficiency problems are common across the world. Though it is widely known that sodium selenite has limited bioavailability, the narrow margin between requirement and toxicity of the nutrient and the specific toxicity of sodium selenite have prompted strict regulation as to the amount that can be added to feed. In fact, the toxicity of sodium selenite to humans has resulted in bans against its use in certain markets, including Japan – one of many selenium-deficient regions in the world.

Bioavailability and regulatory issues have left the animal feed industry in many parts of the world with seemingly insurmountable problems in getting the necessary amount of selenium into animals. Until the advent of organic selenium, the only selenium supplements for feeds were the highly oxidized sodium selenite and sodium selenate. Selenite or selenate selenium, poorly available to begin with, often interact with compounds in water and (or) digesta to become substantially less available; yet addition of higher amounts to feeds in compensation is restricted. In addition, the highly oxidized nature of the inorganic sources is increasingly being seen as a poor method of supplying the antioxidant selenium nutrient from a biochemical perspective. The inorganic sources are pro-oxidative, which has implications for a number of physiological processes. For example, use of selenite tends to increase post-mortem drip loss from poultry and pig meat.

Sel-Plex selenium yeast helps solve this limitation to production by providing selenium in a much more bioavailable form, i.e. the form in which it naturally occurs in plants. Yeast, like other plants, form selenoamino acids such as selenomethionine. Unlike the highly oxidized selenite, selenoamino acids are in very reduced organic selenide (-2) form, which is the form useful in physiology. Selenomethionine, differing only from methionine by substitution of the selenium for the sulfur atom, is metabolized very differently from inorganic selenium. It is absorbed as the amino acid, and instead of being largely excreted via urine, selenomethionine can be used by any tissue taking up methionine. As a result, total retention of selenium is increased, as is the selenium content of meat, milk and eggs.

In addition, selenoamino acids in muscle tissue form a reserve - supplying selenoamino acids through ongoing catabolism of muscle cells. In all animals protein turnover is constant. In the case of broilers, muscle cell turnover can be as much as 15% per week. Since selenoproteins such as GSH-Px are composed entirely of selenoamino acids, it is critical that selenoamino acids be part of the muscle amino acid profile in order that a reserve be present during stress. During stress periods, when dietary amino acids are in short supply due to low intake or digestive dysfunction, proteosomes recycle muscle protein to provide amino acids for a variety of purposes, including fermentation of selenoproteins (Figure 3).

The selenoamino acid cycle

Proteosomes catabolize proteins thereby releasing amino acids for recycling

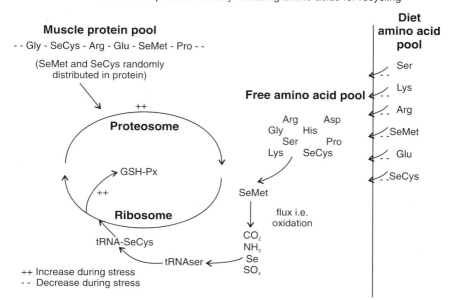

Figure 3. Selenoamino acids are recycled to form critical selenoproteins.

While the value of selenium-rich animal food products has been used to advantage by those marketing specific nutritional or designer foods, the value of organic selenium in animal health and production is of particular note. Substitution of the inorganic selenium with Sel-Plex selenium has resulted in a wide variety of improvements in antioxidant-related response ranging from post-mortem drip loss and meat color to livability of neonates. These factors have wide-ranging impact on animal health, performance and carcass quality (Table 2).

Organic selenium offers a means of supplying sufficient quantities of selenium in metabolizable form without compromising human or animal safety and without the need to add extra-nutritional or extra-legal amounts to feed. The obvious advantages of this alternative to inorganic selenium are becoming apparent to both the livestock feeding industry and regulatory authorities. Already cleared for use in most countries around the world, Sel-Plex has recently completed the FDA food additive petition process in the US and will be marketed in the US beginning in the poultry sector.

Using the yeast cell wall: mannan oligosaccharides and modified cell wall glucan

Viable yeast have always been at the core of many Alltech projects. Products developed using particular strains of yeast include the diet-specific yeast cultures Yea-Sacc[1026] and Yea-Sacc[8417] and biosynthesis of organic selenium (Sel-Plex) and organic chromium (BioChrome). While the ease with which yeast can be grown industrially and the huge variety of strains available are well-suited to finding useful species without the need for genetic modification, the same characteristics have allowed us to explore use of the various fractions of the yeast cell (Figure 4). This exploration includes the variations in cell content and cell wall composition among different strains of Saccharomyces yeast. The result has been development of a number of new products; but even more importantly, it has shown us that the possibilities are limitless.

YEAST CELL WALL MANNAN OLIGOSACCHARIDES: SCIENTIFICALLY PROVEN ALTERNATIVES

Extensive experience with antibiotic growth promoters in all species has given us a general overview of what we need and expect in such an additive:

Pigs: 3-8% faster growth
Calves: lower incidence of digestive disorders, reduced medication use
Poultry: 3-8% improvement in FCR
Physical characteristics: stability during feed processing, mixability with feed ingredients, inert

Table 2. Sel-Plex, selenium status and animal performance: a summary of recent research.

Species and response	Source
Aquaculture	
More bioavailable than inorganic Se for catfish	Wang and Lovell, 1997
Improved flesh color, texture in Atlantic salmon	de Lyons, 1998
Horses	
Higher Se retention, higher blood Se in response to exercise	Pagan *et al.*, 1999
Broilers	
Decreased drip loss	Edens *et al.*, 1996a; Naylor *et al.*, 2000
Increased meat yield	Naylor *et al.*, 2000,
Enhanced feather development	Edens *et al.*, 1996b; 1999;
Decreased ascites, interaction with vitamin E	Roch *et al.*, 2000
Improved performance and/or FCR	Vlahovic *et al.*, 1998; Naylor *et al.*, 2000
Broiler breeders/layers	
Higher egg Se content, increased egg Se associated with higher α-tocopherol content	Cantor, 1997; Paton *et al.*, 1998; Surai and Sparks, 2000a
Egg freshness maintained longer	Wakebe, 1998
Increased Se, vitamin E, reduced GSH and GSH-Px in chicks (with Sel-Plex in the maternal diet).	Surai and Sparks, 2000b
Beef cattle	
Increased whole blood Se and GSH-Px in beef cows and calves	Awadeh *et al.*, 1998a; Pehrson *et al.*, 1999
Increased selenoprotein P	Awadeh *et al.*, 1998b
Higher milk, colostrum Se	Awadeh *et al.*, 1998a; Pehrson *et al.*, 1999
Higher T_3 concentrations in calves at birth	Awadeh *et al.*, 1998a
Dairy cattle	
Higher milk Se	Fisher *et al.*, 1995; Ortman and Pehrson, 1997; Knowles *et al.*, 1999; Hemken *et al.*, 1998
Higher blood Se, GSH-Px	Fisher *et al.*, 1995; Ortman and Pehrson, 1997; Hemken *et al.*, 1998
Sheep	
Improved Se status of ewes at parturition	Hughes *et al.*, 1998
Sows and piglets	
Improved sow Se status	Mahan and Kim, 1996; Mahan, 2000
Increased milk and colostrum Se	Mahan and Kim, 1996; Mahan, 2000
Improved piglet Se status at birth, weaning	Mahan and Kim, 1996; Mahan, 2000
Grow/finish pigs	
Better Se retention, higher tissue Se content, GSH-Px in grow/finish pigs	Mahan and Parrett, 1996;
No pro-oxidative effect in meat, improved meat color	Mahan *et al.*, 1999
Reduced lumbar fat thickness, higher loin eye area	Wolter *et al.*, 1999

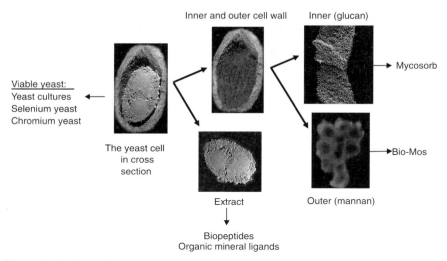

Figure 4. Products of the yeast cell.

In a review of data published on effects of antimicrobial growth promoters, Rosen found that 72% of trials were successful (personal communication). When the search was on for scientific alternatives, the same criteria needed to be satisfied. Investigation of phosphorylated mannan oligosaccharides revealed that these complex carboyhydrates derived from cell walls of certain yeast strains exceeded these requirements. In a wide spectrum of trials, both in research and under commercial conditions, results have shown that subtle changes in the carbohydrate profile of the diet can often have an impact not unlike adding antibiotic growth promoters (Table 3). Bio-Mos has proved efficacious in ~80% of all animal studies; a rate that compares favorably with antibiotics. Furthermore, the product is extremely stable, surviving autoclave temperatures. Bio-Mos is now included as a standard ingredient in many pig and poultry diets around the world; and as our information base grows, we are increasing our understanding of how to maximize its applications.

ESTERIFIED CELL WALL GLUCOMANNAN: MYCOTOXIN ADSORBENTS

Animal feed ingredients, storage bins and transfer equipment frequently present the proper conditions for mold growth; and it is recognized that mycotoxin problems exist in all parts of the world. Alltech has an ongoing commitment to finding ways to reduce animal performance losses due to mycotoxins in stored feed. This commitment is expressed both through supporting university/institute research that seeks to define the nature of mold toxins and toxicity and through projects underway in Alltech laboratories

Table 3. Bio-Mos comparison with antibiotic growth promoters in poultry.

Comparison with:	Research or commercial condition, country	Response: Bio-Mos vs antibiotic growth promoter
Avilamycin[1]	3 flocks of 90,000 commercial broilers grown to 39 days in Britain	Flock 1: FCR: 1.699 vs 1.695; EPEF: 297 vs 294 Flock 2: FCR: 1.75 vs 1.69; EPEF: 294 vs 303 Flock 3: FCR: 1.74 vs 1.7; EPEF: 288 vs 312
Avilamycin*	4720 commercial turkey toms grown to 16 weeks in France	Liveweight 8 wks (g): 3756 vs 3673 Liveweight 16 weeks (g): 11780 vs 12247 Mortality (%): 2.80 vs 4.24
Zn bacitracin*	broiler research (500 birds) grown to 42 days in the Phillipines	Gain (g): 1894 vs 1839 FCR 1.849 vs 1.866
Virginiamycin[2]	broiler research (3500 straight run birds) grown to 42 days in the US	Liveweight (kg): 2.312 vs 2.32 FCR: 1.842 vs 1.827
Bambermycin*	commercial broilers (240 birds) grown to 42 days in Canada	Liveweight (kg): 2.775 vs 2.717 FCR 1.641 vs 1.637
BMD*	broiler research (720 birds) grown to 49 days in the US, stress environment	Liveweight (kg): 2.51 vs 2.58 FCR: 1.815 vs 1.830 Mortality (%): 4.58 vs 5.42

[1]No negative control.
[2]Both Bio-Mos and antibiotic numerically (NS) improved performance relative to negative control
*Both Bio-Mos and antibiotic improved performance relative to negative control.

exploring ways to minimize mycotoxin impact. Mycosorb, a derivative of yeast glucan, is the result of efforts to identify natural compounds that bind mycotoxins. Modifications such as esterification enable us to take greater advantage of the natural porosity of the yeast cell wall glucomamman to adsorb toxins. In cooperation with ETH in Switzerland, adsorption capacity for zearalenone of raw glucan was increased from 2 mg/g to 80 mg/g in Mycosorb, the finished product. Now patented, Mycosorb has proven to successfully bind aflatoxins and fusariotoxins, including T-2 toxin. Binding of T-2 toxin can be as high as 3 mg/g of glucan. Because Mycosorb binding ability is specific, inclusion rates are low in feed and the absorption of other nutrients is not blocked.

Current projects include development of increasingly specific derivations of Mycosorb, *in vitro* assays of binding ability, and work to define solutions to the ergot toxins that cause fescue toxicity and ryegrass staggers. In practical trials, the breakthrough in toxin binding is reflected in improved performance. The lesson appears to be that 1) we have a global problem with mycotoxins, and 2) the esterified glucomannan provides part of the solution.

Extracting new benefits from yeast cell contents

For every ton of yeast, there exists about half a ton of yeast extract, the cell contents of the yeast. Yeast extracts are concentrates of the soluble part of yeast cells following removal of the cell material. This can be accomplished by autolysis (using the enzymes present in the cell) or by hydrolysis (enzymatic or acid). Yeast extracts are used primarily in the fermentation industry as growth substrates or in the food industry as flavor enhancers. The free amino acid content is typically 35-40%; and in addition, there are substantial amounts of small molecular weight (<600 Daltons) peptides (Figure 5) and water-soluble vitamins.

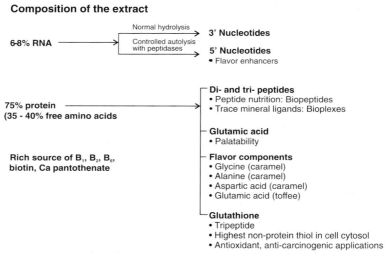

Figure 5. Uses of yeast extract fractions.

The predominant amino acids are glutamic and aspartic acids, both of which lend yeast extract useful characteristics in flavoring agents. Yeast extracts are used in a wide variety of familiar applications including the flavor base of food products such as soups, gravies and sauces as well as microbial growth medium in microbiology. Yeast extracts are valued for their ability to enhance flavors and to mask sour and bitter tastes. During autolysis RNA is broken down into 3´ nucleotides. These nucleotides do not have flavor enhancing characteristics. During enzymatic hydrolysis of yeast, 5´ nucleotides of guanine, adenine, cytosine, and uracil are formed. Only the 5´GMP (guanine) and 5´IMP (inosine) have flavor enhancing ability. By adding an enzyme the 5´AMP can be converted to 5´IMP.

The 5´IMP and 5´GMP enhance flavors and suppress bitterness. By adding these two components to the amino acids, peptides and reaction products already formed, a variety of flavor enhancing properties are obtained. The possibility of developing new flavors based on yeast nucleotides in order to avoid use of MSG has interesting applications in pet food formulations, as well as human food applications.

BIOPEPTIDES FOR ANIMAL FEEDS: REDUCE NITROGEN POLLUTION, PROVIDE NON-MAMMALIAN PROTEIN

Until now, use of such extracts as sources for biopeptides for animal feeds was cost-prohibitive. Today the explosion in use of glucans and mannans has allowed Alltech to offer these extracts to the feed industry. Initially, studies with broiler chicks during the first 7-14 days have shown improvements in feed intake and reductions in mortality. Total replacement of plasma proteins in pig starter diets is possible leading to a savings of 3-5 days to slaughter. Potential uses in aquaculture are also being explored. Indeed a problem, loss of mammalian protein sources, has been transformed into an opportunity – non-GMO high quality protein.

BIOPLEX TRACE MINERALS: DIFFERENT METABOLISM ROUTES

Faster growth rates of meat chickens and pigs, higher reproductive potential in sows and higher production in general have demanded increased ability to extract nutrients from feed. In response to this, researchers went to great lengths to alter energy and protein availability while little attention was given trace element nutrition. Recommended inclusion rates have changed very little; and until recently few studies had investigated effects of mineral forms. As a result, lack of copper, manganese, iron and zinc, critical nutrients for immunity and reproduction, can render animals more susceptible to disease or reproductive dysfunction.

The Bioplex proteinates were designed to more closely simulate the forms in which trace elements naturally occur in plants. Because these nutrient forms are digested and metabolized by different routes than the inorganic oxides and sulfates, mineral retention by the body is higher. Tissue stores can accumulate against periods of peak demand; and adequate amounts can be transferred to the fetus without placing maternal health or subsequent fertility at risk.

Emphasis has been placed on exploring health and reproductive benefits that occur in response to Bioplexes. The practical impact of Bioplex trace mineral forms in dairy cattle diets has been demonstrated in a variety of studies revealing lower mastitis incidence at calving and reduced somatic cell counts in response to improved mineral status. A long term study with sows has recently shown that Bioplex mineral forms have an impact on the reproductive potential of the sow and her longevity in the herd (see chapter by Fehse and Close, this volume).

An equally important benefit of increased mineral retention is reduced trace mineral content of manure. Growing concern about trace minerals in soil profiles is leading pig and poultry researchers to explore use of Bioplexes to allow lower total diet trace mineral content, particularly where high levels of inorganics are used as growth promotants.

ENZYMES: NEW PRODUCTION TECHNOLOGIES, NEW APPLICATIONS

In response to the feed industry's need for non-GMO enzymes, process development at Alltech has focused on appropriate technologies. The result has been the re-emergence of the 'Koji' system of solid state fermentation (Figure 6). Alltech's new manufacturing plant in Serdan, Mexico is currently equipped to produce phytase, xylanases and proteases, all of similar activity to GM-derived enzymes, but with none of the negative connotations. The new plant has the capacity to produce enough enzyme to treat 95 million tons of feed – a fifth of total world animal feed production. Indeed, as we have revisited the old science and applied new technology to the process, we found that our new phytase enzyme is more stable than its GM counterpart and has a much broader range of activity.

In the area of new enzyme applications, we have also been able to sufficiently protect a fiber-digesting enzyme to allow it to be effective in the rumen. The net result has been improved productivity using the farm's cheapest raw material, namely forage. Improvements in milk yield of 1-2 liters per day are consistently observed.

Beyond 2000

"A new scientific truth that does not triumph by convincing its opponents, but rather because its opponents die and the new generation grows up that is familiar with it."

Max Planck

How fast can we adjust our organizations to respond to new challenges and opportunities? In the 1940s and 1950s we perhaps, as Max Planck said, could wait for the opposition to die - however not in the cyberworld where speed is of the essence. Within three years, it is expected that 15% of US households will be purchasing all food via the internet. Are we willing to accept these challenges and become proactive in our approach to meeting consumer demands? The successful feed company of the future will face the reality of today's marketplace and view itself as a link in the food chain (Table 4). If we expect our businesses to grow, we cannot afford to wait until specific technologies such as genetic engineering of food crops become accepted in succeeding generations. We must develop effective and marketable processes and put them into practice - now.

Alltech, a family of 600 people now present in 65 countries, has set itself the task of multiplying sales five-fold. An important part of this effort will

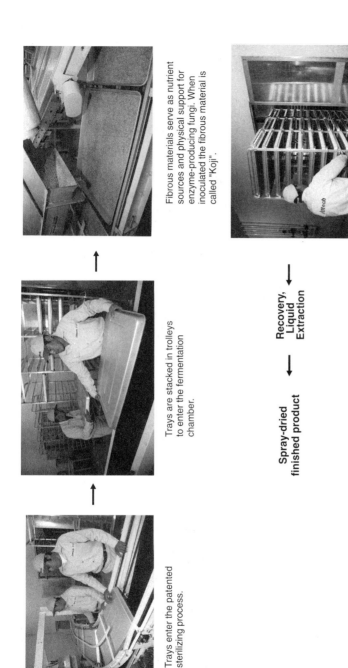

Trays enter the patented sterilizing process.

Trays are stacked in trolleys to enter the fermentation chamber.

Fibrous materials serve as nutrient sources and physical support for enzyme-producing fungi. When inoculated the fibrous material is called "Koji".

Trays enter the fermentation chamber where environmental conditions are maintained for optimum enzyme production.

Spray-dried finished product

Recovery, Liquid Extraction

Figure 6. Flow diagram of the Koji solid state fermentation process.

Table 4. The successful feed company of the future.

- Sees itself as part of the human food chain.
- Is 100% transparent: open to consumer scrutiny.
- Is in business to stay in business: knows that animal production will always be a part of our lives; and as such will always represent opportunity.
- Knows it is not the feed company's job to educate the consumer about antibiotics.
- Understands that the feed company's job is to provide the food animal producer with safe and technically effective nutritional products that help meet the modern definition of safe and nutritious food.

bring to the table 140-180 new M.Sc and Ph.D. students, all of whom will focus on problems facing modern animal production. Through the forums of the Lecture Tour Series and the annual Symposium, information transfer is facilitated; and through a partnership approach, new solutions to the demands of the marketplace are discovered. Success, as always, awaits those with the foresight and flexibility to respond quickly and effectively to these demands.

References

Animal Pharm. 1999. PJB Publications Ltd.

Awadeh, F.T., R.L. Kincaid and K.A. Johnson. 1998a. Effect of level and source of dietary selenium on concentrations of thyroid hormones and immunoglobulins in beef cows and calves. J. Anim. Sci. 76:1204-1215.

Awadeh, F.T., M.M. Abdelrahman, R.L. Kincaid and J.W. Finley. 1998b. Effect of selenium supplements on the distribution of selenium among serum proteins in cattle. J. Dairy Sci. 81:1089-1094.

Cantor, A.H. 1997. The role of selenium in poultry nutrition. In: Biotechnology in the Feed Industry (T.P. Lyons and K.A. Jacques, eds.), Nottingham University Press, Nottingham, UK. pp. 155-164.

de Lyons, M.S. 1998. Organic selenium as a supplement for Atlantic salmon: effects on meat quality. In: Biotechnology in the Feed Industry (T.P. Lyons and K.A. Jacques, eds) Proceedings of the 14th Annual Symposium Nottingham University Press, Nottingham, UK.

Edens, F.W., T.A. Carter and A.E. Sefton. 1996a. Influence of dietary selenium sources on post mortem drip loss from breast meat of broilers grown on different litters. Poultry Sci. 75(Suppl. 1):60.

Edens, F.W., T.A. Carter and A.E. Sefton. 1996b. Improved feathering with dietary organic Se and its modification due to litter material. 1996b. Poultry Sci. 75(Suppl. 1):114.

Edens, F.W. C.R. Parkhurst and G.B. Havenstein. 1999. Effects of conventional *vs* cage housing and inorganic *vs* organic selenium on feathering in broilers. Poultry Sci. 78(Suppl. 1):133.

Fisher, D.D., S.W. Saxton, R.D. Elliot and J.M. Beatty. 1995. Effects of selenium source and Se status of lactating cows. Veterinary Clinical Nutrition 2(2):68.

Hemken, R.W., R.J. Harmon and S. Trammell. 1998. Selenium for dairy cattle: a role for organic selenium. In: Biotechnology in the Feed Industry, Proceedings of the 14th Annual Symposium (T.P. Lyons and K.A. Jacques, eds.) Nottingham University Press, Nottingham, UK pp 497-503.

Hughes, D., S. Kenyon and K.A. Jacques. 1998. Selenium yeast improves selenium status of Welsh ewes. Poster presented at the 6th International Symposium on the Uses of Selenium and Tellurium, Selenium-Tellurium Development Association, May 10-12,1998, Scottsdale, AZ, USA

Knowles, S.O., N.D. Grace, K. Wurms and J. Lee. 1999. Significance of amount and form of dietary selenium on blood, milk and casein selenium concentrations in grazing cows. J. Dairy Sci. 82:429-437.

Mahan, D.C. 2000. Effect of organic and inorganic selenium sources and levels on sow colostrum and milk selenium content. J. Anim. Sci. 2000 78:100-105.

Mahan, D.C. and Y.Y. Kim. 1996. Effect of inorganic or organic selenium at two dietary levels on reproductive performance and tissue selenium concentrations in first parity gilts and their progeny. J. Anim. Sci 74:2711-2718.

Mahan, D.C. and N.A. Parrett. 1996. Evaluating the efficacy of Se-enriched yeast and sodium selenite on tissue Se retention and serum GSH-Px activity in grower and finisher swine. J. Anim. Sci. 74:2967-2974.

Mahan, D.C., T.R. Cline and B. Richert. 1999. Effects of dietary levels of selenium-enriched yeast and sodium selenite as selenium sources fed to grower-finishing pigs on performance, tissue selenium, serum glutathione peroxidase activity, carcass characteristics and loin quality. J. Anim. Sci. 77:2172-2179.

Naylor, A.J., M. Choct and K.A. Jacques. 2000. Effects of selenium source and level on performance, mortality and meat quality in male broilers. Poster presented at Southern Poultry Science, Atlanta, Georgia, Jan. 17-18.

Ortman, K. and B. Pehrsen. 1997. Selenite and selenium yeast as feed supplements for dairy cows. J. Vet. Medicine A 44:373-380.

Pagan, J.D., M.A.P. Kennedy, T. Currier and K.E. Hoekstra. 1999. Effect of selenium source on selenium digestibility and retention in exercised Thoroughbreds. Proceedings, 16th Annual Equine Nutrition and Physiology Symposium, Raleigh, NC, June 2-5, 1999. 135-140.

Paton, N.D., A.H Cantor, M.J. Ford, B.T. Slaugh, A.F. Rizvi, and T.P. Karnezos. 1998. Effect of providing organic selenium and chromium as yeast in laying hen diets on nutrient composition of eggs. Poultry Sci. 77(Suppl. 1):11.

Pehrson, B., K. Ortman, N. Madjid and U. Trafikowska. 1999. The influence of dietary selenium as selenium yeast or sodium selenite on the concentration of selenium in the milk of suckler cows and on the selenium status of their calves. J. Anim. Sci. 77:3371-3376.

Roch, G. M. Boulianne and L. de Roth. 2000. Effects of dietary vitamin E and selenium source on incidence of ascites, growth performance and blood glutathione peroxidase in cold-stressed broilers. Poster presented at Southern Poultry Science, Atlanta, Georgia, January 17-18.

Surai, P.F. and N.H.C. Sparks. 2000a. Effect of the selenium content of the maternal diet on the antioxidant system of the yolk. Proceedings, Winter Meeting, British Society of Animal Science, Scarborough, UK, March 20-22.

Surai, P.F. and N.H.C. Sparks. 2000b. Effect of the selenium content of the maternal diet on the antioxidant system of the newly-hatched chick. Proceedings, Winter Meeting, British Society of Animal Science, Scarborough, UK, March 20-22.

Vlahovic, M., Z. Pavlovski, B. Zivkovic, M. Lukic and G. Marinkov. 1998. Influence of different selenium sources on broiler performance. Yugoslav Poultry Science, Vol. 3:3-4.

Wang, C. and R.T. Lovell. 1997. Organic selenium sources, selenomethionine and selenoyeast, have higher bioavailability than an inorganic selenium source, sodium selenite, in diets for channel catfish (*Ictalurus punctatus*). Aquaculture 1522.

Wakebe, M. 1998. Feed for meat chickens and feed for laying hens. Japanese Patent Office, Application Heisei 8-179629. Published Jan. 27.

Wolter, B., M. Ellis, F.K. McKeith, K.D. Miller and D.C. Mahan. 1999. Influence of dietary selenium source on growth performance and carcass and meat quality characteristics in pigs. 1999. Canadian J. Anim. Sci. Vol. 79(No. 1):119-121.

Supermarkets: powerful consumer advocates. How they came to dominate British, European, Thai and Japanese animal production. Implications for the rest of the world

JON RATCLIFF

Food and Agriculture Consultancy Services, Banbury, Oxon, UK

Introduction

A few years ago, it would have been unlikely that a presentation focusing on supermarkets would have been included in a meeting devoted to animal nutrition. Today, supermarkets are a major influence on animal production throughout the world, and as such are likely to influence many of the future trends in production and nutrition. An explanation of why supermarkets have become such powerful consumer advocates and what happened to bring about the involvement of supermarkets in the animal production and feed industries is the aim of this paper.

Without information, choice has no value. Without choice, information has no relevance

Supermarkets are driven by their customers. They need to create value and loyalty while providing sufficient information and choice. Consumers are becoming increasingly well informed and articulate when it comes to making choices about food. Issues such as quality, safety and integrity are increasingly important factors in consumer decision-making; and guarantees regarding such issues can only be delivered through assured traceability once standards are established. The process of due diligence is fundamental to the relationship between the supermarket and its customers. Given recent events in the food safety arena, it is not surprising that the major supermarkets are no longer prepared to entrust this responsibility to the food and feed industries (Cooke, 2000).

Food safety and the demand for accountability

During the past ten years, consumer confidence in the European feed manufacturing and livestock industries has all but collapsed due to a series of high profile food scares. The most recent of these scares, dioxin contamination of animal feed in Belgium, only served to highlight the ineffectiveness of self regulation and strengthen the deep distrust felt by most European consumers toward political efforts to regulate food safety. Many consumers now perceive the supermarkets as the enforcers of food safety.

Nowhere was food safety more of an issue than in the United Kingdom in the late 1980s. Bovine spongiform encephalopathy (BSE) in beef and salmonella in eggs hit the headlines and consumer attention worldwide focused upon the role of the animal feed industry in the human food chain. The political response to the BSE and salmonella problems was inept; and not surprisingly, consumers demanded a greater control over production methods and food safety. European supermarkets were exposed to the damage caused by the food scares and the subsequent decline in sales of beef and eggs. Consequently, the major British supermarkets were no longer prepared to allow the livestock and feed industries to operate without accountability. Acting in the 'interest of the consumer' a series of controls and regulations (codes of practice) were implemented throughout the supply chain in order to restore consumer confidence and reverse the steep decline in sales. The success of this response is clearly illustrated in the UK, where consumption of beef per capita is now higher than in the period prior to the BSE crisis. Consequently, the production of livestock within Europe for meat, milk and eggs has rapidly changed from a farmer-led industry to a supermarket-led industry.

SUPERMARKETS PERCEIVED AS THE ETHICAL DECISION MAKERS

European consumers viewed the supermarkets as sympathetic allies with the resources to elicit change. Supermarkets, in turn, realised that by taking the lead on such issues as animal welfare and food safety, the strength and image of their brand name (and hence customer loyalty) were enhanced. In the absence of a political lead, the British supermarkets in particular became very proactive throughout the supply chain, making decisions on systems of production and feed ingredients and other aspects of formulation.

In the 1980s animal welfare was gaining widespread publicity thanks to an increasingly vocal and effective lobby group throughout Europe. Issues such as sow stalls and tethers and battery cage production of eggs were high on the agenda, but politicians were slow to react to the feelings of the public. British supermarkets were able to introduce wide-ranging codes of practice sympathetic to the welfare agenda addressing areas such as maximum stocking densities and handling of animals, which gained favourable media attention. It was these codes of practice that led to the move toward more extensive systems of animal production such as the housing of sows outdoors and free range egg production. Since that time, the race to be seen as 'acting on behalf of the consumer' has not stopped. The leading supermarkets continue to monitor consumer attitudes toward sensitive issues and take any steps necessary to maintain confidence in the quality and safety of their products. An indication of some of the areas of animal and feed production in the UK where codes of practice have an impact are given in Tables 1 and 2.

Table 1. Welfare issues regulated by some of the supermarkets in the UK.

Tail docking/castration - pigs
Sow stalls and tethers
Sick animal treatment/disposal
Hard flooring - pigs
Beak trimming – poultry
Toe clipping – poultry
Comb dubbing - breeders
24 hour lighting programmes
Restricted water supply
Feed restrictions, e.g. no skip-a-day
A.I. – turkeys
Leg weakness

Table 2. Feed ingredient restrictions associated with supermarkets in the UK.

Exclusion of meat and bone meal, poultry offal and feather meal, blood meal
Exclusion of animal fat
Restricted use of recovered vegetable oils
Salmonella codes of practice for poultry
Maximum drug residue levels in meat and eggs
Restrictions on the prophylactic and therapeutic use of medication in the water and in the feed
Exclusion of canthaxanthin from layer feeds
Exclusion of fish meal from some layer feeds
Maximum permitted levels of mycotoxins, pesticide residues, heavy metals and dioxins
Exclusion of antibiotic growth promoters in broiler feeds
Segregation and exclusion of genetically modified raw materials

Political inertia prompted European supermarkets to make policy decisions on sensitive issues on behalf of their customers ranging from the feeding of animal by-products to use of genetically modified (GM) feed ingredients and antibiotic growth promoters (AGPs). This leadership caused the supermarkets to be seen as the 'ethical decision makers' championing the rights of the consumer against the large multinational agri-businesses, many of which are perceived as being out of step with public opinion. That the term 'ethical' has entered the food issue vernacular is a clear indication of the judgemental tone of the debate. American Minister Counsellor Thomas Hamby, from the American Embassy in London recently acknowledged this terminology when he referred to the task of "reconciling free trade with ethical production".

Consumer perception is the reality

It is important to understand the role that perception plays in this process and how this is likely to influence future attitudes toward production and feeding of livestock. Ever since the UK government made a statement in the late 1980s about the potential contamination of all eggs with salmonella, the media began to promote the image of a feed industry sadly lacking control. The feed industry response in the UK was to continue to defend the policy of not providing customers with a full and open declaration of feed ingredients. At the time of the salmonella and BSE crises it was not a legal requirement for feed compounders to declare the ingredients on the bag label or bill of sale. Suspicions grew, consumer confidence fell and the public image of the feed industry was severely tarnished.

By the early 1990s, publicity surrounding BSE, welfare issues and doubts about certain feed additives continued to provide the media with shock headlines that reinforced negative perceptions about the feed industry in Europe. In reality the European feed industry has made significant progress in the past few years through the implementation of Good Manufacturing Practice (GMP) and Hazard Analysis Critical Control Point (HACCP) strategies together with the more recent adoption of feed assurance schemes that encompass raw material supply through to delivery on farm. However, the Greenpeace advertising campaign against genetically modified raw materials in animal feed underscores the fact that the industry is still being portrayed as out of step with consumer concerns. The feed industry continues to fail to recognise that its customers are not only farmers, but also the public at large who purchase food animal and other agricultural products.

The EU experience demonstrates that consumer perception frequently bears little relation to scientific evidence. Whether it is AGPs or GM foods, there is always an army of experts including scientists, physicians, researchers, food specialists and microbiologists to provide conflicting information, increase concerns, raise alarms and contribute to media hype. The media have effectively helped to produce a society that is extremely suspicious of scientific experts, particularly those that represent government or industry. One UK politician recalled that when he visited Monsanto some years ago, he was told "we have 900 PhDs working here – that's why we are convinced we are right."

As we enter the 21st century, the reality is that in many cases the scientific argument has been lost. Consumers are more likely to take notice of supermarkets and journalists than they are of scientific committees. Within the EU and particularly the UK, the food agenda is being firmly managed by the supermarkets. Their policies will reflect consumer attitudes and perceptions in an effort to provide a guarantee of food safety.

LEGISLATION *VS.* CONSUMER-DRIVEN SUPPLIER STANDARDS

At this point it is appropriate to ask why EU legislation has not been sufficient to preclude the need for supermarkets to start implementing their own rules and standards relating to the production and feeding of animals. To answer this question it is interesting to look at the fundamental difference between how the US and EU regulate and respond to matters of food safety. In the US the Food and Drug Administration (FDA) and United States Department of Agriculture (USDA) are responsible for screening products and providing answers to consumers on all issues relating to food safety. The FDA is effectively one body, providing a definitive response to each individual consumer issue ranging from hormone implants to genetically modified organisms (GMO). Most importantly, the FDA is generally perceived by US consumers to be acting in their interest.

Despite the recent appointment of a Directorate General for Health and Consumer Protection, the EU has no such organisation capable of representing all the individual member states. The EU is comprised of fifteen member states each with their own agencies responsible for food safety. Consequently, we often find conflicting opinions expressed to the media based upon each country's particular political agenda. Nowhere is this more apparent than in the response to the proposed lifting of the ban on British beef by individual EU countries. The EU Commission ruled that British beef is safe and that the ban should be lifted, but individual countries are still refusing to comply.

In addition, the credibility of individual governments within the EU has been severely dented as a result of their handling of food safety issues. This is particularly true of the UK government due to the inadequacy of its response to the BSE crisis and the Belgian government for its handling of the dioxin scandal. It is within this political vacuum that the supermarkets have been able to extend their influence throughout Europe.

BEYOND EUROPE

The thrust toward consumer protection is not confined to Europe. Japan has long been recognised as a leader in such areas as food safety (Suzuki and Kashima, 1998). Concerns about antibiotic resistance have been recognised for many years and a high proportion of meat supplied to Japan must now be specified antibiotic free. Rigorous tests are carried out by the Japanese authorities on all imported food products. This has had a knock-on effect in other Asian countries actively seeking to export food products to Japan. In Thailand, a number of poultry companies are now rearing broilers without any additives, including in-feed coccidiostats, specifically for the Japanese market. Tests for the presence of residues are carried out at around 30 days of age and at slaughter.

The influence of supermarkets in Asia is not limited to the requirements of export markets. Since purchase of the Lotus chain of supermarkets in Thailand, the British supermarket chain Tesco has committed itself to further expansion into Southeast Asia. Seventy five percent of new Tesco store space is now outside of the UK; and by the end of next year 36% of total retail space will be outside the UK. No doubt Tesco will wish to introduce western styles of producer control in an effort to establish brand identity and differentiation. It remains to be seen how readily Asian consumers respond to this style of marketing.

Eastern Europe has also seen recent rapid expansion by western supermarkets such as Marks and Spencer, Tesco and Auchan. Czech Republic, Poland and Hungary are having to face the reality of western food standards as they prepare to become members of an expanded European Community.

Another potential source of influence, although in reverse, may be seen following the takeover of British supermarket chain ASDA by the US retail giant Walmart. It remains to be seen whether issues sensitive to British consumers start to influence Walmart policy in the US.

The global market – implications for the rest of the world

Consumer concerns do not stop at products produced within national boundaries; and therefore the policy-making activity of supermarkets is not restricted to the countries within which they operate. Sourcing of food products throughout the world is now an established practice and has led to the concept of the 'global market'. In reality, what this means is that sophisticated refrigeration and transport systems make it possible to source food products from virtually anywhere in the world. To the supermarkets, the essential criterion is consistency - not just in quality but also in standards of animal and feed production. Consumers want assurance that all imported products are produced to the standards established for home-grown products. Supermarkets and governments within Europe have come under considerable pressure to ensure that the welfare and production standards applied to indigenous products apply equally to imported products. Consequently, the codes of practice implemented by supermarkets throughout Europe are applied to suppliers throughout the world. To emphasise the influence supermarkets in the UK have on the export market, one only need to look at the change in the percentage of animal products sold through the major retailers during the past 15 years (Table 3).

Table 3. Percent of products sold by supermarkets within the UK.*

	1985	1993	1998
Beef and veal	27	50	70
Lamb	26	41	60
Pork	30	53	72
Bacon	43	62	78
Poultry	47	57	75
Eggs	n/a	n/a	74
Liquid milk**	18	43	65

*Source: Meat and Livestock Commission, British Egg Information Service, British Poultry Meat Federation, Dairy Industry Council.
** England and Wales

The poultry industry is probably the most advanced sector of the meat industry as far as the global market is concerned. Exports to Europe from Brazil and

Thailand have more than doubled in the past 12 months. The media in Europe has highlighted consumer concerns resulting from sourcing such large volumes of product beyond its boundaries. The response of the EU parliament has been to send veterinary delegations to monitor and report on the poultry industries in countries such as Brazil and Thailand.

For the supermarkets, sending out veterinary delegations is not a sufficiently reliable means of ensuring that standards are met. In order to meet the standards expected of their customers, the major supermarkets apply and audit their own codes of practice covering all aspects of feed manufacture and processing. These audit systems are the definitive due diligence process designed to provide the 'guarantees' demanded by their customer base. The major poultry integrators in countries such as Thailand and Brazil have set up dedicated export operations specifically for the European market.

Because of the high profile of supermarkets in Europe, they come under intense scrutiny from farmers, consumers and politicians on such issues as traceability and labelling. The supermarkets are now turning that attention to the catering section, which until now has escaped the same level of scrutiny.

The influence of the supermarkets can be observed across the world. Most countries outside Europe are already assessing strategies in relation to antibiotic growth promoters and GM feed ingredients. Activities and legislation in one country can create major media attention throughout the world. The advent of the internet has reduced the concept of the global market to the level of the individual consumer. Not surprisingly, environmental, welfare and activist groups are therefore quick to pick up on sensitive issues in any part of the world. Likewise, global food companies such as McDonalds and KFC are under pressure to adopt issues of production ethics and apply standards worldwide.

At the recent World Trade Organisation talks in Seattle, the stumbling block between the US and EU was the right of individual countries to legislate against the import of foodstuffs determined not safe for consumers, even when the scientific evidence may be to the contrary. Examples include beef hormones, antibiotic growth promoters and GM technology. More recent statements by US officials indicate a softening of the stance on such issues as GM technology; since unless the US modifies its position, it could continue to be precluded from trade with Europe and many other countries worldwide.

Antibiotic growth promoter ban

The response of the British supermarkets to AGPs and GM ingredients may well set the trend for many other countries. The EU ban on avoparcin in 1997 was a clear signal that politicians were beginning to take seriously consumer concerns surrounding the potential risk of the transfer of antibiotic resistance from animals to humans arising from in-feed antibiotic growth promoters, despite the conclusions of the SCAN report (SCAN, 1996). The ban was extended by the EU in 1998 to include tylosin phosphate, zinc bacitracin, spiramycin and virginiamycin, leaving only avilamycin and bambermycin the only two growth promoters currently registered for use in pigs and poultry.

Despite the EU Commissioner for Consumer Affairs, David Byrne, repeating his concern about the usage of AGPs and signalling their likely ban in Europe within two years, certain retailers, including the UK's largest and most influential supermarket group, Tesco, have taken their own lead by implementing a complete ban on AGPs in broiler feeds. This has come on the back of a number of significant developments in Europe within the past few years.

Firstly, Sweden and Denmark implemented voluntary bans on AGPs in 1986 and 1997, respectively. Their experience has been well documented (Inborr, 2000) and demonstrated that the impact on animal performance and health was less than expected. Their strategy not only focused on alternative products but the type of in-feed coccidiostat used (ionophore or chemical), stocking density, ventilation, hygiene standards, chick quality and feed composition.

Secondly, in October 1999 the UK's largest poultry company, Grampian Country Food Group, announced the removal of AGPs from all broiler and breeder feed. Although not the first company to do so, the impact from a volume perspective was very significant. Their decision came on the back of extensive trials with alternative products under commercial conditions over a two year period in conjunction with a review of management practices. Significantly, there were no reported detrimental effects with regard to bird health, suggesting there would be no greater use of therapeutic antibiotics to treat flocks.

The issue of a possible increase in therapeutic antibiotic use is uppermost in the mind of the supermarkets as they strive to implement a complete ban across all species. Pig and poultry producers are being challenged to review their systems of production to reduce stress and prevent an increase in the therapeutic prescription of antibiotics such as occurred in 1986 when Sweden banned AGPs (Best, 1996). Consumer groups would be quick to condemn any such trend across the rest of Europe.

Genetically modified raw materials

The consumer response to the GM issue within Europe contrasts greatly with the US and is an example of how different attitudes and perceptions apply. Monsanto failed to appreciate these differences despite the experience of their failed attempt to introduce BST into Europe in the 1980s.

Media hysteria and powerful environmental lobby groups have effectively cut off the introduction of GM technology in Europe. That the debate has also included whether genetically modified feed ingredients should be included in animal diets is a clear signal that consumers are not prepared to take chances with their food/environment regardless of the quality or quantity of scientific argument in its favour. The goal of certain supermarkets in the UK to remove genetically modified raw materials from animal feeds by the end of 2000 has raised the question of the long-term future of such raw materials throughout Europe. The necessity to segregate GM free soya and maize and their derivatives will inevitably force a significant number of feed compounders down the road of total GM-free production. Again the supermarkets have been seen to be taking the lead on an issue in advance of any legislation.

Future issues

There are a number of feed-related issues in Europe currently being monitored by the supermarkets that are likely to surface during the coming months:

1. *Maximum permitted dioxin levels.* We are still waiting for the decision on the allowable dioxin levels in raw materials and finished feed and any potential impact upon raw material selection, particularly for the fish feed industry. Associated with the dioxin issue is the decision pending by the EU on use of recovered vegetable oil in animal feed. This is of particular concern in the UK where use of tallow is not an option.

2. *Sustainable fish meal sources.* Fish meal continues to attract media attention due to the concern about sustainable sources. It is likely that pressure will be exerted by environmental groups to reduce fishmeal usage in animal feeds. Concurrent with this is the challenge to find novel but cheaper protein sources.

3. *Genetically modified feed grains and feed supplements.* The fate of genetically modified raw materials such as soya and maize and their derivatives has already been discussed. It may only be a matter of time before attention is turned to the microingredients such as enzymes, amino acids and vitamins.

4. *Colourants.* Synthetic yolk pigments continue to attract adverse publicity in the UK. A number of smaller supermarkets have already banned synthetic and nature-identical yolk pigments.

5. *Coccidiostats.* At present two antibiotic substances listed by the EU are also approved as coccidiostats (salinomycin and monensin sodium). Any move to add these two substances to the banned AGP list could have serious consequences for the poultry industry.

6.   *Alternatives to AGPs.* The removal of AGPs has led to the search for alternative growth promoters. The prerequisite for alternative products must be that they are safe to animals, consumers and the environment. Evaluation of some of these alternative products may be difficult due to the lack of data relating to active ingredient levels and dose response data.

As far as animal production is concerned, we are likely to see an increased trend toward more extensive systems of production. Within the EU the demand for free range, outdoor and organic food is increasing. Supermarkets will continue to promote these alternative systems of production because they are perceived as ethically correct and they are associated with added value. In France approximately 15% of broiler production is Label Rouge, based on an extensive outdoor system taking birds to an older age without in-feed additives or antibiotics. In the UK 20% of eggs are produced from alternative systems and at least 30% of the sow herd is now based outdoors.

Without doubt the move away from AGPs will result in a radical review of current systems of production. This may be particularly true for the pig industry, which has not adopted the level of hygiene present in the poultry industry (Gadd, 1997).

Conclusion

We live in an age where consumer power frequently outweighs scientific evidence. Supermarkets are going to become increasingly responsive to consumer concerns and demands in an effort to promote an encompassing image of absolute food safety. Animal feed will remain a focus of attention because of its emotive association with animals and recent food safety scares and its direct link in the human food chain. Supermarkets will continue to influence and control the systems of animal production in Europe and the content of animal feeds as long as they are perceived as the 'ethical decision makers' on behalf of their customers. Animal feed manufacture will continue to move closer to human food standards through the widespread implementation of HACCP and hygiene control measures.

The influence of supermarkets will continue to spread beyond countries of origin, either through expansion into new markets or through controls applied to import products. Consequently, suppliers outside the EU will be forced to adopt the same standards of animal and feed production if they wish to pursue these lucrative export opportunities.

The global market and spread of the internet will make it much easier for consumers and lobby groups to access public opinion on the other side of the globe. Global food chains are likely to come under more pressure to respond to the ethics associated with animal and feed production.

The 'props' that have supported intensive livestock production are slowly being removed by the major supermarkets. The most significant prop has been AGPs. Their removal from animal feed will have widespread implications not only for animal nutrition but environment, vaccination programmes, hygiene standards and stocking densities.

References

Best, P. 1996. Production without antibiotics: The Swedish experience. Feed International. April. p. 8.

Cooke, M. 2000. The retailers view. In: Topical Feed Issues, Proceedings of the Society of Feed Technologists, February 2000.

Gadd, J. 1997. Life without antibiotic digestive enhancers. In: Biotechnology in the feed industry, Proceedings of the 13th Annual Symposium (T.P. Lyons and K.A. Jacques, eds.) Nottingham University Press, Nottingham, UK. p. 277.

Inborr, J. 2000. Swedish poultry production without in-feed antibiotics – a testing ground or a model for the future? Proceedings of the Australian Poultry Science Symposium. p. 1.

SCAN. 1996. Report on the scientific committee for animal nutrition (SCAN) on the possible risk for humans on the use of avoparcin as a feed additive. VI/6474/96.

Suzuki, T. and Y. Kashima. 1998. Animal production, consumer demands and the role of the feed industry in Japan. In: Biotechnology in the feed industry, Proceedings of the 14th Annual Symposium (T.P. Lyons and K.A. Jacques, eds.) Nottingham University Press, Nottingham, UK. p. 31.

Bio-Mos effects on pig performance: a review

J.E. PETTIGREW

Pettigrew Consulting International, Louisiana, Missouri, USA

Introduction

It is imperative that we find new technologies to reduce the amount of feed resources needed to produce pork. The need is made more acute by the growing societal concern about routine use of antibiotics in livestock feeds. If we are to produce pork without the routine use of antibiotics in feed, we must change some things. The most important changes will be in production systems, sanitation and biosecurity. However, these changes should be supplemented with targeted methods for influencing the microbial ecology of the digestive tract of the pig.

Bio-Mos is a product designed to influence microbial ecology. It is derived from yeast cell walls, and consists primarily of phosphorylated glucomannans. Two modes of action are now recognized:

1.   It binds to the lectins on the cell walls of certain undesirable bacteria. These bacterial lectins normally bind to the intestinal epithelial cells and aid the bacteria in colonization of the gut. However, if the lectins are bound to Bio-Mos they cannot bind to the epithelial cells, and the undesirable bacteria are eliminated from the gut lumen.

2.   It enhances certain actions of the immune system.

These modes of action enable Bio-Mos to help protect the animal from pathogens.

This paper focuses on the empirical evidence concerning the effects of adding Bio-Mos to the diet of pigs on their productive performance.

Starting pigs

The database consists of 17 comparisons in 13 experiments, conveyed in ten reports from eight research groups. Two additional experiments were excluded from the analysis because they were unreplicated.

OVERVIEW

An overview of the data set is provided in Table 1. This broad-brush summary considers only the overall experimental period, not short-term measurements. Where more than one Bio-Mos level was tested in an experiment, the data are averaged across the levels for this summary.

The results are encouraging. Although few of the responses were statistically significant in the individual experiments, the overall picture is of a beneficial effect of Bio-Mos. Of the 17 comparisons, 14 showed a numerical advantage of Bio-Mos, although some of these advantages were quite small.

Some comments about the approach are appropriate. This broad view across experiments has the considerable advantage of simultaneously considering a wide range of production conditions (genetics, diet formulation, environment, health) and providing a general impression of the effect of Bio-Mos across those conditions. However, the approach suffers from two disadvantages. First, it does not provide precise estimates of the response, nor of the impact of specific variables on that response. Second, it is subject to bias if experiments showing 'undesirable' responses are not included. That is a real concern when relying on the published scientific literature for the database, because 'negative' responses are sometimes not considered acceptable for publication. In the present case we believe we have included all data that have been sponsored by Alltech, regardless of the outcome, so this summary is safer than most.

The overall mean percentage response was an increase in growth rate of 4.4% (Table 1). For perspective, that is a somewhat smaller response than we generally expect from antibiotics, which appear to increase growth rate of starting pigs by about 16% on average (NRC, 1998). Most of the antibiotic data were collected many years ago when pigs, diets, weaning ages and production systems were very different from those used now, so the comparison may not be strictly appropriate. However, as described in more detail later, it generally appears that the response to Bio-Mos is smaller than the response to antibiotics, but it clearly exists. The product is a useful tool for improving pig performance.

The overall summary shows that Bio-Mos increases feed intake and improves feed efficiency of starting pigs (Table 2). Both of these responses are smaller than the growth rate response, which is the same pattern of response found with antibiotics (NRC, 1998).

The next sections of the paper examine the nature of the response to Bio-Mos and certain factors that influence the size of the response.

STAGE OF NURSERY PERIOD

A summary of the average daily gain response to Bio-Mos during only the first stage of the nursery period (7 to 14 days, depending on the experiment)

Table 1. Growth rate response to Bio-Mos in controlled studies with starter pigs.

Authors/description	Year	Reps	Weaning age (days)	Length of test (days)	Bio-Mos level (%)[a]	ADG (g) Control	ADG (g) Bio-Mos	Diff[b]	% diff[c]	P[d]
van der Beke	1997	12	28	30	0.2	243	261	18	7.33	ND
Dvorak and Jacques	1998	4	17-18	21	0.2	309	341	32	10.30	NS
Kumprecht and Zoba	1999	3	28	39	0.2	NA	NA	NA	8.50	0.1
LeMieux et al., High Zn	1999	5	17	28	0.2-0.3	307	318	11	3.48	)[e]
LeMieux et al., Low Zn	1999	5	17	28	0.2-0.3	262	291	29	11.04	
Stockland, Trial 1	1999	4	10	28	0.1	243	258	15	6.17	NS
Stockland, Trial 2	1999	5	21	14	0.1-0.4	163	189	26	16.07	ND
Stockland, Trial 3	1999	6	21	33	Varied	418	427	9	2.18	0.01[f]
Stockland, Trial 4	1999	6	21	33	0.2/0.1	452	439	-12	-2.68	NS
Brendemuhl and Harvey	1999	4	25 (30)[g]	28	0.1-0.2	639	649	10	1.56	NS
Davis et al.	1999	18	21	38	0.2	402	427	25	6.30	0.04
Harper and Estienne, No antibiotic	2000	5	24	35	0.3/0.2	445	450	5	1.03	NS
Harper and Estienne, Mecadox	2000	5	24	35	0.3/0.2	490	490	0	0.00	NS
Maxwell et al., Low Zn	1999a	9	21	38	0.3/0.2	406	423	17	4.23	)[h]
Maxwell et al., High Zn	1999a	9	21	38	0.3/0.2	446	439	-7	-1.59	
Maxwell et al., Low Zn	2000	6	18	38	0.2-0.3	413	406	-7	-1.62	NS
Maxwell et al., High Zn	2000	6	18	38	0.2-0.3	427	437	10	2.44	NS
	Total	112			Means	379	390	11	4.40	

[a]Numbers separated by / indicate sequential changes during the experiment; numbers separated by - indicate different treatments.
[b]Bio-Mos minus control.
[c]Bio-Mos minus control, % of control.
[d]Statistical significance level within experiment; ND = not determined; NS = not significant.
[e]Bio-Mos by zinc level interaction, P<0.07.
[f]First 12 days only.
[g]Pigs were weaned at 25 days of age, and the experiment was started at 30 days.
[h]Bio-Mos by zinc level interaction, P<0.08.

Table 2. A summary of feed intake and efficiency responses to Bio-Mos in starter diets for pigs.

Authors/description	Year	Average daily feed intake (g) Control	Bio-Mos	Diff[a]	% diff[b]	P[c]	Feed/gain Control	Bio-Mos	Diff[a]	% diff[b]	P[c]
van der Beke	1997	461	469	8	1.69	ND	1.90	1.80	-0.10	-5.26	ND
Dvorak and Jacques	1998	400	427	27	6.83	NS	1.30	1.26	-0.04	-3.08	NS
LeMieux et al., High Zn	1999	445	463	18	3.96	)[d]	1.45	1.46	0.01	0.34	NS
LeMieux et al., Low Zn	1999	386	422	36	9.34		1.48	1.46	-0.02	-1.35	NS
Stockland, Trial 1	1999	274	299	25	9.12	NS	1.18	1.20	0.02	1.69	NS
Stockland, Trial 2	1999	227	234	7	2.86	ND	1.40	1.25	-0.16	-11.07	ND
Stockland, Trial 3	1999	515	540	25	4.79	0.06[e]	1.23	1.27	0.03	2.85	NS
Stockland, Trial 4	1999	558	578	20	3.55	NS	1.24	1.31	0.07	5.65	NS
Brendemuhl and Harvey	1999	1120	1102	-19	-1.65	NS	1.75	1.69	-0.06	-3.43	NS
Davis et al.	1999	612	617	5	0.83	NS	1.49	1.41	-0.08	-5.37	0.04
Harper and Estienne, No antibiotic	2000	772	772	0	0.00	NS	1.73	1.72	-0.01	-0.58	NS
Harper and Estienne, Mecadox	2000	840	826	-14	-1.62	NS	1.72	1.69	-0.03	-1.74	NS
Maxwell et al., Low Zn	1999a	613	625	12	1.89	NS	1.47	1.43	-0.04	-2.72	NS
Maxwell et al., High Zn	1999a	655	639	-16	-2.38	NS	1.41	1.39	-0.02	-1.42	NS
Maxwell et al., Low Zn	2000	559	571	11	2.00	NS	1.32	1.37	0.05	3.79	ND[f]
Maxwell et al., High Zn	2000	588	594	7	1.17	NS	1.33	1.31	-0.03	-1.88	ND[f]
Means		564	573	9	2.65		1.46	1.44	-0.03	-1.47	

[a] Bio-Mos minus control.
[b] Bio-Mos minus control, % of control.
[c] Statistical significance level within experiment; ND = not determined; NS = not significant.
[d] Bio-Mos by zinc level interaction, P<0.07.
[e] First 12 days only.
[f] Quadratic effect of Bio-Mos level, P<0.01.

shows a more variable response than over the overall period, as expected (Table 3). The mean percentage increase in growth rate is bigger during the early period (Table 3) than during the overall period (Table 1) because of some very high values, but there does not appear to be a strong pattern of bigger responses during the early stage within individual experiments. From this, I infer that the response to Bio-Mos is not concentrated during the first few days after weaning, but is probably of approximately uniform size throughout the nursery phase.

EFFECT OF WEANING AGE

The experiments were divided arbitrarily into three weaning age categories (Table 4). These data suggest that the response to Bio-Mos may decline slightly as weaning age increases, but that the effect is small.

Table 4. Effect of weaning age on the growth rate response to Bio-Mos in starting pigs.

Weaning age (days)	No. experiments	No. replicates	Mean % change in ADG
10	1	4	6.17
17-21	8	79	4.56
24-28	4	29	3.69

EFFECT OF BIO-MOS CONCENTRATION

It is presumably necessary to provide an adequate concentration of Bio-Mos in the diet in order to achieve the desired effects. Four experiments have tested more than one level of Bio-Mos, and they support some tentative conclusions about the best level.

Stockland (1999) compared several levels of Bio-Mos, and found that 0.3% appeared optimal (Figure 1). Maxwell *et al.* (2000) confirmed that 0.3% supported better performance than 0.2%, but that was partially because in that experiment performance on the lower level was actually poorer than on the control diet. Data from LeMieux *et al.* (1999) also show non-significant trends in the same direction when the diet contained a high level (3,000 ppm) of zinc, but not when the zinc level was lower. The study of Brendemuhl and Harvey (1999) can be interpreted to show that 0.2% is better than 0.1%, but the difference was not statistically significant. Overall, it appears that performance of starting pigs is maximized at a Bio-Mos level of about 0.3% of the diet.

Cole (1999) suggested a 'step-down' program, using a high dietary concentration of Bio-Mos in the first feed after weaning when intake is low, and gradually reducing the concentration in successive feeds. Stockland *et al.* (1999) confirmed that such a program (0.4, 0.2, 0.1%) produced better performance than a constant level of 0.2%. Some version of a step-down program appears to be the best choice.

Table 3. Responses to Bio-Mos during Stage I (7-14 days).

Authors/description	Year	Reps	Weaning age (days)	Length of test (days)	Bio-Mos level (%)[a]	Early average daily gain (g) Control	Early average daily gain (g) Bio-Mos	Diff[b]	% diff[c]	P[d]
van der Beke	1997	12	28	14	0.2	130	136	6	4.86	ND
Dvorak and Jacques	1998	4	17-18	7	0.2	168	154	-14	-8.10	NS
LeMieux *et al.*, High Zn	1999	5	17	7	0.2-0.3	122	105	-17	-13.72	NS
LeMieux *et al.*, Low Zn	1999	5	17	7	0.2-0.3	73	126	53	73.14	NS
Stockland, Trial 2	1999	5	21	14	0.1-0.4	163	189	26	16.07	ND
Stockland, Trial 3	1999	6	21	12	Varied	194	246	52	26.80	0.01
Stockland, Trial 4	1999	6	21	13	0.2/0.1	318	323	5	1.57	NS
Brendemuhl and Harvey	1999	4	25 (30)[e]	7	0.1-0.2	509	528	19	3.73	NS
Davis *et al.*	1999	18	21	10	0.2	161	171	10	6.20	NS[f]
Harper and Estienne, No antibiotic	2000	5	24	7	0.3/0.2	254	259	5	1.81	NS
Harper and Estienne, Mecadox	2000	5	24	7	0.3/0.2	282	259	-23	-8.06	NS
Maxwell *et al.*, Low Zn	1999a	9	21	10	0.3/0.2	160	159	-1	-0.69	NS
Maxwell *et al.*, High Zn	1999a	9	21	10	0.3/0.2	200	205	6	2.86	NS
Maxwell *et al.*, Low Zn	2000	6	18	10	0.2-0.3	147	146	-2	-1.02	NS
Maxwell *et al.*, High Zn	2000	6	18	10	0.2-0.3	178	183	5	3.04	ND[g]
	Total	**105**			Means	204	213	9	7.23	

[a]Numbers separated by / indicate sequential changes during the experiment; numbers separated by - indicate different treatments.
[b]Bio-Mos minus control.
[c]Bio-Mos minus control, % of control.
[d]Statistical significance level within experiment; ND = not determined; NS = not significant.
[e]Pigs were weaned at 25 days of age, and the experiment was started at 30 days.
[f]Bio-Mos by copper sulfate level interaction, $P<0.01$.
[g]Quadratic effect of Bio-Mos level, $P<0.01$.

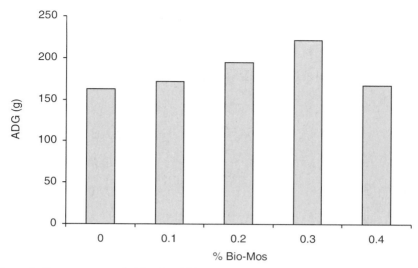

Figure 1. Response to graded levels of Bio-Mos in weanling pigs (adapted from Stockland, 1999).

EFFECT OF PERFORMANCE LEVEL

The proposed modes of action of Bio-Mos are forms of protection against disease challenges. It seems logical that it would be more effective when disease challenges are greater than when they are smaller. It is not possible to evaluate the degree or nature of disease challenges in the experiments under review, but perhaps the overall growth rate of the control treatments can serve usefully as an imperfect index of disease challenge. Pigs that are subjected to a greater disease challenge are likely to grow more slowly. Slower-growing pigs may respond more dramatically to Bio-Mos.

To examine whether that actually happened, it was necessary to sort the data in order to avoid confounding factors. First, two weaning age categories were selected, 17-21 and 24-28 days. Further analyses were made within each of these categories. If performance of pigs in different experiments is to be compared, it must be measured over approximately the same stage of growth. Some experiments cause difficulty in this regard because the experimental period was short. Therefore, all experiments with a growth period less than an arbitrarily selected 28 days were eliminated, leaving a range of 28 to 38 days. One experiment was eliminated because it did not start immediately at weaning, and another because actual growth rates were not reported. That left nine comparisons in the 17-21 day weaning age category (two each from LeMieux *et al.*, 1999; Stockland *et al.*, 1999; Maxwell *et al.*, 1999a; Maxwell *et al.*, 2000; and one from Davis *et al.*, 1999); and three comparisons in the 24-28 day weaning age category (van der Beke, 1997; and two from Harper and Estienne, 2000). The results are plotted in Figures 2 and 3.

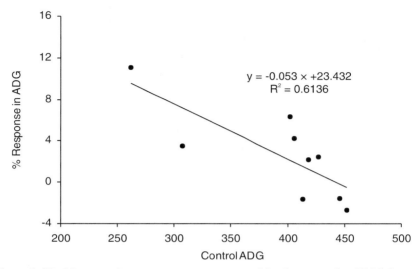

Figure 2. Bio-Mos growth rate response versus control in pigs weaned at 17-21 days.

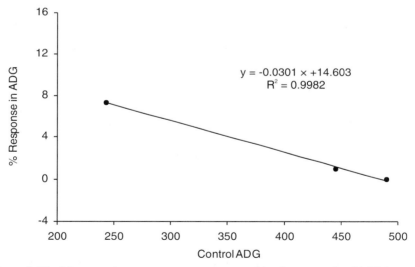

Figure 3. Bio-Mos growth rate response versus control in pigs weaned at 24-28 days.

The data for the older weaning age (Figure 3) show a very clear relationship between percentage improvement in growth rate from using Bio-Mos and growth rate of control pigs. Slower-growing pigs respond more dramatically to Bio-Mos, exactly as we expected. The pattern with the younger weaning age (Figure 2) is less clear, but it appears to show a similar relationship.

From these figures, I draw the following working hypothesis: pigs with growth rate less than 350-400 g/day in the nursery are likely to respond to Bio-Mos with improved growth rate. We should not depend on a response in pigs already growing faster than 400 g/day, although it occurs in some experiments.

This analysis is imperfect, but I believe that when combined with our understanding of the mode of action of Bio-Mos it supports the working hypothesis outlined above. The relationship to performance level is important, because many of the university experiments report excellent growth rate, while the growth rate in many commercial nurseries is substantially slower.

Note that this pattern of response is similar to the pattern of response to antibiotics. Challenged pigs respond more dramatically to antibiotics than do healthier pigs.

COMPARISON TO ANTIBIOTICS, ZINC AND COPPER

Harper and Estienne (2000) found the growth rate of starting pigs was increased by 10.2% (P<0.01) by Mecadox, but only 1.0% (not significant) by Bio-Mos, suggesting the response to Bio-Mos is smaller than the response to antibiotics.

Three experiments (LeMieux *et al.*, 1999; Maxwell *et al.*, 1999; 2000) compared the responses to Bio-Mos and to a high level of zinc oxide (2,300 – 3,000 ppm Zn) when added to a basal diet. In two cases, the response to zinc oxide was bigger. The respective percentage increases in overall growth rate were 17.4, 9.8, and 3.4% for zinc oxide, while the corresponding increases for the best Bio-Mos treatment were 18.3, 4.2, and –0.5%.

Davis *et al.* (1999) found a bigger response to copper sulfate (16.1% increase in overall growth rate) than to Bio-Mos (6.3%), evaluating main effects in a factorial experiment.

It is clear that the responses to Bio-Mos are real and important. Realistically, it appears from the data available to date that they are smaller than the responses to antibiotics, zinc oxide, or copper sulfate.

Interactions with antibiotics, zinc and copper

Harper and Estienne (2000) found no interactions between carbadox (Mecadox) and Bio-Mos, suggesting that the effects are additive.

All three experiments that studied Bio-Mos and zinc oxide found interactions between them, but the patterns were not consistent. The results of Maxwell *et al.* (2000) suggest that pigs may respond to either Bio-Mos or zinc oxide, but that the responses are not additive. LeMieux *et al.* (1999) found a trend in the same direction (smaller response to Bio-Mos in the presence of zinc oxide), but the more striking interaction was between Bio-

Mos levels and zinc oxide. The higher level of Bio-Mos (0.3%) appeared best in the absence of 3,000 ppm zinc, but the lower level (0.2%) seemed better with the zinc supplement. The data of Maxwell *et al.* (1999a) indicated that the response to Bio-Mos was bigger in the presence of a high level of zinc oxide.

Davis *et al.* (1999) found an interaction between Bio-Mos and a high level of copper sulfate, but only during the first few days after weaning. Bio-Mos improved performance in the absence of a high level of copper sulfate, but reduced it in the presence of 185 ppm copper from copper sulfate.

These results do not lead to a clear conclusion regarding interactions between Bio-Mos and the various antibacterial agents. It would be useful to generate more information in situations where a sizable response to Bio-Mos is expected.

Finishing pigs

There is a smaller database on finishing pigs. It consists of five comparisons in four experiments from four research groups. The database is not big enough to support the depth of analysis undertaken on the starting pig database.

A broad overall summary, corresponding to the one presented for starting pigs in Table 1, is offered in Table 5. Unlike the summary for starting pigs, this one does not show a clear pattern of benefits from the use of Bio-Mos. In three of the five cases the pigs fed Bio-Mos grew faster than the controls, but that effect was statistically significant in only one experiment. Feed efficiency data show a similar lack of clear response (Table 6). LeMieux and Southern (1999) found no effects on carcass measurements.

In my view, the appropriate interpretation of the data in Tables 5 and 6 is that:

1) the data available to date do not show clearly that Bio-Mos improves performance of finishing pigs; and

2) if Bio-Mos is eventually shown to improve performance of finishing pigs, the response is likely to be smaller than the response in starting pigs. That is not surprising, as the response to antibiotics is also markedly smaller in finishing pigs than in starting pigs (NRC, 1998).

There is no compelling evidence to date of a bigger response to Bio-Mos during the early part of the finishing period than later (data not shown).

An appropriate dose level is not clear. The only statistically significant increase in growth rate was found in the study by Kavanagh (1999), which used the lowest Bio-Mos concentration in the diet (0.5%). However, results of a direct comparison by Brendemuhl and Harvey (1999) suggest that 0.2% is better than 0.1%.

Table 5. Growth rate responses to Bio-Mos in finishing pigs.

Authors/description	Year	Reps	Weight (kg)		Sex[a]	Bio-Mos level (%)[b]	Average daily gain (g)		Diff[c]	% diff[d]	P[e]
			Initial	Final			Control	Bio-Mos			
Brendemuhl and Harvey	1999	4	25	110	F&C	0.1-0.2	804	835	31	3.86	NS
Kavanagh	1999	4	37	81	NA	0.05	730	755	25	3.42	0.03
Maxwell et al., low Cu	1999b	6	20	104	F&C	0.2/0.1/0.05	843	885	42	4.98	NS
Maxwell et al., high Cu	1999b	6	20	109	F&C	0.2/0.1/0.05	931	911	-20	-2.15	NS
LeMieux and Southern	1999	3	62	110	C	0.3	790	780	-10	-1.27	NS
Total		23				Means	820	833	14	1.77	

[a]F=female; C=castrate; NA=information not available.
[b]Numbers separated by / indicate sequential changes during the experiment; numbers separated by - indicate different treatments.
[c]Bio-Mos minus control.
[d]Bio-Mos minus control, % of control.
[e]Statistical significance level within experiment; NS = not significant.

Table 6. Feed efficiency and intake responses to Bio-Mos in finishing pigs.

Authors/description	Year	Average daily feed intake (g)		Diff[a]	% diff[b]	P[c]	Feed/gain		Diff[a]	% diff[b]	P[c]
		Control	Bio-Mos				Control	Bio-Mos			
Brendemuhl and Harvey	1999	2218	2188	-30	-1.35	NS	2.75	2.62	-0.14	-4.91	ND
Maxwell et al., low Cu	1999b	2308	2435	127	5.50	NS	2.74	2.75	0.01	0.36	NS
Maxwell et al., high Cu	1999b	2448	2437	-11	-0.45	NS	2.63	2.67	0.04	1.52	NS
LeMieux and Southern	1999	2450	2890	440	17.96	NS	3.03	3.70	0.67	22.11	NS
Means		2356	2488	132	5.41		2.79	2.93	0.15	4.77	

[a]Bio-Mos minus control.
[b]Bio-Mos minus control, % of control.
[c]Statistical significance level within experiment; ND = not determined; NS = not significant.

The wide variation in weight ranges among experiments makes it difficult to draw conclusions about the effect of performance level on the response to Bio-Mos. The logic applied to starting pigs, suggesting that slower-growing pigs should respond more markedly to Bio-Mos, would seem to apply to finishing pigs also. However, more data are needed to verify it.

Dvorak (1996) found no differences in overall performance among finishing pigs fed Bio-Mos, bacitracin methylene disalicylate (BMD), or virginiamycin. The experiment did not include a negative control, so it is not clear to what extent the pigs responded to any of the products. Maxwell *et al.* (1999b) found that overall growth rate was increased 5.0% by Bio-Mos, compared to an increase of 10.4% from addition of copper sulfate (175 ppm Cu), when the products were added singly. Combining Bio-Mos and copper sulfate did not produce an additive response.

Nursing piglets

In an experiment in China (Huan, 1999), a daily oral dose of 250 mg Bio-Mos to piglets from birth to weaning at 28 days of age increased growth rate and reduced the incidence of diarrhea. The daily growth rate increased from 220 to 233 g (5.9% increase), and the incidence of diarrhea (not defined) was reduced from 41 to 25%. Bacteriological studies indicated the presence of a pathogenic *E. coli* in the building.

Perhaps Bio-Mos can become a valuable tool for improving piglet performance in the face of an active outbreak of *E. coli* diarrhea.

Summary

The data available to date suggest strongly that adding Bio-Mos to the diet of starting pigs improves their performance. The improvement is especially large and consistent where growth rates are at levels often found in commercial production. The best approach seems to be feeding a high dietary level of Bio-Mos in the first post-weaning diet and then gradually reducing the level as the pigs grow.

The data on finishing pigs allow the possibility that Bio-Mos may improve growth performance, but they do not show it clearly.

There is experimental support for the use of Bio-Mos to improve the health and performance of nursing pigs under a disease challenge.

References

Brendemuhl, J.H. and M.R. Harvey. 1999. Evaluation of Bio-Mos (mannanoligosaccharide) in diets for pigs. I. Growth performance response during nursery and growing-finishing phases. University of Florida, Gainesville, Florida, USA. Report to Alltech Inc.

Cole, D.J.A. 1999. Potential, performance and problems. In: Concepts in Pig Science 1999. The 1st Annual Turtle Lake Pig Science Conference. (T.P. Lyons and D.J.A. Cole, eds.) Nottingham University Press, Nottingham. pp 19-31.

Davis, M.E., C.V. Maxwell, E.B. Kegley, B.Z. de Rodas, K.G. Friesen, D.H. Hellwig and R.A. Dvorak. 1999. Efficacy of mannan oligosaccharide (Bio-Mos) addition at two levels of supplemental copper on performance and immunocompetence of early weaned pigs. J. Anim. Sci. 77 (Suppl. 1):63. (Abstr.).

Dvorak, R.A. 1996. Mannanoligosaccharide as an alternative to growth promotant antibiotics for growing-finishing swine: response under commercial conditions. Poster presented at the 12th Annual Symposium on Biotechnology in the Feed Industry, Lexington, KY.

Dvorak, R. and K.A. Jacques. 1998. Mannanoligosaccharide, fructooligosaccharide and Carbadox for pigs days 0-21 post-weaning. J. Anim. Sci. 76 (Suppl. 2):64. (Abstr.).

Harper, A.F. and M.J. Estienne. 2000. Efficacy of carbadox antibiotic and a mannanoligosaccharide source as growth promoters for weanling pigs. J. Anim. Sci. 78 (Suppl. 2):12. (Abstr.).

Huan, X.-H. 1999. Performance and incidence of coliform scours and immunological response in piglets given Bio-Mos alone or in combination with citric acid or Norfloxacin. College of Animal Science, Fujian Agricultural University, China. Report to Alltech China.

Kavanagh, N.T. 1999. Performance response to Bio-Mos: Grower/finisher pigs. Oldcastle Laboratories, Oldcastle, Co. Meath, Ireland. Report to Alltech Ireland.

Kumprecht, I., and P. Zoba. 1999. Mannanoligosaccharides in weanling pig diets: Effects on performance and nutrient digestibility. Research Institute of Animal Nutrition, Pohoelice, Czech Republic. Report to Alltech Czech Republic.

LeMieux, F.M., T.D. Bidner, and L.L. Southern. 1999. Effect of 0.2 and 0.3% Bio-Mos with and without 3,000 ppm zinc on growth performance of weanling pigs. Louisiana State University, Baton Rouge, LA. Report to Alltech Inc.

LeMieux, F.M. and L.L. Southern. 1999. Effect of Bio-Mos in finishing pigs. Louisiana State University, Baton Rouge, LA. Report to Alltech Inc.

Maxwell, C., K. Friesen, E.B. Kegley, B. de Rodas, D. Hellwig, and E. Davis. 1999a. Efficacy of Bio-Mos in improving gain and efficiency in early weaned pigs fed diets with and without growth promoting levels of Zn. University of Arkansas, Fayetteville, Arkansas, USA, Report to Alltech Inc.

Maxwell, C., B. da Rodas and Z. Johnson. 1999b. Efficacy of Bio-mos in improving gain and efficiency in grow/finish pigs. University of Arkansas, Fayetteville, Arkansas. Report to Alltech.

Maxwell, C., K. Friesen, E.B. Kegley, and E. Davis. 2000. Effect of Bio-Mos addition with and without zinc oxide supplementation on performance and immunocompetence in weanling pigs. University of Arkansas, Fayetteville, Arkansas, USA. Report to Alltech Inc.

National Research Council. 1998. Nutrient Requirements of Swine. Tenth Edition. Washington, D.C.: National Academy Press. p 97.

Stockland, W.L. 1999. Practical solutions to maximise production: The commercial application of oligosaccharides in starter pig diets. In: Concepts in Pig Science. The 1st Annual Turtle Lake Pig Science Conference. (T.P. Lyons and D.J.A. Cole, eds.) Nottingham University Press, U.K.

van der Beke, N. 1997. The use of mannanoligosaccharides (Bio-Mos) and lactic acid bacteria (Lacto-Sacc) in piglet feed. Thesis, Department Biotechnological Sciences, Landscape Management and Agriculture, Gent, Belgium.

The case for mannanoligosaccharides in poultry diets. An alternative to growth promotant antibiotics?

C.W. PARKS, J.L. GRIMES, P.R. FERKET, AND A.S. FAIRCHILD

North Carolina State University, Raleigh, North Carolina, USA

Introduction

Antibiotics have been used in the poultry industry for the past 40 years to improve growth performance of birds. They are fed during the grow-out period to prevent infection by pathogens, maintain health and improve meat quality and wholesomeness. However, antibiotics have come under increasing scrutiny by scientists, consumers and government regulators alike because of the potential development of antibiotic-resistant bacteria (including pathogenic strains) after long use of antibiotic growth promotants in livestock and poultry feed. Antibiotic resistance displayed by field *Escherichia coli* isolates from North Carolina commercial turkey farms has been reported, including resistance to enrofloxacin, one of the most recently approved antibiotics for poultry (Fairchild *et al.*, 1998). Most of the antibiotics used as growth promoters have no specific claims regarding control of disease (Gustafson and Bowen, 1997). Debate over resistance seen among Gram-negative bacteria such as *E. coli* and salmonella has generated the strongest objection to antibiotic use (Evagelisti *et al.*, 1975; Scioli *et al.*, 1983; Gustafson and Bowen, 1997). It has been reported that antibiotic resistance of indigenous *E. coli* in poultry has remained at a relatively high level since the 1950s (Gustafson and Bowen, 1997). Furthermore, the use of these antibiotics could disrupt or destabilize normal gut microflora (Surawicz *et al.*, 1989).

Alternatives to antibiotics: competitive exclusion

Alternatives to antibiotics such as competitive exclusion (CE) treatments have been developed to counter the growth-depressing effects that certain strains of bacteria elicit in poultry. One type of CE aims at the development of a protective barrier bacterial population in the digestive tract to prevent colonization of unfavorable (i.e., growth-depressing and/or pathogenic) microorganisms. Some cultures have included lactobacillus species. (Francis *et al.*, 1978) or undefined normal avian gut flora (Nurmi and Rantala, 1973). Another CE approach exploits the presence of mannose-specific (Type 1) fimbriae on unfavorable Gram-negative bacteria including many strains of *E. coli* and salmonella. These bacteria use the fimbriae to attach to and then colonize the intestinal wall. Mannanoligosaccharides (MOS) derived from mannan on yeast cell surfaces act as high affinity ligands offering a competitive binding site for the bacteria (Ofek *et al.*, 1977). Pathogens with the mannose-specific fimbriae adsorb to the MOS instead of attaching to intestinal epithelial cells and consequently move through the intestine without colonization. Newman (1994) reported that the presence of dietary MOS in the intestinal tract removed pathogenic bacteria that could attach to the lumen of the intestine in this manner. This might provide a more favorable environment for nutrient utilization by the bird (Savage and Zakrzewska, 1996).

In an effort to confirm the inhibitory effect of mannanoligosaccharide on pathogen colonization reported by previous research, Spring *et al.* (2000) screened different bacterial strains for their ability to agglutinate MOS in yeast cell preparations (*Saccharomyces cerevisiae*, NCYC 1026). Five of seven strains of *E. coli* and 7 of 10 strains of *Salmonella typhimurium* and *Salmonella enteritidis* agglutinated MOS and *Sac. cerevisiae* cells. However, strains of *Salmonella choleraesuis*, *Salmonella pullorum*, and campylobacter did not lead to agglutination. They also determined the effect of MOS on cecal fermentation parameters, cecal microflora and enteric pathogen and coliform colonization in chicks. After 3-day old chicks were orally challenged with 10^4 CFU of *S. typhimurium* 29E and received 4000 ppm dietary MOS, cecal *S. typhimurium* 29E concentrations decreased from 5.40 to 4.01 log CFU/g (P<0.05) at day 10. A similar study using *S. dublin* as the challenge pathogen resulted in a decrease in the number of infected birds by day 10 from 90% to 56% (P<0.05). Dietary MOS supplementation also reduced the concentration of cecal coliforms, although less significantly (P<0.10) than with the Salmonella challenges. Dietary MOS supplementation had no effect on cecal concentrations of lactobacilli, enterococci, anaerobic bacteria, lactate, volatile fatty acids or cecal pH.

The effects of hen age, *Escherichia coli*, and dietary Bio-Mos and bambermycin on poult performance from 1 to 21 days were studied previously in our laboratory (Fairchild *et al.*, 1999). Day-of-hatch BUTA (BIG-6) male poults were gavaged (1 ml) with 10^8 CFU/ml *E. coli* composed of four serotypes or sterile carrier broth. A mixture of the same *E. coli* cultures was added to the drinking water (10^6 CFU *E.coli*/ml drinking water) on a weekly basis to ensure a continuous bacterial challenge. Within each *E. coli* split plot treatment group, poults from hens of different ages (33 and 58 wk of age) were fed diets containing Bio-Mos (2 lb/ton feed) and bambermycin (2 g active ingredient/ton feed), alone and in combination, in a randomized complete block design. At week 1 and week 3, one bird per pen (n=128) was randomly chosen for bacterial sampling of liver and intestinal tissue for coliforms, aerobic bacteria, and lactobacilli. Individual bodyweight and feed consumption by pen were recorded weekly and poult mortality was recorded daily. *E. coli* isolates from tissue samples were serotyped. Feed conversion and weight gains were calculated. Under *E. coli* challenge, dietary Bio-Mos and bambermycin improved ($P \leq 0.05$) poult bodyweight gains. When poults were not challenged with *E. coli*, dietary Bio-Mos improved ($P \leq 0.05$) poult growth during week 2 while dietary bambermycin improved ($P \leq 0.05$) poult growth through week 3. Cumulative three week bodyweight gains for unchallenged poults were improved ($P \leq 0.05$) by both Bio-Mos and bambermycin. Two of the four *E. coli* serotypes administered were recovered in cultures of tissue samples. Several serotypes were recovered that were not administered. This work demonstrated that dietary Bio-Mos can improve the overall performance of poults, especially when they are faced with an *E. coli* challenge, as well as traditionally used antibiotics.

Effect of Bio-Mos, bambermycin and virginiamycin on growth performance of turkeys

MATERIALS AND METHODS

Recently, research at North Carolina State University was conducted to evaluate the effects of Bio-Mos and two popular in-feed antibiotics (bambermycin and virginiamycin) on the growth and performance of market turkeys. Poults were randomly assigned to 48 pens on day of hatch and raised from 1 to 140 days of age. There were eight replicate pens per dietary treatment with 20 birds per replicate placed at the start of the trial, and randomly culled to 12 birds per pen at 12 weeks of age. Dietary treatments were randomly assigned to each of 48 pens within blocks of 12 pens each. This experimental design was used to account for any variation in bird performance due to pen location in the turkey house, which might be affected by the environment such as light or temperature differences. Each treatment was replicated twice in each block of pens. The six dietary treatments were as follows:

1. Control: typical US corn/soybean meal diet

2. Bio-Mos (2 lbs/ton to 6 weeks of age then 1 lb/ ton)

3. Bambermycin (2 g/ton active ingredient)

4. Virginiamycin (20 g/ton active ingredient)

5. Bio-Mos + bambermycin (as in Treatments 2 and 3)

6. Bio-Mos + virginiamycin (as in Treatments 2 and 4)

The experimental diets are presented in Table 1. Typical US corn-soy based diets were employed to minimize possible variability due to ingredient digestibility. All diets met or exceeded NRC (1994) nutrient recommendations for turkeys. No coccidiostats were added to the feed in order to avoid any confounding effects with the dietary treatments. Dietary feed additives were added at the expense of washed builder's sand as inert filler to avoid any differences in dilution effects among the diets. All feed was pellet-processed and fed in crumble form up to 6 weeks of age and subsequently as 5/16" pellets.

Table 1. Composition of treatment diets fed from 1 to 140 days of age.

	Week					
	0-3	3-6	6-9	9-12	12-15	15-20
Ingredient						
Corn	46.11	49.70	52.98	57.19	67.92	75.13
Soybean meal (48% CP)	44.03	40.43	36.86	33.21	24.22	15.42
Poultry meal (60% CP)	5.00	5.00	5.00	5.00	2.86	4.76
Dical (18.5% P)	2.01	1.49	1.24	1.09	1.18	0.65
Limestone	1.27	1.04	0.93	0.90	0.85	0.71
Poultry fat	0.44	1.30	2.01	1.70	2.06	2.44
Salt	0.28	0.25	0.26	0.26	0.29	0.28
Minerals[*]	0.20	0.20	0.20	0.20	0.20	0.20
Choline Cl (60%)	0.20	0.20	0.15	0.15	0.10	0.10
DL methionine	0.15	0.09	0.07	0.01	0.02	-
Sand	0.15	0.15	0.15	0.15	0.15	0.15
Vitamins[^]	0.10	0.10	0.10	0.10	0.10	0.10
Selenium	0.05	0.05	0.05	0.05	0.05	0.05
Calculated analysis						
Crude protein, %	28.14	26.67	25.21	23.75	19.00	16.50
ME, kcal/lb	1270	1315	1350	1360	1406	1451
Crude fat, %	3.16	4.10	4.89	4.71	5.12	5.90
Methionine, %	0.59	0.51	0.48	0.40	0.35	0.31
Meth + Cys, %	1.05	0.95	0.90	0.80	0.68	0.61
Lysine, %	1.60	1.50	1.40	1.30	1.00	0.80
Calcium, %	1.20	1.00	0.90	0.85	0.75	0.65
Available phosphorus, %	0.60	0.50	0.45	0.42	0.38	0.32
Sodium, %	0.17	0.15	0.15	0.15	0.15	0.15

* Supplied per kg of feed: 120 mg Zn as $ZnSO_4$; 120 mg Mn as $MnSO_4$; 80 mg Fe as $FeSO_4$; 10 mg Cu as $CuSO_4$; 2.5 mg I as Ca $(IO_3)_2$; and 1.0 mg Co as $CoSO_4$.

^ Supplied per kg of feed: vitamin A, 13,200 IU; cholecalciferol, 4,000 IU; niacin, 110 mg; pantothenic acid, 22 mg; riboflavin, 13.2 mg; pyridoxine, 7.9 mg; menadione, 4 mg; folic acid, 2.2 mg; thiamin, 4 mg; biotin, 0.253 mg; vitamin B_{12}, 0.04 mg; ethoxyquin, 100 mg; selenium, 0.30 mg. The vitamin E premix provided the necessary amount of vitamin E as D,L-α-tocopheryl acetate.

Facilities used in this experiment consisted of an industry-standard curtain-sided house containing 48 pens each with nine square meters of floor space. Pen floors were covered with clean, soft pine shavings top-dressed with used litter from a previous flock to supply some microbial challenge to the birds. Caked litter was removed as necessary throughout the trial. Ventilation was provided by natural air movement through appropriately adjusted curtain sides and air mixing fans located on the ceiling throughout the house. Birds were offered feed *ad libitum* using one 22 kg capacity tube feeder per pen and water by one Plasson drinker per pen. Lighting was provided 23 hrs out of every day for the first week and subsequently by natural length daylight. Standard gas brooders provided heat for each pen. House temperature was kept at approximately 29.5°C during the first two weeks and then gradually stepped down by 2.75°C per week until brooders were no longer used. Brooder temperatures were kept at approximately 35°C at poult level and stepped down to 2.75°C each week in conjunction with house temperature. Ambient temperature outside the turkey house ranged from 37.8°C in the late summer to -4°C in the late fall. High and low ambient temperature within the house was recorded at two places daily throughout the duration of the trial.

Feed consumption (by pen) and individual bird body weights were recorded at 0, 3, 6, 9, 12, 15, 18, and 20 weeks of age. Mortality and culled birds were recorded as they occurred and their weights were used to adjust feed conversion. Body weight, weight gain, feed consumption and adjusted feed conversions were determined for each of these periods. An attending veterinarian (Rollins Diagnostic Laboratory, NCDA, Raleigh, NC) determined cause of mortality.

The data were subjected to the General Linear Models procedure for ANOVA (SAS, 1992). The pen served as the experimental unit. Variables having a significant F-test were compared using the LS Means function of SAS (SAS, 1992) and considered to be significant at $P \leq 0.05$.

RESULTS

Dietary supplementation with Bio-Mos, bambermycin, and virginiamycin all resulted in the improvement of body weight (Table 2) and feed utilization (Tables 3 and 4) when fed to male turkeys. Overall, there were no further improvements in body weights when either of the antibiotics was fed in conjunction with the Bio-Mos. Bio-Mos and virginiamycin fed individually resulted in increased body weights at week 20 when compared to the control diet while birds fed the combination treatment were intermediate in body weight.

Bio-Mos, bambermycin and virginiamycin all improved feed:gain (Table 3) from 0-3 weeks of age. Virginiamycin also improved feed:gain from 3-6 weeks of age. There was a significant improvement in feed:gain from 3-6 weeks of age when Bio-Mos and bambermycin were fed in combination indicating a possible synergistic action between the two compounds. Bio-Mos and virginiamycin also improved feed:gain from 15-18 weeks of age. Cumulative feed:gain (Table 4) was significantly improved for the virginiamycin treatment from 0-6 and 0-9 weeks of age. The combination of Bio-Mos and bambermycin also resulted in improved cumulative feed:gain

Table 2. Effects of Bio-Mos, bambermycin and virginiamycin on the body weights of male turkeys.

Treatment	3	6	9	12	15	18	20
	(g)			(kg)			
Control	668	2.28	4.79	7.84[b]	11.26[b]	15.07	17.48[b]
Bio-Mos	668	2.29	4.82	7.94[ab]	11.56[ab]	15.41	17.94[a]
Bambermycin	674	2.31	4.88	8.12[a]	11.58[a]	15.39	17.81[a]
Virginiamycin	679	2.31	4.80	8.17[a]	11.61[a]	15.41	17.85[a]
Bio-Mos + bambermycin	664	2.37	4.90	8.13[a]	11.73[a]	15.43	17.80[a]
Bio-Mos + virginiamycin	673	2.29	4.84	8.06[ab]	11.63[a]	15.33	17.61[ab]
SEM	9.00	0.03	0.05	0.08	0.11	0.13	0.12

[ab]Means with different superscripts within a column differ significantly (P<0.05). There were no significant differences in poult starting weights at day 1 (60 g).

Table 3. Effects of Bio-Mos, bambermycin and virginiamycin on the period feed:gain of male turkeys.

Treatment	0-3	3-6	6-9	9-12	12-15	15-18	18-20
				Feed:gain from weeks			
Control	1.49[a]	1.72[a]	1.87	2.49	2.83	3.35[a]	3.48
Bio-Mos	1.43[b]	1.72[a]	1.86	2.44	2.77	3.11[b]	3.61
Bambermycin	1.41[b]	1.72[a]	1.85	2.38	2.87	3.22[ab]	3.90
Virginiamycin	1.40[b]	1.63[b]	1.84	2.31	2.80	3.15[b]	3.69
Bio-Mos + bambermycin	1.43[b]	1.65[b]	1.82	2.39	2.76	3.24[ab]	3.65
Bio-Mos + virginiamycin	1.40[b]	1.66[b]	1.85	2.36	2.79	3.07[b]	3.75
SEM	0.02	0.02	0.04	0.05	0.08	0.07	0.14

[ab]Means with different superscripts within a column differ significantly (P<0.05).

Table 4. Effects of Bio-Mos, bambermycin and virginiamycin on the cumulative feed:gain of male turkeys.

Treatment	0-3	3-6	6-9	9-12	12-15	15-18	18-20
				Feed:gain from weeks			
Control	1.49[a]	1.65[a]	1.76	2.04[a]	2.23	2.44[a]	2.55
Bio-Mos	1.43[b]	1.64[a]	1.76	2.02[ab]	2.21	2.40[ab]	2.54
Bambermycin	1.41[b]	1.63[ab]	1.74	2.00[abc]	2.21	2.41[ab]	2.57
Virginiamycin	1.40[b]	1.57[c]	1.71	1.95[c]	2.16	2.36[b]	2.51
Bio-Mos + bambermycin	1.43[b]	1.59[bc]	1.71	1.98[bc]	2.18	2.39[b]	2.53
Bio-Mos + virginiamycin	1.40[b]	1.58[c]	1.72	1.97[bc]	2.18	2.36[b]	2.51
SEM	0.02	0.02	0.02	0.02	0.02	0.02	0.02

[abc]Means with different superscripts within a column differ significantly (P<0.05).

during these same time periods. Cumulative feed:gain from 0-18 weeks of age was slightly improved for birds fed Bio-Mos or bambermycin compared to control fed birds although these differences were not significant. However, birds fed the combination treatment of Bio-Mos and bambermycin had significantly improved feed:gain compared to the feed:gain of birds fed the control diet. Cumulative feed:gain from 0-20 weeks of age was not affected by any treatment. This may have been a result of increased variability due to uncontrollable feed wastage as the large birds became more crowded within the pens at this late age. In addition, during the 18 to 20 week period the outside temperature was much colder than average and may have resulted in increased consumption of feed for thermal regulation purposes, which may not have been available for body weight gain. There were no significant differences due to treatment observed in cumulative feed consumption, mortality, or cull rate from 0 to 20 weeks of age (Table 5).

Table 5. Effects of Bio-Mos, bambermycin and virginiamycin on the cumulative performance (weeks 0-20) of male turkeys.

Treatment	Feed consumption (kg)	Mortality (%)	Cull (%)
Control	44.92	3.13	3.13
Bio-Mos	46.16	2.56	2.20
Bambermycin	46.14	1.88	4.38
Virginiamycin	45.66	2.50	5.63
Bio-Mos + bambermycin	45.23	0.63	1.25
Bio-Mos + virginiamycin	44.78	4.38	5.00
SEM	0.51	1.21	1.53

[a,b]Means with different superscripts within a column differ significantly (P<0.05).

Comparative modes of action: antibiotics and mannan oligosaccharides

The practice of feeding subtherapeutic levels of antibiotics to livestock and poultry has been in use for over fifty years. Their prevalence has become widespread because of the benefits afforded to the producer, the animal and the environment, as well as the consumer (Gadd, 1997). Antibiotics are fed to poultry because they improve the utilization of feed and increase body weight gain. Gastrointestinal disorders caused by the unhealthy microflora can influence feed intake, feed conversion, weight gain and overall animal health (Gedek, 1999). Feed-grade antibiotics may serve to improve performance by several different mechanisms, all of which center on the influence of the gut microflora on the host animal. Research has shown that it is possible to achieve superior performance when rearing birds germ-free versus under normal conditions (Visek, 1978).

The body is specifically designed to withstand the colonization and translocation of microorganisms that can cause harm or dysfunction. Skin, mucous membranes and the inflammatory response to a wound are all designed to defend the animal against microbial attack. The gastrointestinal tract is a front-line defense against the constant invasion of foreign microbes. Antigenic characteristics are deflected by the gut-associated lymphatic tissue (GALT) when challenged by one of any number of microbial agents, which in turn leads to mounting a specific immune response. Two important organs associated with the GALT are the cecal tonsils and bursa. The epithelial tuft cells of the bursa are phagocytic and can present antigens to lymphocytes within the basal cortex, which ultimately allows immunological protection against the organism (Tizzard, 2000). The cellular and humoral complements are stimulated into a defensive mode in order to fend off the attack on the host's internal system. Along with this reaction comes an acute systemic response to infection or disease challenge (Klasing, 1988; Klasing, 1998; Cook, 2000). The acute systemic immune response can be a great consumer of metabolic energy causing alterations such as increased gluconeogenesis, increased lipolysis and an increase in the turnover rate of body proteins and amino acids (Klasing, 1988). Immunologically-challenged birds have been shown to produce several classes of cytokines that can increase metabolic rate, decrease appetite and possibly re-direct nutrients needed for immune response instead of skeletal muscle growth (Ferket and Qureshi, 1999). These actions of mounting an acute immune response may be a greater energetic drain than those of the specific immune responses, such as the manufacturing of B-cells, T-cells, macrophages and neutrophils.

Feeding antibiotics suppresses microbial growth in the gut, thereby reducing the immunological stress described above. Furthermore, antibiotics likely reduce the microbial by-products and toxins that impart negative effects on the energy needs of the animal. Zimber and Visek (1972) reported that microbial products such as ammonia (NH_3) and lactic acid can increase enterocyte cell division and alter mucosal barriers. The animal must then maintain more intestinal tissue with a higher turnover rate when microbes are present, thus robbing it of metabolic energy and possibly inhibiting the maximum absorption of vital nutrients (Visek, 1978). Indeed, the feeding of antibiotics has been shown to reduce the relative weight and length of the intestines (Visek, 1978; Postma *et al.*, 1999). This reduction in gut mass due to dietary supplementation of antibiotics is similar to that observed in germ-free birds. Stutz *et al.* (1983) reported reduced amounts of lamina propria, lymphoid tissue, reticuloendothelial cells, intestinal weight and moisture in germ-free birds.

Antibiotics produce their effects on the microflora by acting on the biochemical machinery of the microbial cell. Bambermycin specifically inhibits the synthesis of the bacterial cell wall by blocking the incorporation of the muramyl-pentapeptide into the cell wall peptidoglycan structure (Huber and Nesemann, 1968). In contrast to bambermycin, virginiamycin functions by inhibiting bacterial protein synthesis by acting on or binding to the 50s ribosomal subunit which blocks normal peptide bond formation (Parfait *et al.*, 1978; Cocito, 1973; Cocito, 1978). These antibiotics have a broad spectrum of activity and act mainly on Gram-positive microbes such as lactobacillus, bifidobacterium, and streptococcus. Antibiotics have been shown to primarily reduce lactic acid-producing bacteria which predominate in the upper gastrointestinal tract of the fowl (Cummings, 1995). Lactic acid is largely responsible for many of the detrimental effects associated with the gut microflora (Cummings, 1995). Both bambermycin and virginiamycin have been shown in numerous reports to increase weight gain and improve feed efficiency when fed to poultry (Waldroup *et al.*, 1970; Caston and Leeson, 1992; Waibel *et al.*, 1991; Buresh *et al.*, 1986). Much of the previously mentioned research agrees with the findings in our study. Overall, the addition of both bambermycin and virginiamycin improved body weights and feed:gain although virginiamycin was more influential on feed conversion than was bambermycin. It is noteworthy that both antibiotics and Bio-Mos improved feed:gain of poults from 0-3 weeks of age; a period when the gut microflora is not fully developed and stabilized. Therefore, these feed additives may convey benefit by stabilizing the gut microflora and limiting the colonization of pathogens.

Controversy over the feeding of antibiotics as growth promotants in Europe has increased because of fears concerning the development of antibiotic resistant microbes stemming from the use of these substances in food animals. Trade with the European Union along with the uncertain future of feeding antibiotics in the US poultry industry makes it prudent to seek alternatives to antibiotics as growth promotants.

In contrast to the mode of action of antibiotics, which limit or suppress growth of common Gram-positive microflora, mannanoligosaccharide (Bio-Mos) and other oligosaccharides can serve to prevent attachment of Gram-negative pathogens, thereby preventing attachment onto enterocytes and subsequent enteric refection. Bio-Mos is an oligosaccharide with a terminal mannose moiety. These mannose units mimic the receptors found on enterocytes on which the Gram-negative pathogens possessing Type-1 fimbriae are able to bind. In most cases, the ability of the pathogenic microbe to attach to the host cell surface is crucial for it to colonize, produce toxins and cause enteric disease. For example, unless *Vibrio cholerae* can successfully attach itself to the enterocyte of the intestinal wall, it is unable to initiate disease conditions despite the presence of large numbers of bacteria (Freter, 1969). Previous research has shown that bacterial adhesion can be mediated by fimbriae on the bacterial cell surface and that mannose and similar sugars can inhibit the agglutination of bacterial cells in culture by occupying cell surface binding sites necessary for bacterial adhesion (Sharon and Lis, 1993; Duguid *et al.*, 1966). Bacteria that bind to the mannose units on the oligosaccharide are ultimately excreted as these oligosaccharides cannot be digested by the host. Before excretion, however, the host may be still able to mount an immunlogical defense against the bacteria bound to the mannanoligosachoride because the barrier would still possess its antigenic properties as detected by the GALT.

The unique mode of action of Bio-Mos may make its application in commercial field conditions more effective than can be observed in university trials. While broad-spectrum antibiotics limit the growth of both beneficial and pathogenic bacteria in the gut, Bio-Mos may be more beneficial by being more specific. Therefore, the use and activity of Bio-Mos differ depending on the specific circumstances of the gut ecosystem. Indeed, Olsen (1995) concluded that turkeys raised under commercial farm conditions showed improvements in livability, performance, efficiency and condemnations when fed a diet supplemented with Bio-Mos. Turkeys fed Bio-Mos during a specific challenge from *Salmonella typhimurium* had decreased incidence of fecal contamination, while broilers fed Bio-Mos had reduced fecal counts of *Salmonella dublin* and *E. coli* (Spring *et al.,* 1996). Schoeni and Wong (1994) also showed a reduction in *Campylobacter jejuni* colonization when birds were fed Bio-Mos. Fairchild *et al.* (1999) observed improved performance of poults challenged with field isolates of *E. coli* and fed Bio-Mos. These responses may not be limited only to growth. Choi *et al.* (1994) reported a reduction in colony-forming units of *Salmonella typhimurium* in broiler chicks challenged while being fed a diet supplemented with fructo-oligosaccharides (FOS) (Fairchild *et al.*, 1999).

In contrast to antibiotics, Bio-Mos has been shown to enhance immune response. Cotter (1997) observed improved secondary and tertiary humoral immune responses during the PHA test in birds fed Bio-Mos while Savage *et al.* (1996) observed an enhancement of immunoglobulin production of both circulatory (plasma IgG) and secretory (IgA) levels in the turkey. The mechanism by which Bio-Mos enhances immunity is not fully understood, although it may be associated with enhanced stimulation of the GALT.

The degree of immunological response differs in various studies of oligosaccharide supplementation of poultry diets. Waldroup *et al.* (1993) demonstrated inconsistent performance results when FOS was fed to broilers, while Kumprecht and Zobac (1997) reported improved performance of broilers fed mannanoligosaccarides (Bio-Mos). Signs of bacterial infection and immune challenge may also be a function of numbers and not just the presence of pathogens. There may exist a certain concentration threshold necessary for blatant infection to occur (Garlich, 1999). Raibaud (1992) reported that clostridium species may be well-tolerated at log 10^7 within the gastrointestinal tract but become potentially toxic at levels of about log 10^8.

In addition to inhibiting bacterial colonization and immune stimulation, Bio-Mos may also improve the structural integrity of the gastrointestinal tract. Choi *et al.* (1994) reported a significant increase in the length of the ileal microvilli in birds challenged with *Salmonella typhimurium* while being fed FOS. Increases in the jejuna villi length (Iji and Tivey, 1999) as well as the length of the small intestine (Trevino *et al.,* 1990) have also been reported in birds fed FOS. Reasons for this response are unknown, although certain biochemical alterations due to the oligosaccharide molecule may be responsible for the long-term regulation of the gastrointestinal tract structure (Iji and Tivey, 1999).

The finding of a possible synergism between Bio-Mos and the antibiotic bambermycin is also an important aspect of this trial. Feeding the Bio-Mos in conjunction with bambermycin improved cumulative feed conversion from

0-12 and 0-18 weeks of age (Table 4). One positive role of the gastrointestinal microflora is that of competitive exclusion. The establishment of the normal microflora serves to occupy binding sites need by pathogenic bacteria to colonize the gut lining. Antimicrobial compounds produced by these microbes may also serve as a pathogen control mechanism. The feeding of antibiotics may increase the host susceptibility to pathogenic colonization because of their growth limiting effects on the normal microflora. George *et al.* (1982) concluded that bambermycins had no effect on the microbial resistance of *Salmonella typhimurium* of experimentally infected broiler chicks. Feeding Bio-Mos may limit the attachment capability of pathogens during this time when more attachment sites are available on the enterocyte, thus providing a secondary mode of protection during Gram-negative pathogenic challenge.

Summary

The bird's gastrointestinal ecosystem is an important aspect of poultry performance and flock health. Antibiotics improve performance by modifying the normal gut microflora, although their future use is questionable. We must increase our understanding of those mechanisms governing gut health and develop novel and alternative gut health management techniques. Oligosaccharides such as Bio-Mos have been demonstrated to improve poultry performance in numerous trials, including the one reported herein. This improvement in performance may be due in part to the reduction of the pathogenic load encountered by the bird under farm conditions. Future research must continue to evaluate the effectiveness of such alternatives and help us learn more about the effects they have on health, metabolism, and nutritional status of the bird.

References

Buresh, R.E., R.H. Harms and R.D. Miles. 1986. A differential response in turkey poults to various antibiotics in diets designed to be deficient or adequate in certain essential nutrients. Poultry Science 65:2314-2317.

Caston, L.J. and S. Leeson. 1992. The response of broiler turkeys to bambermycin. Can. J. Anim. Sci. 72:445-448.

Choi, K.H., H. Namkung and I.K. Paik. 1994. Effects of dietary fructooligosaccharides on the suppression of intestinal colonization of *Salmonella typhimurium* in broiler chickens. Korean Journal of Animal Science 36:271-284.

Cocito, C. 1973. The ribosomal cycle in bacteria treated with an inhibitor of protein synthesis. Biochimie 55:309-316.

Cocito, C. 1978. Pressure dissociation of bacterial ribosomes and reassociation of ribosomal subunits. Mol. Gen. Genet. 162:43-50.

Cook, M.E. 2000. Interplay of management, microbes, genetics, immunity affects animal growth, development. Feedstuffs (Jan 3):11-12.

Cotter, P.F. 1997. Modulation of the immune response: current perceptions and future prospects with an example from poultry and Bio-Mos. In: Biotechnology in the Feed Industry, Proceedings of Alltech's 13th Annual Symposium (T.P. Lyons and K.A. Jacques, eds). Nottingham University Press, Nottingham, UK. pp. 195-203.

Cummings, T.S. 1995. The effect of probiotics and antibiotics on the intestinal microflora of poultry. In: 22nd Annual Carolina Poultry Nutrition Conference. Carolina Feed Industry Association, Dec. 5-6. pp. 88-90.

Duguid, J.P., E.S. Anderson and I. Campbell. 1966. Fimbriae and adhesive properties in salmonella. J. Path. Bact. 92:107-138.

Evangelisti, D.G., A.R. English, A.E. Girard, J.E. Lynch and I.A. Solomons. 1975. Influence of subtherapeutic levels of oxytetracycline on *Salmonella typhimurium* in swine, calves, and chickens. Antimicrobial Agents and Chemotherapy 8:664-672.

Fairchild, A.S., J.L. Grimes, M.J. Wineland and F.T. Jones. 1998. Disk diffusion antimicrobial susceptibility tests against avian *Escherichia coli* isolates. Poultry Sci. 77(Suppl. 1):94.

Fairchild, A.S., J.L. Grimes, F.W. Edens, M.J. Wineland, F.T. Jones and A.E. Sefton. 1999. Effect of hen age, Bio-Mos and bambermycin on susceptibility of turkey poults to oral *Escherichia coli* challenge. In: Under the Microscope: Biotechnology in the Feed Industry, Proceedings of Alltech's 15th Annual Symposium (T.P. Lyons and K.A. Jacques, eds), Nottingham University Press, Nottingham, UK. pp. 185-201.

Ferket, P.R. and M.A. Qureshi. 1999. The turkey immune system and immunomodulators. In: Proceedings of the 12th European Symposium on Poultry Nutrition. (R.P. Kwakkel and J.P.M. Bos, eds). Worlds Poultry Science Association, Dutch branch. Het Spelderholt, Beekbergen, the Netherlands. pp. 17-30.

Francis, C., D.M. Janky, A.S. Arafa and R.H. Harms. 1978. Interrelationship of lactobacillus and zinc bacitracin in the diets of turkey poults. Poultry Sci. 57:1687-1689.

Freter, R. 1969. Studies of the mechanism of action of intestinal antibody in experimental cholera. Tex. Rep. Biol. Med. 27:299.

Gadd, J. 1997. Life without antibiotic digestive enhancers. In: Biotechnology in the Feed Industry, Proceedings of Alltech's 13th Annual Symposium (T.P. Lyons and K.A. Jacques, eds). Nottingham University Press, Nottingham, UK. pp. 277-291.

Garlich, J.D. 1999. Microbiology of the avian intestinal tract. Presented at the XVI Congresso Latinoamerican de Avicultura. Lima, Peru. Sep. 24.

Gedek, B.R. 1999. Mode of actions of probiotics in poultry diets. In: Proceedings of the 12th European Symposium on Poultry Nutrition. (R.P.

Kwakkel and J.P.M. Bos, eds). World's Poultry Science Association, Dutch branch. Het Spelderholt, Beekbergen, the Netherlands. pp. 83-90.

George, B.A., D.J. Fagerberg, C.L. Quarles, J.M. Fenton and G.A. McKinley. 1982. Effect of bambermycins on quantity, prevalence, duration, and antimicrobial resistance of *salmonella typhimurium* in experimentally infected broiler chickens. Am. J. Vet. Res. 43:299-303.

Gustafson, R.H. and R.E. Bowen. 1997. A review: antibiotic use in animal agriculture. J. of Appl. Bacteriol. 83:531-541.

Huber, G. and G. Nesemann. 1968. Moenomycin, an inhibitor of cell wall synthesis. Biochemical and Biophysical Research Communications 30:7-13.

Iji, P.A. and D.R. Tivey. 1999. The use of oligosaccharides in broiler diets. In: Proceedings of the 12th European Symposium on Poultry Nutrition. (R.P. Kwakkel and J.P.M. Bos, eds). World's Poultry Science Association, Dutch branch. Het Spelderholt, Beekbergen, the Netherlands. pp. 193-201.

Klasing, K.C. 1988. Nutritional aspects of leukocytic cytokines. Journal of Nutrition 118:1436-1446.

Klasing, K.C. 1998. Nutritional modulation of resistance to infectious diseases. Poultry Science 77:1119-1125.

Kumprecht, I. and P. Zobac. 1997. The effect of mannan-oligosaccharides in feed mixtures on the performance of chicken broilers. Zivocisna Vyroba 42:117-124.

National Research Council Nutrient Requirements of Poultry. 1994. 9th Revised Edition.National Academy Press, Washington, D.C. 1994.

Newman, K. 1994. Mannan-oligosaccharides: Natural polymers with significant impact on the gastrointestinal microflora and the immune system. *In*: Biotechnology in the Feed Industry, Proceedings of Alltech's 10th Annual Symposium (T.P. Lyons and K.A. Jacques, eds.) Nottingham University Press, Nottingham, UK, pp. 167-174.

Nurmi, E. and M. Rantala. 1973. New aspects of salmonella infection in broiler production. Nature (London) 241:210-211.

Ofek, I., D. Mirelman and N. Sharon. 1977. Adherence of *Escherichia coli* to human mucosal cells mediated by mannose receptors. Nature (London) 265:623-625.

Olsen, R. 1995. Mannanoligosaccharides: Experience in commercial turkey production. In: Biotechnology in the Feed Industry, Proceedings of Alltech's 11th Annual Symposium. (T.P. Lyons and K.A. Jacques, eds), Nottingham University Press, Nottingham, UK. pp. 389-392.

Parfait, R., M.P. de Bethume and C. Cocito. 1978. A spectrofluorimetric study of the interaction between virginiamycin S and bacterial ribosomes. Mol. Gen. Genet. 166:45-51.

Postma, J., P.R. Ferket, W.J. Croom and R.P. Kwakkel. 1999. In: Proceedings of the 12th European Symposium on Poultry Nutrition. (R.P. Kwakkel and J.P.M. Bos, eds). World's Poultry Science Association, Dutch branch. Het Spelderholt, Beekbergen, the Netherlands. p. 188.

Raibaud, P. 1992. Bacterial interactions in the gut. In: Probiotics: The Scientific Basis. (R. Fuller, ed.). Chapman & Hall, New York, NY. Ch2.

SAS Institute. 1992. Version 6.08. SAS Institute, Inc., Cary, NC.

Savage, T.F. and E.I. Zakrzewska. 1996. The performance of male turkeys fed a starter diet containing a mannanoligosaccharide (Bio-Mos) from day old to eight weeks of age. *In*: Biotechnology in the Feed Industry. Proceedings of Alltech's 12th Annual Symposium. (T.P. Lyons and K.A. Jacques, eds.), Nottingham University Press, Nottingham, UK, 47-54.

Savage, T.F., P.F. Cotter and E.I. Zakrzewska. 1996. The effect of feeding a mannan oligosaccharide on immunoglobulins, plasma IgG and bile IgA of Wrolstad MW male turkeys. Poultry Science 75 (Suppl. 1):Abstract S129.

Schoeni, J.L. and A.C.L. Wong. 1994. Inhibition of *Campylobacter jejuni* colonization in chicks by defined CE bacteria. Appl. Environ. Mircobiol. 60:1191-1197.

Scioli, C., S. Esposito, G. Anzilotti, A. Pavone and C. Pennucci, 1983. Transferable drug resistance in *Escherichia coli* isolated from antibiotic-fed chickens. Poultry Sci. 62:382-384.

Sharon, N. and H. Lis. 1993. Carbohydrates in cell recognition. Scientific American 268:82-89.

Spring, P., K.A. Dawson, K.E. Newman and C. Wenk. 1996. Effect of MOS on different cecal parameters and on cecal concentrations of enteric bacteria in challenged broiler chicks. Poultry Science 75 (Suppl. 1):Abstract S138.

Spring, P., C. Wenk, K.A. Dawson and K.E. Newman. 2000. The effects of dietary mannanoligosaccharides on cecal parameters and the concentrations of enteric bacteria in the ceca of salmonella-challenged broiler chicks. Poultry Science 79:205-211.

Stutz, M.W., S.L. Johnson and F.R. Judith. 1983. Effects of diet, bacitracin and body weight restrictions on the intestine of broiler chicks. Poultry Science 62:1626-1632.

Surawicz, C.M., G.W. Elmer, P. Speelman, L.V. McFarland, J. Chinn and G. van Belle. 1989. Prevention of antibiotic-associated diarrhea by *Saccharomyces boulardii*: A prospective study. Gastroenterology 96:552-556.

Trevino, J., C. Centeno, A. Brenes, P. Yuste and L. Rubio. 1990. Effect of dietary oligosaccharides on the digestion of pea starch by growing chicks. Animal Feed Science & Technology 30:313-319.

Tizard, I., 2000. El Sistema immune aviol. Proceedings Curso Actulizacion Sabre immulogia Aviar., Page 33-38, February 18., Mexico City, Mexico.

Visek, W.J. 1978. The mode of growth promotion by antibiotics. J. Animal Science 46:1447-1469.

Waibel, P.E., J.C. Halvorson, S.L. Noll and S.L. Hoffbeck. 1991. Influence of virginiamycin on growth and efficiency of large white turkeys. Poultry Science 70: 837-847.

Waldroup, P.W., C.M. Hillard, R.J. Mitchell and D.R. Sloan. 1970. Response of broilers to moenomycin. Poultry Science 49:1264-1267.

Waldroup, A.L., J.T. Skinner, R.E. Hierholzer and P.W. Waldroup. 1993. An evaluation of fructooligosaccharide in diets for broiler chickens and effects on salmonella contamination of carcasses. Poultry Science 72:643-650.

Zimber, A. and W.J. Visek. 1972. Effect of urease injections on DNA synthesis in mice. Amer. J. Physiology 223:1004.

Maximising nutrient utilisation: from enzymes to nutraceuticals

PAUL J. MOUGHAN AND V. RAVINDRAN

Institute of Food, Nutrition and Human Health, Massey University, Palmerston North, New Zealand

Introduction

Toward the end of last century a major lifestyle trend emerged in the developing nations emphasizing wellness and disease prevention in the human population rather than treatment therapies. This focus is expected to strengthen, rather than diminish, as the relatively affluent and well-educated 'baby boomers' of the 1950s and 1960s progressively reach middle age and begin to contemplate their retirement years. It has been calculated that in the US alone, and in the period from 1996 through to 2006, a 'baby boomer' (defined as someone born between 1946 and 1964) will turn 50 years of age every seven and a half seconds (Sloan, 1998). Such individuals are acutely aware of health and lifestyle issues. A further significant driver of this trend, fuelled at government level, is the escalating cost of traditional disease treatment. Allied to this, there has been a growing realisation of the pivotal role of nutrition in disease prevention and the maintenance of human health. Epidemiological studies have exposed statistical correlations between the intake of certain dietary constituents and the development, or alternatively the prevention, of various non-communicable diseases. In many cases, controlled human intervention studies have supported the epidemiological observations; and a considerable body of knowledge and level of understanding has developed around the nexus of nutrition, health and longevity. It has even been postulated (the Barker hypothesis, Barker, 1994; Barker, 1999), and considerable supportive evidence has been amassed, that a propensity to develop certain diseases in later life may be related to maternal nutrition and subsequently modified by the nutritional habits of the individual. Barker reports that the heavier the baby, the lower the incidence of coronary heart disease in later life. Barker found that a plump baby who gains weight well in the first year of life has a coronary infarct rate in later life one third that of lower weight babies. Barker has also found that blood pressure in the adult is clearly related to infant birth weight and placental size, with a large placenta and a low weight being highly associated with increased systolic pressures in adults, an association stronger than that linking salt consumption to blood pressure. These findings have far-reaching implications.

Nutraceuticals and functional foods

DEVELOPMENTS IN HUMAN NUTRITION

The food industry has been quick to capitalise upon the changes in societal attitudes and today pays far more attention to nutrient contents and bioavailability than was the case in the past. This growing emphasis on lifestyle has also influenced the emergence and vigorous marketing of a completely new category of food, the so-called 'functional foods' and 'nutraceuticals'. Functional foods are foods that when consumed as part of a normal diet elicit specific physiological effects on the consumer in addition to sustenance derived from the food nutrients. Certain foods, when consumed on a sustained basis, may have quite subtle longer-term effects on aspects of physiological function, whereas yet other foods and natural food extracts may have acute pharmacological effects. It is in the latter case that the terms 'nutraceutical' or 'pharmafood' may be applied. Indeed, in the growing market of nutraceutical and functional foods, there is a merging of the traditional food, agribusiness and pharmaceutical industries. Moreover, and as the human genome project gains momentum, the very genetic basis of the so-called lifestyle diseases is being unravelled and described. This will soon allow the early identification (pre-symptomatic) of individuals prone to developing certain diseases, thus heralding specific dietary and lifestyle prescriptions.

Functional foods and their place in a balanced diet are going to become increasingly important. The functional foods revolution began in earnest in the early 1980s with the health-related benefits of materials such as plant fibre, fish oil, calcium and probiotics attaining respectability following publication of clinical studies in the medical literature and with physicians beginning to publicly promote their use. Examples are diverse, including the use of ß-carotene in the prevention of cancer, pyridoxine to treat and prevent depression, tryptophan to induce sleepiness, garlic (allicin) to reduce artherosclerosis, cranberry juice to prevent urinary tract infections, the role of calcium in treating osteoporosis, phytoestrogens, lycopene, antioxidants, and many others. An example of one of the earlier and now well established functional foods is oat bran, whereby the soluble oat fibre acts in the alimentary canal to bring about a reduction in blood cholesterol. For hypercholestrolaemic individuals, the inclusion of oatbran in the diet (e.g. oatbran enriched cereals) can be used as part of an overall strategy to lower blood cholesterol, without resorting to prescription drugs. A further example of a cholesterol-lowering functional food, and one that has been enormously successful commercially, is that of phytosterol enriched margarines and spreads. Animal products may also be manipulated to produce unique functional foods, presenting the animal and feed industries with an opportunity to develop differentiated, branded food products. Examples here include omega-3 enriched hen's eggs ('heart-smart') and high vitamin C/vitamin E pork, with antioxidant potential, reduced drip loss and a superior shelf life.

There are many other examples of functional foods and nutraceuticals and many more products can be expected to enter the market as product development and clinical testing increases apace. The increasing appreciation of the diverse physiological roles of food constituents is also having a profound influence on the contemporary view of nutritional science itself and of the very definition of 'a nutrient'. In the past, for example, volatile fatty acids were viewed as products of the fermentative breakdown of fibre, acting as an energy source for the host animal, whereas now their role in the development and regulation of gut function is being emphasised (Sakata, 1987). Proteins were once viewed as simply supplying amino acids for body protein synthesis whereas now the distinct and diverse physiological effects of dietary peptides are being discovered and documented with an increasing frequency. Fatty acids, far from acting solely as sources of energy or as body energy stores, are now known to quite profoundly affect red blood cell membrane composition, with consequent physiological effects.

WHAT OF THE ANIMAL FEEDSTUFFS INDUSTRY?

The opportunities afforded by the often potent physiological effects of dietary constituents being exploited by the international foods industry are also open to the compound feed industry; and we have only seen the beginnings of biotechnological innovation in this area. The potential to manipulate animal health and performance through understanding the physiological roles of feed constituents is immense and will undoubtedly be a major focal point in research and development for the biotechnology industry in this century. In the following, two biotechnology products already available commercially (namely enzymes and peptides) will be discussed in detail as examples of how animal 'function' can be influenced by diet, other than through nutriment.

Bioactive peptides

A new technology offering considerable potential to the feed and animal industries is that of bioactive peptides. As mentioned above, dietary protein was once viewed as a source of amino acids, primarily acting as building blocks for body proteins. Now, however, it is understood that during the digestive process, peptides which are 'hidden' in an inactive state within the protein sequence may be released to act as physiological modulators, both locally in the gut and systemically. Both animal and vegetable proteins contain potentially bioactive sequences, though much of the research to date has been conducted with milk proteins.

An opioid activity of peptides derived from partial enzymatic digestion of milk proteins and wheat gluten was reported in the literature as early as 1979 (Brantl *et al.*, 1979; Zioudrou *et al.*, 1979). Following on from this discovery, much research into bioactive peptides has been conducted and many sequences and their physiological functions have been defined. In spite of this research effort, however, the area is still very much in its infancy and undoubtedly there is a great deal yet to be discovered. The potential for bioactive peptides in the development of functional foods for humans, farm animals and in the pet food industry is truly great. Bioactive peptides are now understood to have a wide range of physiological effects, some of which are listed in Table 1. Evidence (Lord, 1986; Webb *et al.*, 1992; Gardner, 1998) that peptides can be released during digestion and absorbed to enter the portal blood intact provides a basis to explain the wide range of systemic activities so far discovered and documented. Moreover, the existence of bioactive peptides themselves offers an explanation for the often observed varying effect of diet on physiological response.

Table 1. Some reported physiological effects of bioactive peptides released from foods during digestion.

1.	Modulation of gastrointestinal motility
2.	Stimulation of secretory processes
3.	Mineral binding
4.	Antibacterial properties
5.	Immunomodulation
6.	Antithrombotic activity
7.	Inhibition of angiotensin converting enzyme (ACE) in the control of hypertension
8.	Analgesic (pain relief) and other neuroactive effects

An array of bioactive peptides and protein hydrolysates can now be produced commercially, creating the opportunity for dietary addition. Indeed it is predicted that such materials will be used increasingly in the feed industry (Power and Murphy, 1999) and wider foods industry (Frokjaer, 1994). Casein derived peptides are already being used as food supplements (eg. phosphopeptides) and pharmaceutically (Meisel, 1997).

There have been a number of reports in the literature describing a role for bioactive peptides in regulating stomach emptying rate and gastrointestinal motility in mammals (Daniel *et al.*, 1990, Kil and Froetschel, 1994; Froetschel, 1996), gut secretory and absorptive activity (Schlimme *et al*, 1988; Ben Mansour *et al.*, 1988) and gut tissue growth (Birke *et al.*, 1993). Such observations are consistent with findings from our own group working at Massey University, New Zealand, which has described a central role for diet-derived peptides in influencing gut protein dynamics. The following provides a brief summary of our studies to date and again highlights the importance of diet-derived peptides. The gut is a highly metabolic organ, accounting for a significant proportion of total energetic and protein costs during animal growth, and thus regulatory activities assume a disproportionate order of importance.

In our first set of studies we sought to determine the effect of nitrogenous alimentation *per se* (i.e. excluding effects of proteins and peptides) on the net effect of gut protein secretion and reabsorption (i.e. endogenous loss measured at the end of the small bowel). A semi-synthetic nitrogen-free diet (control) was formulated to mimic the effect of the non-protein component of a diet, along with a series of similar diets containing synthetic free amino acids as the sole source of nitrogen. By not including certain dietary non-essential amino acids in some of the diets and by also omitting certain dietary essential amino acids in others (but with accompanying intravenous infusion), we could directly and unambiguously measure endogenous amino acid loss at the terminal ileum. The studies were undertaken with laboratory rats and pigs as generalised mammalian model animals. The animals consumed the amino acid-containing diets readily, grew normally and were in a positive body nitrogen balance. A comparison of endogenous ileal amino acid loss for animals receiving the synthetic amino acid-based diets and the protein-free control is given in Table 2. In spite of the treatment groups being in positive body nitrogen balance and receiving a gut luminal amino acid supply, the endogenous amino acid flows (the net result of overall gut secretion and reabsorption) were not higher than for the control (protein-free) animals that were in negative body nitrogen balance and deprived of a direct dietary amino acid supply to the gut. The results of these studies indicated that gut protein dynamics do not appear to be influenced by nitrogenous alimentation *per se*.

The second series of experiments sought to determine whether feeding the animal protein rather than amino acids would have any effect. Here it was necessary to devise techniques to distinguish between undigested dietary protein and the endogenous protein flow. Isotopic markers may be used to make such a distinction, but their use is fraught with difficulties leading to inaccuracy. It occurred to us that if we could completely transform lysine in dietary proteins to an analogue such as homoarginine, then we could, by feeding animals the guanidinated protein, directly measure the endogenous loss of lysine. Homoarginine is absorbed in a similar manner to

Table 2. **Mean endogenous ileal amino acid flows (µg/g dry matter intake) in the growing rat and pig determined using purified diets each devoid of a specific amino acid or based on a protein-free dietary control.**

Amino acid[4]	Rat[1]		Rat[2]		Pig[3]	
	Synthetic diet	Control	Synthetic diet	Control	Synthetic diet	Control
Lysine	212	228	-	-	284	252
Aspartic acid	704	585	-	-	-	-
Serine	282	290	254	220	-	-
Glutamic acid	597	615	593	524	-	-
Alanine	-	-	195	200	-	-

[1]Skilton *et al.*, 1988.
[2]Darragh *et al.*, 1990.
[3]Butts *et al.*, 1993. The 15 kg bodyweight pigs received lysine intravenously.
[4]None of the differences between the mean flows for each amino acid were significant ($P>0.05$).

lysine and is partially converted in the liver to lysine. In this case, animals would consume a protein-containing diet and would be in positive body nitrogen balance. We were successful in completely guanidinating proteins (Rutherfurd and Moughan, 1990) and subsequently several studies were conducted with the laboratory rat using this approach. We were also aware that there are naturally occurring proteins that are completely devoid of certain amino acids. An example of such a protein is zein, which can be isolated from the maize grain and is completely devoid of lysine. Accordingly, we prepared semi-synthetic zein-based diets and fed them to young pigs, which were simultaneously infused intravenously with lysine. Here again, the gut tissues were supplied with nitrogenous material and the animals were in positive body nitrogen balance. The ingestion of protein led to a dramatic almost doubling of the endogenous ileal lysine flow (Table 3).

Table 3. Mean endogenous flows of lysine (mg/g dry matter intake)[1] at the terminal ileum of the growing rat fed guanidinated protein-based diets, a zein based diet or a protein-free control diet.

Guanidination study[2]	Guanidinated gelatin	Guanidinated soya	Guanidinated casein	Protein-free
Lysine flow	488[a]	442[a]	472[a]	239[b]

Zein study[3]	Zein	Protein-free		
Lysine flow	389[a]	252[b]		

[1]Means with different superscripts were significantly different ($P< 0.01$).
[2]Moughan and Rutherfurd (1990), Moughan and Rutherfurd (1991). Lysine was supplied by liver conversion from homoarginine.
[3]Butts *et al.*, 1993.

The question now arose as to whether the pronounced effect of dietary protein on gut protein dynamics may be caused by peptides. To test this hypothesis, it was required to develop yet a further experimental technique.

Our resultant methodology, referred to as the enzyme-hydrolysed protein method, is now commonly employed in laboratories throughout the world to determine gut endogenous losses. In this approach an enzymic hydrolysate of protein is fed to the animal as the sole source of nitrogen in a purified diet. The size of the peptides in the hydrolysate is less than 5000 Daltons. Ileal digesta are subsequently collected from the animals and the material is centrifuged and ultrafiltered (10,000 Dalton MW cut-off). Any unabsorbed dietary peptides are discarded in the ultrafiltrate, with the precipitate plus retentate being an estimate of gut endogenous loss. This estimate is slightly low due to the loss of a small amount of endogenous free amino acids and peptides in the ultrafiltrate. Our group has applied this technique widely in a number of studies, with the consistent result of a significant ($P<0.05$) effect of the peptides on gut endogenous amino acid loss (Table 4). Net endogenous ileal amino acid flows, determined after administering peptides, for a range of simple-stomached animal species including humans are shown in Table 5. The inordinately high gut losses in the domestic cat are notable. Further studies have demonstrated that not only do the dietary peptides have a profound effect on gut secretory and reabsorptive activity, but that the effect is dose dependent (Figure 1). It appears that the breakdown products of dietary proteins themselves may assist in regulating the digestive processes. Current research is investigating which of the peptides present in the complex hydrolysates are responsible for the effect, what are the mechanisms of action and what components of the endogenous milieu are affected. Clearly, given the quantitative importance of gut protein dynamics in overall body protein metabolism (Moughan, 1999), there are opportunities here to manipulate the gut processes. One can imagine, for example, enhanced digestive function arising from dietary peptide supplementation or significant increases in growth efficiency brought about by a reduction in endogenous amino acid loss consequent upon removing the effects of key bioactive peptides. This research field is fertile and the future exciting.

The observations described above regarding the role of bioactive peptides in regulating digestive function hopefully serve to underscore the biological importance of these components in production farm animals. Such peptides are potent and have wide-ranging effects. Industrial production of bioactive peptides heralds new opportunities for functional foods in the livestock and pet food industries.

Exogenous enzymes

The potential usefulness of enzyme preparations to improve performance in poultry has been known for many years (Hastings, 1946; Fry *et al.*, 1957). However, it has only been possible in the past decade to produce feed enzymes cheaply enough to warrant their use in commercial situations. This has been due primarily to a better understanding of target substrates and

Table 4. Mean endogenous ileal amino acid flows (µg/g dry matter intake) for rats and pigs determined after administering dietary peptides versus a protein-free control.[*][1]

Amino acid	Rat		Pig	
	Hydrolysate	Protein-free	Hydrolysate	Protein-free
Lysine	275	172**	461	312 *
Methionine	127	53**	-	-
Cysteine	142	56**	-	-
Histidine	223	133**	319	231 [ns]
Phenylalanine	237	212**	278	238 [ns]
Tyrosine	179	161[ns]	244	181 [ns]
Threonine	525	311**	909	572 *
Leucine	386	256**	528	400 *
Isoleucine	313	159**	504	230 ***
Valine	341	234**	593	321 **
Alanine	349	213**	485	436 [ns]
Aspartic acid	748	636**	1531	754 **
Aginine	274	217**	373	480 [ns]
Serine	759	374**	1383	550 ***
Glutamic acid	1366	701**	3378	786 ***
Glycine	796	765[ns]	682	1660 *
Proline	493	584*	1419	3558 *

[*]Donkoh *et al.*, 1995; Moughan *et al.*, 1992.
[1]Animals were fed a semisynthetic enzyme hydrolysed casein (MW <5,000 Da) based diet. Digesta were centrifuged and ultrafiltered (MW cutoff = 10,000 Da) and the precipitate + retentate taken as the endogenous component.

Table 5. Endogenous amino acid loss (µg/g dry matter intake) at the end of the small bowel determined using the enzyme hydrolysed protein (casein) method with the laboratory rat, pig, cat, chicken and human.[*]

Amino acid	Laboratory rat[1]	Pig[1]	Domestic cat	Chicken	Human[1]
Lysine	312	455	1101	303	614
Methionine	125	—	411	—	269
Cysteine	188	—	853	—	367
Histidine	216	339	897	288	561
Threonine	689	951	2127	606	857
Valine	538	640	1687	604	978
Phenylalanine	236	332	1015	278	442
Tyrosine	220	301	1046	283	439
Isoleucine	486	510	1205	530	564
Leucine	560	636	1823	514	808
Aginine	303	442	948	—	478

[*]Butts *et al.*, 1991; Moughan *et al.*, 1992; Butts *et al.*, 1993; Donkoh *et al.*, 1995; Feng Yu *et al.*, 1995; Hendriks *et al.*, 1996.
[1]Overall means representing three rat and two pig studies and a mean for six ileostomised human subjects. The chicken and human data are unpublished.

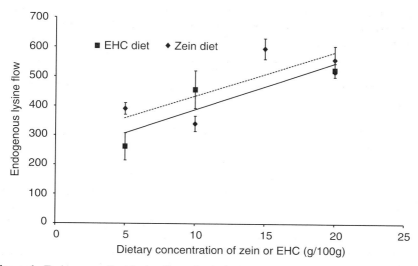

Figure 1. Endogenous ileal lysine flows (μg/g dry matter intake) in growing rats (n=6) receiving diets containing different amounts of zein, and growing pigs (n=7) receiving diets containing different amounts of enzyme hydrolysed casein (EHC). A linear model is fitted to the EHC data (—) and the zein data (- - - -).

advances in microbiological technology. Enzymes may have their effect by directly altering the rate of hydrolysis of bonds thus releasing nutrients or by affecting physico-chemical properties (eg. viscosity of digesta). In either case, physiological mechanisms are being affected and enzymes can be considered as 'functional' additives.

The poultry industry is the largest user of feed enzymes. The highly integrated nature of the poultry sector has enabled the faster uptake of these new technologies, and exogenous enzymes are now well accepted as a feed enhancer to improve nutrient digestibility and efficiency of nutrient utilization in poultry. Progress into pig diets, on the other hand, has been slower due partly to the more fragmented nature of the pig industry and partly to species differences in production responses. However, interest within the pig industry, especially for weaner pigs, is gaining momentum. The popularity of feed enzymes is a consequence of changing social and economic philosophies and emphasis on efficient animal production with minimal environmental damage. Consumers are demanding an all-natural feed supply. Feed enzymes, especially from non-genetically modified organisms, are acceptable alternatives because they are common in daily life.

The primary objective of adding enzymes to animal feeds is to improve the utilization of nutrients in raw materials. This is achieved by one or more of the following mechanisms: 1) degradation of specific bonds in ingredients not usually degraded by endogenous digestive enzymes, 2) degradation of anti-nutritive factors that lower the availability of nutrients, 3) increased accessibility of nutrients to endogenous digestive enzymes, and 4) supplementation of the enzyme capacity of young animals.

BEYOND CEREAL APPLICATIONS: THE POTENTIAL FOR PROTEIN-HYDROLYZING ENZYMES

Although the use of exogenous enzymes in animal nutrition has increased considerably in recent years, most of the use has been in cereal-based diets. The enzymes widely used by the industry are the glycanases (xylanases and ß-glucanases) that cleave the non-starch polysaccharides in some cereals, and more recently, microbial phytases that target the phytate-complexes in plant-derived ingredients. The use of exogenous glycanases in wheat- and barley-based diets is now widespread in many parts of the world. Excellent reviews on the influence of xylanases on animal performance and nutrient utilization and on their modes of action are available (Annison and Choct, 1991; Bedford and Schulze, 1998). The ecological benefits and production responses from the use of microbial phytase are current topics, but this will not be covered herein since a session of the symposium is devoted to this enzyme.

Several enzyme preparations, designed towards improving the utilization of protein, starch or lipids in specific ingredients, are also currently available. In particular, proteases are of interest because protein is the most expensive item in animal diets. Poorly digested proteins not only lower the efficiency of nitrogen utilization, but also contribute to odour problems and ground water pollution. Whenever an ingredient or diet is utilized more efficiently, there is obviously a reduction in manure output per unit weight gain and the ecological benefits can be quite substantial. The use of proteases can be valuable in this context to improve the nutritive value of protein meals by hydrolyzing certain protein types that are resistant to digestive enzymes and/or by complementing the animal's own digestive system.

Studies with Allzyme Vegpro in proteins for pig diets

Allzyme Vegpro, an enzyme complement with protease activity, has been proven to be successful in improving energy utilization, nutrient digestibility and growth performance of poultry and pigs fed on diets containing a variety of vegetable proteins. At the Monogastric Research Centre at Massey University, we have evaluated the influence of Vegpro on the apparent digestible energy content and total tract nutrient digestibility of a number of vegetable proteins, including soyabean meal and canola meal (Pluske *et al.*, 1999). In this study, growing pigs (35 to 45 kg) were housed individually and fed semi-purified assay diets containing the vegetable protein as the sole source of nitrogen. The inert marker chromium oxide was included in the diets to determine digestibility. Following a seven day acclimatisation period, grab faecal samples were obtained daily for five days, pooled, processed and subsequently analysed for chromium, gross energy and nitrogen. Although faecal digestibility is not an accurate measure of amino acid digestion in pigs due to the modifying effects of hindgut microorganisms, the trends observed demonstrate that the utilization of protein and energy were improved by the use of Vegpro (Table 6).

Table 6. Influence of Allzyme Vegpro on the apparent digestible energy (ADE) and faecal digestibilities of nitrogen and amino acids in soyabean meal and canola meal for growing pigs.[1]

	Soyabean meal		Canola meal		Vegpro effect
	Control	Vegpro	Control	Vegpro	
ADE, (MJ/kg DM)	15.9	16.1	14.1	15.5	NS
Digestibility coefficient					
Nitrogen	0.860	0.869	0.783	0.813	NS
Histidine	0.933	0.940	0.857	0.911	**
Isoleucine	0.854	0.870	0.779	0.802	**
Leucine	0.859	0.881	0.808	0.835	**
Lysine	0.866	0.869	0.757	0.787	**
Methionine	0.727	0.777	0.733	0.824	*
Phenylalanine	0.869	0.888	0.800	0.833	**
Threonine	0.842	0.868	0.742	0.812	**
Valine	0.848	0.864	0.794	0.818	**

[1]From Pluske *et al.*, 1999.
*P<0.05; **P<0.01; NS = not significant.

These improvements in nutrient digestibility have been confirmed and benefits in terms of growth responses seen in a subsequent trial with growing-finishing pigs fed barley-based diets containing soyabean meal or canola meal. The most marked responses to Vegpro were observed in a trial involving Australian sweet lupins (*Lupinus angustifolius*). Addition of Vegpro to a barley-based diet containing 300 g/kg lupins improved the digestible energy by 5.4%, growth rate by 8.4% and the feed efficiency by 8.0% (Table 7). As a consequence of improved gain, pigs fed diets with Vegpro had a 4.5% heavier carcass. However, the carcass fat of pigs fed diets with Vegpro was 1.8 mm thicker (at P_2). It appears that the additional energy released by the enzyme was responsible for the increase in fat thickness. Under these circumstances, a revised diet formulation taking into consideration the increments in nutrient digestibility is clearly necessary to maintain the carcass quality at slaughter. An additional benefit from the use of the enzyme is decreased nitrogen excretion. In the study, a 10% decrease in faecal nitrogen output was observed.

Table 7. Influence of Vegpro on apparent digestible energy (ADE), faecal nitrogen (N) digestibility, nitrogen excretion and the performance of pigs fed a barley-based diet containing 300 g/kg sweet lupins.[1]

	Control	Vegpro	Significance
ADE, MJ/kg	12.9	13.6	**
N digestibility	0.768	0.787	†
N excreted, g/day	15.1	13.7	†
Performance data			
n	14	15	
Daily gain, kg	1.01	1.09	*
Feed conversion, kg meal/kg gain	2.98	2.74	*
Dressing out, %	65.3	65.9	NS
Backfat thickness (P$_2$), mm	13.1	14.9	NS

[1]From Pluske, 1999.
**$P<0.01$; *$P<0.05$; †$P<0.10$; NS = not significant.

Increasing fat utilization: studies with Lipozyme

Full-fat rice bran, a by-product of white rice milling, is available abundantly in the Asian region. It is a potentially important feedstuff for broilers containing relatively high levels of crude protein (130-170 g/kg) and fat (130-200 g/kg). Early studies, funded by Alltech and conducted at Massey University, showed that rice bran also contains high levels of non-starch polysaccharides; but it does not appear that these are anti-nutritive for broiler chickens (Annison *et al.*, 1995). However, the AME content of rice bran is lower than anticipated on the basis of its gross energy content (20-22 MJ/kg dry matter); and this may be attributable in part to a low secretion of pancreatic lipase (Warren and Farrell, 1990). Supplementation with exogenous lipases may be beneficial in assisting birds to extract energy from diets containing rice bran. To this end, Allzyme Lipozyme has been tested in a series of trials at Massey University. Initial research, (summarised in Table 8), showed that supplementation with lipase led to a significant reduction in excreta energy concentration (16.57 *vs.* 15.78 MJ/kg dry matter), which translated to a higher apparent metabolisable energy (AME) value for rice bran (12.15 *vs.* 12.47 MJ/kg dry matter) for adult cockerels.

Table 8. The effect of Lipozyme (100 mg/kg diet) on excreta energy concentration and the AME content of rice bran fed to adult cockerels (mean ± SEM).[1]

Treatment	Excreta energy (MJ/kg DM)	AME (MJ/kg, as fed basis)
Without exogenous lipase	16.6 ± 0.18	12.2 ± 0.18
With exogenous lipase	15.8 ± 0.20	12.5 ± 0.17
Significance	$P<0.05$	NS

[1]Thomas *et al.*, 1997.

In subsequent studies (Tan *et al.*, 2000), the use of Allzyme Lipozyme added to diets containing full-fat rice bran resulted in numerical improvements in the AME content of both the complete diet and the full-fat rice bran *per se*. The responses were dependent upon the dietary level of rice bran, with greater response being observed at lower inclusion levels (Table 9). However, observed responses could not be attributed to any improvement in lipid digestibility suggesting that other enzyme activities (i.e. protease, cellulase, and xylanase) present in the preparation may have worked singly or in combination. The overall results suggest that this enzyme preparation offers promise to improve the nutritive value of rice bran for broiler chickens.

Table 9. Influence of Lipozyme on the apparent metabolisable energy (AME), faecal fat digestibility and growth performance in broilers fed diets containing full-fat rice bran.[1]

	90 g/kg rice bran		180 g/kg rice bran	
	Control	Lipozyme	Control	Lipozyme
AME (MJ/kg DM)				
Day 4-7	14.6	14.9	14.1	14.4
Day 11-14	14.6	14.8	14.2	14.3
Faecal fat digestibility				
Day 4-7	0.91	0.92	0.79	0.79
Day 11-14	0.83	0.87	0.80	0.82
Bird performance				
(Day 0-14)				
Average gain, g/bird	475	503[2]	456	449
Feed/gain, g/g	1.19	1.16	1.25	1.24

[1]From Tan *et al.* (2000).
[2]Significant enzyme effect (P<0.05).

LIQUID FEEDS: ENZYME APPLICATIONS

In pig production, liquid feeding systems are becoming increasingly popular. Liquid feeding confers a number of benefits such as a reduction in food wastage, automatic (computerised) and accurate control of feed delivery, lowered dust levels, flexibility in the use of different diets and improved animal performance (Patterson, 1986). Moreover, the liquid medium offers significant opportunities for 'biological' processing of feeds using bacteria or exogenous enzymes. Liquid feeding systems offer a major opportunity for reacting mixed diets or particular feed ingredients with enzymes pre-feeding. Pigs differ from birds in that upon ingestion food directly enters the true stomach rather than a crop and is immediately subjected to a low pH. With careful selection of the appropriate enzymes and taking advantage of the liquid medium, it may be possible to pre-react foods and deliver to the animals partially digested feedstuffs.

With this in mind, we undertook a pilot study (Hartley and Moughan, 1994) to evaluate the effects on pig growth of adding a standard enzyme cocktail to a barley-based diet steeped in water. The composition of the diet is given in Table 10. Before feeding, the cereal component was steeped in water (3 parts water:1 part food, w/w). A crude preparation of carbohydrases was added to one half of the cereal. In a similar manner, the dietary protein component was steeped in water and to half the protein mixture a crude preparation of proteases was added. The animals were fed twice daily with the cereal protein mixture and vitamin/mineral component being mixed before feeding to the pigs. For the morning and evening meals, the cereal (with or without added enzyme) had been steeped for 5 hrs and the protein mixture for 2 hrs. The mean ambient temperature during the study was 16°C. The animals were given the liquid diet at a restricted level of feeding $(0.09 \times W^{0.75})$.

Table 10. Pig grower diet used in a liquid feeding/enzyme trial.

Ingredient	%
Barley	78
Meat and bone meal	12.5
Blood meal	2.5
Fish meal	2.5
Soyabean meal	4.0
Salt	0.25
Premix	0.25

In spite of relatively low and unbalanced numbers of pigs per treatment, the effect of enzyme on food conversion ratio tended toward statistical significance and was significant at P=0.10 (Table 11). The absolute growth rates of both the male and female pigs were higher with the added enzymes. Work in this area is continuing at our institute.

Table 11. Effect of enzymes on the performance of growing pigs (least square means) in a pilot study of the use of enzymes in conjunction with liquid feeding.

	Female		Male		Significance	
	Control	Enzyme	Control	Enzyme	Sex	Enzyme
N	5	9	9	5		
Daily gain	627	677	713	727	#	NS
FCR	3.01	2.74	2.64	2.60	*	#

*P < 0.05
#P < 0.10

Enzyme preparations with higher activity at ambient air temperature should be developed. Enzymes used in conjunction with liquid feeding systems offer potentially increased efficiency in pig production. For a more comprehensive treatment of this topic the reader is referred to Brooks *et al.* (1999).

The above results also highlight the benefits of using enzyme cocktails in diets rather than preparations with single enzyme activity. Given the complexities of the substrates in raw materials, it is only logical to expect greater responses from a broad spectrum of exogenous enzyme activities. A combination of enzymes could facilitate each other's activity by providing greater substrate access. The improvements observed with Vegpro, an enzyme with protease, α-galactosidase, ß-glucanase and endoxylanase activities, in pigs fed diets based on barley and lupin provides a good example of the multi-faceted effect of enzyme cocktails.

During the past decade, the feed enzymes have evolved from a virtually undefined entity to a well-accepted feed additive. The use of feed enzymes has steadily increased over this time and this trend is likely to continue in the future. The role of enzymes in improving precision and flexibility in least-cost feed formulations and, more importantly, narrowing within-flock or herd variability and ensuring more uniformity at market weight is well appreciated by the industry. Most currently available formulations, however, are effective only in specific situations. The challenge for the future is to develop and refine enzyme combinations that are cost effective with a wider applicability.

Conclusion

A case has been made that both bioactive peptides and exogenous enzymes may assist in increasing nutrient uptake and utilization. These technologies bring about their effects by altering overall physiological function in the animal and are thus akin to functional food applications in human nutrition. These and similar technologies are having an increasing application in animal nutrition, where the variation in nutrient digestibility among samples of a feedstuff is notoriously high (Donkoh *et al.*, 1994; van Wijk *et al.*, 1998). Minimising this variation is economically advantageous and is urgently required. Compound feeds that bring about changes in nutrient utilization and animal performance, by altering aspects of animal function (functional feeds), will become increasingly commonplace.

References

Annison, G. and M. Choct. 1991. Anti-nutritive activities of cereal non-starch polysaccharides in broiler diets and strategies minimising their effects. Worlds Poultry Science Journal 47:232.

Annison, G., P.J. Moughan and D.V. Thomas. 1995. Nutritive activity of rice bran arabinoxylans in broiler diets. British Poultry Science 36:479.

Barker, D.J.P. 1994. In: Mothers, Babies, and Disease in Later Life. BMJ Publishing Group, London. p. 180.

Barker, D.J.P. 1999. Commentary: Intrauterine nutrition may be important. British Medical Journal 318:1471.

Bedford, M.R. and H. Schulze. 1998. Exogenous enzymes in pigs and poultry. Nutrition Research Reviews 11:91.

Ben Mansour, A., D. Tome, M. Rautureau, A. Bisalli and J.F. Desjeux. 1988. Luminal antisecretory effects of a beta-casomorphin analogue on rabbit ileum treated with cholera toxin. Pediatric Research 24:751.

Birke H., O. Thorlasius-Ussing, S. Frokjaer and I. Hessov. 1993. Tropic effects of different enteral diets in the rat intestine. Clinical Nutrition 12:20.

Brantl, V., H. Teschemacher, J. Blasig, A. Henschen and F. Lottspeich. 1979. Novel opioid peptides derived from casein (ß-casomorphins). I. Isolation from bovine casein peptone. Hoppe-Seyler's Z. Physiol.Chem. 360:1211.

Brooks, P.H., C. Moran and J.D. Beal. 1999. Liquid feeding of pigs: potential for reducing environmental impact and for improving productivity and food safety. In: Biotechnology in the Feed Industry, Proceedings of the 15th Annual Symposium (T.P. Lyons and K.A. Jacques, eds), Nottingham University Press, Nottingham, UK.

Butts, C.A., P.J. Moughan and W.C. Smith. 1991. Endogenous amino acid flow at the terminal ileum of the rat determined under conditions of peptide alimentation. Journal of the Science of Food and Agriculture 55:175.

Butts, C.A., P.J. Moughan, W.C. Smith and D.H. Carr. 1993. Endogenous lysine and other amino acid flows at the terminal ileum of the growing pig (20 kg bodyweight): The effect of protein-free, synthetic amino acid, peptide and protein alimentation. Journal of the Science of Food and Agriculture 61:31.

Daniel, H., M. Vohwinkel and G. Rehner. 1990. Effect of casein and ß-Casomorphins on gastrointestinal motility in rats. J. Nutr. 120:252.

Darragh, A.J., P.J. Moughan and W.C. Smith. 1990. The effect of amino acid and peptide alimentation on the determination of endogenous amino acid flow at the terminal ileum of the rat. Journal of the Science of Food and Agriculture 51:47.

Donkoh, A., P.J. Moughan and W.C. Smith. 1994. True ileal digestibility of amino acids in meat and bone meal for the growing pig – application of a routine rat digestibility assay. Animal Feed Science and Technology 49:73.

Donkoh, A., P.J. Moughan and P.C.H. Morel. 1995. Comparison of methods to determine the endogenous amino acid flow at the terminal ileum of the growing rat. Journal of the Science of Food and Agriculture 67:359.

Feng, Yu, P.J. Moughan and T.N. Barry. 1995. Effect of condensed tannin in cottonseed hulls on endogenous ileal amino acid loss in the growing rat. Journal of the Science of Food and Agriculture 68:451.

Froetschel, M.A. 1996. Bioactive peptides in digesta that regulate gastrointestinal function and intake. Journal of Animal Science 74:2500.

Frokjaer, S. 1994. Uses of hydrolysates for protein supplementation. Food Technology 48:86.

Fry, R.E., J.B. Allred, L.S. Jensen and J. McGinnis. 1957. Influence of cereal grain components of the diet on the response of chicks and poults to dietary enzyme supplementation. Poultry Science 36:1120.

Gardner, M.L.G. 1998. Transmucosal passage of intact peptides. In: Peptides in Mammalian Protein Metabolism. (G.K. Grimble and F.R.C. Blackwell, eds). Portland Press, London, p. 11.

Hartley, D.G. and P.J. Moughan. 1994. Report on a pilot study to evaluate the use of enzymes in liquid feeding systems. Internal report, Monogastric Research Centre, Massey University, New Zealand, p. 6.

Hastings, W.H. 1946. Enzyme supplements for poultry feeds. Poultry Science. 25:584.

Hendriks, W.H., P.J. Moughan and M.F. Tarttelin. 1996. Gut endogenous nitrogen and amino acid excretions in adult domestic cats fed a protein-free diet or an enzymatically hydrolyzed casein-based diet. Journal of Nutrition 126:955.

Kil, S.J. and M.A. Froetschel. 1994. Involvement of opioid peptides from casein on reticular motility and digesta passage in steers. Journal of Dairy Science 77:111.

Lord, A.P.D. 1986. Intestinal Absorption of ß-Casomorphins in Newborn Animals, B.Sc. Thesis, Department of Animal Sciences, The University of Adelaide, Adelaide, Australia.

Meisel, H. 1997. Biochemical properties of regulatory peptides derived from milk proteins. Biopoly. 43:119.

Moughan P.J. 1999. Protein metabolism in the growing pig. In: A Quantitative Biology of the Pig (I. Kyriazakis, ed), CABI Publishing, Wallingford, p. 299.

Moughan, P.J. and S.M. Rutherfurd. 1990. Endogenous flow of total lysine and other amino acids at the distal ileum of the protein or peptide-fed rat: The chemical labelling of gelatine protein by transformation of lysine to homoarginine. Journal of the Science of Food and Agriculture 55:163.

Moughan, P.J. and S.M. Rutherfurd. 1991. Endogenous lysine flow at the distal ileum of the protein-fed rat: Investigation of the effect of protein source using radioactively labeled acetylated lysine or lysine transformed to homoarginine. Journal of the Science of Food and Agriculture 55:163.

Moughan, P.J., G. Schuttert and M. Leenaars. 1992. Endogenous amino acid flow in the stomach and small intestine of the young growing pig. Journal of the Science of Food and Agriculture 60:437.

Patterson, D.C. 1986. Proceedings of the 14th Annual Symposium of the Pig Health Society. University College, Dublin, Ireland, p.3.

Pluske, J.R. 1999. Effect of Vegpro supplementation on digestibility of vegetable proteins and production indices in growing-finishing pigs. A Report Submitted to Alltech, Inc. Monogastric Research Centre, Massey University, Palmerston North, New Zealand, p. 36.

Pluske, J.R., P.C.H. Morel, E.A.C. James and K.A. Jacques. 1999. Allzyme Vegpro increases faecal digestibility coeffecients in pigs fed soyabean meal and canola meal. Journal of Animal Science. (submitted).

Power, R.F. and R. Murphy. 1999. Biologically active peptides: sources, production and nutritional importance. In: Concepts in Pig Science, Proceedings of the 1st Annual Turtle Lake Pig Science Conference., (T.P. Lyons and D.J.A. Cole, eds.), Nottingham University Press, Nottingham, UK, p. 33.

Rutherfurd, S.M. and P.J. Moughan. 1990. Guanidination of lysine in selected dietary proteins. Journal of Agricultural and Food Chemistry. 38:209.

Sakata, T. 1987. Stimulatory effect of short-chain fatty acids on epithelial cell proliferation in the rat intestine: a possible explanation for trophic effects of fermentable fibre, gut microbes and luminal trophic factors. British Journal of Nutrition. 58:95.

Schlimme, E., H. Meisel and H. Frister. 1988. Bioactive sequences in milk proteins. In: Milk Proteins, Nutritional, Clinical, Functional and Technological Aspects (C.A. Barth and E. Schlimme, eds.) Steinkopff Verlag, Darmstadt, p. 143.

Skilton, G.A., P.J. Moughan and W.C. Smith. 1988. Determination of endogenous amino acid flow at the terminal ileum of the rat. Journal of the Science of Food and Agriculture 44:227.

Sloan, E.A. 1998. Food Industry Forecast: Consumer trends to 2020 and beyond. Food Technology 52:37.

Tan, S.H., D.V. Thomas, B.J. Camden, I.T. Kadim, P.C.H. Morel and J.R. Pluske. 2000. Improving the nutritive value of full-fat rice bran for broiler chickens using a lipase-based enzyme preparation. Asian-Australasian Journal of Animal Science. (in press).

Thomas, D.V., I.T. Kadim, P.J. Moughan and S. Bourne. 1997. Effect of lipase supplementation of rice bran on excreta energy content in adult cockerels. Proceedings of the Australasian Poultry Science Symposium 9:218.

Van Wijk, H.J., P.J. Moughan, S.M. Hodgkinson, P.P. Jansen and G. Pearson. 1998. Variation in apparent and true ileal amino acid digestibility in barley using a rat model. Animal Feed Science and Technology 76:9.

Warren, B.E. and D.J. Farrell. 1990. The nutritive value of full-fat and defatted Australian rice bran. III. The apparent digestible energy content of defatted rice bran in rats and pigs and the metabolisability of energy and nutrients in defatted and full-fat bran in chickens and adult cockerels. Animal Feed Science and Technology 27:247.

Webb, K.E., J.C. Matthews and D.B. DiRenzo. 1992. Peptide absorption: a review of current concepts and future perspectives. Journal of Animal Science 70:3248.

Zioudrou, C., R.A. Streaty and W.A. Klee. 1979. Opioid peptides derived from food proteins, the exorphins. The Journal of Biological Chemistry 254:2446.

Herbs, spices and botanicals: 'Old fashioned' or the new feed additives for tomorrow's feed formulations? Concepts for their successful use

CASPAR WENK

Institute of Animal Sciences, Nutrition Biology, ETH Zurich, Switzerland

Introduction: why all the discussion about herbs?

The various ways in which human food is produced are vigorously discussed and questioned in modern societies. We expect food from plants, farm animals and microorganisms to be of good quality, healthy and inexpensive. Furthermore the food industry and politicians are increasingly concerned about environmental matters and keeping energy inputs low. In addition, arguments for food produced as naturally as possible are increasingly heard from organic farming organizations and consumer organizations. The use of new technologies such as genetic engineering in food and animal feed production is being questioned. Even synthetic amino acids, vitamins or other feed additives produced by modern technologies are banned in certain (organic) production systems. In general, all of us expect our food to be as natural as possible and free of any toxic or undesired substances.

In highly developed countries we do not always feel the impact of the steady growth of world population. In 25 years there will be almost 9 billion inhabitants (FAOSTAT, 1998) on earth who expect to get enough food to meet their nutritional needs. The goal to produce sufficient food for everyone can only be achieved if world food production increases by about 2% per year. It is expected that world animal production will follow this trend. According to FAOSTAT (1998) world production will grow about 2.0% for pigs and poultry in the next 20 years. For beef production a slight reduction of 0.4% is expected, mainly in developed countries.

World food production must also accomplish this growth without increasing the environmental waste load. This precondition demands the efficient and responsible use of all available resources, of traditional and modern technologies and also of feed additives. There is no doubt that worldwide agricultural productivity must increase. However, consumers in highly developed countries, who spend only a minor percentage of income on food (in Switzerland less than 10%), make increasingly pointed demands about quality and have idealistic images of food that focus attention on issues other than yield.

Antibiotic feed additives have been banned in animal nutrition in Sweden since 1986. The ban is being discussed throughout Europe due to increased occurrence of pathogens resistant to therapeutic antibiotics used in both animals and humans. The increase has been viewed to be related to use of antibiotic feed additives as growth promoters in farm animals. Despite the report of the SCAN (1996) showing no evidence that use of avoparcin has led to increased resistance to vancomycin (an antibiotic used in human medicine), avoparcin was banned in the European Union (EU) in April of 1997. After an intensive debate, Switzerland banned all antimicrobial feed additives as performance promoters in 1999. A report of the Swiss Office of Health (1999) stated later that the ban was politically based and that animal feed supplements contributed only marginally to the actual resistance situation. Coccidiostats are still permitted in poultry diets. Recently the EU has banned tylosin phosphate, virginiamycin, zinc bacitracin and spiramycin. A further law banned the use of olaquindox and carbadox as feed additives for 1999.

With the restricted use or outright ban of dietary antimicrobial agents, new ways of improving and protecting the health status of farm animals must be explored. Furthermore, useful additives should ensure optimum animal performance and increase nutrient availability. This goal can be attained by good housing or climate conditions as well as by the best possible combination of the so-called pronutrients (Rosen, 1996) available including pro- or prebiotics, organic acids, dietary fiber, highly available nutrients, herbs, spices or botanicals. Rosen defined the pronutrients as 'micro-feedingstuffs used orally in a relatively small amount to improve the intrinsic value of the nutrient mix in an animal diet'.

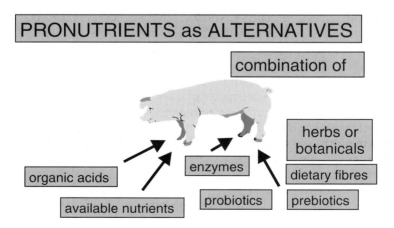

Figure 1. Pronutrients instead of antibiotics.

The effect of a pronutrient on the performance of a farm animal can vary over a wide range. Many reasons for this variation can be considered.

Generally, pronutrients are more effective in animals with low performance and (or) unfavorable health status, those kept under adverse environmental and management conditions and animals receiving diets with low nutritive value.

Beside feed enzymes, probiotics (lactobacilli, yeast culture, etc.), prebiotics (oligosaccharides) and organic acids, the herbs and botanicals can be used as feed additives. In recent years the modern western world has been learning what many Asians (eg. Keys, 1976) and native Americans (eg. Bye and Linares, 1999) have known for centuries, namely that plant extracts and spices can play a significant role in health and nutrition.

What are herbs, spices or botanicals?

Definitions for herbs, spices and botanicals derived from Webster's Encyclopedic Cambridge Dictionary of the English Language (1989) are as follows:

Herb: A flowering plant whose stem above ground does not become woody and persistent. A plant valued for its medical properties, flavor, scent, or the like.

Spice: Any of a class of pungent or aromatic substances of vegetable origin, as pepper, cinnamon, cloves, and the like, used as seasoning, preservatives, etc.

Botanical: A drug made from part of a plant, as from roots, leaves, bark, etc.

Essential oils: Any of a class of volatile oils obtained from plants possessing the odor and other characteristic properties of the plant, used chiefly in the manufacture of perfumes, flavors and pharmaceuticals (extracts after hydro-distillation).

Plants have evolved a wide range of low molecular weight secondary metabolites. Generally these compounds enable the plant to interact with the environment and may act in defense against physiological and environmental stress as well as predators or pathogens. Some plant metabolites are toxic to animals, however several have been reported to provide beneficial effects in food products and also in mammalian metabolism. The latter are primarily in herbs and spices and are specifically enriched and eventually standardized in botanicals.

Modes of action of herbs, spices and botanicals

Herbs and botanicals benefit farm animals by increasing feed intake, improving immune response and by their antibacterial, coccidiostatic, anthelmintic, anti-viral, anti-inflammatory or, particularly, antioxidant properties. Most of these active secondary plant metabolites belong to the flavonoid and glucosinolate classes of isoprene derivatives; and many of these compounds have been suggested to have antibiotic or antioxidant effects *in vivo* and in food. Reviews of physiologically active secondary plant metabolites (e.g. Rhodes, 1996 or Hirasa and Takemasa, 1998) and their principle antioxidant characteristics (e.g. Halliwell *et al.*, 1995) have been presented by several authors.

Herbs are active initially in animal feeds as flavors, and can therefore influence eating patterns, secretion of digestive fluids and total feed intake. The primary site of activity is the digestive tract. Herbs or the phytochemicals can selectively influence the intestinal microflora by either antimicrobial activity or by favorably promoting eubiosis of the microflora resulting in better nutrient utilization and absorption, or stimulation of the immune system. Finally, herbs can contribute to nutrient requirements, stimulate the endocrine system and affect intermediate nutrient metabolism.

The diverse activities of herbs and other feed additives can have considerable importance during the growth phase of animals. In the very young animal nutrient digestion and metabolism are not yet fully functional. Furthermore, the immune system and a stable digestive tract microflora (eubiosis) must be established, for which regular feed intake is of prime importance. After this critical period, digestive processes can be optimized and adapted to the available feedstuffs. In these later stages of growth, factors related to product quality (both feed quality and meat, milk or egg quality) play a major role.

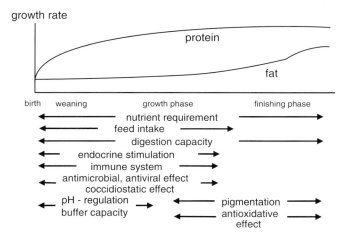

Figure 2. Modes of action of feed additives in growing animals.

Often the desired activity of herbs or spices is not constant. Conflicting results may derive from the natural variability in composition of plant secondary metabolites. Plant composition is affected by variety, many soil and climatic factors and stage of maturity at harvest. In addition, method of conservation and length of storage, the extraction method used and potentially synergistic or antagonistic effects including anti-nutritional factors or microbial contamination are factors which may substantially affect the results of *in vivo* experiments. For example, rosemary and sage from different geographical locations and types of processing (dried herbs vs. essential oil (Svoboda and Deans, 1992)) or from different suppliers (Wenk *et al.*, 1998) had significant differences in antioxidant capacity. Furthermore, several plant metabolites have strong flavors, which may alter feed sensory characteristics and therefore affect feed intake. Additionally, antibacterial properties (probably concentration-dependent) and effects on feed intake and nutrient digestion should be expected and taken into consideration when conducting *in vivo* experiments with phytochemicals in farm animals.

INFLUENCE OF HERBS ON FEED INTAKE

After the ban on antibiotic use in practical pig production, herbs are increasingly used as feed additives to promote growth and general health. A product from the rhizomes of *Sanguinaria canadensis* is frequently used in Europe. Other herb mixtures such as Porcin Herba (Bourne, personal communication) lead to increased feed intake as well as better growth performance in piglets and grow/finish pigs.

We have studied the influence of dietary supplementation of five single herbs and two mixtures on feed intake and growth performance of weanling pigs (Table 1). All additives were added at 0.5% of the diet; and performance was compared with an unsupplemented basal diet. The basal diet consisted of barley, wheat, oats, corn, soybean meal, potato protein, fish meal, fat, amino acids and a mineral/vitamin premix. The analyzed nutrient content of the basal and experimental diets was almost identical (Gebert *et al.*, 1999a).

Table 1. Herbal supplements used in growth experiments with piglets.

Herba epimedii
Rhubarb
Magnoliavine fruit
Gold thread
Tibet bitter root
Phyto starter 004
Porah Herba W-15

There were no animal losses during the four week experimental period. Added at 0.5% of the diet, only one of the herbs tested (Phyto starter 004) led to an increase in daily feed intake (Table 2). A distinct reduction in feed intake was observed in response to rhubarb and Tibet bitter root inclusion. The increase in feed intake did not correspond to higher growth rate, but the reduced feed intake was clearly reflected in lower daily body weight gain, especially for piglets given diets containing rhubarb or Tibet bitter root. It was concluded that the herbs tested did not generally increase feed intake and growth performance, but some herbs reduced growth performance.

Table 2. Effect of different herbs and two herbal mixtures on performance of piglets weeks 1-4 post-weaning.

Treatment	Initial weight (kg)	End weight (kg)	Intake (g/day)	Body weight gain (g/day)	Feed conversion (kg/kg)
Control	9.58	21.90	698	440[a]	1.60
Herba epimedii	9.91	21.40	672	410[ab]	1.65
Rhubarb	9.37	19.50	570	362[b]	1.59
Magnoliavine fruit	9.58	21.97	703	455[a]	1.55
Gold thread	9.79	21.93	662	434[a]	1.52
Tibet bitter root	9.45	19.53	598	360[b]	1.68
Phyto starter 004	10.28	22.18	728	425[a]	1.74
Porah Herba W-15	9.88	21.48	703	414[ab]	1.71
SEM	*0.27*	*0.51*	*19*	*15*	*0.03*
P values	*0.158*	*0.100*	*0.149*	*0.040*	*0.143*

Gebert *et al.*, 1999b.
[ab]Means in a column differ, P<0.05

In addition to the growth parameters, fecal consistency and organic matter digestibility were evaluated. Fecal consistency scores were unaffected by treatment with the exception of lower scores and dry matter content for pigs given diets containing rhubarb (Table 3). Although the variation in organic matter digestibility was extremely low, no significant differences between treatments were noted. There was a trend toward increased digestibility in the diet containing Magnoliavine fruit and a similar trend toward reduced digestibility in the diet containing *Herba epimedii*.

Table 3. Effect of different herb supplements on organic matter digestibility, fecal dry matter content and fecal score of piglets.

Treatment	Fecal score[1]	Fecal dry matter (%)	Organic matter digestibility
Control	1.36[a]	31.1[a]	0.843
Herba epimedii	1.29[a]	31.0[a]	0.829
Rhubarb	1.80[b]	24.4[b]	0.837
Magnoliavine fruit	1.12[a]	30.6[a]	0.852
Gold thread	1.17[a]	29.9[a]	0.842
Tibet bitter root	1.12[a]	31.6[a]	0.844
Phyto starter 004	1.21[a]	30.9[a]	0.841
Porah Herba W-15	1.19[a]	30.9[a]	0.839
SEM	*0.05*	*0.58*	*0.002*
P values	*0.001*	*0.022*	*0.175*

[1]1 = normal; 2 = wet; 3 = diarrhea
[ab]Means in a column differ, P<0.05

The reduced intake and higher fecal water content when pigs were given rhubarb can be explained by chemical constituents of this herb. In addition to the presence of oxalic acid, anthrachino-glycans in rhubarb can have specific effects on the digestion processes. According to Engelshowe (1975), anthrachino-glycans can be used to prevent constipation and chronic diarrhea as well as other digestive disorders. Furthermore, there are some indications that rhubarb reduces cholesterol and has antioxidant effects in humans (Goel *et al.*, 1997).

In this experiment, the herbs were added at 0.5% of the experimental diets. Therefore, it was of interest to evaluate whether there was a dose-response effect of rhubarb on performance. This was evaluated by adding rhubarb to the starter diet of piglets at 0.1, 0.25 or 0.5% and to the broiler diet at 0.25 or 0.5%. In these experiments, a further treatment was included with an antimicrobial supplement as a positive control. Piglet growth was evaluated over a four week period.

Feed intake and growth performance significantly increased with carbadox supplementation compared to the unsupplemented control (Table 4). In all treatments with rhubarb, feed intake and performance were reduced. Daily weight gain of pigs given 0.5% rhubarb was half that of pigs fed the control diet. Addition of 0.1% rhubarb slightly reduced growth rate, however feed intake was markedly lower than controls. As in the previous trial, rhubarb reduced fecal dry matter content. In further experiments with rhubarb from another origin, addition of 0.1% increased feed intake and growth rate; however 0.25 and 0.5% led to a significant decrease (Gebert *et al.*, 1999b).

Table 4. Growth experiments with rhubarb in piglets.

	Control	Carbadox (50 ppm)	Rhubarb (%)		
			0.1	0.25	0.5
Start weight, kg	10.4	9.8	10.2	10.0	10.3
End weight, kg	27.2[b]	28.3[b]	26.6[b]	26.0[b]	20.5[a]
Feed intake, g/day	922[b]	956[b]	875[b]	848[ab]	604[a]
Weight gain, g/day	597[b]	659[b]	586[b]	569[b]	361[a]
Feed conversion ratio	1.54	1.45	1.54	1.47	1.75
Fecal dry matter, %	34.9	36.6	34.9	31.9	30.4

Gebert *et al.*, 1999b.
[ab]Means in a row differ, P<0.05.

In an experiment with growing chickens, rhubarb supplements were compared with zinc bacitracin as antimicrobial agents. The feeding experiment began following a week adaptation period post-hatch and continued throughout the 39 day growth period. Seven birds from the negative control treatment had to be excluded from the experiment while only two birds were lost in each of the other treatments. Deaths or removals from treatment were due to heart failure, ascites and leg weakness (mainly caused by fast growth). Zinc bacitracin increased feed intake and growth rate slightly (Table 5). In contrast to the piglet experiments, 0.25% rhubarb increased feed intake and growth rate by about 8%. There was no detrimental effect on excreta dry matter content and no effect on water intake. However, supplementation of 0.5% rhubarb reduced feed intake and performance, an observation which corresponds well with the piglet experiments. Obviously, the birds were less influenced by the rhubarb than the pigs.

Table 5. Growth experiments with rhubarb in broilers.

Treatment	Negative control	Zn bacitracin	Rhubarb (0.25%)	Rhubarb (0.5%)
Initial weight, g	162	166	166	165
End weight, g	2294[ab]	2332[ab]	2382[b]	2163[a]
Feed intake, g/day	115.5[ab]	118.4[ab]	122.1[b]	112.1[a]
Daily gain, g	63.9[ab]	67.3[b]	69.0[b]	61.4[a]
Feed conversion	1.81	1.76	1.77	1.83
Water:feed	1.83[ab]	1.75[a]	1.84[ab]	1.90[b]
Fecal dry matter, %	34.7	36.1	33.3	34.1
Losses, n	7	2	2	3

Messikommer, 1999; personal communication.
[ab]Means in a row differ, $P<0.05$.

ANTIMICROBIAL AND COCCIDIOSTATIC ACTIVITIES OF HERBS AND BOTANICALS

The antimicrobial activity of herbs and botanicals has been studied in many different *in vitro* assays (Huang, 1999; Baratta *et al.*, 1998; Deans and Richie, 1987). In Table 6 some examples for Chinese herbs are presented. Some of the herbs tested had a wide spectrum of antimicrobial activity against Gram-positive and Gram-negative bacteria. Others were mainly active against Gram-positive species (Spring *et al.*, 1998, personal communication).

Results of *in vitro* tests as shown in Table 6 indicate that herbs can have specific antimicrobial activities. Transforming such results into the digestive tract of an animal is not easy. Herbs or botanicals added to a diet must compete with the major nutrients as well as with other possible secondary plant constituents present in the feed. Furthermore the microbial population of the digestive tract varies with factors such as pH, transit time, nutrient density, absorption rate, etc.

An interesting approach was made by Gàbor and Boros (personal communication), in which an oil extract of several plants (clove, thyme, peppermint and citrus) was tested under practical farm conditions in comparison with a diet containing a standard coccidiostat. Birds given the oil extract performed similarly to the flocks given diets containing coccidiostat (Table 7). Allen *et al.* (1998) also found that certain plant products have coccidiostatic activity and can be used as feed additives.

Table 6. Antimicrobial activity of Chinese herbs in comparison to garlic.

	Activity against:		
Goldthread rhizome	Gram+	Gram-	
Scullcap root	Gram+	Gram-	
Arnefia root	Gram+		
Barberry root	Gram+		
Cassia seed	Gram+	Gram-	
Flavescent sophora root	Gram+		
Forsythia fruit	Gram+		
Honeysuckle fruit	Gram+		
Honeysuckle stem	Gram+		
Houttuynia	Gram+	Gram-	
Oriental wormwood	Gram+		
Philodendron bark	Gram+		
Quad leaf	Gram+		
Tibet bitter root	Gram+	Gram-	
Ash bark	Gram+	Gram-	
Garlic, positive	Gram+	Gram-	

Recent tests with Chinese herbs (Spring, Wang and Ding, 1998 personal communication).

Table 7. Comparison of an oil extract of clove, thyme, peppermint and lemon and a standard coccidiostat in diets for broilers.

	Oil extract	Control (standard coccidiostat)	
Experiment 1			
Initial number of birds	17,097	17,600	
Days to slaughter	44	44	
Mortality, %	8.9	8.4	
Average weight, kg	1.84	1.80	
FCR	2.17	2.16	
Experiment 2			
Initial number of birds	64,320	58,055	
Days to slaughter	45	48	
Mortality, %	9.9	10.7	
Average weight, kg	2.05	1.91	
FCR	2.07	2.41	

HERBS AND BOTANICALS AS ANTIOXIDANTS

The antioxidant status of an animal depends on several different factors (Wenk *et al.*, 2000). The animal itself represents a homeostatic balance regulated by the available enzymes. Nutrients with different potentials for oxidation are ingested in feed, with the polyunsaturated fatty acids (PUFA) representing the highest risk for oxidation. In addition, feedstuffs may contain substances like iron, copper or phytases that can catalyze nutrient oxidation. Finally, antioxidants like tocopherols, carotenoids, flavonoids, etc. protect compounds prone to oxidation.

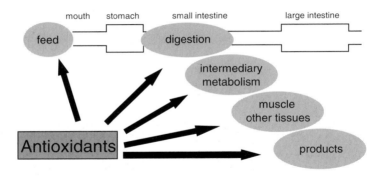

Figure 3. Activity of antioxidants in monogastric animals.

Activity of various antioxidants varies with the type of antioxidant, polarity, solubility and site of activity (Figure 3). Some antioxidants protect nutrients in feed during storage. Others are primarily active in the digestive tract where they may also aid absorption of the nutrients they protect. Antioxidants are responsible for many functions in intermediary metabolism including protection of intact membranes. In farm animals dietary antioxidants can ultimately influence shelf life of animal products.

The antioxidant activity of herbs can be measured by methods such as the Rancimat test (Metrohm, Herisau, CH). Herbs or botanicals are added to an oil that is heated and ventilated by an air stream for accelerated oxidation. The results are expressed as an antioxidant factor which corresponds to the induction time of oxidation relative to the untreated oil. Thus high values indicate high oxidative stability. The antioxidant capacity of several Chinese herbs or their ethanol extracts was measured in comparison to rosemary using the Rancimat test with soybean oil as the carrier. Rosemary is well-known as a potent antioxidant, especially in countries around the Mediterranean Sea. Soybean oil itself contains high amounts of tocopherols and therefore has natural capacity for protection against oxidation. In comparison to rosemary, only *Radix et Rhizoma Rhei* showed similar effects on AF (Figure 4). The ethanol extracts of *Herba epimedii*, Magnoliavine fruit, *Radix puerariae* and *Ramulus taxilii* also had some antioxidant activity.

The Rancimat test used as described selects only for lipid soluble antioxidants; however it is of interest to know whether other water soluble constituents also have antioxidant activity. Therefore, in a further study the Rancimat test was compared with the microsome peroxidation assay in which thiobarbituric acid reactive substances were measured after starting oxidation of rat liver microsomes using $FeCl_2/H_2O_2$. In the microsome peroxidation test, primarily water soluble antioxidants are detected. The values given in Figure 5 are relative to the control with low values indicating

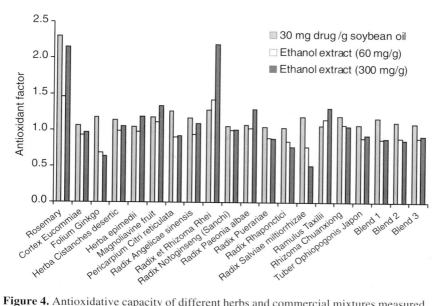

Figure 4. Antioxidative capacity of different herbs and commercial mixtures measured with the Rancimat system (AF = antioxidative factor) (Scheeder *et al.*, 1999).

delayed oxidation. Oleic acid was used instead of soybean oil in the Rancimat test.

In the Rancimat test *Cortex eucommiae* and Magnoliavine fruit were the most effective antioxidants, but other Chinese herbs showed significant activity. *Cortex eucommiae* did not react at all. Other herbs like *Herba epimedii* or *Radix et Rhizoma rhei* had excellent antioxidant activity in the water soluble fraction. These data indicate that *in vitro* tests will not be able to characterize the antioxidant actives of a herb properly.

Deans *et al.* (1993) studied the antioxidant activity of essential oils from different herbs in detail. Some of the results are shown in Table 8. The essential oils extracted by hydro-distillation from rosemary, thyme etc. had distinct antioxidant activity in this test. On the other hand, essential oils from estragon or sage had pro-oxidative activity. Some other herbs showed no activity against oxidation. In experiments with mice Deans *et al.* (1993) demonstrated that essential oils from thyme were able to protect highly polyunsaturated fatty acids (C20:4 and C22:6) and prevent rapid aging. From these experiments, it can be concluded that the antioxidant activity of thyme also had a significant role for animal metabolism.

The effects of phytochemical antioxidants on lipid oxidation in meat and meat products is of major concern. Plant oils used as feed ingredients in monogastric nutrition may readily alter fatty acid composition of all body lipid fractions by generally increasing the amount of PUFA and therefore

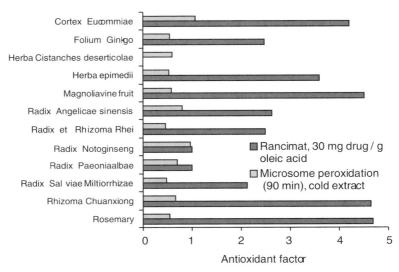

Figure 5. Antioxidant capacity of different herbs in the Rancimat as well as microsome peroxidation test.

Table 8. Anti- and pro-oxidative properties of essential oils (Deans *et al.*, 1993).

Anti-oxidative	Pro-oxidative	No activity
Bitter almond	Cardamom	Sweet almond
Clove	Coriander	Anise
Cinnamon	Estragon	Fennel
Laurel	Eucalyptus	Ginger
Mint	Lime	Lemon
Nutmeg	Sage	Marjoram
Pepper	Verbena	Melissa
Peppermint		
Rosemary		
Thyme		

Deans *et al.*, 1993.

their susceptibility to oxidation. Concomitantly, plant oils usually contain natural antioxidants which may contribute to an improved oxidative stability of meat and meat products, compensating for the increased degree of unsaturation. These antioxidants are mainly tocopherols. However, phenols present in appreciable amounts in olive oil may serve as examples of effective non-tocopherol antioxidants (Baldioli *et al.*, 1996). Their antioxidant capacity (Papadopoulus and Boskou, 1991) and free radical-scavenging properties (Visioli *et al.*, 1998) have been reported as well as specific antioxidant effects on biomembranes (Saija *et al.*, 1998) and inhibition of low density lipoprotein oxidation *in vitro* (Visioli *et al.*, 1995) and in rabbits (Wiseman *et al.*, 1996).

In a recent study, we demonstrated that supplementation of olive oil in pig diets led to a significantly increased proportion of oleic acid in lard and consequently decreased firmness of salami produced (Scheeder *et al.*, 1998). On the other hand, oxidative stability was higher in the lard of olive-oil supplemented pigs than expected from the degree of unsaturation compared to lard of pigs fed diets without fat, or supplemented with soybean oil or pork fat (Gläser *et al.*, 1999; Figure 6).

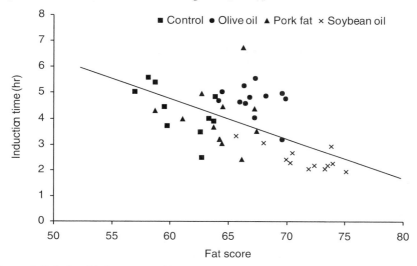

Figure 6. Relationship between oxidative stability of lard from pigs fed different fat supplements and the fat score (a measure of double bonds) showing the elevated oxidative stability of lard from olive oil supplemented pigs (Gläser *et al.*, 1999).

The effects of herbs or herb extracts used as dietary supplements were examined in two other studies. Greber (1997) fed dried sage to pigs and reported a significant decrease of TBARS (thiobarbituric acid resistant substances) in the lard with increasing concentration of sage from 0.6% to 1.2% of the diet. In contrast, the Rancimat test showed no significant effect.

Lopez-Bote *et al.* (1998) also reported that they did not find an antioxidant effect in pork when oleoresins of rosemary and sage were fed. However, feeding the same oleoresins (500 mg/kg) to broilers led to improved oxidative stability in red (leg) and white (breast) meat (measured as TBARS) as well as a lower amount of cholesterol oxidation products. The oleoresins were not as effective as α-tocopherol acetate (200 mg/kg), but it may be concluded that at least part of the ingested antioxidant compounds were retained in the muscle and that they were still active in the meat.

However, investigations on effects of dietary secondary plant metabolites on muscle and adipose tissues of farm animals are still rare. In addition, knowledge about effects of secondary plant metabolites in feed and in the gut, their bioavailability with respect to absorption and metabolism, and the extent to which they might be retained in animal tissues is not readily available.

Lopez-Bote *et al.* (1998) used extracts of rosemary and thyme in their experiments. It was therefore of interest to know whether entire herbs were also able to react as antioxidants in diets for chickens. In experiments of Ding *et al.* (1999) the antioxidative effects of rhubarb, *Herba epimedii* and Magnoliavine fruit were evaluated. The herb supplements were added to a standard diet based on corn, soybean meal and fish meal in amounts of 0.25 and 0.5% fed for an eight week period. Mortality was unaffected by treatment (Table 9). Daily body weight gain in the treatments with rhubarb were slightly higher, and in the treatments with Magnoliavine fruit slightly lower, compared to the control diet containing avilamycin as antimicrobial agent (200 ppm). The improved body weight gain was associated with improved feed conversion.

Table 9. Daily body weight gain and feed conversion of broilers given diets containing antioxidant Chinese herbs.

Herb	Dosage (%)	Final body weight gain (kg)	Body weight (g/day)	FCR (g/g)
Control	200 ppm avilamycin	2.2 ± 0.45	52.2 ± 6.38	2.8
Rhubarb	0.25	2.3 ± 0.5	55.0 ± 5.1	2.6
	0.50	2.3 ± 0.2	55.6 ± 3.2	2.4
Herba epimedii	0.25	2.2 ± 0.2	52.5 ± 3.0	2.6
	0.50	2.2 ± 0.2	51.8 ± 3.2	2.6
Magnoliavine fruit	0.25	2.1 ± 0.5	48.7 ± 6.1	2.8
	0.50	2.0 ± 0.4	47.2 ± 7.1	2.6

Ding *et al.*, 1999.

Antioxidant activity of the herbs was measured as superoxide dismutase activity (SOD) and as malondialdehyde (MDA) in liver, in blood serum and in abdominal fat issues. With an increased antioxidant status in the three different tissues (high SOD values) a reduced amount of oxidative products is expected (lower MDA values). The results in Table 10 confirm this relationship for all herbs. Moreover, improved stability of the tissues against oxidation was observed. Thus it can be concluded that in addition to extracts, the entire herb added in amounts of 0.25 and 0.5% will have a positive effect. This means that these herbs were able to increase shelf life, reduce off flavors and therefore improve quality of the products.

Conclusions: the need for alternative strategies

Beneficial effects on health status, performance, and nutrient and energy utilization are the main reasons for the wide use of antibiotic feed additives. The trend toward more 'natural' animal production systems has led to an increasingly critical attitude on the part of consumers about in-feed

Table 10. Superoxide dismutase (SOD) activity and malondialdehyde (MDA) content of liver, serum and abdominal lipids (means ±sd).

Herb	Dosage	Liver		Serum		Abdominal lipids	
		SOD	MDA	SOD	MDA	SOD	MDA
Control	200 ppm avilamycin	137.4±2.2	2.2±0.3	98.5±7.6	0.6±0.02	56.3±5.6	37.1±3.3
Rhubarb	0.25 %	163.2±5.4	1.7±0.2	134.9±4.6	0.4±0.02	83.7±5.4	27.6±2.7
	0.50 %	168.0±3.5	1.6±0.2	146.6±6.6	0.37±0.03	73.7±5.0	31.7±3.5
Herba epimedii	0.25 %	150.7±3.1	2.0±0.2	130.7±7.5	0.4±0.04	62.1±3.9	14.1±2.9
	0.50 %	145.4±2.9	1.6±0.1	133.6±3.1	0.4±0.03	73.8±3.0	18.9±3.9
Magnoliavine	0.25 %	175.3±5.7	1.9±0.1	130.0±5.2	0.4±0.04	59.1±5.8	12.0±2.1
Fruit	0.50 %	178.4±2.3	1.8±0.1	136.7±5.9	0.3±0.03	65.4±4.4	11.0±1.9

antimicrobial agents. Therefore, agriculture is looking for 'friendly' supplements with better acceptance by the consumer. Whether herbs, spices or botanicals (eg. essential oils) are appropriate must be considered in each practical application.

The banning of antibiotics in Europe and in other countries in the near future has brought about discussion of alternative strategies. They are of primary interest in veal production and in young pigs, in addition to poultry. Such strategies must be based primarily on optimal management and housing conditions. The main aspects of environmental management are:

- temperature (microclimate of the calves and piglets)
- fresh air, no draughts
- space allowance and appropriate floor surface
- straw bedding, if possible
- low humidity and minimal dust
- good rotation system

Nutrition must primarily focus on supplying animals with all essential nutrients and energy in adequate amounts. Adequate feed trough space is necessary where large groups of animals are fed. Overeating by heavier animals should be avoided in order to prevent digestive disorders. With the following measures the risks of digestion problems, especially in the young pig, can be minimized:

Low acid binding capacity

- reduced mineral content (< 6 g Ca and < 5 g P per kg feed)
- reduced protein content (essential amino acids according to requirement)
- organic acids (mainly fumaric and lactic acid)

Enzymes, prebiotics and dietary fiber sources

-    mainly phytases and carbohydrases
-    fructose and mannose oligosaccharides
-    pectins or other soluble dietary fibers

Liquid feeding systems with the possibility of fermentation before feeding

-    herbs, botanicals, spices or essential oils
-    probiotics (lactobacilli)
-    avoidance of anti-nutritional factors

In the concept of production of healthy farm animals without using antibiotics, herbs can be relevant in many different ways. There is evidence that they can regulate feed intake and stimulate digestive secretions. An optimized digestion capacity and a reduced risk of digestive disorders are the consequence. Several phytochemicals like essential oils or dietary fiber can contribute to a balanced microflora, an optimal precondition for an effective protection against pathogenic microorganisms and an intact immune system. In addition, herbs and botanicals contain many different antioxidants with a high potential for the protection of nutrients against oxidation in the digestive tract, in intermediary metabolism as well as in meat, milk and eggs.

References

Allen, P.C., H.D. Danforth, P.C. Augustine and M. Shirley. 1998. Dietary modulation of avian coccidiosis. International Journal for Parasitology 28:1131-1140.

Baldioli, M., M. Servili, G. Perretti and G.F. Montedoro. 1996. Antioxidant activity of tocopherols and phenolic compounds of virgin olive oil. Journal of the American Oil Chemists Society 73:1589-1593.

Baratta, M.T., H.J.D. Dorman, S.G. Deans, D.M. Biondi and G. Ruberto. 1998. Chemical composition, antimicrobial and antioxidative activity of laurel, sage, rosemary, oregano and coriander essential oils. J. Essent. Oil Res. 10:618-627.

Bye R. and E. Linares. 1999: Medicinal plant diversity in Mexico and its potential for animal health sciences. In: Proc. Alltech's 15th Annual Symposium on Biotechnology in the Feed Industry (T.P. Lyons and K.A. Jacques, eds.) pp. 265–294.

Deans, S.G. and G. Ritchie. 1987. Antibacterial properties of plant essential oils. International Journal of Food Microbiology 5:165-180.

Deans, S.G., R. C. Noble, L. Penzes, S.G. Imre. 1993. Promotional effects of plant volatile oils on the polyunsaturated fatty acid status during aging. Age 16:71-74.

Ding, H., X. Wei and D. Xia. 1999. Chinese herbs in the diet for broilers. Report, p. 15.

Engelshowe, R. 1975. Eine alte Droge – noch immer aktuell. Pharmazie in unserer Zeit 14, Jg. 2:40–49.

FAOSTAT. 1998. Food and Agriculture Organization of the United Nations Data Base. Faostat.fao.org.

Gebert, S., R. Messikommer and W. Wenk. 1999a. Chinesische Kräuter im Ferkelfutter. In: Gesunde Nutztiere: Umdenken in der Tierernährung? (F. Sutter, M. Kreuzer and C. Wenk, eds.) pp. 163-164.

Gebert, S., F. Stahel, R. Messikommer and C. Wenk. 1999b. Rhubarb als Alternative zu antimikrobiellen Leistungsförderern (AML) im Ferkel- und Broilerfutter. In: Gesunde Nutztiere: Umdenken in der Tierernährung? (F. Sutter, M. Kreuzer and C. Wenk, eds.) pp. 165-166.

Gebert, S., G. Bee, H.P. Pfirter and C. Wenk. 1999. Phytase and vitamin E in the feed of growing pigs: 1. Influence on growth, mineral digestibility and fatty acids in digesta. J. Anim. Physiol. and Anim. Nutr. 81:9-19.

Gebert, S., G. Bee, H.P. Pfirter and C. Wenk. 1999. Phytase and vitamin E in the feed of growing pigs: 2. Influence on carcass characteristics as well as meat and fat quality. J. Anim. Physiol. and Anim. Nutr. 81:20-30.

Gläser, K.R., M.R.L. Scheeder and C. Wenk. 1999. Influence of C 18 - monoenoic- and polyenoic fatty acids in feedstuff on the fat properties in pigs. In: 5.Tagung Schweine- und Geflügelernährung (1.-3.12.1998), Martin-Luther-Universität Halle-Wittenberg (H. Jeroch, H. Nonn, K. Eder, Hrsg), pp. 32-35.

Goel, V., B. Ooraikul and T.K. Basu. 1997. Cholesterol lowering effects of rhubarb stalk fiber in hypercholesterolemic men. J. Am. Col. Nutr. 16(6):600-604.

Greber, A. 1997. Salvia Officinalis L. als Futteradditiv in der Schweinemast. Ph.D. dissertation, Veterinärmedizinische Universität, Vienna.

Halliwell, B., R. Aeschbach, J. Loeliger and O.I. Aruoma. 1995. The characterization of antioxidants. Food and Chemical Toxicology 33:601-617.

Hirasa, K. and M. Takemasa. 1998. Spice science and technology. Marcel Dekker, New York, pp. 220.

Huang K.C. 1999. The pharmacology of Chinese herbs. CRC Press Inc.; Boca Raton, Florida; USA. pp. 512.

Keys, J.D. 1976. Chinese Herbs. Charles E. Tuttle Co., Tokyo.

Lopez-Bote, C.J., J.K. Gray, E.A. Gomaa E.A. and C.J. Flegal. 1998. Effect of dietary administration of oil extracts from rosemary and sage on lipid oxidation in broiler meat. British Poultry Science 39:235-240.

Papadopoulos, G. and D. Boskou. 1991. Antioxidant effect of natural phenols on olive oil. Journal of the American Oil Chemists' Society 68:669-671.

Rhodes, M.C. 1996. Physiologically-active compounds in plant foods: an overview. Proceedings of the Nutrition Society 55:371-384.

Rosen, G.D. 1996. World's Poultry Sci. J. 52:53-56.

Saija, A., D. Trombetta, A. Tomaino, R. LoCascio, P. Princi, N. Uccella, F. Bonina and F. Castelli. 1998. *'In vitro'* evaluation of the antioxidant activity and biomembrane interaction of the plant phenols oleuropein and hydroxytyrosol. International Journal of Pharmaceutics 166:123-133.

SCAN (Scientific committee for animal nutrition) of EU. 1996. Possible risk for humans on the use of avoparcin as a feed additive. European Commission, Brussels.

Scheeder, M. R. L., K. Gläser, D. Schwörer and C. Wenk. 1998. Oxidative stability and texture properties of fermented sausage produced from pork differing in fatty acid composition. 44st ICoMST, Barcelona, 1998, "Meat Consumption and Culture".Congress Proceedings, Published by Institute for Food and Agricultural Research and Technology (IRTA) and EUROCARNE. pp. 866-867.

Scheeder, M. R. L., C. Spleiss, H. Bossi and C. Wenk. 1999. Screening of chinese herbs as antioxidants for their use in diets of farm animals. Schweizer Forschung begegnet Hunger und Armut. 1. Forum für Internationale Landwirtschaft, ETH Zürich, 30.3.

Stahel, F. 1999. Kräuter als Alternative zu antimikrobiellen Leistungsförderern im Ferkelfutter, Ms. Thesis ETH Zurich, pp. 92.

Svoboda, K.P. and S.G. Deans. 1992. Variability of rosemary and sage volatile oils on the British market obtained from various geographical sources: their antioxidative properties. Flavour and Fragrance Journal.

Swiss Federal Office of Public Health (BAG). 1999: Bakterielle Antibiotikaresistenz in den Bereichen Humanmedizin, Veterinärmedizin und Lebensmittel. BAG, Infodienst Bern, CH. pp. 146.

Visioli, F., G. Bellomo, G. Montedoro and C. Galli. 1995. Low density lipoprotein oxidation is inhibited *in vitro* by olive oil constituents. Atherosclerosis 117:25-32.

Visioli, F., G. Bellomo and C. Galli. 1998. Free radical-scavenging properties of olive oil polyphenols. Biochemical and Biophysical Research Communications 247:60-64.

Wenk, C., M.R.L. Scheeder and C. Spleiss. 1998. Sind Kräuter Allerheilsmittel? In: Gesunde Nutztiere: Umdenken in der Tierernährung? (F. Sutter, M. Kreuzer and C. Wenk, eds.) pp. 95-109.

Wenk, C., M. Leonhardt and M. Scheeder. 2000. Monogastric nutrition and potential for improving muscle quality. In: Antioxidants in Muscle foods, (E. Decker, C. Faustman and C. Lopez-Bote, eds.). J. Wiley & Sons, New York. pp. 199–227.

Webster's Encyclopedic Cambridge Dictionary of the English Language (1989). Gramercy Books, New York.

Wiseman, S.A., J.N. Mathot, F.N. de, and L.B. Tijburg. 1996. Dietary non-tocopherol antioxidants present in extra virgin olive oil increase the resistance of low density lipoproteins to oxidation in rabbits. Atherosclerosis 120:15-23.

The interplay between modern management practices and the chicken: how immune response and the physiological mechanisms for growth and efficiency have adapted over time. Where do we go from here?

MARK E. COOK

University of Wisconsin, Madison, Wisconsin, USA

Introduction

Although plants and animals began to be acquired as domesticants nearly 10,000 years ago, it has only been the last 50 years in which animals have been intensively raised for food. In 1892 Wehman wrote "Poultry, to be successful on a large scale must be kept in small colonies of about 50 birds, for many more than that number in a single house is apt to cause sickness or disease ere long among". Given the scale and concentration of the modern poultry industry, one must ponder whence we have come and question how it was accomplished.

Two developments, namely vaccination and antibiotics, allowed the microbial villain of the piece to be overcome sufficiently for the movement from small animal husbandry schemes to the large scale consolidated units of today. Intensive rearing, vaccination and antibiotic use along with other more subtle changes have in the short period of animal domestication and consolidation had dramatic consequences on the nature of the bird. Contemplation of the role of management decisions on animal change is critical in determining the future and sustainability of those decisions. In the following paper, discussion will be narrowed to one well-defined system I will call 'the ecosystem of the chicken house'. Since this ecosystem is far more complex than can be dealt with here, the discussion will be limited to several ecological interfaces: 1) the interface of select management decisions and the chicken, 2) the interface between the chicken and its microbes and 3) the interface between time and the chicken which reflects management-induced genetic change. It is in this context that we begin to understand how our rearing practices, including antibiotic use, have altered the nature and physiology of the chicken. It is also in this context that we must view the value and the cost of using antimicrobials and seek new directions to maximize growth of intensively-reared birds.

Consolidation

One of the most obvious phenotypes that needed to be modified in the process of animal domestication and consolidation was behavior. The pheasant, one of the more recent wild animals in the US to be placed into domestic conditions in large scale will serve to illustrate domesticated selection. To produce a released bird, ready for hunting season and capable of building a stable flock (the long term goal) these fowl had to be brought into captivity. However, this had unintended consequences in that captivity adjusted behavior as successive generations over time were bred in confined space. When wild pheasants were first placed into confinement, they were put into outdoor flight pens often 200-300 feet long and 50 feet wide. They were rectangular in configuration with posts holding containment wire or nylon netting. However, the posts supporting the wire or nylon netting needed interior support to prevent post collapse, especially during heavy snow and ice. Hence, the original flight pens had an obstacle to flight (the support post) that would accidentally kill the flying pheasant. The consequences of breeding 30 generations of pheasants in this consolidated environment were that birds surviving to breeding age were the least likely to fly. When confronted by the caretaker, the most likely survivor fled on foot. Hence, over the course of many generations, game farm pheasants became runners, not fliers. Leading game breeders recognized the problem, namely that management practices had selected for a tame species. Recognition of this problem led game producers to import wild individuals from China. These were used to breed back traits lost in the more domesticated birds. However, current flight pen construction had to change. Confinement and rearing of a wild species, pheasant, serves to illustrate the consequences of consolidation and the rapid change of a species based upon a simple decision on whether the support beam is on the inside of a flight pen or on the outside.

THE ROLE OF VACCINES AND ANTIBIOTICS IN INTENSIVE REARING

The modern poultry industry has moved from 50 bird flocks to the 1 million plus flocks (layers) or 1 million processed broilers per week in a 30 mile radius of an integrated broiler unit. Vaccine and antibiotic strategies were adopted by early leaders in the poultry sector in order to consolidate animal units and to maintain a competitive edge in animal agriculture. This assured, in the case of chickens, that a valuable food (eggs and meat) would be available to the consumer at a fraction of its cost in 1900. The success of these two management strategies remain a marvel, and assured the modern Western world that food shortages would not limit human pursuits.

The entire animal food industry hinges on the discovery and production technologies of vaccination and antibiotics. Vaccination was not only one of the most brilliant discoveries of mankind, one only need examine the history of poultry science to learn the value gained from vaccination strategies to prevent disease. Once scientists realized that the microscopic world had its own weaponry, antibiotics, we began using them against microbes. This brilliant strategy in disease prevention was quickly moved to the chicken house. An added benefit appeared in that when using antibiotics in animal agriculture to fight disease, animals grew faster and used less food per unit body weight gain. The reason for this remained a mystery until the explanation was provided by Kirk Klasing of U.C. Davis (discussed later).

Vaccination and antibiotics became crucial tools in the consolidation of the poultry industry; and the interface between the chicken and the microbial world was subdued through their use. The revelation that continual feeding of antibiotics promoted growth and feed efficiency resulted in subtherapeutic use of antibiotics on a continual basis in the chicken ecosystem. The ramifications of continual antimicrobial use for performance effects in the chicken house were far-reaching. Poultry products became affordable to all households. Soon antibiotic use in animal feeds represented 50% of antibiotics made in the US. This meant that pharmaceutical companies could finance the discovery of new human cures, partly on the back of profits realized by antibiotic use in animal agriculture. Had it not been for this link between chicken growth and the cures of human diseases, we may have never enticed pharmaceutical companies to risk investments required to generate some of these products. The cost of launching a new antibiotic for use in human medicine, from concept to product, is a staggering $350 million investment. In view of such an investment, one can begin to realize the contribution of the chicken's growth response to financing development of antibiotics for human use. More than 7.5 billion broilers are raised a year in the US. Antibiotics have historically improved growth by 5-10%. With these numbers, the importance of the chicken in medicinal development is evident.

Consolidation was, in its own right, a pressure for change in disease patterns that all of us recognize. Once winter sets in, and people spend more time indoors, the disease of one becomes the disease of all in the household, classroom, office or movie theatre. When we brought chickens together in densities less than one square foot per bird, we created an environment in which disease could quickly spread. In the chicken house we have seen two events that were catastrophic to the poultry industry in recent history: the Newcastle disease outbreak of the early 1970s in California and the influenza outbreak in the 1980s in Lancaster, Pennsylvania. Both outbreaks, while closely contained within their respective regions, cost the consumer hundreds of millions of dollars in increased food costs. Few realize that our animal food production does not far exceed human demand. The fact is that our production, particularly for inelastic markets such as eggs, barely exceeds human needs, hence the low price. During the two historical outbreaks, prices for poultry products reached an all time high even though only a small part of the nation's production was affected.

Consolidation of an animal species increases the likelihood of the transmission of a pathogen among individuals. If we consider the strategy of the villain, the infectious organism, consolidation is the perfect medium to achieve its goals. Keeping a flock of no more than 50 birds was a perfect strategy for prevention in the 1890s, but is not sustainable if we are to maintain a low cost food supply. Hence, the greater the consolidation, the lower the food cost, but the greater the chance of the spread of an introduced infectious pathogen. Ultimately, consolidation and low food prices have driven the need for vaccination and antibiotics.

The tool of vaccination (not to be discussed at length here) was the most important vehicle for consolidation of humans and their animals. Controlled exposure to potential insults could assure that an army of educated defenders (antibodies) were in place if the attack came. Most interesting, the agricultural community largely ignored the cost of maintaining a specifically trained militia designed for only one purpose: to destroy only one enemy and often at only one frontal attack. This cost will be explored in more detail later.

Bacteria, antimicrobials and immune response: why the chicken responds to antibiotics

Of all management strategies for consolidation, none have come under more scrutiny than the use of antimicrobials. It is interesting that we group a wide range of biologically active compounds under a single term; but however diverse their activity in controlling infectious diseases, they, like vaccines and consolidation, result in change of the chicken ecosystem. For many generations, forced change has occurred rapidly.

Despite the modern misconception that if it was not published yesterday, it is not relevant to the problems of today, many of the answers to today's questions can only be found in works dating back decades. Lev and Forbes (1959) published a paper that is pivotal in the understanding of the ecosystem of the chicken house. They showed that chickens raised in germ free environments grew faster than those exposed to conventional bacterial flora. More importantly, they showed that the feeding of penicillin (an antibiotic known to be a growth stimulant in poultry) had no growth promoting effects in germ free environments in contrast to potent growth stimulation in bacterially contaminated environments. The improvement in growth for germ free vs. normally-exposed birds was greater than 10%. Even more importantly, antibiotics only partially alleviated the growth suppression associated with the exposure to naturally occurring microbes. Hence, their work showed that there was room for expression.

Kirk Klasing showed that injecting the cell wall of *Escherichia coli* (endotoxin) into chickens caused them to grow more slowly or lose weight. Why? Because the exposure of an animal to a normal flora antigen had such a negative impact on growth. The reduction in body weight gain following endotoxin exposure was 30%. His work also showed that the type of immune stimulant was not responsible for the reduction in gain. Chicks injected with sheep red blood cells also grew 17% slower than the control birds.

While never published in a full length manuscript, a group at Mississippi State University reported that "vaccination of broilers resulted in lower final body weights, poorer feed conversion and higher 8 day and 42 day mortality. Vaccination reduced overall performance in the absence of overt disease" (Chamberlee *et al.*, 1992). We also observed a similar effect in ducks. In a study with a commercial line of ducks, we injected either a saline control or a standard killed bacterin of *Pasteurella antipestifer*. The injections were given at day 12 and again 10 days later. The ducks were then raised to market age. The final carcass weight of the ducks injected with the killed bacterin was reduced by 9% and the amount of breast meat was reduced by 5.4%. These data clearly showed that there was a significant cost associated with vaccination. In addition, the decreased growth and feed efficiency observed with a diverse range of antigens suggested that the reduced performance was not antigen mediated, but perhaps related to the immune response.

During the response of the immune system to a stimulus, immune cells such as the macrophage destroy and process (degrade) the stimulant and present specific parts of the stimulant to white blood cells known as lymphocytes. There are two primary classes of lymphocytes known as T and B cells. These cells proliferate to form clones of cells specifically targeted to the antigen presented. The cloned cells have increased capacity to respond in a rapid defense if exposed to the antigen in the future. The macrophage is also responsible for producing cell signals, known as cytokines, which up-regulate the immune cells during their cloning. The cytokines, interleukin-1 (IL-1) and tumor necrosis factor (TNF), are two major cytokines released from the macrophage during the immune response to an antigen.

Klasing *et al.* (1987) went on to show that the growth depression associated with endotoxin (*E. coli* cell wall) injection could be produced by a direct injection of IL-1. He also showed that IL-1, when placed on cultured muscle strips, increased muscle degradation and decreased protein synthesis. Hence, the growth depression associated with immune stimulation was the result of the release of the immune cytokines and not the direct effect of the immune stimulant. Everyone can relate to the consequence of immune stimulation. When we develop an infectious disease, we lose our appetite and we lose weight. The pathogen is not responsible for these physiological changes, it is the result of immune cytokines. The use of recombinant cytokines as immunotherapy was of great interest when first discovered. However the side effects were so severe that routine use of IL-1 and TNF was never realized in human medicine. Those of you who are actively involved in poultry production can relate to the effects of immune stimulation. In our research involving growing broilers or turkeys, we often go into the growing facility to weigh birds. During the process of data collection, litter is stirred causing the air to be filled with dust. In this dust is fecal matter rich in killed bacterial cells and hence endotoxin. After breathing this dust for several hours, we all experience similar signs: loss of appetite, low grade fever and fatigue. These effects are immune related. Within the next 24 hrs, the immune system slows and the adverse effects of immune stimulation are resolved. Since it is the immune products that suppress growth, it becomes evident that immune suppression or removal of the immune stimulant should enhance growth in the absence of disease.

Both immune suppression and reduction of immune stimulants (reduced bacterial load through the use of antibiotics) represent two major management strategies used to consolidate poultry. While both management strategies have moved animal agriculture toward more efficient production of food, there is a long term cost associated with them.

THE COST OF ANTIMICROBIAL USE

If animals could be reared in the absence of immune stimulation, the added performance would be valued in the hundreds of millions of dollars in the US alone. However, it is unlikely that such a process could be economic. Improved sanitation has been shown to minimize decreases in growth associated with the immune response (Roura and Klasing, 1993). In certain species one strategy used to reduce immune stimulation is 'all in/all out' management. In this scenario, animals are placed in a growing setting only with others of the same age. By doing so, older animals, which often become carriers of infectious pathogens, do not expose younger animals to disease agents. The swine industry experienced major improvements in growth rates when they moved from facilities containing multi-age animals to segregated early weaning strategies where piglets were removed from the sow at an early age and reared in isolation.

Since the 1950s, another management practice used to reduce immune-induced growth suppression involved the use of antibiotics. It was observed that feeding low levels of dietary antibiotics on a continuous basis improved growth and feed efficiency. The reason for the improved performance was that antibiotics reduced the bacterial load (immune stimulants) in the gut, decreased the level of immune stimulation, and hence prevented the catabolic nature of the immune response. By the 1970s, over 50% of all antibiotics produced in the US went into animal feeds (Von Houwelling, 1978). In some countries, antibiotic use in animal feed was more than 1000 times the use in human medicinals (Witte, 1998).

Witte (1998) reported the consequence of antimicrobial use in animal feeds. The study he reported was perhaps the best longitudinal study illustrating that using antimicrobials in animal feed confers resistance to organisms in humans. In 1983 in East Germany, pigs were tested for microbes resistant to the antibiotic nourseothricin prior to its use in swine diets. No resistance was observed. Beginning in 1983, nourseothricin was used as a growth promotant in swine diets. By 1985, microbes with resistance to the antibiotic were observed in the intestinal tract of pigs and on the processed meats.

By 1990, resistant *E. coli* was found in the farmers and individuals in the community. In 1987, Shigella (a human pathogen and an organism not associated with pigs) was expressing resistance to nourseothricin. It is now well recognized that antibiotic resistance can be transferred across bacterial species. This resistance can be transferred both by plasmids as well as genomically. Hence, targeting these immune stimulants as a strategy for enhancing growth rate ultimately confers resistance.

What alternatives are available to assure improved growth and feed efficiency without directing the therapy to the microbial flora, or without suppressing the inflammatory response? Dafwang *et al.* (1987) showed that when broilers were provided with more floor space, the depressed performance associated with consolidation was reduced. In fact, these studies showed that at only the highest densities were antibiotics effective at enhancing growth rate. While these results looked promising, the cost associated with doubling the floor space for 7.5 billion broilers would be prohibitive. Our data also showed that increasing the density of broilers resulted in a reduced size of selected lymphoid organs (Bursa of Fabricius and thymus). While antibiotics enhanced the growth rate of broiler chicks raised at high densities, the use of antibiotics was ineffective at restoring the size of the bursa and thymus associated with dense populations of broilers.

A number of antibiotics have been banned in Europe, in part because it is feared that the generation of antibiotic resistance will increase human disease with no effective therapeutic treatment. Logic would have it that similar bans should be proposed in the United States. Many have expressed concerns about the consequent effects on animal health and efficiency. The removal of antibiotics as growth promotants could cost poultry and swine producers as much as a billion dollars. One must also consider that the poorer feed efficiency could significantly increase the demand for corn and soybean meal. In addition, animals not fed antibiotics would grow more slowly and hence would not reach their market weight until days later than those fed antibiotics. This would decrease the number of animals moving through the existing infrastructure. Unless new animal units were constructed, total animal numbers produced would decline. Even more important is the potential negative effect antibiotic removal could have on human health. The continuous use of antibiotics reduces the bacterial load on an animal and hence the final meat products. Would animal products from animals not fed antibiotics represent an even more serious food safety risk? Another indirect means by which a ban on antibiotics could affect human health involves the pharmaceutical manufacturers. Since animal agriculture represents a source of income for antibiotic manufacturers, what will be the likely outcome if this source of income is lost? Will a company be eager to spend the $350 million needed to create a new antibiotic if it will have lost a major market which helps defray these costs? If so, then the future generation of new antimicrobials for human health could be (or is) at great risk. As one thinks about these issues, it would appear that we have created a trap that may be difficult to avoid without a major restructuring of the animal industry and allied industries. It is clear that research is needed to clearly define the costs associated with both the use and avoidance of antibiotics in animal feeds.

Genetic selection and the microbial/immune interface

Our discussion to this point clearly shows that the interface between management strategies and the microbial world is greatly linked to the immune response of an animal, with critical points of growth and feed efficiency being the driving variables needing optimization. Most of our management strategies in consolidated animal units attempt to minimize the inflammatory process, whether intentionally or by chance. The unexpected consequence, particularly with regard to the microbial world, of antibiotics was increased resistance and hence a potential human hazard. The microbial immune interface has another dimension worthy of discussion: the effects on genetic selection. While improved growth was achieved by reducing immune stimulation (Lev and Forbes 1957 only showed a partial restoration of growth through the use of antibiotics), genetic selection for growth rate and feed efficiency was not without its effect. As previously discussed, symptoms associated with an immune reaction include decreased body weight (or rates of weight gain) and poorer feed efficiency (or anorexia). In addition, immune stimulation can actually increase mortality. These are the very endpoints we wished to improve and the reason for our desire to reduce the level of immune stimulation using antibiotics. However, if you were an animal geneticist selecting commercial breeding stock and looking for the birds which grow the fastest and convert feed the most efficiently, which bird would you select? Would the bird with the greater or lesser inflammatory response perform best? The birds that are selected as the superior performers in theory should have the poorest immune response. In fact, from the geneticist's point of view, the less growth depression due to immune stimulation the better. Generation after generation of selecting animals that perform in the top 20% in the typical immune stimulating environment loaded with airborne endotoxin has resulted in an animal that is less likely to mount an inflammatory response associated with the cytokines IL-1 and TNF.

We became very interested in the effects of genetic selection on the immune response of an animal. Access to such genetic lines however proved difficult. Fortunately, a duck company, Maple Leaf Farms, was interested in this question as well. This highly vertically-integrated company had its own breeding program where performance traits were selected. While the studies conducted were not pure and ideal, we were able to gain limited insight into the influence of selection for performance on immune responses. In our first study, we compared a T cell dependent immune response to phytohemagglutinin-P. Fortunately, the company had a line of ducks that did not have heavy selection pressures (we called this line the control). The other lines were selected for rate of gain, breast meat yield, or feed efficiency. All lines selected for performance traits had reduced immunoreactivity of 28% or more when compared to the line with less (or no) selection pressure. We expanded our test to include antibody synthesis in response to an antigenic stimulus. The antibody response was 29 to 79% less in lines selected for improved performance when compared to our control. Dr. Venelin Kounev soon joined my laboratory to try to improve our understanding of growth and immune function. Working within a given elite duck line (the great grandparent lines) he was able to show a direct inverse correlation between body weight and cell-mediated immunity (r = -0.38). This means that in this line of ducks, if the top performers were selected as grandparents for the next generation, those selected would have the poorest ability to generate an immune response to a stimulus.

Others were making similar observations. In a study by Sharaf *et al.* (1988), turkeys selected for enhanced egg production had decreased antibody titers in response to Newcastle Disease virus vaccination. Hence, these data suggested that genetic selection for enhanced performance (whether for growth, feed efficiency, or egg production) is associated with suppressed immunological function. Work has shown that the genetic overexpression of genes for tumor necrosis factor (TNF) greatly retards growth and thriftiness of animals. Hence, the obvious effect of selection for growth in immune stimulating environments is the selection against catabolic cytokines. However, no data are available to directly support this hypothesis. We are actively engaged in such research but have failed to convince the scientific community of its merits. Hence, grant proposals are rejected with comments of "no need to reapply".

It appears that not only are management practices changing to enhance animal performance, but also that the immune system of our agricultural species is being modified to improve animal growth and feed efficiency. As there are consequences associated with an attempt to modify immune stimulation, there are likewise consequences in modification of the inflammatory process and other immune reactions. One consequence involves physiological processes that cells of the immune response are involved in that have little relationship to defense. Select cells of lymphoidal origin are responsible for the maintenance of tissue structure and function. The macrophage is essential in the repair and remodeling of tissues associated with growth, development and injury. Hence, one can predict that selection against inflammatory or immune processes may lead to physiological aberrations.

Out of the trap?

Clearly, new strategies are needed to assure animal growth, to maintain an immunologically expressive animal and to reduce pressure on the microbial ecosystem. Such approaches should target neither the immune system nor the microbial flora. While these targets have rewarded us with improved animal growth and perhaps even wellbeing, these targets have limitations that can be pushed only so far. We have signs that suggest that it is time to remove pressures on the microbial flora and the animal's immune system. What are those new targets going to look like? If we need to find alternatives for maintaining the existing level of growth in animals, how will we structure these alternatives? It is now time to explore these ideas. We are landed in a kind of trap in that our management strategies of antibiotic use may lead to resistant disease organisms and our genetic selection practices result in 'immune suppressed' animals. Where is the door of opportunity? We have created a system of unintended consequences that demands creative thinkers.

Alternatives

Initial work with nutrition and immunity examined pharmacological levels of certain nutrients in an effort to enhance immune function and was not promising. Working with two integrated turkey companies in the early 1990s, we reformulated the diets based on experience and literature reviewed (Cook, 1991). Both companies said the results were disastrous. It was then that I realized that there was a cost to immunological function, much as Kirk Klasing was demonstrating in his work. Other works in the literature, although sketchy, were showing similar effects. Nockels (1979) had shown that immune enhancement of guinea pigs using vitamin E had a deleterious effect on growth rate when the pigs were infected with equine encephalomyelitis virus. Gross (1992) also showed that while high dietary levels of ascorbic acid reduced lesions associated with Mycoplasma and *E. coli*, chickens fed the high ascorbic acid had much poorer feed conversion. It appeared that implementation of nutritional regimes proven to reduce pathogenesis of select infectious disease was costly. Enhanced immunoreactivity suppressed performance and hence an alternative appeared necessary in the management of performance in immunoreactive animals.

CONJUGATED LINOLEIC ACID

To understand alternative methods to prevent the immune-induced growth suppression and to find ways to improve animal performance without the aid of antibiotics, a basic understanding of immune-induced growth suppression was needed. The question that had to be answered was how do immune cytokines suppress growth? Rodemann and Goldberg (1982) had shown that muscle degradation associated with IL-1 was associated with increased production of prostaglandin E_2 (PGE_2). They went on to show (Goldberg *et al.*, 1984) that when PGE_2 was directly applied to muscle strips, the muscle degradation was increased. Based on these works, we began a series of studies to identify dietary factors that would prevent the wasting of body weight during the immune response. A number of compounds were identified; however, they all appeared to be immunosuppressive. Our goal was to prevent the loss of body weight in the immune challenged animal without having a negative effect on immune function.

We began work with conjugated linoleic acid (CLA) when Mike Pariza, a collegue in Food Microbiology and Toxicology, proposed feeding some laying hens CLA as he had found that it had potent anticarcinogenic activity. At that time, he believed that the anticancer activity of the compound might be related to antioxidant capacity. His goal was to feed laying hens CLA so he could harvest the eggs, make mayonnaise and determine if shelf life was extended. Since one mechanism in the reduction of tumor formation involved the immune system, we began collaborative studies on CLA and immunological function.

What was most appealing about CLA with regard to the Klasing model of immune-induced growth suppression was that CLA is a fatty acid markedly similar to linoleic acid (18:2, cis 9, cis 12), which was the precursor for PGE_2, the lipid mediator that caused muscle wasting. The double bond configuration of CLA (18:2) prepared in his laboratory was predominately cis 9, trans 11, or trans 10, cis 12. Even more perfect was that these fatty acids were naturally occurring (see *www.wisc.edu/cook* for more detail). As predicted, CLA prevented growth suppression resulting from immune stimulation (Cook *et al.*, 1993; Miller *et al.*, 1994). Later we found that it even protected against growth suppression associated with the direct injection of TNF and wasting autoimmune disease. More exciting, CLA did not prevent immune-induced growth suppression by suppressing the immune system. In fact, it enhanced the immune response. This became our first alternative to the growth suppression caused by immune stimulation. Instead of targeting the microbial world (which would only develop resistance) or the immune system (a potentially bad idea) we targeted how nonlymphoidal tissue responded to the immune system (see US Patents: 5,430,066; 5,428,072; 5,827,885; 5,674,901 and 5,725,873).

An analogy may aid in explaining these results: If one thinks of the immune system as a military force, the immune reaction as a battle, and the animal's nonlymphoidal tissue (such as muscle) as the nonmilitary citizen where the battle is taking place, during conflict there is always collateral damage to nontargeted sites. Our hope is to minimize this collateral damage by erecting barriers. CLA was found to be a biological barrier to the collateral damage associated with the immune response.

Another area we thought would be a beneficial control point in protecting against the collateral damage of the immune response is the intestine. Of all places in the animal's body, the intestine hosts the greatest quantity of immune stimulants. As was previously mentioned, one of the consequences of the immune response is a reduction in feed intake. Work on our campus by Donna McCarthy (Daun and McCarthy, 1993) had shown that IL-1 induces anorexia in part by causing the release of the gut peptide, cholecystokinin (CCK). CCK in turn induces a satiety effect and alters gut motility. We reasoned that if we could interfere with the actions of CCK, then we could prevent reduced feed intake associated with the immune response. Literature suggested that CCK was released into the lumen of the intestine. This source of CCK was targeted using antibody generated against CCK. We selected the laying hen as our source of anti-CCK production since hens can be stimulated to produce high quantities of antibodies in the egg yolk. When egg powder containing antibodies to CCK was fed to broiler chickens, growth rate and feed efficiency improved. Antibodies to other gut peptides also showed similar benefits (see US patents 5,827,517; 5,725,873 and 5,989,584). While these anti-CCK antibodies were not found to stimulate food intake, they proved very effective as growth promotants. We have continued our efforts to make antibodies to other physiological processes involved in the immune response with remarkable success.

Another area in regulating immune-induced growth suppression involved the development of a method to continuously monitor when an animal is immunologically challenged. We reasoned that if we could know rapidly and noninvasively when an animal was undergoing an immunological reaction, that animal could be treated accordingly. For example, is there a means to continuously monitor layers in a large complex (a million or more) to know if a disease is in the early stages of development? If rapid detection was possible, then these diseased animals could be removed from the flock or specifically treated. To accomplish this goal we used the natural fractionation of isotopes of carbon (US patent 5,912,178). During enzymatic processes, enzymes discriminate against substrates containing ^{13}Carbon and preferentially use substrate with ^{12}Carbon. We reasoned that during the immune response, as skeletal muscle is degraded and amino acids are released, these amino acids have two pathways of metabolism. They can be reused for acute phase protein synthesis or burned to CO_2 and expired. Since the complete metabolism to CO_2 has many enzymatic steps, we predicted that the amount of ^{13}C in breath would decrease during the catabolic response and indeed it does. Hence, one could envision the continuous sampling of CO_2 from ventilation exhaust for monitoring ^{12}C:^{13}C ratios.

Summation

New strategies for the control of the microbial/immune and immune/nonlymphoidal interfaces are critical in discovering alternatives to antibiotics as growth promotants. These strategies must not result in resistant microbes and must enhance or maintain immune function.

References

Chamberlee, T.N., J.R. Thompson and J.P. Thaxton. 1992. Effects of day old vaccination on broiler performance. Poultry Sci. 71(Suppl. 1):144 (Abstr.).

Cook, M.E., C.C. Miller, Y. Park and M. Pariza. 1993. Immune modulating by altered nutrient metabolism: Nutritional control of immune-induced growth depression. Poultry Sci. 72:1301-1305.

Dafwang, I.I., M.E. Cook and M.L. Sunde. 1987. Interaction of dietary antibiotic supplementation and stocking density on broiler chick performance and immune response. Brit. Poultry Sci. 28:47-55.

Daun, J.M. and D.O. McCarthy. 1993. The role of cholecystokinin in interleukin-1 induced anorexia. Physiology and Behavior 54:237-241.

Goldberg, A.L., V. Baracos, Rodemann, L. Waxman and C. Dinarello. 1984. Control of protein degradation in muscles by prostaglandins, Ca++ and leukocyte pyrogen (interleukin-1). Federation Proc. 43:1301-1306.

Klasing, K.C., D.E. Laurin, P.K. Peng and D.M. Fry. 1987. Immunologically mediated growth depression in chicks: Influence of feed intake, corticosterone and interleukin-1. J. of Nutr. 117:1629-1637.

Lev, M. and M. Forbes. 1959. Growth response to dietary penicillin of germ-free chicks with a defined intestinal flora. Brit. J. Nutr. 13:78-84.

Miller, C.C., Y. Park, M.W. Pariza and M.E. Cook. 1994. Feeding conjugated linoleic acid to animals partially overcomes catabolic response due to endotoxin injection. Biochem. Biophys. Res. Comm. 198:1107-1112.

Nockels, C.F. 1979. Protective effects of supplemental vitamin E against infection. Fed. Proc. 38:2134-2138.

Rodemann, H.P. and A.L. Goldberg. 1982. Arachadonic acid, prostaglandin E2 and F2 influence rates of protein turnover in skeletal and cardiac muscle. J. Biol. Chem. 257:1632-1638.

Roura, E. and K.C. Klasing. 1993. Dietary antibiotics reduce immunological stress elicited by poor sanitation or consumption of excreta in broiler chicks. J. Nutr. 122:2383-2390.

Sharaf, M.M., K.E. Nestor, Y.M. Saif, R.E. Sacco and G.B. Havenstein. 1988. Antibody response to Newcastle Disease virus and *Pasteurella multocida* of two strains of turkeys. Poultry Sci. 67:1372-1377.

Von Houwelling, C.D. 1978. Draft environmental impact statement. Subtherapeutic agents in animal feeds. Food and Drug Admin. Washington, D.C.

Wehman, H.J. 1892. Wehman's Practical Poultry Book. Wehman Bros., New York, pp. 110. Quoted in: Wilson, W.O. 1974. Housing In: American Poultry History 1823-1973. American Printing and Publishing, Inc., pp. 221.

Witte, W. 1998. Medical consequences of antibiotic use in agriculture. Sci. 279:996-997.

Efficacy, use and application of microbial phytase in pig production: a review

AGE W. JONGBLOED, PAUL A. KEMME, ZDZISLAW MROZ AND HANS TH.M. VAN DIEPEN

Institute for Animal Science and Health (ID-Lelystad), ID TNO Animal Nutrition, Lelystad, The Netherlands

Summary

In this paper the current status of knowledge on the impact of microbial phytases in pig production is reviewed. In most studies, exogenous phytases supplemented to diets for pigs are obtained from Aspergilli. They produce 3-phytase (EC 3.1.3.8), a non-specific phosphomonoesterase, catalysing dephosphorylation of myoinositol hexakisphosphate (phytate) in a stepwise manner, producing orthophosphate, which can be absorbed by the animal. During the last decades various experiments have been conducted all over the world with commercially available microbial phytases. Supplementation of these enzymes to diets for pigs (and poultry) results in enhancement of phosphorus (P) digestibility/availability, as assessed by different criteria. In studies at our institute, mostly with Natuphos®, doses of microbial phytase in the range of 500 to 2000 phytase units per kg of feed resulted in generation of 0.8 to 1.0 g digestible phosphorus per kg of feed. The dose-response relationship seems to be dependent on the type of feed and the dose of microbial phytase. In addition, digestible calcium (Ca) content is increased in amounts averaging from 50 to 80% of the increase in digestible phosphorus content. Apart from the well-defined positive effects of this enzyme on calcium and phosphorus digestibility, ileal digestibility of amino acids and total tract digestibility of magnesium and trace elements (mainly zinc) are enhanced by microbial phytase. The amount and origin of phytate appear to have a substantial effect on the efficacy of microbial phytase. Feeding frequency and amount of feed exert minor effects on the efficacy of microbial phytase. Performance (daily gain, feed conversion ratio) of pigs fed microbial phytase appears to be better as compared with a non-supplemented diet or even with a positive control diet. Microbial phytase is now used in most pig and poultry diets in The Netherlands and can be used as a feed ingredient in linear programming of the diets. Microbial phytase supplementation to diets for pigs can substantially reduce phosphorus excretion and also to a certain extent nitrogen excretion, and can therefore reduce environmental pollution from pig production.

Introduction

Phytate is the main phosphorus-containing constituent (P content 28.2%) of many seeds and tubers; and its primary physiological role is P storage for germination (Cosgrove, 1980). In general, phytates constitute about 1-2% by weight of many cereals and oilseeds. Approximately 60-90% of total P in these seeds is present in phytate-bound form (Cheryan, 1980). Phytates are of very limited digestibility/availability for pigs (Cromwell, 1980; Jongbloed, 1987). It therefore contributes to the P pollution in regions where land and water resources are limited and animal production is intensive such as in The Netherlands.

A possible structure of the phytate molecule (myoinositol 1,2,3,4,5,6-hexakisphosphate) when complexed with minerals and protein and starch in acidic medium is presented in Figure 1.

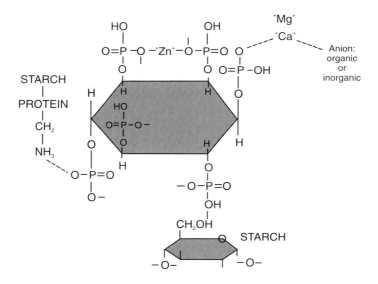

Figure 1. Phytate-protein-starch complex molecule: a potential structure (modified after Thompson, 1986; and Kies, 1998).

Phytic acid is strongly negatively charged (six reactive phosphate groups) over a wide pH range, indicating tremendous potential for complexing or binding positively charged molecules such as cations or proteins below the isoelectric point. The binding is possible within a phosphate group or between two phosphate groups on either the same or different phytic acid molecules; and the resulting structure is said to be a chelate compound (Cheryan, 1980).

Usually, phytate-bound nutrients are poorly available in the digestive tract of monogastric animals due to the lack of phytase enzyme required to cleave the phytate molecule (Cosgrove, 1980; Reddy *et al.*, 1982; Jongbloed *et al.*, 1993). Numerous animal experiments have documented the nutritional implications of phytates in binding dietary macro- and microelements (Ca, Mg, Fe, Zn, Cu, Mn, Mo and Co), thus reducing their solubility and bioavailability (Erdman, 1979; Torre *et al.*, 1991). The effect of phytic acid on mineral bioavailability is influenced by pH, amount of phytic acid, mineral concentration, association/configuration of phytic acid with dietary protein/fiber/starch, heat treatment, pre-feeding processing and the presence of other metal ions in a diet (Cheryan, 1980; Torre *et al.*, 1991). Phytates are generally soluble at low pH, but almost completely insoluble at intestinal pH (Cheryan, 1980). The interaction between phytates and minerals leads to formation of complexes that precipitate in the duodenum (Reddy *et al.*, 1982). Since the small intestine is the principal site of divalent cation absorption (Jongbloed *et al.*, 1993), this implies that bioavailability of minerals can be affected by the presence of phytate. The availability of dietary minerals bound to phytate is low, especially when two or more cations are present so that a synergistic binding effect can occur (Maga, 1982).

To enable dephosphorylation of dietary phytates, there is increasing interest all over the world in supplementing such diets with purified preparations of exogenous (microbial) phytases (often obtained from genetically modified microorganisms) instead of additional phosphorus from feed phosphates.

In this paper, the effects of exogenous phytases in pig rations on animal performance and availability of P, N and some other minerals will be discussed. In addition, dietary and management factors that affect the efficacy of microbial phytase, its use in practice and the environmental impact will be considered.

Some characteristics of microbial phytases

There are several commercial microbial phytases now on the market either in dry powder or liquid forms. The phytases may differ slightly in their physical properties and enzyme activity. This may imply different efficacies of the phytase preparations. Natuphos® was the first commercially available phytase from a genetically modified *Aspergillus niger* strain. Since 1991 the Dutch feed industry has been using this exogenous microbial phytase, an enzymatic product obtained by fermentation of *Aspergillus niger*, into which the gene encoding phytase from *Aspergillus niger* var. Van Tieghem has been cloned using recombinant DNA technology. Therefore, it is obvious that most knowledge concerning microbial phytase has been obtained with this enzyme, although subsequently several other phytase preparations have been used. Phytase activity of this product (FTU) is assayed by measuring the amount of orthophosphate released from phytic acid within a period of linear increase with time. One unit of phytase activity is equal to 1 µmol of orthophosphate liberated from 1.5 mM Na-phytate in 1 min. at 37°C and pH 5.5 (Engelen *et al.*, 1994). The activity of other phytase sources may be assayed under slightly different conditions.

Phytase is a phosphomonoesterase capable of hydrolyzing phytic acid (myoinositol hexakisphosphate) to yield inorganic orthophosphate that can be absorbed through the gastrointestinal wall of the pig along with a series of lower phosphoric esters of myoinositol. The dephosphorylation is necessary not only for digestibility of phytate P, but also for the utilization of minerals and proteins bound to phytates.

Intrinsic phytase present in the seeds of higher plants (e.g. wheat) is recognized by the International Union of Pure and Applied Chemistry and the International Union of Biochemistry as 6-phytase (EC 3.1.3.26). Exogenous phytase produced by microorganisms inhabiting the gastrointestinal tract such as fungi, bacteria, yeasts or intestinal endogenous phytase secreted into the lumen from the intestinal mucosa of some species is recognized as 3-phytase (EC 3.1.3.8; Wise, 1980). However, the endogenous phytase activity in the intestinal mucosa of pigs is negligible (Pointillart *et al.*, 1984). Jongbloed *et al.* (1992) detected no phytase activity in the ileal digesta, which indicates that phytases from the bacterial flora up to the terminal ileum and intestinal mucosal phytases are negligible. For that reason, the ability of the pig to utilize nutrients bound to phytate complexes is primarily dependent on intrinsic phytase activity of the feed ingredients or enzymatic preparations of microbial phytase added to diets. The mode of action of phytase is illustrated in Figure 2.

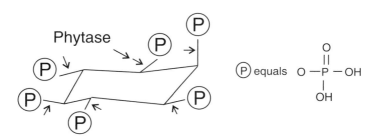

Figure 2. Schematic mode of action of microbial phytase on dietary phytates.

The enzyme cannot stand high temperatures. For instance, by pelleting a pig diet at 70°C, the initial activity is reduced by 15-25% (Schwarz and Hoppe, 1992). Microbial phytases are active over a wide range of pH, with optima at pH 2.5 and 5.5 (Simons *et al.*, 1990). Jongbloed *et al.* (1992) reported from studies on cannulated pigs (ileal and duodenal cannulae) that hydrolysis of phytate in diets by microbial phytase takes place mainly in the stomach (43%), and decisively less in the small intestine (7%). This indicates that only half of the phytate was hydrolyzed by microbial phytase, which can be explained by the limited retention time in the stomach.

Effect of microbial phytase on digestibility/availability of phosphorus

Since 1990 various experiments with exogenous microbial phytases have been reported to quantify their effect on the apparent digestibility/availability of phosphorus. A survey of a large part of these studies was presented by Jongbloed *et al.* (1993) and Düngelhoef and Rodehutscord (1995). One of the first and most interesting experiments was the dose-response effect of microbial phytase (Natuphos®) on apparent digestibility of P in growing pigs from 20 to 55 kg (Beers and Jongbloed, 1992). Six doses of phytase (from 0 to 1800 FTU/kg) were used in two types of grower diets (based either on corn-soybean meal or phytate-rich by-products). The efficacy of microbial phytase appeared to be related to its dose and the type of diet (Figure 3). For the corn-soybean meal diet the relation could be described by an exponential curve with the following formula:

Digestible P (g/kg) = 1.86 - 0.9963^{dose},
R^2 = 96.7%; r.s.d. = 0.067 g digestible P/kg.

From 0 to 400 FTU/kg there was a rapid increase in microbial phytase efficacy, which flattened afterwards. For the phytate-rich by-product diet, the response could be illustrated by a logistic curve using the following formula:

Digestible P (g/kg) = 0.95 + 1.31/(1 + e$^{(-5.51 \times 10 - 3(dose-377.8))}$),
R^2 = 95.5%; r.s.d. = 0.092 g digestible P/kg.

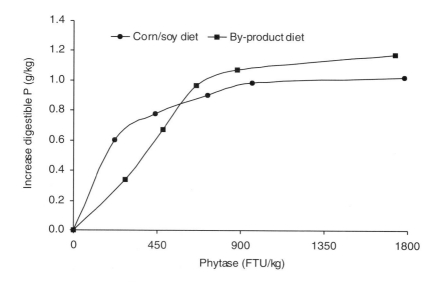

Figure 3. Improvement in digestible P by microbial phytase (Natuphos®) in two diets for growing pigs (Beers and Jongbloed, 1992).

In most cases the dose-response relationship can best be described by an exponential curve. This can also be concluded from studies of Cromwell *et al.* (1995) with the phytase preparation Allzyme Phytase® (Figure 4). The conclusion of the experiment of Beers and Jongbloed (1992) was that the efficacy of microbial phytase per FTU appeared to be the largest up to 500 FTU/kg diet. This dose was estimated to be equivalent to 0.8 g digestible P/ kg diet.

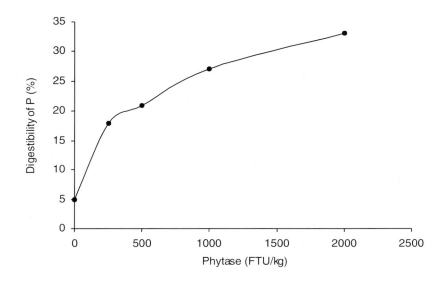

Figure 4. Improvement of availability of P (%) by microbial phytase (Allzyme Phytase®) in a corn-soybean meal diet (Cromwell *et al.*, 1995).

Based on the curve for the corn-soybean meal based diet (Figure 3), the responses of a large number of our own experiments have also been plotted (figures not shown). This showed that responses in other experiments in our laboratory fit quite well with the curve for corn-soybean meal. In all experiments it is shown that microbial phytase is considerably effective in enhancing P digestibility and so increases the amount of digestible/available P in the feed for pigs.

The efficacy of microbial phytase also depends on animal related factors such as physiological status and housing conditions (Kemme *et al.*, 1997a). Kemme *et al.* (1997b) showed that the efficacy of phytase in generating digestible P decreased in the order of lactating sows, growing-finishing pigs, sows at the end of pregnancy, piglets and sows at midpregnancy.

Dietary factors affecting efficacy of microbial phytase

A prerequisite for a good evaluation of microbial phytase efficacy is that the animals be fed below their P requirement. This is due to intestinal regulation of P absorption when animals are fed above their P requirement.

There is little information available on dietary factors affecting efficacy of microbial phytase. It is commonly known that higher dietary Ca levels decrease apparent absorption of P (Jongbloed, 1987). However in most experiments dietary treatments with different Ca levels were implemented only in diets with microbial phytase and not simultaneously in diets without microbial phytase (Lei *et al.*, 1994; Lantzsch *et al.*, 1995). Mostly a linear decrease of P absorption is observed. In two experiments we studied whether a possible interaction could be demonstrated between dietary Ca level and microbial phytase supplementation on P absorption (Mroz *et al.*, 1994b; Jongbloed *et al.*, 1995). We observed a linear decrease in apparent digestibility of P at higher Ca levels, but no interaction with microbial phytase could be demonstrated.

Another dietary factor is the amount and source of phytate. In two experiments we studied the effect of phytate amount and source on the efficacy of microbial phytase (Dekker *et al.*, 1992). For this purpose we used diets based on either corn or sunflower seed meal at two inclusion levels (and so two levels of phytate P). The concentrations of phytate P were 1.2 and 1.8 g/kg; and phytase activities in the corn and sunflower-based diets were 450 and 340 FTU/kg, respectively. We observed that in the corn-based diet the higher level of phytate generated substantially more digestible P, while in the sunflower-based diet slightly more digestible P was generated at the higher phytate level. It was concluded firstly that in both diets the lower level of phytate was too low to get maximal effect of the enzyme; and secondly that phytate in corn is more readily available than phytate in sunflower seed meal. Lack of substrate (phytate) may occur in piglet diets formulated with large proportions of animal products as a protein or P source or with diets that already contain a high concentration of intrinsic phytase like wheat, wheat bran, barley, rye or triticale (Düngelhoef *et al.*, 1994; Eeckhout and De Paepe, 1992).

Jongbloed *et al.* (2000) performed two experiments in which diets were supplemented with or without microbial phytase and/or lactic acid and formic acid. Supplementary lactic acid and formic acid exerted a synergistic effect on apparent digestibility of P. This means that efficacy of microbial phytase could be further enhanced by some organic acids.

Effect of phytase on calcium digestibility

As stated earlier, phytate complexes may be formed with various di- and trivalent cations (Wise, 1980). Microbial phytase supplementation also

117

increases Ca digestibility. To quantify this effect the ratio was calculated between the increase in amount of digestible Ca and the amount of digestible P. All available data from our own experiments and those in the literature were used (Figure 5). The ratios in our own experiments (n=12) were on average 0.55±0.19, while those from data in the literature (n=20) were significantly higher 0.84±0.33. We have no clear explanation for this difference, but the levels of dietary Ca and digestible P certainly play a part (Mroz *et al.*, 1994b). In practical diet formulation the higher Ca digestibility means that supplementation of Ca in diets with microbial phytase can be slightly reduced, which may be beneficial as this lowers buffering capacity of the diet (less digestive disorders). Using 500 FTU/kg of feed generates 0.8 g/kg of digestible P and 0.4 to 0.7 g/kg of digestible Ca. Assuming a Ca digestibility of supplemental limestone of 60%, then between 1.7 and 3.0 g less limestone per kg of feed need be supplied.

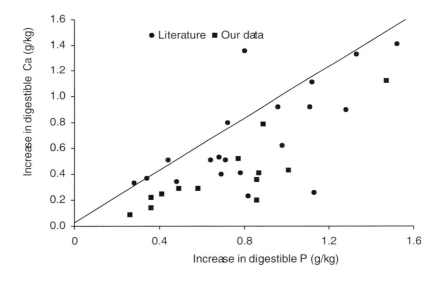

Figure 5. Effect of microbial phytase on the improvement of both digestible Ca and digestible P in the same diet.

Apart from its effect on P and Ca digestibility, phytase affects the availability of other minerals and nutrients. Microbial phytase can improve the apparent absorption of Mg, Na, K, Zn, Cu and Fe (Jongbloed *et al.*, 1999).

Effect of phytase on digestion and/or utilization of dietary protein, amino acids and energy

Some *in vitro* and *in vivo* studies on rats have documented that dietary protein and amino acid digestibilities may be reduced by phytates due to ability to form insoluble complexes under gastrointestinal conditions and to inhibit some endogenous proteolytic enzymes (Atwal *et al.*, 1980; Knuckles, 1985; Ritter *et al.*, 1987). Based on these studies, it is assumed that dietary phytases (intrinsic and extrinsic) may prevent the negative effects of phytates on protein and starch digestibilities by hydrolysing the phytate-protein-starch complexes and returning dietary protein, amino acids and starch to soluble and absorbable form in the small intestine of the pig.

APPARENT TOTAL TRACT DIGESTIBILITY AND UTILIZATION OF PROTEIN BY PIGS FED EXOGENOUS PHYTASE

From a nutritional point of view, total tract digestibility of dietary protein and amino acids is not an accurate measure of nutritive value. However, in practice it may be important to determine the environmental burden of nitrogen in response to various doses of phytase. Data on total tract digestibility of dry matter, organic matter and crude protein in relation to microbial phytase addition as extracted from the publications of Mroz *et al.* (1994a) and Näsi *et al.* (1995) are presented in Table 1. Data from studies of Mroz *et al.* (1994a) indicate that microbial phytase (Natuphos®) significantly increased apparent total tract digestibility of crude protein by 2.3 percentage units. In addition, nitrogen retention tended to be higher though the difference was not statistically significant. In contrast, Näsi *et al.* (1995) showed only a marginal improvement in crude protein total tract digestibility whereas N retention was minimally negative.

Table 1. Apparent total tract digestibility of dry matter (%), organic matter and crude protein and N retention (as % of intake) in pigs fed diets without or with microbial phytase.

	Mroz *et al.* (1994a)			Näsi *et al.* (1995)		
Microbial phytase FTU/kg of diet	0	800	Difference	0	1000	Difference
Dry matter	83.2[a]	85.0[b]	+1.8	80.1	80.4	+0.3
Organic matter	85.6[a]	87.2[b]	+1.6	81.8	82.0	+0.2
Crude protein	83.3[a]	85.6[b]	+2.3	78.0	78.8	+0.8
N retained	40.1	42.8	+2.7	40.6	39.4	-1.2

[ab]Means within a row (for each experiment) lacking a common superscript letter differ (P<0.01).

In another study, Khan and Cole (1993) fed a barley-based diet to six cannulated gilts without or with *Aspergillus niger* phytase (1000 FTU/kg). The authors found that total tract crude protein digestibility for the control and microbial phytase groups was 81.4 and 85.5% (SED=1.7), respectively. Total tract digestibility of gross energy increased also by 1.2 percentage units in the presence of microbial phytase, but this difference was not statistically significant.

119

Ketaren *et al.* (1993) fed 60 gilts (initial weight 20 kg) a soybean meal-sucrose-based diet without and with microbial phytase (1000 FTU/kg). After 35 days the gilts were slaughtered to assess the deposition of protein, fat and energy (Table 2). The authors observed that microbial phytase (1000 FTU/kg) significantly increased protein deposition (+15 g/d), protein retained:protein intake ratio (+0.031 kg/kg), energy retained:DE intake (+0.02 MJ/MJ) and protein retained:DE intake (+0.4 g/MJ).

Table 2. Retention of protein, fat and energy in growing pigs given a soybean-sucrose-based diet with and without microbial phytase (1000 FTU/kg)[1].

	Protein retained:protein intake (kg/kg)	Protein retained:DE intake (g/MJ)	Fat retained:DE intake (g/MJ)	Energy retained:DE intake (MJ/MJ)
No phytase	0.328	4.1	6.6	0.36
Phytase	0.359	4.5	6.9	0.38
SEM	0.0093	0.12	0.20	0.008
P value	<0.05	<0.05	>0.05	<0.05

[1]After Ketaren *et al.*, 1993.

Han *et al.* (1997) used 48 pigs over 10 to 90 kg to study the effects of supplemental microbial phytase (1000-1200 FTU/kg), cereal phytase (230-460 FTU/kg) and inorganic P (0.20-0.24%) on apparent total tract digestibility and retention of N. Microbial phytase in this study resulted in a higher crude protein digestibility (+3.0 percentage units), but this difference was not statistically significant from the control group. Biehl and Baker (1996) concluded from studies with 15 young pigs (9.1 kg initial weight) that phytase supplementation (1200 FTU/kg) improved amino acid utilization in amino acid-deficient corn-soybean meal diets. Kemme and Jongbloed (1994) reported that both *Aspergillus niger* phytase and intrinsic phytase from wheat middlings exerted no effect on crude protein digestibility in diets for piglets, sows or growing-finishing pigs. In line with these findings were the conclusions of Näsi (1990), Näsi and Helander (1994), Pallauf *et al.* (1994), Bruce and Sundstøl (1995), Kornegay *et al.* (1996) and Valaja *et al.* (1998).

We calculated the effect of microbial phytase on apparent fecal digestibility of some nutrients. In our studies microbial phytase enhanced average dry matter digestibility by 0.54 ±0.81 percentage units (n=18), organic matter by 0.33 ±0.72 (n=9) and N by 1.21±1.73 (n=7). From these data it can be concluded that there is a tendency toward increased fecal digestibilities of dry matter, organic matter and N in response to supplementary microbial phytase. Data from the literature showed a slightly different picture. Fecal digestibilities of dry matter and organic matter were slightly reduced by 0.11±0.69 (n=9) and 0.37±0.57 (n=3), respectively, while digestibility of N was increased by 0.60±1.66 (n=10) by supplementary phytase.

APPARENT ILEAL DIGESTIBILITY

There is a limited number of reports on the apparent ileal digestibility of crude protein in pigs in relation to phytase supplementation. Ileal digestibility of N and amino acids is usually considered a proper criterion of dietary protein value (Low, 1989). Officer and Batterham (1992) reported that ileal digestibility of crude protein and essential amino acids increased by 7-12 percentage units. Also, Khan and Cole (1993) observed an increase in ileal nitrogen digestibility of 12.8 percentage units (P<0.077) when feeding a high-phytate barley-based diet with *Aspergillus niger* phytase (1000 FTU/kg) to six cannulated gilts. Mroz *et al.* (1994a) observed a lower effect (+3.5 percentage units); and in a second experiment Kemme *et al.* (1999) showed a significantly higher ileal digestibility for several amino acids (Table 3). However, there are a few reports showing that microbial phytase exerted no effect on apparent ileal digestibility of crude protein or amino acids (Lantzsch *et al.*, 1995; Valaja *et al.*, 1998).

Table 3. Effect of microbial phytase on apparent ileal digestibility of N and some amino acids.

Nutrient	Phytase			Phytase		
	no[1]	yes[1]	std. dev.[1]	no[2]	yes[2]	SSD.[2]
N	71.7	74.2	ns	74.2	75.8	ns
Lysine	81.0	81.9	ns	77.5	79.9	*
Methionine	76.9	80.6	**	80.6	81.7	ns
Cysteine	70.5	74.1	ns	73.5	72.2	ns
Tryptophan	72.4	73.7	ns	68.3	72.7	*
Isoleucine	80.1	79.8	ns	77.9	80.0	*
Threonine	73.8	72.0	ns	68.3	71.2	**

[1]Mroz *et al.*, 1994a.
[2]SSD: Statistically significant difference, Kemme *et al.*, 1999.

Effect of management factors on efficacy of microbial phytase

In practice, pigs are raised under a wide variety of housing and feeding conditions. Therefore, it is important to know the effects of different feeding regimens and housing conditions on the efficacy of microbial phytase. In one study we could not show any effect of feeding level (2.3 and 2.8 times maintenance requirement for metabolizable energy) on the efficacy of microbial phytase (Mroz *et al.*, 1994a). In the same experiment no effect on phytase efficacy was noted between feeding two and seven times a day, while efficacy was slightly decreased when pigs were fed once daily.

The efficacy of microbial phytase (500 FTU/kg) is increased by soaking a phytate-rich diet (maize, tapioca, beans, phytase-inactivated wheat bran and extracted sunflower meal) for 8-15 hrs prior to feeding (Kemme and

Jongbloed, 1993). Some results of this treatment in a trial with growing pigs from 30 to 70 kg body weight are presented in Table 4. Soaking a barley-soybean meal diet supplemented with microbial phytase for 3 hrs, however, did not result in a higher P digestibility (Näsi and Helander, 1994). This may have been due to the short soaking time and the rather high dietary Ca content. In a second experiment of Näsi *et al.* (1995), soaking a barley-rapeseed meal diet for 3 hrs with dried whey at 40°C increased P digestibility by 4%.

Table 4. Effects of soaking a phytate-rich diet without or with microbial phytase on the apparent digestibility of Ca and total P[1].

Dose, FTU/kg	0		500		SED	Significance
Soaking	-	+	-	+		
Ca digestibility, %	38.3	36.2	44.2	51.7	2.99	P<0.05
P digestibility, %	26.5	25.3	44.2	52.4	1.54	P<0.001

[1]Kemme and Jongbloed, 1993.

Effect of microbial phytase on pig performance

Jongbloed *et al.* (1999) presented results on the effect of microbial phytase on performance of pigs compared, where possible, with both negative control and positive control treatments. However, the choice of a positive control treatment was not always evident. Therefore, they chose for the positive control a treatment with about 1 g of supplementary P from a feed phosphate. However, in half of the experiments the difference with the negative control treatment was often between 2 and 3 g of P. For their review, they chose 11 experiments where a reasonable comparison was possible. Relative values were calculated based on a value for the negative control diet of 100 (Table 5). Data in Table 5 show that the performance of both the positive control and the phytase groups were superior to the negative control group. The positive control group and the phytase supplemented group were almost identical. From the eleven experiments there were six in which the positive control group was also supplemented with microbial phytase. Performance of the pigs receiving the positive control group with supplementary phytase was slightly better than those without phytase. The relative ratios compared with the positive control diet for growth rate, feed intake and feed conversion ratio were 106.0±5.5, 103.0±3.2 and 95.7±4.9, respectively. This may imply that either the P requirement was not yet met, which is unlikely, or there is another positive effect of microbial phytase on performance.

Further calculations were performed on the effect of Natuphos® on the performance of piglets fed above their P requirement (Kies, 1997). Feed conversion ratio (corrected for differences in weight gain using 25 g equal

Table 5. Relative performance of pigs using the negative control diet as 100 (n=11) and effect of phytase when added to the positive control diet (n=6).

	Negative control	Positive control	Phytase effect	Positive control	Phytase effect
Growth rate	100	115.0 ± 6.5	116.7 ±10.6	100	106.0 ± 5.5
Feed intake	100	105.4 ± 5.2	107.6 ± 7.8	100	103.0 ± 3.2
FCR	100	93.0 ± 4.9	93.2 ± 5.0	100	95.7 ± 4.9

to 0.01 unit FCR) was taken as the response variable. In total, 11 experiments comprising 17 trials met this criteria. The experiments were analysed using the model:

Corrected FCR = Experiment$_i$ + b*FTU/kg added

Experiment$_i$ (i=1.17) is a constant per experiment and b is the regression coefficient. The mean corrected FCR was 1.483. The value for b was -0.000094, with a 95% confidence interval of -0.000051 to -0.000136; R^2 =0.94.

It can be derived from the equation that dietary supplementation of 500 FTU Natuphos®/kg improved the corrected FCR by 0.047 units, which is close to the value reported by Jongbloed *et al.* (1999). Due to lack of sufficient data he could only use a linear model, while it may be speculated that an exponential curve might be more physiologically appropriate. From the experiments of Campbell *et al.* (1995) and Selle *et al.* (1996) it can also be concluded that dietary level of phytate influences the improvement in FCR. The improvement in FCR can be attributed to a higher digestibility of protein/amino acids and a slightly higher energy digestibility. Also, other unknown factors may play a part.

Environmental impact of microbial phytase

In the absence of microbial phytase only ~16% of P in corn and ~38% of P in soybean meal is digested by pigs. Because of the large amount of undigested dietary P, a substantial amount of P is excreted via feces. Based on the estimates of Cromwell *et al.* (1993), a dose of microbial phytase equal to 1000 FTU/g converted approximately one-third of the unavailable P to an available form. About 500 FTU/kg of diet generates approximately 0.8 g digestible P/kg, which is equivalent to 1.0 g P from monocalcium phosphate or 1.23 g P from dicalcium phosphate, which is often used in the United States. This is illustrated in Table 6. This table shows that with supplementation of 500 FTU/kg of feed, total P content is 1.3 g/kg lower. With the same performance as the control diet between 20 and 50 kg live weight and a feed conversion ratio of 2.5, it can be calculated that P excretion per kg growth is 4.75 instead of 8.0 g, which is 40% lower.

123

Table 6. Effect of microbial phytase (500 FTU/kg feed) on diet formulation and mineral content in a grower diet (g/kg).

	Phosphorus	Calcium	Digestible P (%)	Feed-	Feed+
Corn	2.9	0.3	20	798.7	801.0
Soybean meal dehulled	6.4	2.7	39	178.0	179.0
Dicalcium phosphate	200	250	64	8.5	2.3
Limestone	-	380	-	8.3	11.1
Salt + premix	-	-	-	6.5	6.5
Phytase premix	-	-	-	-	0.1
Total P	-	-	-	5.2	3.9
Digestible P	-	-	-	2.0	2.0
Calcium	-	-	-	6.0	5.5

Use and application of microbial phytase in The Netherlands

In The Netherlands, legislation has been imposed to allow a maximum amount of P to be spread per hectare of land. When this amount has been exceeded, the farmer must pay a levy and has to transport the manure elsewhere (Jongbloed and Lenis, 1998). This has stimulated the replacement of inorganic feed phosphates by microbial phytase in pig and poultry diets.

Microbial phytase is considered as a raw material containing a high phosphorus value and can be used in linear programming for feed formulation. Therefore, in most cases the feed compounder chooses a certain amount of phytase units, which is linked to the amount of digestible P generated. In general, between 300 and 500 FTU/kg is added. Beyond that, inorganic feed phosphate can be added to meet the P requirement as necessary. Microbial phytase can be used as a dry or liquid raw material. The latter is increasingly used, because the phytase is not completely resistant to high steam-pelleting temperatures (exceeding 80°C). Much effort has gone into developing a more heat-resistant phytase and to choosing formulations in which phytase can better resist high temperatures. Microbial phytase is most effective in layer diets, and is therefore highly competitive to inorganic feed phosphates for this category. In general, microbial phytase is incorporated in most pig and poultry diets in The Netherlands, but is becoming increasingly popular in other countries for reasons beyond its positive effect on the reduction of P excretion. This is predominantly due to associated enhanced effects on the digestibility of protein and amino acids, energy, calcium and zinc, and last but not least on animal performance.

In The Netherlands, the concentrations of several minerals in animal diets are occasionally monitored. Therefore, it is possible to estimate the excretion of P by several categories of pigs. In Table 7 a survey is presented for growing-finishing pigs from 1973 to 1998. In that period performance increased considerably. Growth rate increased from 625 to 755 g/day, while feed conversion ratio improved from 3.37 to 2.69. Despite the better performance, P content in pig diets decreased by more than 2.0 g/kg. From 1988 onwards it has been common to feed a starter diet and a grower-finisher diet. Data in Table 7 show that the excretion of P in growing-finishing pigs has reduced by more than half in 20 years. This lower P excretion has, apart from increased nutritional knowledge, undoubtedly been stimulated by legislation based on P. As microbial phytase has been commercially available in The Netherlands since late 1991, the decrease in P excretion since then is predominantly due to microbial phytase. Incorporation levels of microbial phytase will undoubtedly increase in the coming years resulting in a further decrease of P excretion by pigs.

Table 7. Mean excretion of P of a growing-finishing pig from 25 to 110 kg in The Netherlands.

Year	P in feed (g/kg)	FCR	Excretion (kg/pig)
1973	7.4	3.37	1.62
1983	6.2	3.08	1.18
1988	6.0/5.0*	2.96	0.88
1992	5.5/4.9	2.87	0.80
1998	5.43/4.7	2.69	0.67

*first figure starter diet; second grower-finisher diet.

References

Atwal, A.S., N.A.M. Eskin, B.E. McDonald and M. Vaisey-Genser. 1980. The effects of phytate on nitrogen utilization and zinc metabolism in young rats. Nutr. Rep. Int. 21(2)257-267.

Beers, S. and A.W. Jongbloed. 1992. Apparent overall (total tract) digestibility of P in relation to doses of *Aspergillus niger* phytase in diets for pigs. J. Anim. Sci. 70(Suppl. 1):242.

Biehl, R.R. and D.H. Baker. 1996. Efficacy of supplemental 1α-hydroxycholecalciferol and microbial phytase for young pigs fed phosphorus- or amino acid-deficient corn-soybean meal diets. J. Anim. Sci. 74:2960-2966.

Bruce, J.A.M. and F. Sundstøl. 1995. The effect of microbial phytase in diets for pigs on apparent ileal and faecal digestibility, pH and flow of digesta measurements in growing pigs fed a high-fibre diet. Can. J. Anim. Sci. 75:121-127.

Campbell, R.G., D.T. Harrison, K.J. Butler and P.H. Selle. 1995. Effects of dietary available phosphorus and phytase (Natuphos) on the performance of pigs from 19 to 40 days post-weaning. In: Manipulating pig production V (D.P. Hennessy and P.D. Cranwell, eds), Proc. of the Fifth Biennial Conf. of the Australasian Pig Science Association, Werribee, Victoria, Australia, p. 193.

Cheryan, M. 1980. Phytic acid interactions in food systems. CRC Crit. Rev. Food Sci. 13: 297-335.

Cosgrove, D.J. 1980. Inositol phosphates. Their chemistry, biochemistry and physiology. Elsevier Science Publishers, Amsterdam, p.175.

Cromwell, G.L. 1980. Biological availability of phosphorus in feedstuffs for swine. Feedstuffs 52:(9)14-16.

Cromwell, G.L., T.S. Stahly, R.D. Coffey, H.J. Monegue and J.H. Randolph. 1995. Efficacy of phytase in improving the bioavailability of phosphorus in soybean meal and corn-soybean meal diets for pigs. J. Anim. Sci. 71:1831-1840.

Cromwell, G.L., R.D. Coffey, H.J. Monegue and J.H. Randolph. 1993. Efficacy of low-activity phytase in improving the bioavailability of phosphorus in corn-soybean meal diets for pigs. J. Anim. Sci. 73:449-456.

Dekker, R.A., P.A. Kemme and A.W. Jongbloed. 1992. Methodological comparison of the assessment of P digestibility of tapioca and maize, and the influence of amount and origin of phytic acid on the efficacy of microbial phytase from *Aspergillus niger*. Report IVVO-DLO, Lelystad, nr. 244.

Düngelhoef, M., M. Rodehutscord, H. Spiekers and E. Pfeffer. 1994. Effects of supplemental microbial phytase on availability of phosphorus contained in maize, wheat and triticale to pigs. Anim. Feed Sci. Technol. 49:1-10.

Düngelhoef, M. and M. Rodehutscord. 1995. Effects of phytases on the digestibility of phosphorus in pigs. Übers. Tierernährg. 23:133-157.

Eeckhout, W. and M. De Paepe. 1992. Betere benutting van de voeders. 1.1. Synthetische fytase. 1.1.2. Tarwefytase en een microbieel fytasepreparaat en de schijnbare fosforverteerbaarheid van een eenvoudig biggenvoeder. Landbouwtijdschrift-Revue de l'Agriculture 45:193-204.

Engelen, A.J., F.C. van der Heeft, H.G. Randsdorp and E.L.C. Smit. 1994. Simple and rapid determination of phytase activity. J. AOAC Intern. 77:760-764.

Erdman, J.W. 1979. Oilseed phytates: nutritional implications. J. Am. Oil Chem. Soc. 56:736-741.

Han, Y.M., F. Yang, A.G. Zhou, E.R. Miller, P.K. Ku, M.G. Hogberg and X.G. Lei. 1997. Supplemental phytases of microbial and cereal sources improve dietary phytate phosphorus utilization by pigs from weaning through finishing. J. Anim. Sci. 75:1017-1025.

Jongbloed, A.W. 1987. Phosphorus in the feeding of pigs. Effect of diet on absorption and retention of phosphorus by growing pigs. PhD thesis, Report IVVO-DLO nr. 179, Lelystad, The Netherlands, 343 pp.

Jongbloed, A.W. and N.P. Lenis. 1998. Environmental concerns about animal manure. J. Anim. Sci. 76:2641-2648.

Jongbloed, A.W. and Z. Mroz. 1999. Influence of phytase on availability of phosphorus, amino acids and energy in swine. In: Proc. BASF Technical Symposium. Use of Natuphos® Phytase in Swine and waste Management Midwest Series 1999, 1-20.

Jongbloed, A.W., Z. Mroz and P.A. Kemme. 1992. The effect of supplementary *Aspergillus niger* phytase in diets for pigs on concentration and apparent digestibility of dry matter, total phosphorus, and phytic acid in different sections of the alimentary tract. J. Anim. Sci. 70:1159-1168.

Jongbloed, A.W., P.A. Kemme and Z. Mroz. 1993. The role of microbial phytases in pig production, In: Enzymes in Animal Production (C. Wenk and M. Boessinger, eds), Proceedings of the 1st Symposium, Kartause Ittingen, Switzerland, p. 173-180.

Jongbloed, A.W., P.A. Kemme, Z. Mroz and R. ten Bruggencate. 1995. Apparent total tract digestibility of organic matter, N, Ca, Mg and P in growing pigs as affected by levels of Ca, microbial phytase and phytate. In: W. van Hartingsveldt, M. Hessing, J.P. van der Lugt and W.A.C. Somers (Eds). Proceedings of Second Symposium on Feed Enzymes (ESFE2), Noordwijkerhout, Netherlands, TNO Nutrition and Food Research Institute, Zeist, p. 198-204.

Jongbloed, A.W., R. van der Weij-Jongbloed, P.A. Kemme and Z. Mroz. 2000. The effects of microbial phytase, organic acids and their interaction in diets for growing pigs. Livestock. Prod. Sci. (in press).

Kemme, P.A. and A.W. Jongbloed. 1993. Effect of *Aspergillus niger* phytase and soaking on the digestibility of P in diets for pigs. J. Anim. Sci. 71: (Suppl. 1):181.

Kemme, P.A. and A.W. Jongbloed. 1994. Effekt van plantaardig en Aspergillus niger fytase, leeftijd en voerniveau op de verteerbaarheid van Weende analyse komponenten, Ca en P bij biggen [Effect of intrinsic and *Aspergillus niger* phytase, age and feeding level on digestibilities of proximate components, Ca en P in diets for piglets]. Report IVVO-DLO no. 257.

Kemme, P.A., J.S. Radcliffe, A.W. Jongbloed and Z. Mroz. 1997a. The effects of body weight, housing, and calculation method on mineral digestibility and the efficacy of microbial phytase in diets for growing-finishing pigs. J. Anim. Sci. 75:2139-2146.

Kemme, P.A., A.W. Jongbloed, Z. Mroz and A.C. Beynen. 1997b. The efficacy of *Aspergillus niger* phytase in rendering phytate phosphorus available for absorption in pigs is influenced by their physiological status. J. Anim. Sci. 75:2129-2138.

Kemme, P.A., A.W. Jongbloed, Z. Mroz, J. Kogut and A.C. Beynen. 1999. Digestibility of nutrients in growing-finishing pigs is affected by *Aspergillus niger* phytase, phytate and lactic acid levels. 1. Apparent ileal digestibility of amino acids. Livest. Prod. Sci. 58:107-117.

Ketaren, P.P., E.S. Batterham, E.B. Dettmann and D.J. Farrel. 1993. Phosphorus studies in pigs. 3. Effect of phytase supplementation on the digestibility and availability of phosphorus in soyabean meal for grower pigs. Br. J. Nutr. 70:289-311.

Khan, N. and D.J.A. Cole. 1993. The effect of dietary inclusions of phytase and yeast on apparent phosphorus digestibility in pigs. Proc. of the Winter Meeting of the British Society of Animal Production. Scarborough, England. p. 2.

Kies, A. 1997. Niet-fosfor effecten van Natuphos®. In: BASF Symposium "Enzymen en organische zuren in de Nederlandse mengvoederindustrie", Arnhem, The Netherlands. p. 11.

Kies, A. 1998. The influence of Natuphos® phytase on the bioavailability of protein in swine. In: BASF Technical Symposium, World Pork Expo, De Moines, IA. p. 1-12.

Knuckles, B.E., D.D. Kuzmicky and A.A. Betschart. 1985. Effect of phytate and partially hydrolyzed phytate on *in vitro* protein digestibility. J. Food Sci. 50:1080-1082.

Kornegay, E.T., D.M. Denbow, Z. Yi and V. Ravindran. 1996. Response of broilers to graded levels of Natuphos® phytase added to corn-soybean meal based diets containing three levels of nonphytate phosphorus. Br. J. Nutr. 75:839-852.

Lantzsch, H.J., S. Wjst, and W. Drochner. 1995. The effect of dietary calcium on the efficacy of microbial phytase in rations for growing pigs. J. Anim. Physiol. and Anim. Nutr. 73:19-26.

Lei, X.G., P.K. Ku, E.R. Miller, M.T. Yokoyama and D.E. Ullrey. 1994. Calcium level affects the efficacy of supplemental microbial phytase in corn-soybean meal diets of weanling pigs. J. Anim. Sci. 72:139-143.

Low, A.G. 1989. Research into the digestive physiology of pigs. In: Nutrition and digestive physiology in monogastric farm animals (E.J. van Weerden and J. Huisman, eds.). Wageningen, The Netherlands. p. 1-12.

Maga, J.A. 1982. Phytate: Its chemistry, occurrence, food interactions, nutritional significance, and methods of analysis. J. Agric. Food Chem. 30:1-8.

Mroz, Z., A.W. Jongbloed and P.A. Kemme. 1994a. Apparent digestibility and retention of dietary nutrients bound to phytase complexes as influenced by microbial phytase and feeding regimen in pigs. J. Anim. Sci. 72:126-132.

Mroz, Z., A.W. Jongbloed and P.A. Kemme. 1994b. The influence of graded calcium supply on microbial phytase efficacy in starter diets for pigs. In: 45th Annual Meeting of the EAAP, Edinburgh; paper P4.3.

Näsi, M. 1990. Microbial phytase supplementation for improving availability of plant phosphorus in the diet of the growing pigs. J. Agric. Sci. in Finland 62:435-443.

Näsi, M. and E.H. Helander. 1994. Effects of microbial phytase supplementation and soaking of barley-soybean meal on availability of plant phosphorus for growing pigs. Acta Agric. Scand., Sect. A, Animal Sci. 44:79-86.

Näsi, M., E.H. Helander and K.H. Partanen. 1995. Availability for growing pigs of minerals and protein of a high phytate barley-rapeseed meal diet treated with *Aspergillus niger* phytase or soaked with whey. Animal Feed Sci. Technol. 56:83-98.

Officer, D.I. and E.S. Batterham. 1992. Enzyme supplementation of Linola™ meal. In Proc. Wollongbar Pig Industry Seminar on Feed Enzymes, p. 56-57.

Pallauf, J., G. Rimbach, S. Pippig, B. Schindler and E. Most. 1994. Effect of phytase supplementation to a phytate-rich diet based on wheat, barley and soya on the bioavailability of dietary phosphorus, calcium, magnesium, zinc and protein in piglets. Agribiol. Res. 47:39-48.

Pointillart, A., N. Fontaine and M. Thomasset. 1984. Phytate phosphorus utilization, intestinal phosphatases in pigs fed low phosphorus: wheat or corn diets. Nutr. Report Int. 29: 473-483.

Reddy, N.R., S.K. Sathe and D.K. Salunkhe. 1982. Phytates in legumes and cereals. Adv. Food Res. 28:1-92.

Ritter, M.A., C.V. Morr and R.L. Thomas. 1987. *In vitro* digestibility of phytate-reduced and phenolic-reduced soy protein isolates. J. Food Sci. 52:325-327.

Schwarz, G. and P.P. Hoppe. 1992. Phytase enzyme to curb pollution from pigs and poultry. Feed Magazine 1:22-26.

Selle, P.H., V. Ravindran, D.J. Cadogan, A.R. Walker and W.L. Bryden. 1996. The role of microbial phytases in poultry and pig production. Proc. Tenth Australian Poultry and Feed Convention, Melbourne, Australia, p. 219-224.

Simons, P.C., H.A.J. Versteegh, A.W. Jongbloed, P.A. Kemme, P. Slump, K.D. Bos, M.G.E. Wolters, R.F. Beudeker and G.J. Verschoor. 1990. Improvement of phosphorus availability by microbial phytase in broilers and pigs. Brit. J. Nutr. 64:525-540.

Thompson, L.U. 1986. In: Phytic acid chemistry and applications (E. Graf, ed.), Pilatus Press, Minneapolis. p 173-194.

Torre, M., A.R. Rodriguez and F. Saura-Calixto. 1991. Effects of dietary fiber and phytic acid on mineral availability. Crit. Rev. Food Sci. Nutr. 1(1):1-22.

Valaja, J., S. Plaami and H. Siljander-Rasi. 1998. Effect of microbial phytase on digestibility and utilisation of phosphorus and protein in pigs fed wet barley protein with fibre. Animal Feed Sci. Technol. 72:221-233.

Wise, A. 1980. Dietary factors determining the biological activities of phytate. Nutr. Abstr. Rev. 53:791-806.

Production of enzymes for the feed industry using solid substrate fermentation

KEITH FILER

North American Biosciences Center, Alltech Inc., Nicholasville, Kentucky, USA

Introduction: industrial enzyme applications

Virtually all chemical reactions in biological systems are catalyzed by macromolecules called enzymes. Chemical reactions *in vivo* rarely proceed at perceptible rates in the absence of enzymes while reaction rates increase as much as a million times when enzymes are present. These proteins are among the most remarkable biomolecules known.

The name 'enzyme', meaning 'in yeast', was not used until 1877; however much earlier it was suspected that biological catalysts were involved in the fermentation of sugar to form alcohol. These catalysts were termed ferments (Lehninger, 1975). Eduard Buchner extracted the enzymes catalyzing alcoholic fermentation in 1897. This demonstrated that enzymes could function independently of cell structure. In 1860, Louis Pasteur postulated that enzymes are linked with the structure of the yeast cell. The ability of enzymes to function outside a cell has greatly increased their use in a large variety of commercial products and reactions.

A wide range of industries use commercial enzymes. The world annual sales of industrial enzymes was recently valued at $1 billion (Bron *et al.*, 1999). Three quarters of the market is for enzymes involved in the hydrolysis of natural polymers, of which about two-thirds are proteolytic enzymes used in the detergent, dairy and leather industries; and one third are carbohydrases used in the animal feed, baking, brewing, distilling, starch and textile industries. Detergent manufacturers use 45% of all industrial enzymes produced in spot remover and detergent products containing proteases and lipases. This industry is expected to have a 10% annual growth rate for the next five years. Food processing enzymes including α-amylases, glucose isomerase and pectinases account for about 45% of enzyme usage. The starch processing industry uses half of the enzymes in the food industry, approximately 25% are used by the dairy industry and 10% by the brewers, fruit juice and wine producers. The textile and paper industry (6%) uses primarily amylases and hemicellulases and the leather industry (2%) uses proteases. Enzyme supplements for animal feeds account for about 1% (Amado, 1993). Table 1 lists some industrially important enzymes and their applications.

Table 1. Commercial applications of enzymes.*

Industry	Application	Enzyme	Source
Baking and milling	Reduction of dough viscosity, acceleration of fermentation, increase in loaf volume	Amylase	Fungal
	Improvement of dough texture, reduction in mixing time	Protease	Fungal/bacterial
Brewing	Mashing	Amylase	Fungal/bacterial
	Chillproofing	Protease	Fungal/bacterial
	Improvement of fine filtration	ß-glucanase	Fungal/bacterial
Coffee	Coffee bean fermentation	Pectinase	Fungal
	Preparation of coffee concentrates	Pectinase, hemicelllase	Fungal
Confectionery	Manufacture of coffee concentrates	Invertase, pectinase	Fungal/bacterial
Corn syrup	Manufacture of low dextrose-equivalent syrups	Amylase	Bacterial
	Production of glucose from corn syrup	Amyloglycosidase	Fungal
	Manufacture of fructose syrups	Glucose isomerase	Bacterial
Dairy	Manufacture of protein hydrolysates	Protease	Fungal/bacterial
	Production of whole milk concentrates and ice cream	Lactase	Yeast
Feed	Reduce antinutritional factors	Xylanase, ß-glucans, phytase	Fungal
	Improve feed utilization	Amylase, cellulase, protease	Fungal/bacterial
Fruit juices	Clarification	Pectinases	Fungal
	Oxygen removal	Glucose oxidase	Fungal
Laundry	Detergents	Protease, lipase	Bacterial
Leather	Dehairing, baiting	Protease	Fungal/bacterial
Pharmaceutical	Digestive aids	Amylase, protease	Fungal
	Anti-blood clotting	Streptokinase	Bacterial
Soft drinks	Stabilization	Glucose oxidase, catalase	Fungal
Textiles	Desizing of fabrics	Amylase	Bacterial
Vegetables	Preparation of purees, soups	Pectinase, amylase, cellulase	Fungal

*Modified from Stanbury *et al.*, 1995.

The acceptance of enzymes by the animal feed industry has become widespread in the last decade. As the understanding of enzymes and their properties has grown, so have both their use and their effectiveness as feed supplements. The purpose of using enzymes in monogastric animals is to improve availability of nutrients in feedstuffs. The result is improved feed utilization and reduced impact of anti-nutritional components.

Methods for production of commercial enzymes

Industrial enzymes are produced by plants, animals, and microbes. By far the most exploited for the use of industrial enzymes has been the microbial population. Short generation times and high yields, together with the fact that microorganisms produce extracellular enzymes, which are easy to harvest, make microbes the enzyme source of choice. Production of enzymes by microorganisms has also expanded because of the vast amounts of genetic information now available. Several industrially important microbial genomes have been sequenced; and the understanding of gene expression systems in microorganisms is much more advanced when compared to other gene expression systems. This knowledge has made it possible to select a variety of microorganisms suitable for enzyme production with traditional submerged liquid fermentation (Bailey and Ollis, 1986). An alternative fermentation method for enzyme production is solid substrate fermentation (Mitchell and Lonsane, 1992).

SUBMERGED LIQUID FERMENTATION

Submerged liquid fermentations are traditionally used in the United States for the production of microbially derived enzymes. Submerged fermentation involves submersion of the microorganism in an aqueous solution containing all the nutrients needed for growth. A research team led by Chaim Weizmann in Great Britian developed a process for production of acetone by submerged liquid fermentation using *Clostridium acetobutylicum,* which eventually led to the first large-scale aseptic fermentation vessel (Stanbury *et al.,* 1995). The first large-scale aerobic fermenters were used in central Europe in the 1930s for production of compressed yeast (de Becze and Liebmann, 1944). In 1943, the British government decided that solid substrate fermentation was inadequate for the production of penicillin. This decision forced the development of liquid fermenters that are aseptic and contain adequate aeration and agitation. Construction of the first large-scale plant to produce penicillin by liquid fermentation began in 1943 (Callahan, 1944).

Organisms used in submerged fermentations

Fermentation using bacillus species accounts for about half of the world's production of industrial enzymes. The main classes of bacillus enzymes and the strains used to produce them are listed in Table 2. Two enzymes dominate the industrial market: alkaline protease and α-amylase. Alkaline protease used in detergents represents the single largest enzyme market. Although bacillus species are the primary enzyme-producing organisms, other microbes are also used. Through genetic modifications the bacterium *Escherichia coli* is able to produce insulin and human growth hormones. *Penicillum chrysogenum* is used to produce penicillin. Other microorganisms used on an industrial scale include *Saccharomyces cerevisiae* for ethanol production and the fungi *Aspergillus* and *Trichoderma* for carbohydrase production.

Table 2. Industrial enzymes produced by Bacillus species.*

Enzyme	Producer strains
α-amylase	*B. amyloliquefaciens, B. circulans, B. licheniformis,*
ß-amylase	*B. polymyxa, B. cerus, B. megaterium*
Alkaline phosphatase	*B. licheniformis*
Cyclodextran glucotransferase	*B. macerans, B. megaterium*
ß-galactosidase	*B. stearothermophilus*
Metalloprotease	*B. lentus, B. polymyxa, B. subtilis*
Serine protease	*B. amyloiquefaciens, B. amylosaccharicus, B. subtilis*
Urease	*Bacillus* sp.
Uricase	*Bacillus* sp.

Bron *et al.*, 1999.

Selection of microorganisms for the fermentation industries in the past involved a hit-and-miss screening approach. With the development of genetic engineering techniques, organisms can be engineered to produce high yields of a great variety of products. Most of the information has been developed in bacterial systems and has resulted in very efficient enzyme production. Genetic manipulation of organisms can increase yield 100 fold or more over wild type strains (Stanbury *et al.*, 1995). The genetic manipulation of genomes is common for organisms used in submerged liquid fermentations.

Fermenter design

The main function of a fermenter is to provide a controlled environment for growth of microorganisms in order to obtain a desired product. Two important criteria for a submerged liquid fermenter include the ability to operate aseptically for a number of days and provide adequate aeration and agitation to meet the metabolic requirements of the microorganism. Many different types of fermenters have been described in the literature, but very few proved satisfactory for industrial aerobic fermentations. The most common designs are based on a stirred upright cylinder with sparger aeration (Stanbury *et al.*, 1995). Fermenter sizes can range from flasks used in the laboratory to production fermenters of 8,000 liters or more (Figure 1).

Fermenter operation

Many biochemical processes involve batch growth of cell populations. After seeding a liquid medium with an inoculum of living cells, only gas is added or

Figure 1. Deep tank liquid fermenter (250 liter).

removed from the culture as growth proceeds. Typically in such a batch reactor, the concentrations of nutrients, cells and products vary with time as growth proceeds. In addition, it is often desirable to add liquid streams to a batch bioreactor as the reaction process occurs. This can be done to add precursors for desired products, to add regulating compounds such as inducers at a point in the batch operation, to maintain low nutrient levels to minimize catabolite repression or to extend the stationary phase by nutrient addition (Baily and Ollis, 1986). When the fermenter is used in this manner it is known as a 'fed-batch' fermentation.

The success of a fermentation depends upon the existence of defined environmental conditions for biomass and product formation. The temperature, pH, degree of agitation, oxygen concentration in the medium and other factors may need to be kept constant during the process. Careful monitoring of the fermentation is performed to regulate these parameters. Table 3 lists the variety of process sensors included in a submerged liquid fermentation.

SOLID SUBSTRATE CULTIVATION

In addition to submerged liquid fermentation, an ancient fermentation technology known as solid substrate fermentation is also used to produce enzymes. Solid substrate fermentations are generally characterized by growth of microorganisms on water-insoluble substrates in the presence of varying

Table 3. Process sensors and their possible control functions.*

Category	Sensor	Possible control function
Physical	Temperature	Heat/cool
	Pressure	
	Agitator shaft power	
	Rpm	
	Foam	Foam control
	Weight	Change flow rate
	Flow rate	Change flow rate
Chemical	pH	Acid or alkali addition, carbon source feed rate
	Redox	Additives to change redox potential
	Oxygen	Change feed rate
	Exit-gas analysis	Change feed rate
	Medium analysis	Change in medium composition

*Stanbury *et al.*, 1995.

amounts of free water (Mitchell and Lonsane, 1992). This process is also referred to as solid state fermentation (SSF). Table 4 shows differences between the SSF and submerged liquid fermentation.

Table 4. Differences between solid-substrate fermentation and submerged liquid cultures.*

Solid-substrate culture	Submerged liquid culture
Culture medium is not free flowing	Culture medium is always free-flowing
Depth of medium is usually shallow except for a few bioreactors	Medium depth varies
Single water insoluble substrate provides carbon, nitrogen, minerals and energy	Different water-soluble sources of nutrients are used
Gradients in nutrient concentration are common	Nutrients are uniformly distributed throughout the fermentation
Water availability is just sufficient to sustain optimum growth of the culture	Water availability is abundant
Culture systems involves three phases, solid, liquid, and gaseous	Two phases, liquid and gaseous
Culture system is not aseptic beyond medium cooking	Whole system is always under aseptic conditions
Rigorous control of parameters is not required except for heat removal, oxygen supply and moisture	Rigorous control of all parameters during fermentation is essential
Inoculum ratio is always larger	Inoculum ratio is usually low
System may or may not involve agitation	Agitation is often essential
Fungal growth involves penetration of the hyphae deep into solid substrate particles	Fungal mycelial cells grow in the form of individual mycelium or mycelial pellets
Bacterial and yeast cells grow by adhering to solid particles	Bacterial and yeast cells are uniformly distributed throughout the liquid

*Mitchell and Lonsane, 1992.

136

In 1896, Takamine produced a digestive enzyme, Takadiastatse, by SSF employing *Aspergillus niger* on wheat bran (Takamine, 1914). This led to the application of SSF in other food and beverage industries. The most profitable applications of SSF are in Asian and African countries where SSF processes have been perfected over long periods. In western countries, traditional applications of SSF are scarce. Solid substrate fermentation has been largely neglected since the 1940s; and negligible research and development efforts have been made. The selection of submerged liquid instead of SSF in western countries was not based on economic comparisons of submerged liquid and SSF techniques; the choice was linked to slow growth of the microbial cultivation industries across the world (Ralph, 1976; Hesseltine, 1976).

The origin of SSF can be traced back to bread-making in ancient Egypt. Solid substrate fermentations also include a number of well known microbial processes such as soil growth, composting, silage production, wood rotting and mushroom cultivation. In addition, many familiar western foods such as mold-ripened cheese, bread, sausage and many foods of Asian origin including miso, tempeh and soy sauce are produced using SSF. Beverages derived from SSF processes include ontjom in Indonesia, shao-hsing wine and kaoliang (sorghum) liquor in China and sake in Japan (Mudgett, 1986). Table 5 gives examples of foods that involve an SSF process at some point in production.

Table 5. Examples of foods produced by solid substrate fermentation.

Product	Microorganism	Materials
Natto	*Bacillus natto*	Soybean
Tempeh	*Rhizopus oligosporus*	Soybean
Tape	*Amylomyces rouxii, Rhizobium chinensis*	Rice, cassava, maize
Ontjum	*Neurospora sitophila*	Peanut meal
Cheese	*Penicillium roqueforti*	Wheat powder
Bread dough	*Saccharomyces cerevisiae, Lactobacillus sanfrancisco*	Wheat powder
Sake	*Aspergillus. oryzae, A. kawachii*	Rice, barley
Miso	*A. oryzae*	Soybean, rice
Soy sauce	*A. sojae*	Soybean, wheat

Mitchell and Lonsane, 1992.

While commercial use of SSF is not widespread in North America, industrial enzyme production by SSF has occurred for a number of years (Takamine, 1914; Underkofler *et al*, 1958). After World War II, Underkofler *et al*. (1947) and Terui *et al*. (1957) used heaped bed cultures with forced aeration to produce enzymes and citric acid. Tempeh production has been established on a small scale in the US (Hesseltine, 1987) because it has been accepted as a meat substitute by vegetarians. Mushrooms are cultivated in western countries; and soy sauce production has become highly industrialized and is widely used across the world. Kikkoman Foods has built a state-of-the-art facility completed in 1998 for soy sauce production in Folsom, California.

General features of solid substrate fermentation

The single most important feature of SSF is the low moisture content of the medium, which makes SSF very different from submerged liquid cultures. Water is essential for microbial growth; and the limited water in SSF has several consequences. It is adsorbed and to some extent held tightly; and there may even be some free water in the interior and on the surface. Water activity can be below 0.99 in SSF, where free water is virtually absent. These conditions favor filamentous fungi, many of which grow well between water activities of 0.93 and 0.98 (Corry, 1973). Bacteria and yeast grow above a water activity of 0.99.

Heat transfer is restricted in SSF, which can lead to overheating problems in large scale fermentations (Laukevics *et al.*, 1984). Evaporative cooling is the most effective cooling method, although this will reduce water availability (Trevelyan, 1974). Proper temperature conditions during the fermentation are a balance between the need for heat removal and the necessity of keeping the substrate sufficiently moist to support growth.

The insoluble substrates used in SSF are composite and heterogeneous products from agriculture or by-products of agro-industries. For many processes, substrates are chosen because they are readily available and therefore inexpensive. Most substrates have a common macromolecular structure. The macromolecular portion often provides a structural matrix for the substrate as well as serve as the carbon and energy source (e.g. cellulose) for the microorganism. If the macromolecule serves as a structural matrix only, the carbon and energy source is provided by a non-structural macromolecule such as starch or a smaller, soluble compound (e.g. soluble sugar).

Differences in enzymes produced by SSF and submerged liquid fermentation

Evidence has been accumulating to support the view that SSF processes are qualitatively different than submerged liquid fermentations. The data suggest that microbial physiology and regulation within the cell are influenced by the fermentation environment (Viniegra-Gonzalez, 1997). Ayers *et al.* (1952) reported that pectinases produced by SSF had noticeable biochemical differences from those produced by submerged fermentation. A glucosidase produced by *Aspergillus phoenicis* in SSF was more thermotolerant than when produced in submerged liquid fermentation (Deschamps and Huet, 1984). Alazard and Raimbault (1981) showed that amylases produced by *A. niger* using SSF were more resistant to heat denaturation than those produced in submerged liquid fermentation by the same strain. Other differences have also been reported (Romero *et al.*, 1993; Villegas *et al.*, 1993) and reinforced by the observation that the induction and repression patterns of pectinase production by *A. niger* are different for each fermentation technique (Solis-Pereira *et al.*, 1993).

Exoenzyme production in SSF systems results in increased amounts of some enzymatic activities not produced by cultures in liquid fermentation. A phytase produced by SSF (Allzyme Phytase, Alltech Inc.) also contained a mixture of activities not found in enzyme preparations from submerged culture systems (Table 6). The complex nature of feedstuffs makes these side activities beneficial to the animal industry (Classen, 1996). *In vitro* comparisons have shown increased rates of reducing sugar and amino nitrogen, and an associated increase in phosphate release by an SSF phytase product (Allzyme Phytase) (Figures 2-4, Filer *et al.*, 1999).

Table 6. Comparison of enzyme activities of two commercially available phytases.

Enzyme assayed	Production method of enzyme	
	Submerged liquid	SSF
Phytase	1,500 PU/g	1,500 PU/g
Fungal α-amylase	Below detectable level	240 FAU/g
ß-glucanase	Below detectable level	2,160 BGU/g
Cellulase	Below detectable level	310 CMCU/g
Fungal protease	Below detectable level	7,380 HUT/g

Microorganisms for solid state fermentation

Bacteria, yeast and fungi can all grow on solid substrates and have applications in SSF processes. However, filamentous fungi are the best adapted species for SSF and dominate in the research and practical applications around the world. Bacterial SSF fermentations are rarely used for large scale enzyme production, but are very important in nature and in the fermented food industry. In composting, moist solid organic wastes are decomposed by a succession of naturally-occurring microorganisms. Ensiling processes are dominated by lactobacilli producing lactic acid. Natto is a fermented food involving *Bacillus subtilis*. The fermentative yeast *Endomycopsis burtonii* is involved in the production of a traditional Indonesian fermented food, tape (Steinkraus, 1983).

Filamentous fungi are the most important group of microorganisms for enzyme production in SSF. The hyphal mode of growth gives a major advantage to filamentous fungi over unicellular microorganisms in the colonization of solid substrates and the utilization of available nutrients. The filamentous fungi have the power to penetrate solid substrates. Hydrolytic enzymes are excreted at the hyphal tip, without large dilution. This makes the action of hydrolytic enzymes very efficient and allows penetration into most solid substrates. This is critical for the growth of the fungi. Fungi cannot transport macromolecular substrates across the cell wall, so the macromolecule must be hydrolyzed externally into soluble units that can be transported into the cell (Knapp and Howell, 1980).

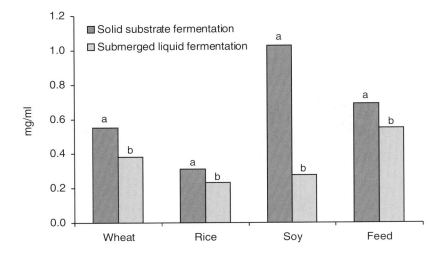

Figure 2. Effect of phytase enzyme source on reducing sugar release from four substrates at recommended use rates ([ab]Means differ, $P<0.05$).

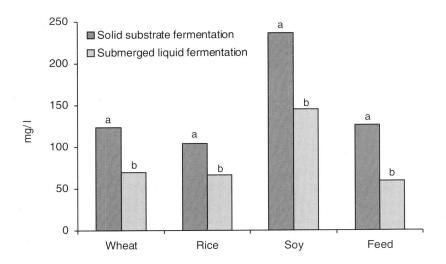

Figure 3. Effect of phytase enzyme source on amino nitrogen release from four substrates at recommended enzyme use rates ([ab]Means differ, $P<0.05$).

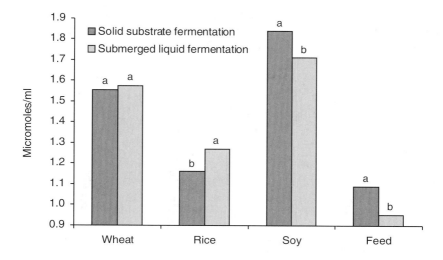

Figure 4. Effect of phytase enzyme source on phosphate release from four substrates at recommended enzyme use rates ([ab]Means differ, P<0.05).

Many submerged liquid fermentations are performed using pure cultures. The substrate is sterilized and then inoculated with a single culture. In the case of SSF a range of culture types are commonly used:

Single organism culture processes:	Many non-traditional processes are inoculated with a single microbial species. Strict aseptic conditions are not followed; and selective pressures such as water content and inoculation rate are used to control contamination.
Defined mixed culture:	A defined mixed culture involves inoculation of the substrate with more than one pure culture.
Sequential culture:	A second organism is inoculated after growth of the first microorganism has stopped. This is a modification of the mixed culture.
Undefined mixed culture:	The substrate is inoculated with a mixture of cultures that have not been identified: either the natural microflora of the substrate itself, or inocula consisting of natural sources of mixed populations of microorganisms. Traditional SSF methods are prepared in this way.

Most applications involve one of these inoculation schemes using fungi. Among the filamentous fungi, three classes have gained importance: phycomycetes such as the genera mucor and rhizopus, the ascomycetes with the genera aspergillus and penicillium, and basidiomycetes (Moo-Young *et al.*, 1983).

Advantages and disadvantages of using solid substrate fermentations

Solid state fermentation systems have a number of advantages (Cannel and Moo-Young, 1980; Mudgett, 1986):

a) *The medium is often simple*, consisting of unrefined agricultural product, which may contain all the nutrients for microbial growth. Examples of substrates are cereal grains, wheat bran, and wheat straw.

b) *Substrates require less pretreatment* compared to liquid fermentation. Pretreatment for SSF must increase the accessibility of nutrients, while pretreatment for liquid fermentation must achieve extraction of the nutrients into the bulk liquid phase.

c) *The restricted availability of water* helps to select against undesirable contaminants, especially bacteria and yeast.

d) *Forced aeration is often easier* in solid state cultures than in liquid cultures because the interparticle spaces allow transfer of fresh air to thin films of water at the substrate surfaces.

e) *Downstream processing and waste disposal is simplified* or minimized. If drying is required, less water is present to be removed.

Solid state fermentation as an enzyme production technique is not without difficulties that must be overcome. A number of disadvantages must be addressed to make a successful product (Cannel and Moo-Young, 1980; Mudgett, 1986):

a) *Restricted to microorganisms that grow at reduced moisture levels*. The majority of commercially profitable processes involve fungi, however.

b) *Removal of metabolic heat* can be a problem in large scale fermentations. Depending on the organism, heat can drastically influence end product production. This problem can be lessened by using organisms that are heat tolerant.

c)   *The solid nature of the substrate presents problems in monitoring process parameters.* Changes in pH are not easily identified and controlled in SSF; and the control of moisture content and substrate concentrations is extremely difficult. Heat production, oxygen consumption and carbon dioxide are parameters that can be measured.

d)   *Many important basic scientific and engineering aspects are poorly understood.* Little is known about the mode of growth of fungi within substrate masses composed of irregularly shaped solid particles.

e)   *Cultivation times* are often longer.

Bioreactor design

Reactor design is important in developing an efficient SSF process. The design of solid state reactors has to date been mostly empirical. Three basic types of reactors can be distinguished based on the mixing regime and the aeration mode. These include tray bioreactors, packed bed reactors, and agitated bioreactors.

The simplest SSF reactor is the tray. In a tray bioreactor a relatively thin layer of substrate is spread over a large horizontal area. There is no forced aeration, although the base of the tray may be perforated and air forced around the tray. Mixing, if any, is by simple automatic devices or manual. Internal temperature may vary with ambient temperature; or the tray may be placed in a temperature-controlled room. Tray bioreactors have been used successfully at laboratory, pilot, semi-commercial and commercial scale (Ahmed *et al*, 1987; Hesseltine, 1987). Although the design of the reactor is simple, extensive mechanization and automation have been reported in Japan (Lonsane *et al*., 1985).

Packed bed bioreactors are characterized by having a static substrate supported on a perforated base plate through which forced aeration is applied. Many variations of this basic design are possible (Lonsane *et al*., 1985). A tall, thin cylindrical column is the typical design. Most commonly the forced air is applied to the bottom. The humidity of the incoming air is kept high to minimize water loss from the substrate. The temperature of the incoming air can be changed to aid in temperature regulation of the substrate (Narahara *et al*., 1984). The advantage of packed bed reactors is that they remain simple while allowing better process control than trays.

Two general types of agitated fermenters have been designed. The first is a rotating drum reactor consisting of a horizontal or inclined cylinder that rotates around a central axis and causes a tumbling motion of the substrate. Aeration is supplied in the headspace. Mixing is gentle, although problems can arise if microorganisms are sensitive to the agitation. Temperature control is difficult because the reactor is difficult to water jacket (Lonsane *et al.*, 1985). The second type of agitated fermenter, a stirred reactor, has the reactor placed either on a horizontal or a vertical axis. Horizontal reactors are similar to rotating drums except the mixing is provided by an internal scraper or paddles, rather than rotation of the reactor. Vertical stirred reactors are subjected to forced aeration and are agitated continuously or intermittently.

Process methodology

The steps involved in solid state fermentation process consist of (Lonsane *et al*, 1985):

1   The preparation of a solid substrate, often with pretreatment to decrease the particle size or increase the availability of nutrients in the substrate.

2   A cooking step which sterilizes or at least pasteurizes the substrate and causes the absorption of water into the substrate particles.

3   Growth of a suitable inoculum.

4   Inoculation of the moist solids.

5   Incubation in appropriate culture vessels.

6   Maintenance of optimal conditions to the extent possible.

7   Harvest of the solids.

8   Drying or extraction of the product from the solids

9   Downstream processing.

The Alltech solid state fermentation program

The many advantages of enzyme production by SSF have convinced Alltech that it is a valuable technology for the production of enzymes. As a result of this commitment an entire SSF program has been developed. The program includes small-scale lab fermentations up to production size facilities. The development from idea to commercial production employed the following steps:

1   Culture isolation, screening and selection.

2   Standardization of the process at small scale.

3   Scale-up studies.

4   Design and construction of the plant.

5   Operation of the plant.

The development of a SSF fermentation program at Alltech is intended to produce a more useful enzyme employing a procedure with economics that make it practical for the animal feed and fuel ethanol industries. With the completion of a production facility in Serdan, Puebla, Mexico the idea became a reality.

CULTURE ISOLATION, SCREENING AND SELECTION: NON-GMO ORGANISMS

The SSF program starts with the cultures. Two isolates have gone through a rigorous screening and selection process and are currently used extensively in the program. An *Aspergillus niger* has been naturally selected for overproduction of phytase. Of all the organisms surveyed, *A. niger* produces the most active extracellular phytase reported (Wodzinski and Ullah, 1996). Through numerous rounds of screening and selection, overproduction by about 400 fold has been achieved. A point that is becoming more and more critical for many consumers is that the organism is a non-genetically modified organism (non-GMO) able to produce phytase at a significant level for commercial production. Use of non-GMO organisms in SSF processes is common. The SSF growth environment is conducive to overproduction of a number of different enzymes; and genetic engineering is not required for production of large amounts. In contrast, submerged liquid systems generally use GMOs designed for overproduction of a particular enzyme.

The second organism currently being studied extensively is *Rhizopus oryzae*, which produces glucoamylase. Glucoamylase sequentially cleaves glucose molecules from the nonreducing end of a starch molecule and is used extensively in the ethanol industry. The organism is not genetically modified and has been naturally selected for overproduction of glucoamylase. *Rhizopus* sp. have been reported to produce amylases (Raimbault, 1998). This organism is currently being used in lab scale and pilot scale tray fermentations and deep bed lab scale fermentations. Completion of these studies will allow the organism to be used at a commercial level.

STANDARDIZATION OF THE PROCESS AT SMALL SCALE

The selection of strains involves SSF on a small scale. Small scale fermentations occur in 500 ml flasks. The substrate used for the majority of fermentations is wheat bran. In these flasks the typical moisture, temperature and extraction conditions as well as the length of fermentation and inoculation rate have been determined and maximized. The information from these systems is important, although certain limitations do exist.

In addition to thin layer tray systems, deep bed systems of 30–50 cm will be used in production. In order to determine if organisms are suitable for growth in deep layer fermentations, lab scale deep layer fermenters have been designed. Conditioned air is blown in through the bottom with an exit port on the top. The substrate sits on top of a perforated screen. The vessel has ports for thermocouples to monitor temperature. The airflow, relative humidity of the air, and oxygen content within the chamber can all be measured. These parameters are monitored and the data collected and sent to a computer. The entire fermenter is placed in a temperature and humidity controlled room. With this system we are able to generate data that reflect the heat produced during the fermentation and determine the amount of air required to maintain temperature in the target range. The substrate cannot be agitated during the fermentation and water is not easily added. These systems can produce data on the success of the fermentation in deep layers and the amount of heat produced during the fermentation.

SCALE-UP STUDIES

The scale-up step is a crucial linkage in the process since it determines whether the process will operate at a commercial scale. The scale-up should theoretically result in the same overall performance that can be achieved in the laboratory. This is rarely the case since a number of additional parameters influence the fermentation. Heat removal must be addressed; and there are no simple solutions since thermodynamic and kinetic properties become more complex.

Once the fermentation conditions have been determined in the flasks, the organism can be grown in lab scale tray systems. These systems are designed to mimic the conditions in a production tray system. The initial system designed was a plexiglass chamber able to hold 12 trays that hold up to 200 g of substrate. The chamber is incubated in a temperature-controlled room. Water saturated air is added from the top. In order to gain more information from tray fermentations, a second-generation tray fermenter was designed and built by the Departmento de Biotechnologia, Universidad Autonoma Metroplitana Iztapalapa. Figure 5 depicts a tray fermentation system. Four trays fit inside the reactor and conditioned air is forced in at the lower left portion of the reactor. Deflectors direct airflow over the tray or away from it. The reactor is equipped with thermocouples, flow meter, oxygen sensor and relative humidity sensor. Data acquisition equipment allows better understanding of heat and carbon dioxide production. This information is then used in designing production systems.

Figure 5. Pilot scale tray fermentation system.

Alltech is interested in production of enzymes in deep layers as well as thin layer tray systems. A pilot scale deep bed fermentation system was constructed (Figure 6). The reactor is a vertical stirred reactor based on a modified lauter tun design. The system is designed to be used at a maximum depth of about 50 cm. The entire unit sits on load cells to measure weight loss during the fermentation. The substrate is sterilized by a rotary mixer that can be pressurized and heated. During the fermentation, temperature, oxygen, carbon dioxide, airflow and relative humidity can be monitored. The reactor will enable studies to determine if organisms can perform in deep layers at pilot scale levels and develop an understanding of heat production.

Figure 6. A pilot scale deep bed fermenter.

DESIGN AND CONSTRUCTION OF THE SSF PLANT

There is no information available in the literature on SSF with respect to the theoretical and experimental comparisons of different kinds of bioreactors, methods for controlling cultivation parameters, automation, design and scale up criteria or downstream processing options. The design process for large scale production of enzymes has been based on information obtained in lab scale and pilot scale studies as well as experience gained in the areas of fermentation and downstream processing.

From the data generated and the scant literature available it became apparent that for initial production a tray fermentation system would reach optimum production levels in the shortest amount of time. The data generated in the lab and pilot tray systems were used in the development of a production tray fermentation system. The facility has been built in Serdan, Pueblo, Mexico. This facility houses pretreatment, inoculation facilities, fermentation facilities, and downstream processing facilities. A separate building at the site contains a laboratory for initial strain manipulation. The initial phase of the design was intended for construction of a facility that will contain about 10,000 trays.

Future potential

Most profitable applications of SSF are confined to Asian and African countries and are scarce elsewhere in the world. A resurgence of interest has occurred in western and European countries in response to the ever-increasing demand for economy in enzyme production. The facility in Serdan is believed to be the first commercial enzyme production facility in North America that uses SSF technology. Its success will lead to expansion. The future of the SSF program at Alltech includes the development of new strains for enzyme production, to enhance current enzyme systems and development of new enzyme applications. Solid substrate fermentations will also lead us in the direction of new substrates. The use of a variety of waste products will be investigated as well as the potential for using inert supports for fermentation. The SSF technology also has the potential to be used for purposes other than enzyme production. Other metabolites such as ethanol, flavors, and other microbial by-products can be produced. SSF can be used for upgrading agro-industrial by-products that can be used in animal feed applications. Knowledge gained about the SSF process will allow construction of systems that better monitor and control fermentation parameters and utilize a wider range of substrates, as well as micro-organisms.

References

Ahmed, S.Y., B.K. Lonsane, N.P. Ghildyal and S.V. Ramakrishna. 1987.
   Design of solid state fermentation for production of fungal metabolites on

large scale. Biotechnol. Tech. 1:97-102.

Alazard, D. and M. Raimbault. 1981. Comparative study of amylolytic enzymes production by *Aspergillus niger* in liquid and solid state cultivation. Eur. J. Appl. Microbiol. 12:113-117.

Amado, R. 1993. Enzymes in food and food processing-a review. In: Enzymes in animal nutrition. Proceedings of the 1st symposium. Kartause Ittingen, Switzerland. (C. Wenk and M. Boessinger, eds.) pp. 5–15.

Ayers, A., J. Dingle, A. Phipps, W.W. Reids and C.L. Solomons. 1952. Enzymatic degradation of pectic acid and the complex nature of polygalacturonase. Nature London 170:834-836.

Bailey, J.E. and D.F. Ollis. 1986. Biochemical Engineering Fundamentals. Second Edition. McGraw Hill Publishing Company. New York. p. 984.

Bron, S., R. Meima, J.M. van Dijl, A. Wipat and C.R. Harwood. 1999. Molecular biology and genetics of *Bacillus sp.* In: Manual of Industrial Microbiology and Biotechnology (A.L. Demain and J.E. Davies, eds.) ASM Press, Washington, D.C. pp. 392-416.

Bull, A.T. and A.P.J. Trinci. 1977. The physiology and metabolic control of fungal growth. Adv. Microbial Physiol. 15:1–84.

Callahan, J.R. 1944. Large scale production by deep fermentation. Chem. Metal. Eng. 51:94–98.

Cannel, E. and M. Moo-Young. 1980. Solid state fermentation systems. Proc. Biochem. 15:2-7.

Classen, H.L. 1996. Enzymes in action. Feed Mix 4:22-28.

Corry, J.E.L. 1973. The water relations and heat resistance of microorganisms. Progr. Ind. Microbiol. 12:73-108.

De Becze, G. and A.J. Liebmann. 1944. Aeration in the production of compressed yeast. Ind. Eng. Chem. 36:882-890.

Deschamps, F. and M.C. Huet. 1984. Beta-glucosidase production in agitated solid fermentation, a study of its properties. Biotechnol. Lett. 6:451-456.

Filer, K., J. Evans, K. Newman and P. Spring. 1999. *In vitro* comparison of two commercial phytase products. Poultry Sci. 78(Suppl 1):74.

Hesseltine, C.W. 1976. Solid state fermentation. Biotechnol. Bioeng. 14:517–532.

Hesseltine, C.W. 1987. Solid state fermentation-an overview. Int. Biodeterioration. 23:79-89.

Knapp, J.S. and J.A. Howell. 1980. Solid substrate fermentation. In: Topics in Enzyme and Fermentation Biotechnology, vol. 4. (A. Wiseman. Ellis Horwood Ltd, Chichest, England, pp. 85-143.

Laukevics, J.J., A.F. Apsite, U.S. Viestures and R.P. Tengerdy. 1984. Solid substrate fermentation of wheat straw to fungal protein. Biotechnol. Bioeng. 26:1465-1474.

Lehninger, A.L. 1975. Biochemistry: The Molecular Basis of Cell Structure and Function. 2nd edition. Worth Publishers, Inc. New York, N.Y.

Lonsane, B.K., N.P. Ghildyal, S. Budiatman and S.V. Ramakrishna. 1985. Engineering aspects of solid state fermentation. Enzym. Microbiol. Technol. 7:258-265.

Mitchell, D.A. and B.K. Lonsane. 1992. Definition, characteristics and potential. In: Solid Substrate Cultivation. (H.W. Doelle, D.A. Mitchell and C.E. Rolz, eds.) Elsevier Applied Biotechnology Series.

Moo-Young, M., A.R. Moreira and R.P. Tengerdy. 1983. Principles of solid-substrate fermentation. In: the Filamentous Fungi, vol. 4. (J.E. Smith, D.R. Berry and B. Kristiansen, eds). Edward Arnold, London, pp. 117-144.

Mudgett, R.E. 1986. Solid-state fermentations. In: Manual of Industrial Microbiology and Biotechnology (A.L. Demain and H.A. Solomon, eds). American Society for Microbiology, Washington, D.C. pp. 66-83.

Narahara, H., Y. Koyama, T. Yoshida, S. Pichangkura and H. Taguchi. 1984. Control of water content in a solid-state culture of *Aspergillus oryzae*. J. Ferment. Technol. 62:453-459.

Oliver, S.G. and A.P.J. Trinci. 1985. Modes of growth of bacteria and fungi. In: Comprehensive Biotechnology, vol. 1 (Moo-Young, eds). New York Pergan Press, pp. 159 –187.

Raimbault, M. 1998. General and microbiological aspects of solid substrate fermentation. EJB. Vol. 1 No.3.

Ralph, B.J. 1976. Solid substrate fermentations. Food Technol. Australia 28:247-251.

Romero, S., M.E. Acuna and G. Viniegra-Gonzalez. 1993. Efecto de la actividad de aqua sobre la produccion de pectinasas por mutantes de *Aspergillus niger* en fermentacion solida y liquida. Biotechnologia (Mexico) 3(1-2):FS65-FS69.

Solis-Pereira, S., E. Favela-Torres, G. Viniegra-Gonzalez, M. Gutierrez-Rojas. 1993. Effects of different carbon sources on the synthesis of pectinases by *Aspergillus niger* in submerged and solid state fermentations. Appl. Microbiol. Biotech. 39:36-41.

Stanbury, P.F., A. Whitaker and S.J. Hall. 1995. An Introduction to Fermentation Processes. In: Principles of Fermentation Technology, Second Edition. Pergamon Publishers, Great Britian.

Steinkraus, K.H. 1983. Fermented foods, feeds, and beverages. Biotechnol. Adv. 1:31–46.

Takamine, J. 1914. Enzymes of *Aspergillus oryzae* and the application of its amyloclastic enzyme to the fermentation industry. Ind. Eng. Chem. 6:824-828.

Terui, G., I. Shibazaki and T. Mochizuki. 1957. Industrial fermentation by a highly heaped culture with forced aeration. I. citric acid fermentation. Hakkokogaku 35:105-116.

Trevelyan, W.E. 1974. The enrichment of cassava by moist-solids fermentation. Tropical Science 16:179–194.

Underkofler, L.A., G.M. Steverson, K.J. Goering and L.M. Christensen. 1947. Commercial production and use of mold. Cereal Chem. 24:1–22.

Underkofler, L.A., R.P. Barton and S.S. Rennert. 1958. Production of microbial enzymes and their applications. Appl. Microbiol. 6:212-221.

Villegas, E., S. Aubague, L. Alcantara, R. Auria, C. Vega and S. Revah. 1993. Solid state fermentation: acid protease production in controlled CO_2 environments. Biotech. Adv. 11:387-397.

Viniegra-Gonzalez, G. 1997. Solid state fermentation: Definition, characteristics, limitations and monitoring. In: Advances in Solid State Fermentation. (S. Roussos, B.K. Lonsane, M. Raimbault and G. Viniegra-Gonzalez, eds.). Kluwer Publishers, The Netherlands, pp. 5–22.

Wodzinski, R.J. and A.H.J. Ullah. 1996. Phytase. Advances in Applied Microbiology. Vol. 42, pp. 263–302.

Do non-GMO enzymes work as well as GMO sources? A comparison of phytase sources in low phosphorus diets fed to layers

D.A. ROLAND, M. BRYANT AND A. BATEMAN

Auburn University, Auburn, Alabama, USA

Introduction: evolution of practical phytase use

The beneficial effects of phytase on the availability of phytate phosphorus have been known since the 1960s (Nelson, 1967) with considerable research having been undertaken and reported in the intervening years. Phytases have been available for many years; but not until the environmental impact of agriculture and urban sprawl became a political issue was there pressure to develop and utilize phytase in livestock feeds. The first sign of things to come was the elimination of phosphorus-based laundry detergents. This had a dramatically beneficial effect on the ecology of the Great Lakes of North America. Commercial fishery has returned to this area. More recently, pressure has been very intense in Western Europe, where the Dutch have pioneered agricultural nutrient management. Similar pressure has surfaced in North America. The Maryland General Assembly established the Water Quality Improvement Act of 1998 and the Nutrient Management Practices Act of 1998. These acts mandate that all feed for monogastric animals must be supplemented with a phytase enzyme or other additives that reduce phosphorus in the manure to the maximum extent commercially and biologically feasible by the end of the year 2000 (Harter-Dennis, 1999).

Phytase enzyme has become widely utilized as a method of reducing the requirement for supplemental phosphorus in monogastric diets. It is currently estimated that over two-thirds of the layers in the United States are already fed reduced phosphorus diets and the percentage is growing. Many of these birds are in locations that have not yet legislated use of phosphorus reducing technologies. These technologies are being employed because producers want to be good custodians of the environment. It is an added benefit for producers that with sound ration formulation addition of phytase can improve production economics.

Changes in the economics of phytase production have allowed practical use of this enzyme to support sound environmental management. It was not until process technology allowed production of cost effective phytase that its use became widespread. The first breakthrough took place when genetic engineering techniques allowed use of *Aspergillus niger* to express the enzyme. This was followed by re-examination of the much older solid substrate fermentation techniques. This method allows non-genetically modified organisms to produce useful quantities of enzyme using modern process technology (Nokes, 1999). Thus, there are two distinct phytases in the marketplace, one derived from a genetically modified organism (GMO) the other based on a non-genetically modified organism (non-GMO). Both are marketed for their ability to release approximately 40% of the phytate phosphorus in practical diets. In monogastric rations this translates into a reduction of 0.1% in the amount of non-phytate phosphorus added to feed.

A reduction of 0.1% in the requirement for non-phytate phosphorus results in a 25% reduction in phosphorus excretion by layers (Balander and Flegal, 1997). Given the number of commercial egg layers in the United States alone, this represents a huge reduction in the environmental impact of poultry production.

Objectives

The present studies were undertaken to compare ability of GMO and non-GMO sources of phytase to release plant-bound phosphorus in commercial layer diets. While phytase is also known to improve utilization of other minerals, amino acids and energy in poultry diets, this study was designed to focus only on phosphorus utilization.

Materials and methods

Two experiments were designed to compare the phytase sources using performance of mature layers fed a phosphorus-inadequate basal diet as the criterion. When phosphorus reserves are depleted, birds are unable to maintain performance levels. Appetite declines, and with feed consumption inadequate to sustain production, egg production and egg size drop, along with specific gravity. Phytase, by releasing phytate phosphorus, slows the rate of depletion of phosphorus reserves. The effectiveness of the phytase is judged by the ability to slow the rate of phosphorus depletion and thus maintain appetite and performance. In these experiments, the phytase sources were added to a basal diet containing 0.10% available phosphorus in order to increase the sensitivity of the enzyme source comparison.

EXPERIMENT 1: EFFECTS OF GMO AND NON-GMO PHYTASE LEVELS IN DIETS CONTAINING ADEQUATE (0.4%) OR INADEQUATE (0.1%) AVAILABLE PHOSPHORUS

The GMO and non-GMO phytase sources used in the study were Natuphos® (BASF Corp., Mount Olive, NJ) and Allzyme Phytase® (Alltech Inc.,

154

Nicholasville, KY), respectively. The enzyme sources were added at either the manufacturers' recommended use rates (Natuphos, 600 FTU/kg, Allzyme Phytase 11,500 PTU/kg) or half that rate to diets containing either adequate phosphorus (0.4%) or inadequate (0.1%) available phosphorus. The unsupplemented basal diet formulated at either 0.4 or 0.1% available phosphorus served as positive and negative control treatments.

Caged Hy-Line W-36 layers (Hy-Line International, West Des Moines, IA), aged 43 weeks were randomly assigned eight replicate pens of 16 birds per treatment. Feed and water were supplied *ad libitum*. Feed consumption was recorded weekly for the six week experiment. Egg production was summarized weekly. Egg weight and specific gravity were measured bi-weekly.

EXPERIMENT 2: COMPARATIVE DOSE-RESPONSE

Experiment 2 was designed to provide a more severe test for the GMO and non-GMO phytases. The GMO phytase was added at 50, 100, 150 or 200 FTU/kg and the non-GMO source was added at either 1900, 3800, 5700 or 7600 PTU/kg. The basal diet contained 0.1% available phosphorus, and a positive control treatment (0.4% available phosphorus) was included. The Hy-Line W-36 hens were 85 weeks of age for this eight week experiment and had been molted.

Results

EXPERIMENT 1: EFFECTS OF GMO AND NON-GMO PHYTASE LEVELS IN DIETS CONTAINING ADEQUATE (0.4%) OR INADEQUATE (0.1%) AVAILABLE PHOSPHORUS.

Feed consumption (Table 1) was lower in birds given the negative control in all weeks relative to the positive control. The difference between the two treatments became progressively greater with time. Feed intake of the positive control group remained relatively constant throughout the experiment. The lower feed intake of the negative control reflects lower appetite for hens fed the phosphorus-inadequate ration. Both phytase sources at both levels maintained feed intake levels comparable to the positive control for the six week experiment.

Egg production (Table 2) of birds fed the negative control diet began to fall after two weeks and by the end of the six week experiment was about half that of the positive control. This was expected as feed consumption declines slightly in advance of egg production. Both phytase sources at both levels supported production comparable to the positive control.

Egg weight (Table 3) of the positive control treatment group followed an upward trend over the six week experimental period while the negative

Table 1. Effect of GMO and non-GMO phytases added at recommended or half the recommended dosage on feed consumption (g/day) in low phosphorus diets (Experiment 1).

	Week					
	1	2	3	4	5	6
Positive control (0.4% AP)	94.75	95.51[a]	94.70[a]	92.55[a]	88.12[abc]	92.57[a]
Negative control (0.1% AP)	90.32	86.42[c]	81.49[c]	72.76[d]	68.13[d]	71.54[b]
Non-GMO, 0.5 kg/T	93.59	94.75[a]	94.12[ab]	93.28[a]	90.42[a]	94.17[a]
GMO, 0.5 kg/T	92.04	93.61[a]	92.73[ab]	91.34[ab]	89.33[ab]	91.71[a]
Non-GMO, 1 kg/T	92.45	92.68[ab]	92.40[ab]	90.14[bc]	87.53[bc]	92.03[a]
GMO, 1 kg/T	90.98	89.95[b]	91.07[b]	88.58[c]	86.01[c]	89.63[a]

[abd]Means in a column differ, P<0.001.

Table 2. Effect of GMO and non-GMO phytases added at recommended or half the recommended dosage on egg production (%) in low phosphorus diets (Experiment 1).

	1	2	3	4	5	6	Average
Positive control (0.4% AP)	87.39	88.73	87.39[a]	86.61[a]	85.49[a]	81.58[a]	86.20[a]
Negative control (0.1%)	87.84	86.61	80.58[b]	66.33[b]	50.11[b]	45.57[b]	69.51[b]
Non-GMO, 0.5 kg/T	87.50	88.39	88.58[a]	85.71[a]	85.86[a]	82.66[a]	86.45[a]
GMO, 0.5 kg/T	87.95	87.72	88.06[a]	87.72[a]	86.27[a]	84.49[a]	87.04[a]
Non-GMO, 1 kg/T	87.39	89.40	87.50[a]	85.27[a]	85.01[a]	82.11[a]	86.11[a]
GMO, 1 kg/T	86.72	88.62	87.61[a]	87.61[a]	86.94[a]	84.82[a]	87.05[a]

[a-b]Means in a column differ, P<0.001.

control followed a downward trend. Both phytase sources and both levels followed the same upward trend as the positive control. These results indicate that both phytases were able to sustain egg weight when given the inadequate phosphorus rations for the six weeks of this experiment.

Egg specific gravity (Table 4) of the positive control, contrary to expectations, tended to increase over the experimental period. The negative control had lower specific gravity at all times compared to the positive control, as expected of birds fed an inadequate ration. It was interesting that the negative control mean specific gravity dropped at week 4 (relative to week 2) then increased to week 6. This indicates that the birds still in lay had a greater genetic ability to utilize the low levels of available phosphorus provided. Both phytase sources and both levels followed the same trend as the positive control; indicating that both phytase sources were able to sustain shell quality on the inadequate phosphorus diets for the duration of this experiment.

In summary, both the GMO and the non-GMO phytase at either the recommended use rate or half the recommended rate were able to sustain performance in birds given diets containing 0.1% available phosphorus at levels comparable to birds given 0.4% available phosphorus. There were no apparent differences between the two phytase sources under the conditions of this six week experiment.

Table 3. Effect of GMO and non-GMO phytases added at recommended or half the recommended dosage on egg weights (g) in low phosphorus diets (Experiment 1).

	Week			
	2	4	6	Average
Positive control (0.4% AP)	59.46	59.86[a]	60.47[a]	59.93[d]
Negative control (0.1%)	58.50	57.93[b]	56.94[b]	57.79[f]
Non-GMO, 0.5 kg/T	58.61	58.90[ab]	59.44[a]	59.20[de]
GMO, 0.5 kg/T	58.45	59.19[a]	59.96[a]	58.98[e]
Non-GMO, 1.0 kg/T	59.66	59.69[a]	60.95[a]	59.43[de]
GMO, 1.0 kg/T	58.49	59.62[a]	60.17[a]	61.10[d]

[a-f]Means in a column differ, P<0.001.

Table 4. Effect of GMO and non-GMO phytases added at recommended or half the recommended dosage on egg specific gravity in low phosphorus diets (Experiment 1).

	Week			
	2	4	6	Average
Positive control (0.4% AP)	1.08078	1.08145	1.08341	1.08188[b]
Negative control (0.1% AP)	1.07974	1.07715	1.08093	1.07928[a]
Non-GMO, 0.5 kg/T	1.08085	1.08192	1.08341	1.08206[a]
GMO, 0.5 kg/T	1.08217	1.08183	1.08351	1.08250[a]
Non-GMO, 1 kg/T	1.08127	1.08174	1.08377	1.08226[a]
GMO, 1 kg/T	1.08105	1.08130	1.08235	1.08157[a]

[ab]Means in a column differ, P<0.001.

EXPERIMENT 2: COMPARATIVE DOSE-RESPONSE

Feed consumption (Table 5) followed a similar pattern to that in Experiment 1. Intake of the negative control diet decreased initially, then stabilized at about 75 g per bird per day. The pattern for the two sources of phytase however differed. Consumption of diets containing GMO phytase declined as the level of use decreased, indicating that the lower levels were at the borderline of ability to counter inadequate dietary available phosphorus. It is important to note that available phosphorus in the phytase-supplemented diets had been reduced from the recommended 0.4 to 0.1% while manufacturers of both enzyme sources only recommend reduction to 0.30%. Allzyme Phytase did not show a dose-related pattern for feed consumption and all non-GMO phytase inclusion rate treatments were similar to the positive control. Given this response it would appear that the non-GMO phytase had more phytase activity than had been assumed.

Egg production also showed a similar pattern to Experiment 1 in that production in the positive control group remained relatively constant for theeight week study while the negative control group had lower production after two weeks on the experiment and then stabilized after five weeks at about 40%. Egg production in the phytase-supplemented treatment groups

157

Table 5. Effect of phytase level and source on feed intake (g/day) (Experiment 2).

	Week 1	2	3	4	5	6	7	8	Average
Positive control (0.4% AP)	87.22[a]	94.05[a]	93.68[a]	95.96[a]	95.22[a]	94.03[a]	94.63[a]	88.55[a]	92.92[a]
Negative control (0.1%)	84.86[b]	79.67[b]	73.03[b]	67.07[b]	75.23[b]	75.52[b]	74.46[b]	74.09[b]	75.49[b]
GMO phytase[1], FTU/kg	NS	NS	NS	**LQ	NS	**L	**L	*L	*L
50	87.00	87.49	84.23	83.80	91.23	86.38	88.06	84.64	86.60
100	86.75	89.67	87.47	90.61	90.58	90.27	91.55	87.34	89.28
150	88.35	90.02	89.44	92.59	93.40	92.19	93.60	88.28	90.98
200	91.33	91.27	91.49	92.11	93.82	93.78	94.09	89.92	92.22
Non-GMO phytase[1], PTU/kg	NS	NS	NS	NS	NS	NS	NS	NS	NS
1900	87.43	90.78	89.20	91.83	94.21	92.56	93.73	88.87	91.07
3800	88.72	91.62	89.83	92.82	93.73	93.37	93.60	88.47	91.52
5700	87.36	90.98	89.20	90.37	92.29	91.38	93.53	88.30	90.43
7600	88.01	92.63	92.11	94.10	93.71	92.64	93.41	87.54	91.77

[1]Phytase enzyme sources were added to the negative control diet containing 0.1% AP.
[a,b]Column means differ, P<0.05.
*L (linear effect, P<0.05), **L (linear effect, P<0.01), **LQ Linear, quadratic.

followed feed intake patterns. Average egg production on the GMO phytase diets was dose-related while all supplementation levels of the non-GMO source were similar (Figure 1).

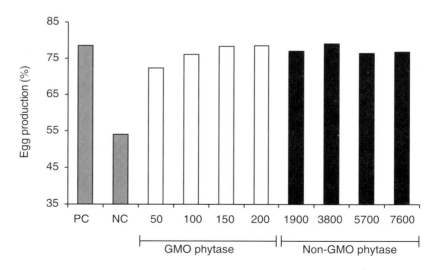

Figure 1. Effect of phytase source and level on average egg production in an eight week trial (PC = positive control, NC = negative control) (Experiment 2).

Egg weight (Table 6) did not follow the age-related pattern exhibited in Experiment 1. Both the positive and negative control treatment egg weights were relatively constant over the eight week experimental period, although there were weekly fluctuations, especially in the positive controls. A dose-related effect of the GMO phytase was similar to that noted in egg production and feed intake, however it was less pronounced. The non-GMO phytase showed no dose-related pattern and did not differ from the positive control.

Table 6. Effect of phytase source and dosage on egg weight (Experiment 2).

	Week						
	2	4	5	6	7	8	Average
Positive control (0.4% AP)	62.66[a]	62.40[a]	63.74[a]	62.19[a]	62.84[a]	62.84[a]	62.78[a]
Negative control (0.1%)	60.13[b]	60.46[b]	60.20[b]	59.86[b]	59.87[b]	59.96[b]	60.08[b]
GMO phytase[1], FTU/kg							
50	61.45	61.87	61.70	62.48	61.84	60.61	61.66
100	61.13	61.29	61.41	62.33	62.13	61.81	61.68
150	61.52	61.62	61.70	62.06	61.93	62.24	61.85
200	61.57	62.78	62.50	62.60	62.75	62.42	62.44
Non-GMO phytase[1], PTU/kg							
1900	61.71	61.80	62.19	62.30	62.44	62.28	62.12
3800	61.69	62.51	62.23	61.94	62.54	62.61	62.25
5700	61.44	62.71	62.03	62.78	61.78	62.84	62.26
7600	61.89	62.71	62.17	62.43	62.22	62.61	62.34

[1]Phytase enzyme sources were added to the negative control diet containing 0.1% AP.

Differences in egg specific gravity (Table 7) between the positive and negative control groups were similar to those in Experiment 1. The specific gravity was lower for the negative controls and decreased in the final weeks of the experiments indicating that only birds with the ability to utilize low available phosphorus levels remained in lay. As for egg production, feed intake and egg weight, specific gravity in the GMO phytase-supplemented groups responded in a dose-related manner while the non-GMO enzyme groups did not.

Both phytase sources had similar dose-related patterns in mortality (Table 8) with death losses decreasing with increased enzyme dose. Mortality in groups receiving the lowest phytase dose from either source was less than the negative control. This indicated that both are active even at these low use rates. Mortality at higher enzyme dosages for either source was comparable to the positive control.

Conclusions

These data demonstrate that both the GMO and non-GMO phytases can be used as recommended to reduce the non-phytate phosphorus allowances

Table 7. Effect of phytase source and level on egg specific gravity (Experiment 2).

| | Week | | | | |
	2	4	6	8	Average
Positive control (0.4% AP)	1.07967[a]	1.08013[a]	1.07773[a]	1.07718[a]	1.07867[a]
Negative control (0.1% AP)	1.07605[b]	1.07578[b]	1.07489[b]	1.07803[b]	1.07619[b]
GMO phytase[1], FTU/kg	**L	NS	*L	NS	*L
50	1.07770	1.07828	1.07620	1.07788	1.07752
100	1.07935	1.07902	1.07734	1.07807	1.07844
150	1.07956	1.08014	1.07662	1.07657	1.07822
200	1.07972	1.07953	1.07818	1.07775	1.07880
Non-GMO phytase[1], PU/kg	NS	NS	NS	NS	NS
1900	1.07944	1.08055	1.07713	1.07744	1.07864
3800	1.07965	1.08056	1.07819	1.07621	1.07865
5700	1.08062	1.08017	1.07811	1.07704	1.07899
7600	1.07933	1.07985	1.07708	1.07662	1.07822

[1]Phytase enzyme sources were added to the negative control diet containing 0.1% AP.
[a,b]Column means differ, P<0.05.
*L (linear effect, P<0.05), **L (linear effect, P<0.01).

Table 8. Effect of phytase source and level on average hen weight and mortality.

	Hen weight (kg)	Hen mortality
Positive control (0.4% AP)	3.97[a]	0.047[b]
Negative control (0.1% AP)	3.63[b]	0.625[a]
GMO phytase[1], FTU/kg	NS	***LQ
50	3.83	.297
100	3.88	0.063
150	3.87	0.047
200	4.05	0.031
Non-GMO phytase[1], PTU/kg	NS	NS
1900	3.79	0.094
3800	3.81	0.063
5700	3.82	0.063
7600	3.77	0.016

[1]Phytase enzyme sources were added to the negative control diet containing 0.1% AP.
NS = non significant, ***LQ (linear, quadratic responses, P<0.001).

for layers. It is of interest to note that in both experiments feed consumption was the first criteria affected when inadequate available phosphorus rations were fed without enzyme supplementation. Appetite is critical to achieving many performance criteria. Low nutrient intake during heat stress leads to lower growth rates of pullets (Stanley *et al.*, 1999a) and lower early egg production (Stanley *et al.*, 1999b).

It should be noted that both experiments were relatively short term, i.e., six and eight weeks. The normal first lay cycle extends from 16 to in some cases over 80 weeks of age, a total of 64 weeks. Thus, it is not recommended that phosphorus levels be reduced in commercial diets to the extent they were in these experiments. Manufacturer's recommendations of a 0.1 percentage point decrease in dietary available phosphorus content with recommended use rates of the GMO or non-GMO phytases would be appropriate.

There are indications in Experiment 2 that the non-GMO phytase activity was under-calculated. Further work will be required to determine the precise phytase activity of the non-GMO product. More side activities (i.e. innate protease and carbohydrase) would be expected in the enzyme produced by solid state fermentation. This was demonstrated by Filer *et al.* (1999), who showed the non-GMO phytase released more amino nitrogen and reducing sugars, and that this was associated with greater *in vitro* phosphate release. Given the complex nature of feed ingredients, a broader spectrum of activity would be expected to ultimately result in similarly higher *in vivo* phytate phosphorus activity, which may enhance its effectiveness in poultry feed.

References

Balander, R.J. and C.J. Flagel. 1997. The effect of phytase on egg production and specific gravity in laying hens. Poultry Sci. 77(Suppl. 1):3.

Filer, K., J. Evans, K. Newman and P. Spring. 1999. *In vitro* comparison of two commercial phytase products. Poultry Sci. (Suppl. 1):74.

Harter-Dennis, J. 1999. Phytase applications in commercial broiler diets in Maryland. In: Biotechnology in the Feed Industry, Proceedings of the 15th Annual Symposium (T.P. Lyons and K.A. Jacques, eds.) Nottingham University Press, Nottingham, UK.

Nelson, T.S. 1967. The utilization of phytate P by poultry- A review. Poultry Sci. 46:862-871.

Nokes, S.E. 1999. Enzyme production using surface culture fermentation. In: Biotechnology in the Feed Industry, Proceedings of the 15th Annual Symposium (T.P. Lyons and K.A. Jacques, eds.) Nottingham University Press, Nottingham, UK.

Stanley, V.G., J. Robertson and V. Vaughn. 1999a. Growth performance, egg size, production and feed consumption of pullets fed dietary protease enzyme. Poultry Sci. 78(Suppl. 1):111.

Stanley, V., J. Robertson and V. Vaughn. 1999b. The response of laying hens to the feeding of dietary protease enzyme, phase II. Poultry Sci. 78(Suppl. 1):44.

Phytase application variations in broiler diets and legislative update

JEANNINE HARTER-DENNIS

University of Maryland-Eastern Shore, Princess Anne, Maryland, USA

Update on environmental legislation in Maryland, Delaware and Virginia

During the summer of 1997 the state of Maryland experienced outbreaks of *Pfiesteria* in several of its rivers and tributaries. These dinoflagellate microorganisms were implicated in several fish kills that closed affected rivers to fishing and tourism. Similar outbreaks were experienced in North Carolina and other eastern coast areas. Although not proven, there was thought to be a link between these outbreaks and nutrient over-enrichment of the soil due to manure application since phosphorus runoff into surface water has been identified as one of the possible causative agents.

The Delmarva Peninsula accounts for the production of over 625 million broilers annually, with an economic value of over $1.6 billion dollars. This results in approximately 53 million pounds of manure nitrogen and 22 million pounds of manure phosphorus. In an effort to reduce both phosphorus and nitrogen pollution in the Delmarva area, the states of Maryland, Delaware and Virginia are in the process of initiating and/or enacting legislation which will regulate poultry waste. The information in Table 1, summarized from the DPI January and February 2000 newsletters, is an update on the information presented at last year's symposium.

MANDATORY USE OF PHYTASE IN MARYLAND

The state of Maryland has passed legislation requiring the addition of 'phytase or other additive' that will reduce the phosphorus content of poultry waste. Simons *et al.* (1990) reported that 60-80% of the total phosphorus present in many grains, oilseed meals and plant products is bound in the form of phytic acid (myoinositol hexaphosphate). Since nonruminants contain relatively little intestinal phytase (Nelson, 1967), the phosphorus content of plant source ingredients is considered to be only 30-40% bioavailable. Due to this poor bioavailability of plant source phosphorus, nutritionists are forced

163

Table 1. Summary of relevant legislation in Maryland, Delaware and Virginia.

	Maryland	Delaware	Virginia
Overall description	Nutrient management legislation	Nutrient management legislation	Poultry waste management program
Regulatory agency	Maryland Department of Agriculture (MDA), Maryland Department of the Environment will have authority in cases of water quality violations.	Delaware Department of Agriculture (DDA) appointed Delaware Nutrient Management Commission	Virginia Department of Environmental Quality (DEQ). The Department of Conservation and Recreation (DCR) sets standards for nutrient management plans and litter storage requirements.
Properties covered	Ag operations with >$2500 annual gross income or livestock operations with >8 animal units. Non-agricultural land of ≥3 acres per parcel or state-owned land if commercial nutrients (i.e. not manure or biosolids) are applied.	Ag operations with >8 animal units or any person who owns, leases or otherwise controls >10 acres of farmland	Ag operations with ≥200 animal units (i.e. 20,000 chickens).
Nutrient plan required ?	Yes	Yes	Yes
Phosphorus plan	• Chemical fertilizers: P-based plan required by 12/31/01 and implemented by 12/31/02. • Manure & Sludge: P-based plan required by 7/1/04 and implemented by 7/1/05.	Application of P to high P soils cannot exceed a 3 year crop removal rate (based on best 4 out of 7 year data).	P application shall not exceed crop removal rate or requirements for plans developed after 10/1/01. Plans must also minimize runoff and leaching.
Nitrogen plan	• Chemical fertilizers: N-based plan required by 12/31/01 and implemented by 12/31/02. • Manure & Sludge: P-based plan required by 12/31/01 and implemented by 12/31/02.	Application of N cannot exceed the crop removal rate (based on best 4 out of 7 year data). Regulation must be adopted by 7/1/00.	N application shall not exceed crop nutrient needs. Plans must also minimize runoff and leaching.
Timetables	See Phosphorus and Nitrogen Plans	The DDA secretary will develop and adopt regulations to implement the law by 7/1/00	DEQ to develop regulations by 10/1/00
Mandatory feed additives	Feeds must include phytase or other additive which will reduce P in manure to the maximum commercially and biologically feasible extent. Must be in place by the end of 2000. May be overridden by MDA.	None required.	None required.
Poultry company requirements	A four-year 'voluntary' program will be followed by the State and poultry companies to facilitate the transportation of poultry manure from high to lower P soils for application. State matching funds will be available for up to $750,000 annually.	Companies must have filed a plan by 7/1/00 in which they will provide technical assistance on poultry waste storage and management, conduct research in P reduction in poultry waste and nutrient reduction strategies to minimize the addition of nutrients to the environment.	Companies must have filed a plan by 1/1/00 in which they will provide technical assistance on poultry waste storage and management, assist in the movement of manure from high to lower P areas, conduct research in P reduction in poultry waste and nutrient reduction strategies in feed formulation.

Table 1 (contd.). Summary of relevant legislation in Maryland, Delaware and Virginia.

	Maryland	Delaware	Virginia
Licensing/ certification	Required for nutrient applicators on agricultural land	All persons who conduct designated activities shall be certified by 1/1/04.	Poultry growers covered by general permit. Violators may be required to obtain individual permit.
State assistance	• Animal Waste Technology Fund created for 3 years at $1 million annually to reduce waste and improve waste management. • Requires the State to provide funding for not less than 110 field personnel in the Soil Conservation Districts. • State cost share for the development of commercially written nutrient management plans will be 50% per acre, not to exceed $4 per acre. • Tax credits available to persons changing from manure to commercial fertilizers. Tax deduction for purchase of manure spreaders. • Funding provided for cover crops on the Eastern Shore. • $800,000 Research funding provided for 3 years. • MDA poultry litter matching service.	• Educational programs will be developed to curtail use of nutrients by individuals not covered by this law. • Consider development of a program to move nutrients from areas of overabundance to deficient areas. • Cost-sharing for practices to help persons covered by this law is contained in other legislation. • The State shall provide free nutrient management planning consultants and provide financial assistance to those using private consultants.	State agencies were required to make recommendations to the Governor by 12/20/99 on ways to improve the economic feasibility of transporting and marketing poultry waste, alternative used of poultry waste and establishment of a matching grant program
State legislative bills under consideration	• HB 20 Maryland Energy Efficient Technology Tax Act • HB 257 Nongerminating Genetically Engineered Seed-Prohibition • HB 292 Land Application of Animal Processing Sludge • HB 293 Agriculture-Interim Protection Act • HB 283 & SB 210 Water Resources Protection Act • HB 327 Department of Agriculture – Nutrient Management • SB 416 University of Maryland – Soil Testing – Fees and Procedures	• HB 434 Nutrient Management Plans • HB 467 Land Use and Prohibition of Incineration Facilities in Certain Areas. • SB 280 Incinerators • SB276 Governor's Budget	• HB 1307 Agricultural Stewardship Act • HJ 92 Study; farmland protection • HB30/SB30 Governor's Budget

to supplement practical feeds with inorganic phosphorus to ensure proper growth and bone development. It has been demonstrated, however, that the phosphorus in this phytate ring can be released through the action of the phytase enzyme. Typically, phytase has been reported to increase phosphorus bioavailability by 25-50% and reduce phosphorus excretion by 15-40% in grain based diets for swine and poultry (Simons *et al.,* 1990; Edwards, 1991; Broz *et al.,* 1994; Kornegay *et al.,* 1996; Mitchell and Edwards, 1996a;b; Qian *et al.,* 1997). Denbow *et al.* (1995) has demonstrated a range of 31 to 58% release of phytate phosphorus when phytase was added to soybean meal/cornstarch-based diet.

Application of phytase to broiler feeds: coefficient of variation

The addition of phytase to pelleted broiler feeds presents a unique challenge because of the nature of the product. Since phytase is an enzyme, it is heat labile and is destroyed during the pelleting process. Pelleting temperatures can easily reach 180°F, which would result in denaturation of the functional proteins in the enzyme. Until the development of a heat stable phytase enzyme, it will be necessary to apply current phytase products post-pelleting. Since addition of fat to pelleted broiler diets also requires post-pellet application, spray technologies have been developed and are in place that may be adapted for use with phytase. Several commercial feed mills on Delmarva have installed spray equipment for the post-pellet application of phytase. There has been concern, however, about the consistency of application of spray liquid application. While the efficacy of phytase has been well established in research trials where incorporation of the enzyme into experimental diets has been carefully ensured, there is little known about the effect of application variations that may exist in commercial mills. A statistical parameter known as the coefficient of variation (CV) is used as an indicator of variability. The CV is determined by taking a series of samples from the same location at predetermined intervals and analyzing them for the substance of interest, in this case phytase. The CV is then calculated by dividing the standard deviation of all the samples taken by the sample mean and multiplying by 100 to express the value as a percentage (Agricultural Experimentation Design and Analysis, 1978). The advantage of using the CV as an indicator of variation is that it allows for the comparison of mixing variability regardless of the units of measure. This will allow for the comparison of mixing accuracy of phytase (or other materials) that have different units of measure (i.e., PTUs can be compared to FTUs). The total variability among samples includes variation due to sampling, analytical assay, laboratory technicians, and the actual application of the enzyme. We are interested in the variation of actual application that would be expressed as a 'corrected CV'. Since this is very difficult to determine, the overall CV is usually reported. Under normal feed mixing of dry ingredients, a CV of 10-15% is usually considered to be in the target range.

Some feed additives, however, such as drugs and vitamins may have CVs in the 20% range. The post-pellet application of phytase may result in even higher CVs due to the nature of the spray application i.e. where a liquid is sprayed on a dry feed traveling past the applicator at a non-uniform rate.

The purpose of this research was to determine the possible effects of a high coefficient of variation in phytase consumption. The parameters of interest were growth rate, feed efficiency, bone ash and bone breaking strength as well as serum calcium and phosphorus levels.

EXPERIMENTAL PROCEDURES

Two hundred and twenty four one-day old commercial male broilers were purchased from a commercial hatchery on Delmarva. Birds were vaccinated *in ovo* for Marek's disease at 18 days of incubation and spray vaccinated for Infectious Bronchitis and Newcastle disease at one day of age. Birds were wing-banded and randomly allotted to pens after removing any obvious culls. Birds were housed in floor pens with wood shaving/sawdust litter. Temperature and ventilation requirements were similar to commercial conditions.

The experiment consisted of four treatments (Table 2) with eight repli-cate pens per treatment and seven male broilers per pen. Treatments were blocked by location in the research facility and treatments were randomly assigned within block. The CV of each treatment was calculated based on daily phytase levels in the feed. The CVs associated with treatments 1-3 was calculated to be 0% while that associated with treatment 4 was 103%.

Table 2. Dietary treatments.

Treatment	Available phosphorus (%)	Enzyme supplement	Coefficient of variation (%)
1.	0.45	None (diet 1)	0
2.	0.25	None (diet 2)	0
3.	0.25+	11,500 PTU Allzyme Phytase daily (diet 3)	0
4.	0.25+	23,000 PTU Allzyme Phytase every other day (diet 4), no phytase on alternate days (diet 2)	103%

Birds were fed their respective diets from 0-20 days of age. On the 21st day the birds on treatment 4 were allowed to remain on their day 20 feed (diet 2). Feed was not removed prior to termination due to blood sampling. At this time all birds were weighed, bled for serum calcium and phosphorus determinations, humanely sacrificed and the right tibias removed and frozen for analysis of bone breaking strength and bone ash content.

The experimental diets were based on corn and soybean meal supplemented with vitamins and minerals (Table 3). Deflourinated phosphate and limestone were added to the diets as sources of available phosphorus (AP) and calcium (Ca). The test diets were formulated to contain 1.0% Ca and 0.45 or 0.25% AP. All diets contained the NRC-recommended crude protein level of 23% and ME level of 3,200 kcal/kg. Treatments consisted of a positive control using the NRC recommended level of 0.45% AP, a negative control (0.25% AP) and the 0.25% AP diet supplemented with the Alltech recommended level of 11,500 PTU Allzyme Phytase fed daily or double the recommended level (23,000 PTU) fed on alternate days. Feed and water were offered *ad libitum*. Data were analyzed using the General Linear Model with treatment and replicate as sources of variation. Duncan's Multiple Range Test was used to separate treatment means where appropriate.

Table 3. Composition of experimental diets (%).

	Diets			
	1	2	3	4
Corn	53.01	53.14	52.87	52.82
Soybean meal	37.60	37.58	37.65	37.65
Corn oil	5.92	5.88	6.02	6.02
Limestone	0.90	1.83	1.83	1.83
CDP	1.70	0.59	0.59	0.59
Salt	0.26	0.38	0.38	0.38
Coccidiostat	0.10	0.10	0.10	0.10
DL-methionine	0.17	0.17	0.17	0.17
Mineral mix	0.075	0.075	0.075	0.075
Vitamin mix	0.25	0.25	0.25	0.25
Allzyme Phytase premix[1]	—	—	0.05	0.10
Calculated analysis				
ME, kcal/kg	3200	3200	3200	3200
Crude protein, %	23.00	23.00	23.00	23.00
Lysine, %	1.32	1.32	1.00	1.00
Sulfur amino acids, %	0.90	0.90	0.90	0.90
Calcium, %	1.00	1.00	1.00	1.00
Available P %	0.45	0.25	0.25+	0.25+
Phytase PTU/kg feed	—	—	11,500	23,000

[1]Allzyme premix contained 23,000 PTU/g

Bone breaking strength was determined using an Instron machine as shown in Figure 1. All right tibias were thawed, flesh removed manually and tibial caps removed. Once the bones reached room temperature they were placed on the rollers of the Instron. A constant pressure was applied and the bone breaking strength was determined to be the pressure required to break the center of the bone.

Figure 1. Inston bone-breaking procedure.

Results

As seen in Table 4 and Figures 2 and 3, reducing the available phosphorus content from 0.45% (diet 1) to 0.25% (diet 2) in the corn/soy diets resulted in significant reductions of 37.5% in weight gain (590 vs. 369 g, respectively) and 11.4% in feed efficiency (0.719 vs. 0.637 gain/feed, respectively) (P<0.001). Average feed consumption was reduced by 28.2% (820 vs. 589 g, respectively, P<0.001) while percent mortality increased from 1.8 to 12.5 (P=0.001). The continuous addition of phytase (diet 3: 11,500 PTU/kg Allzyme Phytase) in the feed resulted in improvements in weight gain (486 g), feed efficiency (0.725) and mortality (0%) when compared to the negative control diet containing 0.25% AP (P<.001). Similar improvements were observed with birds fed double the recommended level of phytase on an every other day basis (483 g, 0.721, 1.8%). While the improvements in performance in birds fed continuous supplemental phytase were not surprising, the almost equal improvements seen in the birds fed a double dose on alternate days was unexpected.

Table 4. Effect of dietary available phosphorus level and Allzyme Phytase on performance of male broilers from 0-21 days of age.

Treatment	Weight gain (g)	Gain/ feed	Feed intake (g)	Mortality (%)
0.45% AP	590[a]	0.719[a]	820[a]	1.8[a]
0.25% AP	369[c]	0.637 [b]	589[c]	12.5[b]
0.25% AP + 11,500 PTU Allzyme daily	486[b]	0.725[a]	671[b]	0.0[a]
0.25% AP + 23,000 PTU Allzyme on alternate days	483[b]	0.721[a]	671[b]	1.8[a]
Probability value	P<.001	P<.001	P<.001	P=.001

[a,b,c]Means within a column with different superscripts differ significantly.

The bone parameters measured (% bone ash and bone breaking strength) showed a similar patter to the growth data (Table 5, Figures 4 and 5). Birds consuming the negative control diet (0.25% AP) had significant (P<0.001) reductions in bone breaking strength and bone ash content of 72.2% (3.20 vs. 11.51 kg) and 32.9% (34.2% vs. 51.0% respectively), when compared

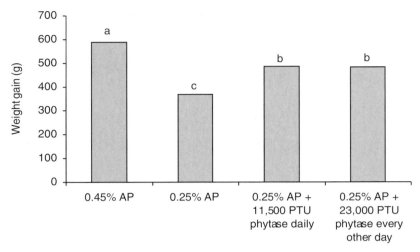

Figure 2. Effect of dietary available phosphorus and phytase supplementation pattern on weight gain.

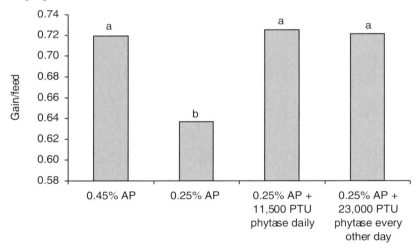

Figure 3. Effect of dietary available phosphorus and phytase supplementation pattern on feed efficiency.

to the positive control diet of 0.45% AP. When 11,500 PTU Allzyme Phytase were added to the feed on a continuous basis, bone breaking strength improved from 3.2 kg to 4.9 kg (53.1%, P<0.001). However, this improvement was still significantly less than the value for birds fed the 0.45% AP diet (11.5 kg). There was no significant difference in bone breaking strength between birds fed 11,500 PTU Allzyme Phytase daily and those fed 23,000 PTU Allzyme Phytase every other day (4.9 kg vs. 4.5 kg, respectively). While this is difficult to explain, it is consistent with work done by BASF with Natuphos® where they reported no differences in performance or bone parameters with CVs up to 69%.

170

Table 5. Effect of dietary available phosphorus level and Allzyme Phytase on bone breaking strength and percent bone ash of male broilers at 21 days of age.

Treatment	Bone breaking strength (kg)	Bone ash (%)
Corn/soy 0.45% AP	11.5[a]	51.0[a]
Corn/soy 0.25% AP	3.2[b]	34.2[c]
Corn/soy 0.25% AP + 11,500 PTU Allzyme daily	4.9[b]	38.5[b]
Corn/soy 0.25% AP + 23,000 PTU Allzyme on alternate days	4.5[b]	37.2[b]
P value	P<.001	P <.001

[a,b,c]Means within a column with different superscripts differ significantly.

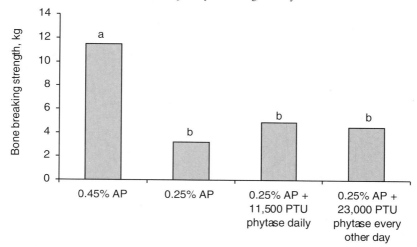

Figure 4. Effect of dietary available phosphorus and phytase supplementation pattern on bone breaking strength.

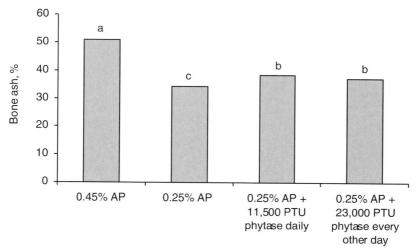

Figure 5. Effect of dietary available phosphorus and phytase supplementation pattern on bone ash content.

A similar pattern was seen with bone ash content in birds fed 23,000 PTU Allzyme Phytase every other day when compared to continuous feeding of 11,500 PTU Allzyme Phytase (38.5 vs. 37.2%). As with bone breaking strength, these values were significantly higher than those of birds fed the 0.25% AP diet (34.2%) but were significantly lower than birds fed the 0.45% AP diet (51.0%).

While growth parameters were dramatically improved by adding phytase to a 0.25% AP diet for young broilers, the modest improvements in bone parameters would suggest that older birds, which have greater skeletal demands to support heavier body weights, would have to be monitored more closely to ensure adequate bone development.

The reduction in dietary available phosphorus from 0.45 to 0.25% had no significant effect on serum calcium (7.26 vs. 7.72 mg/dl), but resulted in a dramatic drop (P<0.001) in serum inorganic phosphorus (5.87 vs. 3.15 mg/dl) (Table 6, Figures 6 and 7). The addition of supplemental phytase, either daily or every other day, to the 0.25% AP diet had no effect on serum calcium (7.84 vs. 7.56 mg/dl) or serum inorganic phosphorus (2.95 vs. 2.93 mg/dl) when compared to the 0.25% AP diet without phytase (7.56 and 3.15 mg/dl, respectively). This would suggest that neither serum calcium nor serum inorganic phosphorus would be a good indicator of phosphorus status in the young broiler.

Table 6. Effect of dietary available phosphorus level and Allzyme Phytase on blood calcium and inorganic phosphorus of male broilers at 21 days of age.

Treatment	Serum calcium (mg/dl)	Serum phosphorus (mg/dl)
Corn/soy 0.45% AP	7.26	5.87[a]
Corn/soy 0.25% AP	7.72	3.15[b]
Corn/soy 0.25% AP + 11,500 PTU Allzyme daily	7.84	2.95[b]
Corn/soy 0.25% AP + 23,000 PTU Allzyme on alternate days	7.56	2.93[b]
P value	NS	P<.001

[a,b]Means with different superscripts differ significantly.

Conclusions

The purpose of this experiment was to determine the effects on performance of a wide coefficient of variation of phytase intake resulting from application via post-pellet spray application systems. The results of this trial suggest that coefficients of variation in feed sampling as high as 103% will not adversely affect the use of Allzyme Phytase when used at recommended levels in a post-pellet spray application system. This level of variation is well within the limits of the commercial post-pellet spray application systems in use today by the commercial broiler industry. It is important that sampling procedures be established which outline when and where samples should be taken from the system (i.e. the same location at regular intervals). It is

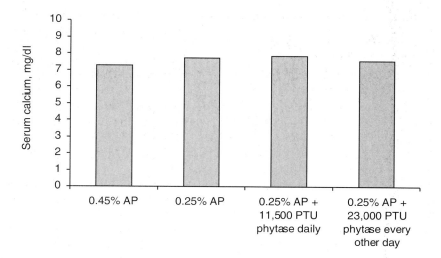

Figure 6. Effect of dietary available phosphorus and phytase supplementation pattern on serum calcium concentration.

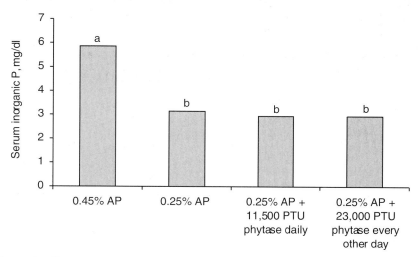

Figure 7. Effect of dietary available phosphorus and phytase supplementation pattern on serum inorganic phosphorus concentration.

also important to realize that while a wide range in CV may be tolerated by the bird, it is critical that the total recommended dose be consumed over a period of time. In this trial, the total dose of phytase consumed over a 48 hr period by birds fed a diet containing double the recommended dose every other day was the same as that consumed by the birds given the recommended dose daily.

References

Agricultural Experimentation Design and Analysis. 1978. John Wiley & Sons, Inc. Publisher. p18.

Broz, J., Oldale, A.H. Perrin-Voltz, G. Tychen, J. Schulze and C. Simones Nines. 1994. Effects of supplemental phytase on performance and phosphorus utilization in broiler chickens fed a low phosphorus diet without addition of inorganic phosphates. Br. Poult. 35:273-280.

Denbow, D.M., V. Ravindran, E.T. Kornegay, Z. Yi and R.M. Hulet. 1995. Improving phosphorus availability in soybean meal for broilers by supplemental phytase. Poultry Sci. 74:1831-1842.

Edwards, H.M. Jr. 1991. Effects of phytase utilization on monogastric animals. Proc. of the Georgia Nutr. Conf. For Feed Manufacturers, Atlanta, pp.1-6.

Kornegay, E.T., Z. Yi, V. Ravindran and D. Denbow. 1996. Improving phytate phosphorus availability in corn and soybean meal for broilers using microbial phytase and calculation of phosphorus equivalency values for phytase. Poultry Sci. 75:240-249.

Mitchell, R.D. and H.M. Edwards, Jr. 1996a. Effects of phytase and 1,25-dihydroxycholecalciferol on phytate utilization and the quantitative requirement for calcium and phosphorus in young broiler chickens. Poultry Sci. 75:95-110.

Mitchell, R.D. and H.M. Edwards, Jr. 1996b. Additive effects of 1,25-dihydroxycholecalciferol and phytase on phytate phosphorus utilization and related parameters in broiler chickens. Poultry Sci. 75:111-119.

Nelson, T.S. 1967. The hydrolysis of phytate phosphorus by poultry: a review. Poultry Sci. 46:862-871.

Qian, H., E.T. Kornegay and D.M. Denbow. 1997. Utilization of phytate phosphorus and calcium as influenced by microbial phytase, cholecalciferol, and the calcium:total phosphorus ratio in broiler diets. Poultry Sci. 76:37-46.

Simons, P.C., H.A.J. Versteegh, A.W Jongbloed, P.A. Kemme, P. Stump, K.D Bos, M.G.E. Wolters, R. F. Beudeker and G.J. Verschoor. 1990. Improvement of phosphorus availability by microbial phytase in broilers and pigs. Br. J. of Nutr. 64:525-540.

Enzyme supplementation of corn/soybean meal diets improves ileal digestibility of nutrients in broiler chicks

H.S. ROSTAGNO, A.A. TEJEDOR, L.F.T. ALBINO and J.H.V. SILVA

Departamento de Zootecnia, Universidade Federal de Viçosa, Viçosa, Minas Gerais, Brazil

Introduction: impact of enzyme supplementation

In Brazil, as in many countries of the world, about 90% of the poultry diets are based on corn and soybean meal. The possibility of using enzyme supplementation to improve nutrient digestibility and utilization of these ingredients is very important for the broiler industry due to feed cost reductions and because of the significant role improved digestibility plays in reducing output of fecal nitrogen and phosphorus (P). Until a few years ago, enzyme supplementation of poultry diets based on corn/soybean meal showed little or no improvement in broiler performance and nutrient digestibility. Recently, Zanella *et al.* (1999) showed clearly that both nutrient digestibility and broiler performance were improved with the use of a mixture of enzymes (amylase, protease and xylanase) in corn/soybean meal diets. Marsmann *et al.* (1997) also found that supplementation of soybean meal with protease and carbohydrase enzymes, individually or in combination, improved crude protein and non-starch polysaccharide digestibility. Allzyme Vegpro, an enzyme complement formulated to better reflect the chemical structure of soybean nutrients, increased the true metabolizable energy (TME) value determined with chicks and the true digestibility of all amino acids except valine in soybean meal (Pugh and Charlton, 1995; Charlton, 1996).

Another important antinutritional factor present in feedstuffs is phytic acid, which binds minerals, proteins, lipids and starch (Cosgrove, 1966; Thompson and Yoon, 1984) reducing the digestibility of these nutrients for poultry (Sebastian *et al.*, 1997). The role of microbial phytase addition in poultry diets in increasing calcium and phosphorus availability has been well established in the scientific literature. Recent studies have also shown a beneficial effect of phytase addition (1200 FTU/kg) to broiler diets on metabolizable energy and total amino acid ileal digestibility (Namkung and Leeson, 1999 and Ravindran *et al.*, 1999).

Objectives: experiments with enzyme combinations

Various methods for the determination of feed ingredient nutrient digestibilities have been tested, but the method based on the analysis of ileal digesta samples (using chromic oxide as a marker) is used with increasing frequency and would appear to be the clear choice for the determination of nutrient ileal digestibility (Zanella *et al.*, 1999).

The possibility exists that the addition of both Vegpro and Allzyme Phytase to chick diets will further enhance nutrient ileal digestibility. Vegpro may release cell-trapped nutrients and facilitate the action of phytase resulting in an added increase in nutrient absorption. Two experiments were run using broiler chicks with the objective of investigating the efficacy of Allzyme Phytase and Vegpro supplementation, separately or in combination, on nutrient ileal apparent digestibility of corn/soybean meal diets containing either normal or low calcium and phosphorus levels.

Materials and methods

A total of 600 day-old male broiler chicks (Avian Farms strain) were purchased from a commercial hatchery and fed a practical broiler starter diet days 1-8. At nine days of age birds were weighed individually and assigned to battery cages (10 birds/pen) with raised wire floors. All birds were exposed to continuous fluorescent light; and feed and water were provided *ad libitum* throughout the 10 day trial. Each of the four treatments in Experiment 1 and six treatments in Experiment 2 was replicated six times.

EXPERIMENT 1. EFFECTS OF ALLZYME PHYTASE IN DIETS
CONTAINING NORMAL OR LOW LEVELS OF CALCIUM AND
AVAILABLE PHOSPHORUS

The completely randomized experimental design utilized a 2 x 2 factorial treatment structure with two Ca/available P (P_{AV}) levels (normal and low) and two levels of Allzyme Phytase addition (0 and 1 kg/T). The normal Ca/ P_{AV} diet contained 1% Ca and 0.45% P_{AV}. The low Ca/P_{AV} diet contained 0.70% Ca and 0.32% P_{AV}. The composition of the basal diet used in the experiment is shown in Table 1.

EXPERIMENT 2. EFFECTS OF VEGPRO AND ALLZYME PHYTASE IN
DIETS CONTAINING NORMAL OR LOW LEVELS OF CALCIUM AND
AVAILABLE PHOSPHORUS

The completely randomized experimental design contained a 3 x 2 factorial arrangement of treatments. There were three experimental diets containing either no enzyme (Control), Vegpro (2 kg/T of soybean meal) or

Vegpro plus Allzyme Phytase (1 kg/T). Each diet was formulated with either normal Ca/P$_{AV}$ levels (1.0% Ca and 0.45% P$_{AV}$) or low Ca/ P$_{AV}$ levels (0.70% Ca and 0.32% P$_{AV}$). In this experiment the metabolizable energy and amino acid values for soybean were increased by 7% (Table 1).

Table 1. Composition of experimental diets (%).

	Experiment 1		Experiment 2	
		Ca/P$_{AV}$ level		
	Normal	Low	Normal	Low
Corn	57.839	60.069	62.522	64.698
Soybean meal, 45% CP	35.398	34.985	...	...
Soybean meal + 7%*	...	...	32.274	31.898
Limestone	1.132	0.781	1.155	0.803
Dicalcium phosphate	1.807	1.097	1.814	1.105
Soybean oil	2.680	1.916	1.077	0.332
Salt	0.400	0.400	0.400	0.400
DL-Methionine	0.196	0.194	0.192	0.190
L-Lysine-HCl	0.023	0.032	0.041	0.049
Premix[1]	0.325	0.325	0.325	0.325
Inert filler/enzymes[2]	0.200	0.200	0.200	0.200
Total	100.000	100.000	100.000	100.000
Calculated composition				
Crude protein	21.20	21.20	21.20	21.20
ME, kcal/kg	3,040	3,040	3,040	3,040
Calcium	1.00	0.70	1.00	0.70
Phosphorus	0.68	0.56	0.68	0.56
Available phosphorus	0.45	0.32	0.45	0.32
Met+Cys	0.88	0.88	0.88	0.88
Lysine (total)	1.18	1.18	1.18	1.18

* For Experiment 2, ME and amino acid values for soybean meal were increased by 7%.

[1] Supplied per kg of diet: vitamin A, 10,000 IU; vitamin E, 30 IU; menadione, 3 mg; vitamin B$_1$, 2 mg; vitamin B$_2$, 6 mg; vitamin B$_6$, 4 mg; Ca pantothenate, 12 mg; niacin, 50 mg; vitamin B$_{12}$, 0.015 mg; biotin, 0.07 mg; folic acid, 1 mg; choline chloride, 360 mg; selenium, 0.25 mg; iron, 50 mg; manganese, 80 mg; copper, 10 mg; cobalt, 2 mg; iodine, 1 mg; BHT, 100 mg; salinomycyn, 60 mg and virginiamycin, 10 mg.

[2] Enzyme products: Allzyme Phytase, 1 kg/ton of diet and Allzyme Vegpro, 2 kg/ton of soybean meal.

In both experiments, the apparent ileal digestibilities of dry matter, protein, energy, Ca and P were measured at 19 days of age. All chicks of each replicate were killed by cervical dislocation at the end of the experiment. A portion of the terminal ileum from 20 cm to a point 5 cm anterior to the ileocecal junction, was obtained. The ileal segment, of approximately 15 cm, was bisected transversely and its contents gently expressed. Ileal samples were pooled for the ten birds in a pen. The samples were freeze-dried, ground through a 1 mm mesh screen and immediately prepared for laboratory analysis. Diets and ileal contents were analyzed using the procedures described by Silva (1990). Nitrogen was determined by the Kjeldahl method and gross energy was measured using an adiabatic bomb calorimeter. Phosphorus was determined by colorimetry and calcium and chromium by atomic absorption spectrophotometry. All samples were assayed in duplicate.

Apparent ileal digestibility coefficients of dry matter, crude protein, energy, calcium and phosphorus were estimated by adding 0.5% chromic oxide (Cr_2O_3) as an indigestible marker to the experimental diets.

The data were analyzed using the SAEG (Universidade Federal de Viçosa, 1983) procedure for statistical analysis. Significant differences among main effects means were obtained by F test (Experiment 1) and Newman Keul's multiple range test (Experiment 2) with significance indicated at the 5% level of probability.

Results and discussion

EXPERIMENT 1. EFFECTS OF ALLZYME PHYTASE IN DIETS CONTAINING NORMAL OR LOW LEVELS OF CALCIUM AND AVAILABLE PHOSPHORUS

Allzyme Phytase improved ileal dry matter, crude protein and energy digestibilities (P<0.05) by 5.2, 2.4 and 3.9%, respectively (Table 2). It is known that phytic acid forms phytate-protein complexes and that it also inhibits a number of digestive enzymes (Sebastian *et al.*, 1998). Since phytase increases hydrolysis of phytic acid, it is reasonable to expect improved nutrient digestibility. Recently published studies also demonstrated a positive effect of supplemental phytase (1200 FTU/ kg) of about 2% on protein or total amino acid digestibility in broiler chicks (Namkung and Leeson, 1999), in broilers (Ravindran *et al.*, 1999) and in cecaectomized roosters (Biehl and Baker, 1997). Namkung and Leeson (1999) also reported a 2.3% increase in nitrogen-corrected apparent metabolizable energy value (AMEn) of a corn/soybean meal diet due to phytase addition. On the other hand, Biehl and Baker (1997) found no phytase effect on nitrogen-corrected true metabolizable energy (TMEn) with cecaectomized roosters using a semipurified diet containing 21% dehulled soybean meal.

Table 2. Effect of calcium/available phosphorus levels and Allzyme Phytase on ileal digestibilities of dry matter, crude protein and energy (Experiment 1).

	Dry matter			Crude protein			Energy		
	Ca/P_{AV} *level*			Ca/P_{AV} *level*			Ca/P_{AV} *level*		
	Normal	Low	Mean	Normal	Low	Means	Normal	Low	Means
Control	64.98	66.88	65.93[B]	77.82	76.64	77.23[B]	69.75	70.14	69.95[B]
AZ Phytase	68.74	70.02	69.38[A]	79.47	78.62	79.05[A]	72.22	73.07	72.65[A]
Mean	66.86[b]	68.45[a]		78.64[a]	77.63[b]		70.99[b]	71.61[a]	

[ab]Means in a row with different letters differ (P<0.05).
[AB]Means in a column with different letters differ (P<0.05).

A significant interaction between Allzyme Phytase and Ca/P_{AV} level was observed for calcium and phosphorus digestibilities (Figure 1). In the present experiment, phytase supplementation of the low Ca/P_{AV} diet improved calcium digestibility by 4.9% and available phosphorus digestibility by 10.6 %, respectively (P<0.05).

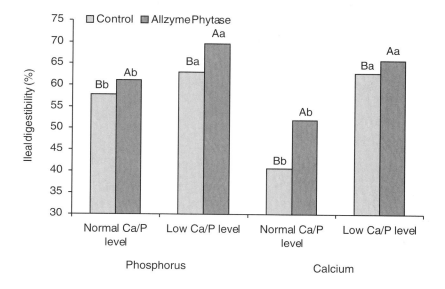

Figure 1. Effects of Allzyme Phytase and calcium/available phosphorus levels on ileal digestibilities of phosphorus and calcium in chicks ([ab]Ca/P levels effect, P<0.05), [AB]Allzyme Phytase effect, P<0.05).

EXPERIMENT 2. EFFECTS OF VEGPRO AND ALLZYME PHYTASE IN DIETS CONTAINING NORMAL OR LOW LEVELS OF CALCIUM AND AVAILABLE PHOSPHORUS

As expected, Vegpro addition to the corn/soybean meal diet improved crude protein digestibility in chicks by 3% (P<0.05) (Table 3). Interestingly, the enzyme complement also improved phosphorus (+4.7 %) and calcium (+7.9 %) ileal digestibilities (P<0.05) (Table 4). The combination of Vegpro and Allzyme Phytase resulted in a further increase in calcium and phosphorus digestibilities (P>0.05).

There was a significant interaction between Vegpro and Ca/P_{AV} level in dry matter and energy digestibility. In the normal Ca/P_{AV} level diet, both Vegpro and Vegpro plus Allzyme Phytase improved dry matter and energy digestibility when compared with the control (P<0.05). In the low Ca/P_{AV} level diets, Vegpro plus Allzyme Phytase also improved dry matter and energy digestibilities relative to the control diet and the diet containing Vegpro alone (P<0.05). These results suggest that it may be advantageous to add a combination of Vegpro and Allzyme Phytase to low Ca/P_{AV} corn/soybean diets.

Table 3. Effects of calcium/available phosphorus level and enzyme supplementation on apparent ileal digestibility coefficients (%) for dry matter, crude protein and energy (Experiment 2).

	Dry matter			Crude protein			Energy		
	Ca/P_{AV} level			Ca/P_{AV} level			Ca/P_{AV} level		
	Normal	Low	Mean	Normal	Low	Means	Normal	Low	Means
Control	69.78[Ba]	69.98[Ba]	69.88	76.90	78.20	77.55 [B]	72.82[Ba]	71.57[Cb]	72.20
Vegpro	72.70[Aa]	70.48[Bb]	71.59	79.43	80.30	79.86 [A]	73.84[Aa]	72.48[Bb]	73.16
Vegpro + Phytase	73.40[Aa]	72.05[Ab]	72.73	79.27	81.45	80.36 [A]	73.46[ABa]	73.85[Aa]	73.66
Mean	71.96	70.84		78.53 [b]	79.98 [a]		73.38	72.64	

[ab]Means in a row with different letters differ (P<0.05).
[AB]Means in a column with different letters differ (P<0.05).

Table 4. Effects of calcium/available phosphorus level and enzyme supplementation on apparent ileal digestibility coefficients (%) for phosphorus and calcium (Experiment 2).

	Phosphorus			Calcium		
	Ca/P_{AV} level			Ca/P_{AV} level		
Enzyme[2]	Normal	Low	Mean	Normal	Low	Mean
Control	58.60	62.36	60.48[C]	47.11	59.38	53.24[C]
Vegpro	63.06	63.56	63.31[B]	51.68	63.15	57.42[B]
Vegpro + Phytase	65.17	66.69	65.93[A]	54.12	66.10	60.11[A]
Mean	62.28[b]	64.20[a]		50.97[b]	62.88[a]	

[ab]Means in a row with different letters differ (P<0.05).
[AB]Means in a column with different letters differ (P<0.05).

Previously published studies also show the beneficial effect of a multi-enzyme cocktail on dietary energy and protein digestibility in chickens (Charlton, 1996; Marsmann *et al.*, 1997; Pugh and Charlton, 1995 and Zanella *et al.*, 1999). No research, however, has reported effects of the multienzyme on dietary P and Ca ileal digestibilities.

Conclusions

Results of these two ileal digestibility experiments with broiler chicks fed corn/soybean meal diets demonstrated that Allzyme Phytase improves not only ileal digestibilities of calcium and phosphorus, but also increases protein and energy digestibility. Vegpro improved protein, energy, calcium and phosphorus ileal digestibilities. The combination of Vegpro and Allzyme Phytase improved ileal protein digestibility by 3%, and also increased ileal digestibilities of phosphorus and calcium. This information can be used by the nutritionist in either of two ways. Decreasing the broiler requirement of protein, energy, P and Ca or by attributing a nutritional value in the nutrient matrix to Allzyme Phytase and Vegpro.

References

Biehl, R.R. and D.H. Baker. 1997. Microbial phytase improves amino acid utilization in young chicks fed diets based on soybean meal, but not in diets based on peanut meal. Poult. Sci. 76:355-360.

Charlton, P. 1996. Expanding enzyme applications: Higher amino acid and energy values for vegetable proteins. In: Biotechnology in the Feed Industry, Proceedings of the 12th Annual Symposium (T.P. Lyons and K.A. Jacques, eds.). Nottingham University Press, Nottingham, UK. pp. 317-326.

Cosgrove, D.J. 1966. The chemistry and biochemistry of inositol polyphosphates. Ver. Pure Appl. Cem. 16:209-224.

Marsmann, G.J., H. van der Poel, A.F. Gruppen, R.P. Kwankkel, M.W. Verstegen and A.G. Voragen. 1997. The effect of thermal processing and enzyme treatments of soybean meal on growth performance, ileal nutrient digestibilities, and chyme characteristics in broiler chicks. Poult. Sci. 76:864-872.

Namkung, H. and S. Leeson. 1999. Effect of phytase enzyme on dietary nitrogen-corrected apparent metabolizable energy and the ileal digestibility of nitrogen and amino acids in broiler chicks. Poult. Sci. 78:1317-1319.

Pugh, R. and P. Charlton. 1995. Enzyme applications for plant proteins: Time to look beyond cereals. In: Biotechnology in the Feed Industry, Proceedings of the 11th Annual Symposium (T.P. Lyons and K.A. Jacques, eds.). Nottingham University Press, Nottingham, UK. pp. 393-396.

Ravindran, V., S. Cabahug, G. Ravindran and W.L. Bryden. 1999. Influence of microbial phytase on apparent ileal amino acid digestibility of feedstuffs for broilers. Poult. Sci. 78:699-706.

Sebastian, S., S.P. Touchburn, E.R. Chavez and P.C. Lague. 1997. Apparent digestibility of protein and amino acids in broiler chickens fed a corn-soybean diet supplemented with microbial phytase. Poult. Sci. 76:1760-1769.

Sebastian, S., S.P. Touchburn and E.R. Chavez. 1998. Implications of phytic acid and supplemental microbial phytase in poultry nutrition: a review. Worlds Poult. Sci. J. 54:27-47.

Silva, D.J. 1990. Análises de alimentos: Métodos químicos e biológicos. Viçosa, MG, UFV, Brazil. p. 166.

Thompson, L.U. and J.H. Yoon. 1984. Starch digestibility as affected by polyphenol and phytic acid. J. Food Sci. 49:1228-1229.

Universidade Federal de Viçosa. 1983. SAEG - Sistema para análise estatística e genética - UFV - CPD.. Viçosa, MG Brazil. p. 59.

Zanella, I., N.K. Sakomura, F.G. Silversides, A. Fiquerdo and M. Pack. 1999. Effect of enzyme supplementation of broiler diets based on corn and soybeans. Poult. Sci. 78:561-568.

Perspectives on selenium nutrition in horses

LAURIE LAWRENCE

University of Kentucky, Lexington, Kentucky, USA

Introduction

Knowledge regarding selenium nutrition in horses lags far behind other livestock species and humans, especially in regard to health and optimal immune function. In dairy cattle, there is a well-accepted relationship between selenium status and udder health. In humans, there are active research efforts relating selenium to decreased cancer risk and enhanced immune function. In the horse, there are relatively clear data linking selenium deficiency to nutritional muscular dystrophy in foals, but information regarding optimal levels of selenium intake for optimal health status in all classes of horses is lacking. Many of the beneficial responses to selenium supplementation in humans and other animals may have application to horses. In particular, the relationship of selenium intake to health and production responses in horses should be considered in view of the expanded understanding of the biological functions of selenium. It is of note that most of the research on selenium in horses was performed prior to 1990, when only the function of glutathione peroxidase was known. Currently, there are several selenoproteins of known function in mammals, and it has been suggested that dozens of others exist. To date, the effect of selenium nutrition on these selenoproteins and their biological role in horses has not been investigated.

Biological function of selenium

Selenium is both a toxic element and a required nutrient. In horses, the best recognized deficiency sign is muscular dystrophy, or white muscle disease, in foals. Additional deficiency signs have been identified in other species including a cardiomyopathy in humans, liver necrosis in pigs and exudative diathesis in chicks. Until the early 1970s when glutathione peroxidase (GSH-Px) was identified as a selenium containing enzyme, the biological function of selenium was unknown. GSH-Px functions in the reduction of hydroperoxides, and thus is an important component of cellular antioxidant mechanisms. GSH-Px activity is observed to be low in selenium deficiency, and many of the manifestations of selenium deficiencies are related to increased oxidative damage.

After the initial research identified GSH-Px as a selenoprotein, four specific enzymes were categorized. These include GSH-Px 1 (the initial cytosolic GSH-Px); GSH-Px 2, which is present in plasma; GSH-Px 3, which is associated with the gastrointestinal tract and GSH-Px 4, which is characterized as a phospholipid-hydroperoxide glutathione peroxidase (Allan *et al.*, 1999). GSH-Px 4 is associated with membrane-bound lipids and thus may be the mechanism through which selenium and vitamin E function synergistically. In addition, it has been suggested that this is the means through which selenium affects leukotriene synthesis (Wolfram, 1999).

Selenium has now been associated with selenoproteins that have other essential functions. Type 1 iodothyronine deiodinase (5' DI), which is responsible for the conversion of thyroxin to tri-iodothyronine is also a selenium containing enzyme. Two other deiodinases important in thyroid hormone metabolism also contain selenium. In addition, two thioredoxin reductases are now known to be selenoproteins. Other selenoproteins that are recognized, but do not have well accepted biochemical roles are selenoprotein P and selenoprotein W. Selenoprotein P is found in relatively high concentrations in plasma, and selenoprotein W is found in muscle.

EFFECT OF SELENIUM INTAKE ON SELENOPROTEINS

The effect of dietary selenium status varies with the individual selenoprotein, the specie of animal and the tissue being evaluated. It has been proposed that there is a hierarchy for selenium supply within the body and/or for different selenoproteins. When rats were fed a selenium deficient diet, selenium content was reduced by 50% in muscle and 91% in liver, compared to control animals. By comparison, the selenium content of the testes was not affected by the selenium deficiency (Behne *et al.*, 1982). When selenium retention by deficient rats was measured, the rate of retention by the testes was much higher than in liver. Although Yeh *et al.* (1997b) reported a decrease in testes selenium concentration in rats fed a deficient diet, the extent of the decrease was much less than in muscle or spleen. These authors also reported that GSH-Px activity was decreased to a much greater extent by selenium deficiency in muscle and plasma than in testes. Marin-Guzman *et al.* (1997) reported that selenium deficiency decreased GSH-Px activity in the testes of growing boars, but the extent of the decrease was less than in the liver or serum. Selenium deficiency did not affect testicular weight or semen quality (volume, sperm number, etc), but fertilization rate was decreased. Decreased fertility of sperm from the deficient boars may have been related to decreased GSH-Px activity in sperm and seminal plasma.

The thyroid is another tissue with a high selenium content and may be superior at retaining selenium in the face of a deficiency (Kohrle, 1999).

Brain tissue also appears to be resistant to effects of selenium deficiency (Yeh *et al.*, 1997a; Yeh *et al.*, 1997b). Consequently, it appears that a preferential conservation of selenium in reproductive organs and brain tissue may occur in selenium deficiency. Conversely, liver and muscle tissue are susceptible to depletion in periods of inadequate selenium supply.

Within a tissue, certain selenoproteins appear to be affected by selenium status more than others. In rats, Arthur and coworkers (1997) reported liver 5' DI activity and GSH-Px 1 activity were reduced more than 90% by selenium deficiency but GSH-Px 4 activity was only reduced 47%. In the thyroid, there was a 25% decrease in 5' DI activity in response to selenium deficiency compared to a 45% reduction in GSH-Px 1 activity and a 75% reduction in GSH-Px 4. Vadhanavikit and Ganther (1993) reported that liver 5' DI activity in rats reached a plateau when the diet contained 0.05 ppm Se, whereas GSH-Px activity continued to increase with additional selenium supplementation. These researchers also reported that 5' DI activity in the thyroid was not affected by selenium intake, even though an effect on GSH-Px activity occurred. Because 5' DI is involved in the conversion of thyroxin (T4) to tri-iodothyronine (T3), an expected effect of selenium deficiency might be an increased level of T4 and a decreased level of T3. Selenium deficiency appears to result in an increase in circulating T4 concentrations (Hotz *et al.*, 1997; Ortman *et al.*, 1999). However, a decrease in circulating T3 concentrations is not typically reported (Hotz *et al.*, 1997; Ortman *et al.*, 1999; Vadhanavikit and Ganther, 1993; Wu *et al.*, 1997), although Wu *et al.* (1997) did find decreased myocardial T3 in deficiency.

Yeh and coworkers (1997a; 1997b) studied the effects of selenium intake on selenoprotein W concentration and GSH-Px activity of several tissues in rats. In muscle, both variables were affected by dietary selenium. However, the relative effect of selenium concentration on GSH-Px activity was less than the effect on selenoprotein W. These researchers also found that selenoprotein W was very responsive to supplemental selenium in both sheep and rats and suggested that selenoprotein W may play a role in defending against white muscle disease.

Selenoprotein P exists in plasma and is associated with other tissues as well (Hill *et al.*, 1996a; Hill *et al.*, 1996b; Mork *et al.*, 1998). There is no clear consensus regarding the biological function of selenoprotein P, but it may have transport or storage functions (Motsenbocker and Tappel, 1984) and a role in antioxidant cell defense (Mork *et al.*, 1998). Typically, more selenium is found in selenoprotein P in plasma than in GSH-Px (Gu *et al.*, 1998; Hill *et al.*, 1996; Motsenbocker and Tappel, 1984). Species differences exist in the levels of selenoprotein P found in plasma, and levels appear to be responsive to dietary selenium intake. Selenoprotein P concentrations were about 10-fold higher in rats receiving 0.1 ppm Se compared to rats receiving 0.01 ppm Se (Motsenbocker and Tappel , 1984). These authors observed a similar increase in plasma GSH-Px acitivity. Hill and coworkers (1996b) found that selenoprotein P concentrations increased in humans with increasing selenium intake within one week of initiating supplementation. It was suggested that selenoprotein P and GSH-Px were similarly predictive of dietary selenium status. Supplementation at 1 ppm did not increase selenoprotein P or GSH-Px activity in plasma beyond the levels observed at 0.1 ppm (Motsenbocker and Tappel, 1984). Yang and coworkers (1989) reported that plasma GSH-Px activity and plasma selenoprotein P concentrations decreased at similar rates when rats were given selenium deficient diets. However, when rats were repleted using various levels of selenium, selenoprotein P concentrations responded to lower intakes than either plasma GSH-Px or liver GSH-Px activity. Persson-Moschos *et al.* (1998) reported on increases in selenoprotein P levels in Finnish men supplemented with 0.2 mg Se per day. Basal selenium intake was approximately 0.04 mg per day. Supplementation resulted in about a 30% increase in selenoprotein P concentrations. From previously reported data on the same subjects, the increase in plasma GSH-Px activity was 10 to 16%, depending upon the form of selenium used. However, the increase in platelet GSH-Px was between 60 and 106%, and plasma selenium increased 66 to 144% (Levander *et al.*, 1983).

Not all selenium in plasma is present in GSH-Px or selenoprotein P. Some selenium can be incorporated in albumin and other plasma proteins as selenomethionine or selenocysteine. These selenoamino acids can also be incorporated into tissue and milk proteins. Consequently, when high levels of selenium are fed, it is possible for the activities of GSH-Px, 5' DI, etc. to plateau while levels of selenium in the tissues continue to increase. The advantage to increasing stores of selenomethionine or selenocysteine in animals has not been clearly defined.

SELENIUM IN HEALTH AND DISEASE

Many years of effort have focused on the relationship between selenium intake and cancer in human and animal models. Selenium is considered to have chemopreventive effects, although all of the mechanisms for this function are not understood (Ganther, 1999). In human medicine, selenium is also being studied for its beneficial effects during certain types of diseases. Selenium concentrations and plasma GSH-Px activities have been reported to be reduced in certain infectious and non-infectious diseases. In addition, many disease processes involve increased production of reactive oxygen species, which could increase the need for antioxidant protection. Angstwurm and coworkers (1999) recently reported that selenium supplementation of critically ill patients improved the clinical outcome in severe systemic inflammatory response syndrome. Plasma selenium concentrations and GSH-Px activity of the patients were below normal at the time of admission but increased with selenium supplementation. Selenium status is also of great interest in regard to human immunodeficiency virus (HIV) where cellular antioxidant defenses may be compromised. Among HIV-positive children, low plasma selenium concentrations were associated with faster disease progression and increased mortality risk (Campa *et al.*, 1999). Similarly, Look and coworkers (1997) reported that low selenium concentrations were related to increased indicators of disease and inflammatory responses in HIV-positive patients. *In vitro,* selenium has been shown to decrease replication of the virus in T lymphocytes (Hori *et al.*, 1997). *In vivo,* selenium supplementation can increase GSH-Px activity in HIV infected patients (Delmas-Beauvieux *et al.*, 1996) and has been promoted as a supportive therapy (Hori *et al.*, 1997; Schrauzer and Sacher, 1994).

Selenium status has been shown to affect disease resistance in several animal species (Bowers, 1997). In dairy cows, research has focused on the relationship between selenium intake and mammary health. Increased incidence of mastitis is correlated with low selenium status (Weiss *et al.*, 1990) and under conditions of low selenium intake, somatic cell counts and resistance to mastitis may be improved with selenium supplementation (Erskine *et al.*, 1989; Malbe *et al.*, 1995; Morgante *et al.*, 1999). One of the mechanisms for increased susceptibility to infection in selenium deficient animals may be impaired leukocyte function. In swine, increasing dietary selenium concentration from less than 0.1 ppm to Se 0.3 ppm Se improved microbicidal activities of blood polymorphonuclear cells (PMN) of gestating sows and also increased the microbicidal activity of PMN in colostrum. The impaired ability of PMN to kill bacteria in selenium depleted animals (Grasso *et al.*, 1990; Wuryastuti *et al.*, 1993), may occur because of alterations in ability to neutralize reactive oxygen species (Smith *et al.*, 1997) or because of altered arachadonic acid metabolism (Eskew *et al.*, 1993). In addition to affecting the microbiocidal activity of PMN, selenium status may also affect the ability of PMN to migrate to infected mammary tissue (Maddox *et al.*, 1999).

Selenium status has also been shown to affect lymphocyte function. Selenium may influence the ratio or number of various subclasses of T lymphocytes in human patients with HIV. Selenium has been reported to influence B cell function *in vitro* (Stabel *et al.*, 1991). Peplowski *et al.* (1980) reported a response to selenium in weanling swine when hemagglutination titers to sheep red blood cells were measured. Increased antibody responses with selenium supplementation have also been reported in weaned beef calves (Swecker *et al.*, 1989), horses (Knight and Tyznik, 1990) and chickens (Larsen *et al.*, 1997). In some studies, selenium supplementation has not produced consistent results. In rats fed deficient or adequate diets, IgG production was not markedly affected, but IgM concentrations were reduced in deficiency (Bauersachs *et al.*, 1993). Sheep vaccinated against *Chlamydia psittaci* had an enhanced antibody response when they received injectable sodium selenite, but not when the selenium was administered with vitamin E (Giandinis *et al.*, 2000). Conversely, Baalsrud and Overnes (1986) reported enhanced antibody response in hyperimmune horses to selenium and vitamin E together, but not selenium alone.

In the last several years, a number of research studies have focused on the effect of selenium nutrition on gestating females and their progeny. Passive transfer of antibodies through the colostrum is an important factor influencing neonatal disease resistance. Selenium supplementation of cows grazing selenium deficient pastures increased IgG concentrations in the colostrum and in calves (Swecker *et al.*, 1995). Awadeh *et al* (1998) reported a similar response in beef cows and their calves. Although antibody levels in the colostrum were not reported, selenium supplementation increased the microbicidal activity of PMN in colostrum of sows (Wuryastuti *et al.*, 1993), which might also be important to neonates. As the immunity conveyed by passive transfer wanes, young animals must mount their own immune response. Lacetara *et al.* (1999) recently reported that lymphocytes from lambs born to ewes supplemented with selenium had greater responsiveness to mitogenic stimulation than lymphocytes from lambs born to unsupplemented ewes. An enhancement of immune function in neonatal animals might be gained by enhancing selenium transfer from the dam. Selenium can be transferred from the dam to progeny through the placenta or milk. Blood selenium levels in most livestock species appear to relatively low at birth (Stowe and Herdt, 1992) and may be below the level believed to provide optimal immune function (Pehrson *et al.*, 1999). Selenium intake has been reported to influence milk selenium concentration in gilts (Mahan and Kim, 1996), sows (Mahan *et al.*, 1975; Mahan, 2000) and dairy cows (Ortman and Pehrson, 1999). Selenium intake of gilts and sows can influence serum selenium concentrations of their progeny, but may not affect serum GSH-Px activity (Mahan *et al.*, 1975; Mahan and Kim, 1996; Mahan, 2000). An important factor affecting the response of dams and their progeny to supplemental selenium appears to be the dietary form of the selenium. Currently, organic selenium appears to be more effective in raising milk selenium concentrations than inorganic selenium (Pehrson *et al.*, 1999; Mahan, 2000).

Most studies evaluating PMN or antibody responses have compared deficient diets (usually less than 0.09 ppm selenium) with one or two levels of supplementation. Diets that have enhanced PMN responses have contained from 0.14 ppm selenium (Erskine *et al.*, 1989) to 0.35 ppm selenium (Wuryastuti *et al.*, 1993). Diets that have enhanced antibody responses have contained from 0.2 ppm (Bauersachs *et al.*, 1993) to 0.45 ppm (Larsen *et al.*, 1997). The current NRC (1998) recommendation for gestating swine is 0.15 ppm diet dry matter. The recommendation for lactating dairy cows is 0.3 ppm of diet dry matter. By comparison, the recommended level of dietary selenium for horses is 0.1 ppm (NRC, 1989). It is unknown whether this level of dietary selenium is adequate for optimal immune response in horses.

Dietary selenium supplementation of broodmares

The relationship between selenium status and immunity is of interest in management of the broodmare and neonatal foal. Risk of septicemia, a

188

leading cause of death in foals, is reduced by ensuring adequate passive transfer of antibodies. The primary source of antibodies for neonatal foals is colostrum. Any management strategy that enhances colostral antibody transfer has potential to improve foal health. Appropriate rates of selenium supplementation of mares in late gestation may be one such strategy. In addition, increasing milk selenium concentration, and thus selenium consumption by foals, may enhance the selenium status of the foal. The current NRC (1989) recommendation for selenium intake is 0.1 ppm in diet dry matter for horses of all physiological classes. For a 600 kg mare consuming 12 kg of dry matter per day this concentration of selenium would result in a daily intake of 1.2 mg. Although this level of dietary selenium appears adequate to prevent classical signs of selenium deficiency, it is not known whether it is adequate for optimal immune function. Lewis (1995) suggests a selenium concentration of 0.2 ppm in the total diet for pregnant and lactating mares (at least 2.4 mg/day). Based on the information in other species, it seems likely that the broodmare requires more than the 1.2 mg selenium recommended by the current NRC (1989).

In 1999, a study was initiated at the University of Kentucky to evaluate the effect of dietary selenium intake on broodmares and their foals (Janicki *et al*, 2000). Fifteen pregnant mares were blocked by expected foaling date and then randomly assigned to one of three treatment programs. The three treatment programs were: 1 mg selenium as sodium selenite; 3 mg selenium as sodium selenite and 3 mg selenium as selenium yeast (Sel-Plex, Alltech, Inc., Nicholasville KY). Treatments were initiated approximately 55 days prior to foaling and all mares were fed a diet consisting of hay, pasture and a mixed grain concentrate without supplemental selenium. Treatments were individually topdressed on the concentrate feed of each mare once a day. Treatments were continued for 8 weeks post foaling. As has been reported in other studies, selenium intake did not influence birth weight of foals or average daily gain. Placental weight and time for placental expulsion were not affected by treatment. Serum IgG concentrations were measured in mares and foals, with foal IgG concentrations responding to treatment. Thus far, the data from this study are consistent with those from Knight and Tyznik (1990) that demonstrated an effect of dietary selenium intake on antibody responses in horses. With supporting data on levels of selenium and GSH-Px in the mares and foals, these results may support a suggestion that optimal dietary selenium concentrations for broodmares may be greater than 0.1 ppm of diet dry matter.

Other roles for selenium in equine nutrition

Based on information in other species, it appears that muscle tissue has a relatively low priority for selenium in times of marginal or deficient intakes. This may have particular importance in the management of performance horses. During exercise, the opportunity for oxidative stress is increased and thus the selenium requirement for optimal GSH-Px activity could be elevated. Furthermore, increased urinary excretion of selenium may occur in exercising horses (Pagan *et al.*, 1999). Changes in concentrations of blood and plasma selenium are known to occur in exercising horses, but effects of exercise on specific selenoproteins have not been described. Training may increase GSH-Px activity in plasma and erythrocytes in humans (Tessier *et al.*, 1995), and presumably could have the same effect in horses. Avellini *et al.* (1999) have recently suggested a beneficial effect of vitamin E and selenium supplementation in exercising horses. Yeh and coworkers (1997a) have suggested that selenoprotein W could be an important determinant in susceptibility of muscle to nutritional muscular dystrophy. This selenoprotein appears to be more sensitive to changes in dietary selenium than GSH-Px, and thus could be of interest to study in exercising horses.

In addition to potential effects on muscle, selenium status may have implications for horses with lung related problems. Exercise has been noted to increase free radical generation in lung tissue in vitamin E and selenium deficient rats (Reddy *et al.*, 1998). It is possible to speculate that selenium status could be of importance in the incidence or severity of exercise induced pulmonary hemorrhage. Selenium has been linked to bone and cartilage development and may be of interest in the prevention or treatment of osteoarthritis and osteochondrosis in horses (Jeffcott, 2000). Perhaps the most interesting potential for selenium in equine management relates to the relationship between selenium status and disease. Low selenium concentrations have been reported in severely ill human patients, and may increase the rate of progress of certain diseases. The effect of disease on serum selenium concentrations does not appear to have been evaluated in horses. However, a number of disease conditions exist where horses may be critically ill for an extended period. Some of these diseases, such as laminitis, involve significant inflammatory responses, where a beneficial role for selenium could be envisioned. Future research should examine the potential role of selenium as a preventive or supportive therapy in critically ill horses.

References

Allan, C. B., G. M. Lacourciere and T. Stadtman. 1999. Responsiveness of selenoproteins to dietary selenium. Annu. Rev. Nutr. 19:1.

Angstwurm, M., J. Schottdorf, J. Schopohl and R. Gaertner. 1999. Selenium replacement in patients with severe systemic inflammatory response syndrome improves clinical outcome. Crit. Care Med. 27:1807.

Arthur, J., F. Nicol, J. Mitchell and G. Beckett. 1997. Selenium and iodine deficiencies and the control of selenoprotein expression. In: Trace Elements in Man and Animals-9: Proceedings of the Ninth International Symposium on Trace Elements in Man and Animals. (P. Fischer *et al.*, eds). NRC Research Press, Ottawa Canada, p 574.

Avellini, L., E. Chiaradia and A. Gaiti. 1999. Effect of exercise training, selenium and vitamin E on some free radical scavengers in horses. Comp. Biochem Physiol B. 123:147.

Awadeh, F. T., R.L. Kincaid and K.A. Johnson. 1998. Effect of level and source of dietary selenium on concentrations of thyroid hormones and immunoglobulins in beef cows and calves. J. Anim Sci. 76:1204.

Baalsrud, K. and G. Overnes. 1986. Influence of vitamin E and selenium supplement on antibody production in horses. Equine Vet. J 18:472.

Bauersachs, S., M. Kirchgessner and B. Paulicks. 1993. Effects of different levels of dietary selenium and vitamin E on the humoral immunity of rats. J. Trace Elem. Electrolytes Health Dis. 7:147.

Behne, D., T. Hofer, R. v. Bergswordt-Wallrabe and W. Elger. 1982. Selenium in the testis of the rat: Studies on its regulation and its importance for the organism. J. Nutr. 112:1682.

Bowers, T.L. 1997. Nutrition and Immunity Part 2: The role of selected micronutrients and clinical significance. Vet. Clin Nutr. 4:96.

Campa, A, G. Shor-Posner, F. Indacochea, G. Zhang, H. Lai, D. Asthana, G. Scott and M. Baum. 1999. Mortality risk in selenium deficient HIV positive childen. J. Acquir. Immune Defic. Syndr. Hum. Retrovirol. 20:508.

Delmas-Beavieux, M., E. Peuchant, A Couchouron, J. Constans, C. Sargeant, M. Simonoff, J. Pellegrin, B. Leng, C. Conri and M. Clerc. 1996. The enzymatic antioxidant system in blood and glutathione status in human immunodeficiency virus infected patients: effects of supplementation with selenium or beta-carotene. Am J.Clin. Nutr. 64:101.

Erskine, R.J., R. Eberhart, P.J. Grasso and R.W. Scholz. 1989. Induction of *Escherichia coli* mastitis in cows fed selenium deficient or selenium supplemented diets. Am. J. Vet Res. 50:2093.

Eskew, M.L., A. Zarkower, W. Scheuchenzuber, G. Hildenbrandt, R. Scholz and C. Reddy. 1993. Increased thromboxane A2 synthesis by rat lung neutrophils during selenium deficiency. Prostaglandins 46:319.

Ganther, H. 1999. Selenium metabolism, selenoproteins and mechanisms of cancer prevention: complexities with thioredoxin reductase. Carcinogenesis 20:1657.

Giandinis, N., G. Koptopoulos, N. Roubles, V. Siarkou and A. Papasteriades. 2000. Selenium and vitamin E effect on antibody production of sheep vaccinated against enzootic abortion. Comp. Immunol. Microbiol. Infect. Dis. 23:129.

Grasso, P., R. Scholz, R. Erskine and R. Eberhart. 1990. Phagocytosis, bactericidal activity and oxidative metabolism of milk neutrophils from dairy cows fed selenium supplemented or selenium deficient diets. Am. J. Vet Res. 51:269.

Gu, Q-P., Y-M. Xia, P-C. Ha, J. Butler and P.D. Whanger. 1998. Distribution of selenium between plasma fractions in guinea pigs and humans with various intakes of dietary selenium. J. Trace Elements Med. Biol. 12:8.

Hill, K.H. Chittum, P.R Lyons, M. Boeglin and R. Burk. 1996a. Effect of selenium on selenoprotein P expression in cultured liver cells. Biochem. Biophys. Acta. 1313:29.

Hill, K.H., Y. Xia, B. Akesson, M. Boeglin and R. Burk. 1996b. Selenoprotein P concentration in plasma is an index of selenium status in selenium deficient and selenium supplemented Chinese subjects. J. Nutr. 126:138.

Hori, K., D. Hatfield, F. Maldarelli, B.J. Lee and K. Clouse. 1997. Selenium supplementation suppresses tumor necrosis factor induced human immunodeficiency virus type I replication *in vitro*. AIDS Research and Human Retroviruses 13:1325.

Hotz, C., D. Fitzpatrick, K. Trick and M. L'Abbe. 1997. Dietary iodine and selenium interact to affect thyroid hormone metabolism of rats. J. Nutr. 127:1214.

Janicki, K.M., L.M. Lawrence, T. Barnes and C.I. O'Connor. 2000. The effect of dietary selenium source and level on broodmares and their foals. ASAS Annual Meeting, Baltimore (submitted).

Jeffcott, L. and M. Davies. 2000. Osteochondrosis into the new millenium. Equine Vet. Ed. 2:67.

Knight, D. and W. Tyznik. 1990. The effect of dietary selenium on humoral immunocompetence of ponies. J. Anim. Sci. 68:1311.

Kohrle, J. 1999. The trace element selenium and the thyroid gland. Biochemie 81:527

Lacetara, N., U. Bernabucci, B. Ronachi and A. Nardone. 1999. The effects of injectable sodium selenite on immune function and milk production of Sardinian sheep receiving adequate dietary selenium. Vet. Res. 30:363.

Larsen, C.T., F.W. Pierson and W.B. Gross. 1997. Effect of dietary selenium on the response of stressed and unstressed chickens to *Escherichia coli* challenge and antigen. Biol. Trace Elem. Res. 58:169.

Levander, O., G. Alfthan, H. Arvilommi, C. Gref, J. Huttunen, M. Kataja, P. Koivistoinen and J. Pikkarainen. 1983. Bioavailability of selenium to Finnish men as assessed by platelet glutathione peroxidase activity and other blood parameters. J. Clin. Nutr. 37:887.

Lewis, L.D. 1995. Equine Clinical Nutrition. Williams and Wilkens, Philadelphia PA.

Look, M.P., J.K. Rockstroh, G.S. Rao, K.A. Kreuzer, U. Spengler and T. Sauerbruch. 1997. Serum selenium versus lymphocyte subsets and markers of disease progression and inflammatory response in human immunodeficiency virus-1 infection. Biol. Trace Elem. Res. 56:31.

Maddox, J.F., K.M. Aherne, C.C. Reddy and L.M. Sordillo. 1999. Increased neutrophil adherence and adhesion molecule mRNA expression in endothelial cells during selenium deficiency. J. Leukoc. Biol. 65:658.

Mahan, D.C. 2000. Effect of organic and inorganic selenium sources and levels on sow colostrum and milk selenium concentration. J. Anim. Sci. 78:100.

Mahan, D.C. and Y.Y. Kim. 1996. Effect of inorganic or organic selenium at two dietary levels on reproductive performance and tissue selenium concentrations in first parity gilts and their progeny. J. Anim. Sci. 74:2711.

Mahan, D.C., A.L. Moxon and J.H. Cline. 1975. Efficacy of supplemental selenium in reproductive diets on sow progeny serum and tissue selenium values. J. Anim. Sci. 40:624.

Malbe, M., M. Klaassen, W. Fang, V. Mylls, M. Vikerpuur, K. Nyholme, S. Sankari, K. Suoranta and M.Sandholm. 1995. Comparisons of selenite and selenium yeast feed supplements on Se-incorporation, mastitis and leukocyte function in Se-deficient dairy cows. Zentralbl Veterinarmed A 42:111.

Marin-Guzman, J., D.C. Mahan, Y.K. Chung, J.L. Pate and W.F. Pope. 1997. Effects of dietary selenium and vitamin E on boar performance and tissue responses, semen quality and subsequent fertilization rates in mature gilts. J. Anim Sci. 75:2994.

Morgante, M., D. Beghelli, M. Pauselli, P. Dall'Ara, M. Capuccella and S. Ranucci. 1999. Effect of administration of vitamin E and selenium during the dry period on mammary health and milk cell counts in dairy ewes. J.Dairy Sci. 82:623.

Mork, H., B. Lex, M. Scheurlen, I. Dreher, N. Schutze, J. Hohrle and F. Jakob. 1998. Expression pattern of gastrointestinal selenoproteins-Targets for selenium supplementation. Nutrition and Cancer 32:64.

Motsenbocker, M. and A. Tappel. 1984. Effect of dietary selenium on plasma selenoprotein P, selenoprotein P1 and glutathione peroxidase in the rat. J. Nutr. 114:279.

NRC, 1989. Nutrient Requirements of Horses. 5th edition. National Academy Press, Washington D.C.

NRC, 1998. Nutrient Requirements of Swine. 10th revised edition. National Academy Press, Washington D.C.

Ortman, K., R. Anderson and H. Holst. 1999. The influence of supplements of selenite, selenate and selenium yeast on the selenium status of dairy heifers. Acta Vet. Scand. 40:23.

Ortman, K. and B. Pehrson. 1999. Effect of selenate as a feed supplement to dairy cows in comparison to selenite and selenium yeast. J. Anim. Sci. 77:3365.

Pagan, J.D., P. Karnezos, M.A.P. Kennedy, T. Currier and K.E. Hoekstra. 1999. Effect of selenium source on selenium digestibility in exercised thoroughbreds. In: Biotechnology in the Feed Industry (T.P. Lyons and K.A. Jacques, eds). Nottingham University Press, UK, p547.

Pehrson, B., K. Ortman, N. Madjid and U. Trafikowska. 1999. The influence of dietary selenium as selenium yeast or sodium selenite on the concentration of selenium in the milk of suckler cows and on the selenium status of their calves. J. Anim Sci. 77:3371.

Peplowski, M.A., D.C. Mahan, F.A. Murray, A.L. Moxon, A.H. Cantor and K.E. Ekstrom. 1980. Effect of dietary and injectable vitamin E and selenium in weanling swine antigenically challenged with sheep red blood cells. J. Anim. Sci. 51:344.

Perrson-Moschos, M., G. Althan and B. Akessson. 1998. Plasma seleno-protein O levels of healthy males in different selenium status after oral supplementation with different forms of selenium. Eur. J. Clin Nutr. 52:363.

Reddy, K.V., T.C. Kumar, M. Prasad and P.Reddanna. 1998. Pulmonary lipid peroxidation and antioxidant defenses during exhaustive physical exercise: the role of vitamin E and selenium. Nutrition 14:448.

Schrauzer, G.N. and J. Sacher. 1994. Selenium in the maintenance and therapy of HIV-infected patients. Chem. Biol. Interact. 91:199.

Smith, K.L., J.S. Hogan and W.P. Weiss. 1997. Dietary vitamin E and selenium affect mastitis and milk quality. J. Anim Sci. 75:1659.

Stabel, J.R., T.A. Reinhardt and B.J. Nonnecke. 1991. Effect of selenium and reducing agents on *in vitro* immunoglobulin M synthesis by bovine lymphocytes. J. Dairy Sci. 74:2501.

Stowe, H.D. and T.H. Herdt. 1992. Clinical assessment of selenium status of livestock. J. Anim Sci. 70:3928.

Swecker, W.S. Jr., D.E. Eversole, C.D. Thatcher, D.J. Blodgett and G.G. Shurig. 1989. Influence of supplemental selenium on humoral immune responses in weaned beef calves. Am. J. Vet. Res. 50:1760.

Swecker, W.S. Jr., C.D. Thatcher, D.E. Eversole, D.J. Blodgett and G.C. Schurig. 1995. Effect of selenium supplementation on colostral IgG concentration in cows grazing selenium-deficient pastures and on post-suckle serum IgG concentration in their calves. Am. J. Vet. Res. 56:450.

Tessier, F., I. Margaritis, M.Richard, C. Moynot and P. Marconnet. 1995. Selenium and training effects on the glutathione system and aerobic performance. Med. Sci Sports. Exerc. 27:390.

Vadhanavikit, S. and H. Ganther. 1993. Selenium requirement of rats for normal hepatic and thyroidal 5'deiodinase (type I) activities. J. Nutr. 123:1124.

Weiss, W. P., J.S. Hogan, K.L. Smith and K.H. Hoblet. 1990. Relationships among selenium, vitamin E and mammary gland health in commercial dairy herds. J. Dairy Sci. 73:381.

Wolfram, S. 1999. Absorption and metabolism of selenium: differences between organic and inorganic sources. In: Biotechnology in the Feed Industry (T.P. Lyons and K.A. Jacques, ed). Nottingham University Press, UK, p547.

Wu, H.Y., Y.M. Hia, P.C. Ha and X.S. Chen. 1997. Changes in myocardial thyroid hormone metabolism and α-glycerophosphate dehydrogenase activity in rats deficient in iodine and selenium. Br. J. Nutr. 78:671.

Wuryastuti, H., H.D. Stowe, R.W. Bull and E.R. Miller. 1993. Effects of vitamin E and selenium on immune responses of peripheral blood, colostrum and milk leukocytes of sows. J. Anim. Sci. 71:2464.

Yang, J., K. Hill and R. Burk. 1989. Dietary selenium intake controls rat plasma selenoprotein P concentration. J. Nutr. 119:1010.

Yeh, J.Y., Q. Gu, M. Bellstein, N. Forsberg and P. Whanger. 1997a. Selenium influences tissue levels of selenoprotein W in sheep. J. Nutr. 127:394.

Yeh, J.Y., S.Vendeland, Q. Gu, J. Butler, B. Ou and P. Whanger. 1997b. Dietary selenium increases selenoprotein W levels in rat tissues. J. Nutr. 127:2165.

Vitamin E levels and selenium form: effects on beef cattle performance and meat quality

B.S. CLYBURN, C.R. RICHARDSON, M.F. MILLER, C.E. CLOUD, J.H. MIKUS AND G.V. POLLARD

Texas Tech University, Lubbock, Texas, USA

Summary

Effects of vitamin E level and selenium supplement form on performance and carcass characteristics were evaluated in a completely randomized design involving 96 Angus crossbred steers (374 kg). Two sources of dietary selenium, sodium selenite and organic selenium (Sel-Plex selenium yeast, Alltech Inc.) added at 0.3 mg Se/kg and three levels of vitamin E (500, 250, and 125 IU/head/day) were evaluated over a 103 day finishing period. Steers were divided into six equal groups and fed diets based on steam-flaked corn with 10% roughage. The basal ration was a typical southwestern feedlot diet with all test diets formulated to be isonitrogenous and isocaloric. Steers given organic selenium showed improvements in performance measurements during the high growth period. Cattle receiving inorganic selenium and a moderate level of vitamin E had higher longissimus muscle area; however, no effects of selenium source and vitamin E level were noted for other variables measured.

Introduction

In 1987, the Food and Drug Administration (FDA) approved the addition of selenium (sodium selenite or sodium selenate) to all livestock diets at a 0.3 mg/kg concentration (Ullrey, 1992). Since that time, several changes have been made with regard to the level at which selenium can be administered in feeds for various animals. In August 1997 a final rule was published by the FDA that supports 3.0 mg/hd/d for beef cattle. There have been numerous reports about the clinical importance of selenium in the prevention of white muscle disease in ruminants (McDowell, 1992). However, few data are available on animal performance and carcass quality responses to dietary selenium in beef cattle.

Vitamin E has been recognized as an essential nutrient for growth and health of all species of animals (McDowell, 1989). The diverse roles of vitamin E are due to its involvement in nutritional myopathy, prostaglandin biosynthesis and immune responsiveness (Liu *et al.*, 1995; Tengerdy, 1989). Asghar *et al.* (1991) recorded improvements in animal performance when pigs were supplemented with 100 mg vitamin E/kg of feed. Selenium and vitamin E are nutritionally associated because of their relatively common deficiency symptoms. There have been a number of studies indicating a relationship between selenium and vitamin E in animal health (Van Ryssen *et al.*, 1989; Weiss *et al.*, 1990). However, there were also beneficial responses in carcass and sensory characteristics when selenium and/or vitamin E were included in the diet (Liu, *et al.*, 1995; Cannon *et al.*, 1996; Liu *et al.*, 1996). The objectives of this research were to determine the effects of organic or inorganic selenium with vitamin E on performance and carcass characteristics of growing/finishing feedlot steers.

Materials and methods

Ninety-six Angus crossbred steers (374 kg) were utilized in an experiment to compare the effects of organic and inorganic selenium supplementation with different levels of vitamin E on performance and carcass characteristics. The feeding study was conducted at the Alltech Biotechnology research feedlot located at the Texas Tech University research farm on the southern high plains during the fall and winter of 1999.

Steers were randomly assigned by weight to 24 pens (four steers per pen and four pens per treatment) and fed for 103 days. Feed for each treatment was individually batched and delivered at approximately 0900 hrs each morning. Prior to feeding, feed remaining in the bunks was visually estimated and used to adjust feed amounts offered.

Typical feedlot diets used in this study were based on steam-flaked corn and 10% roughage from cottonseed hulls and chopped alfalfa hay (Table 1). All diets were formulated to meet requirements for crude protein, calcium, phosphorus, and vitamin A (NRC 1996). Selenium (Se) was added to supply 0 or 3 mg Se per head daily in the form of inorganic selenium (sodium selenite) or organic selenium yeast (Sel-Plex, Alltech Inc.). Vitamin E was added at either 125, 250 or 500 IU per head to provide the following dietary treatments:

Basal diet (no added vitamin E or selenium)
Basal diet plus 3.0 mg Se/head/day from Sel-Plex and 250 IU vitamin E
Basal diet plus 3.0 mg Se/head/day from selenite and 250 IU vitamin E
Basal diet plus 3.0 mg Se/head/day from Sel-Plex and 125 IU vitamin E
Basal diet plus 3.0 mg Se/head/day from selenite and 500 IU vitamin E
Basal diet plus 3.0 mg Se/head/day from Sel-Plex and 500 IU vitamin E

Individual animal weights were recorded at 28 day intervals during the experiment. Average daily gain (ADG), dry matter intake (DMI) and feed

Table 1. Ingredient composition (%) of the six experimental diets.

	Basal diet	Organic selenium			Inorganic selenium	
Vitamin E level, IU/kg	0	125	250	500	250	500
Steam flaked corn	76.5	75.25	75.0	74.5	75.0	74.5
Cottonseed hulls	4.7	4.7	4.7	4.7	4.7	4.7
Ground alfalfa hay	4.7	4.7	4.7	4.7	4.7	4.7
Urea	0.8	0.8	0.8	0.8	0.8	0.8
Cottonseed meal	3.66	3.66	3.66	3.66	3.66	3.66
TTU supplement[a]	2.14	2.14	2.14	2.14	2.14	2.14
Fat	2.5	2.5	2.5	2.5	2.5	2.5
Cane molasses	5	5	5	5	5	5
Sodium selenite Premix[b]	0	0	0	0	1	1
Sel-Plex premix[c]	0	1	1	1	0	0
Vitamin E premix[d]	0	0.25	0.5	1	0.5	1
Total	100	100	100	100	100	100

[a]TTU supplement formulated to meet NRC 1996 requirements for beef cattle containing cottonseed meal, calcium carbonate, dicalcium phosphate, potassium chloride, magnesium oxide, ammonium sulfate, salt, cobalt carbonate, copper sulfate, iron sulfate, EDDI, manganese oxide, zinc sulfate, vitamin A, Rumensin, and Tylan. Texas Tech University supplement contained no added selenium or vitamin E.
[b]Sodium selenite premix 1 = 3 mg/hd/d.
[c]Sel-Plex premix 1 = 3 mg/hd/d.
[d]Vitamin E premix 0.25 = 125 IU/hd/d, .50 = 250 IU/hd/d, and 1 = 500 IU/hd/d of vitamin E.

efficiency (feed:gain) ratios were calculated for each 28 day period. At the conclusion of the study, steers were transported to a commercial packing plant where final yield grade, dressing percentage, longissimus muscle area, quality grade, kidney, pelvic and heart (KPH) fat, and fat thickness were recorded by trained personnel.

Performance and carcass characteristics were analyzed with pen as the experimental unit. A completely randomized design was used, and computations were made with the GLM procedure of SAS (1987). The following five orthogonal contrasts were used to evaluate treatment effects:

1) Control *vs* the average of all other treatments;

2) Average of the organic *vs* the average of the inorganic selenium treatments;

3) Organic Se/125 IU vitamin E *vs* inorganic Se/500 IU vitamin E;

4) Organic Se/250 IU vitamin E *vs* inorganic Se/500 IU vitamin E

5) Organic Se/125 IU vitamin E *vs* inorganic Se/250 IU vitamin E.

Results and discussion

PERFORMANCE EFFECTS

Selenium source and supplemental vitamin E level did not affect overall performance of steers (Table 2). These results are consistent with those of Mahan and Parrett (1996), Ortman and Pehrson (1998) and Mahan *et al.* (1999), who demonstrated no overall growth or performance response to selenium form and various levels of vitamin E added to finishing swine diets. Nicholson *et al.* (1991) found no effect on daily gain or efficiency of calves supplemented with different selenium sources.

Table 2. **Effects of vitamin E level and selenium source on performance of finishing beef steers.**

	Basal diet[a]	Organic selenium			Inorganic selenium		SE[b]	OC[c]	OSL[d]
Vitamin E, IU	0	125	250	500	250	500			
Initial BW, kg	377.77	369.7	373.78	377.72	372.27	377.64	34.33		NS
Final BW, kg	548.04	537.43	546.56	545.23	551.21	544.23	45.62		NS
Daily gain, kg									
0 to 28 days	1.92	2.15	2.22	2.02	2.09	1.88	.20	2,3,4	.09,.05,.01
0 to 56 days	1.85	1.96	1.97	1.90	1.98	1.75	.19	3,4	.09,.08
0 to 84 days	1.73	1.72	1.81	1.72	1.80	1.63	.17		NS
0 to 103 days	1.69	1.64	1.70	1.64	1.76	1.66	.16		NS
DM intake, kg/day									
0 to 28 days	8.29	8.45	8.57	8.21	8.24	8.16	.65		NS
0 to 56 days	9.35	8.08	8.29	8.96	8.10	8.69	.37	1,3	.0001,.02
0 to 84 days	8.83	8.51	8.83	8.70	8.58	8.44	.71		NS
0 to 103 days	8.76	8.41	8.80	8.45	8.62	8.55	.70		NS
Feed:gain									
0 to 28 days	4.31	3.97	3.88	4.09	3.94	4.37	.19	4	.08
0 to 56 days	5.07	4.14	4.22	4.74	4.12	5.04	.23	1,3,4	.02,.01,.02
0 to 84 days	5.09	4.85	4.86	5.07	4.77	5.19	.10	3,4	.03,.04
0 to 103 days	5.20	5.14	5.20	5.15	4.92	5.14	.13		NS

[a]Basal diet = no added vitamin E or selenium.
[b]Pooled standard error; n = four pens/treatment.
[c]Orthogonal contrasts: 1) control vs the average of all other treatments; 2) average of organic Se treatments vs average of inorganic Se treatments; 3) Sel-Plex/125 E vs selenite/500 E; 4) Sel-Plex/250 E vs selenite/500 E, and 5) Sel-Plex/125 E vs selenite/250 E.
[d]OSL = observed significance level of orthogonal contrast; NS = non-significant, P>0.10.

While there were no significant differences for performance over the entire feeding period, orthogonal contrasts revealed differences during the growing period. During the first 28 days, cattle fed diets containing organic selenium had higher (P = 0.09) average daily gain compared to those fed inorganic selenium-supplemented diets. Improvements in daily gain were also detected for cattle given Sel-Plex plus either 125 (P = 0.05) or 250 IU (P = 0.02) vitamin E when compared to the group given inorganic selenium plus 500 IU vitamin E. Furthermore, at 56 days, cattle given Sel-Plex plus 125 or 250

IU vitamin E continued to have higher daily gains compared to those given inorganic selenium plus 500 IU vitamin E (P = 0.09 and 0.08, respectively).

Dry matter intake was similar among treatments, except at 56 days. Steers fed the unsupplemented control diet had higher dry matter intake (P = 0.0001) at 56 days when compared to the average of all other treatments. Furthermore, dry matter intake for cattle given Sel-Plex with 125 IU E decreased (P = 0.02) by 7% compared to the group receiving Sel-Plex with 500 IU vitamin E. At 56 days, steers on the unsupplemented basal diet had poorer feed efficiency (P = 0.02) when contrasted with the average of all other treatments. During the same period, improved efficiencies were noted for cattle given Sel-Plex with either 125 or 250 IU vitamin E (P = 0.01 and 0.02, respectively), when compared to those fed diets containing inorganic selenium and 500 IU vitamin E. Responses in efficiency were similar at 84 days with cattle given organic selenium and either 125 or 250 IU vitamin E being more efficient (*P* = 0.03 and P= .04) than cattle receiving inorganic selenium and 500 IU vitamin E. While the two organic selenium treatments were more efficient for the majority of the feeding study, in the last 21 days of the study there was a decline in daily gain which affected overall efficiency. Cattle supplemented with organic selenium responded with an increase in performance for the first 56 days; however, selenium source and vitamin E level did not change performance over the entire experiment.

CARCASS CHARACTERISTICS

The same orthogonal contrasts used to compare means for performance were used to compare effects of treatments on carcass characteristics. Neither selenium source nor dietary vitamin E level influenced hot carcass weight, final yield grade, fat thickness, or marbling score (Table 3). While few differences were noted for carcass data among treatments, cattle fed the unsupplemented basal diet had higher (P = 0.01) dressing percentage when compared to the average of all other treatments. The Sel-Plex/125 IU E group had more KPH fat (P=0.06) than cattle given selenite/500 IU E. The average of the organic selenium treatments had lower LMA (P = 0.10) compared to the inorganic selenium treatments. No statistical analyses were performed on quality grade percentage; however, more cattle fed Sel-Plex/250 IU E graded Choice. On average, 83% of the cattle graded USDA Choice, with an average fat thickness of 1.49 cm, indicating that the cattle had reached the desired degree of finish by the end of the 103 day study.

Conclusions

While performance over the over the entire 103 days was unaffected, cattle supplemented with organic selenium showed improvements in performance

Table 3. Effects of vitamin E level and selenium source on carcass characteristics of finishing feedlot steers.

Vitamin E, IU	Basal diet[a] 0	Organic selenium 125	250	500	Inorganic selenium 250	500	SE[b]	OC[c]	OSL[d]
Initial BW, kg	377.77	369.7	373.78	377.72	372.27	377.64	34.33		NS
Hot carcass weight, kg	345.87	324.93	334.82	327.33	335.21	336.90	29.31		NS
Dressing %	63.29	60.43	61.20	60.07	60.77	61.88	0.75	1	0.01
Longissimus area, cm^2	86.84	82.84	86.26	82.52	89.49	86.46	0.40	2,5	0.1
Final yield grade	3.44	3.46	3.64	3.45	3.22	3.29	0.21		NS
Fat thickness, cm	1.55	1.40	1.63	1.37	1.55	1.47	0.05		NS
Kidney, pelvic and heart fat, %	2.88	3.29	3.13	2.75	2.94	2.73	0.19	3	0.06
Marbling score[e]	508.75	470.00	521.25	483.75	495.63	485.30	15.52		NS
Percent choice, %[f]	81.25	78.57	93.75	81.25	87.50	73.33			
Percent select, %	18.75	21.43	6.25	18.75	12.50	26.67			

[a]Basal diet = no added vitamin E or selenium.
[b]Pooled standard error; n = four pens/treatment.
[c]Orthogonal contrasts: 1) control vs the average of all other treatments; 2) average of organic Se treatments vs average of inorganic Se treatments; 3) Sel-Plex/125 E vs selenite/500 E; 4) Sel-Plex/250 E vs selenite/500 E, and 5) Sel-Plex/125 E vs selenite/250 E.
[d]OSL = observed significance level of orthogonal contrast; NS = non-significant, P>0.10.
[e]300 = Slight^0; 400 = Small^0; 500 = Modest^0; 600 = Moderate^0; 700 = Slightly abundant^0.
[f]Choice % includes cattle that graded Prime.

during the high growth period. While supplementation of feedlot steers with inorganic selenium increased LMA, no differences were noted due to selenium source for other carcass variables measured. Animals supplemented with selenium and vitamin E had lower dressing percentage compared to animals that received no supplementation. Animals fed organic selenium and the lowest level of vitamin E had a larger percentage of KPH than all other treatments.

References

Asghar, A., J.I. Gray, A.M. Boorman, E.A. Gommaa, M.M. Abouzied, E.R. Miller and D.J. Buckley. 1991. Effects of supranutritional dietary vitamin E levels on subcellular deposition of alpha-tocopherol in the muscle and on pork quality. J. Sci. Food Agric. 57:31.

Cannon, J.E., J.B. Morgan, G.R. Schmidt, J.D. Tatum, J.N. Sofos, G.C. Smith, R.J. Delmore and S.N. Williams. 1996. Growth and fresh meat quality characteristics of pigs supplemented with vitamin E. J. Anim. Sci. 74:98.

Liu, Q., M.C. Lanari and D.M. Schaefer. 1995. A review of dietary vitamin E supplementation for improvement of beef quality. J. Anim. Sci. 73:3131.

Liu, Q., K.K. Scheller, S.C. Arp, D.M. Schaefer and M. Frigg. 1996. Color coordinates for assessment of dietary vitamin E effects on beef color stability. J. Anim. Sci 74:106.

Mahan, D.C. and N.A. Parrett. 1996. Evaluating the efficiency of selenium-enriched yeast and sodium selenite on tissue selenium retention and serum glutathione peroxidase activity in grower and finisher swine. J. Anim. Sci. 74:2967.

Mahan, D.C., T.R. Cline and B. Richert. 1999. Effects of dietary levels of selenium enriched yeast and sodium selenite sources fed to growing-finishing pigs on performance, tissue selenium, serum glutathione peroxidase activity, carcass characteristics, and loin quality. J. Anim. Sci. 77:2172.

McDowell, L.R. 1989. Vitamin E. In: Vitamins in Animal Nutrition. Academic Press, Inc. San Diego.

McDowell, L.R. 1992. Selenium. In: Minerals in Animal and Human Nutrition. Academic Press, Inc. San Diego.

Nicholson, J.W.G., R.E. McQueen and R.S. Bush. 1991. Response of growing cattle to supplementation with organically bound or inorganic sources of selenium or yeast cultures. Can. J. Anim. 71:803.

NRC. 1996. Nutrient Requirements of Beef Cattle (7th Ed.) National Academy Press, Washington, DC.

Ortman, K and B. Pehrson. 1998. Selenite and selenium yeast as feed supplements to growing fattening pigs. J. Vet. Med. A 45:551.

SAS. 1987. SAS/STAT Guide for Personal Computers (Version 6th Ed.). SAS inst. Inc., Cary, NC.

Tengerdy, R.P. 1989. Vitamin E, immune response, and disease resistance. Ann. N. Y. Acad. Sci. 570:335.

Ullrey, D.E. 1992. Basis for regulation of selenium supplements in animal diets. J. Anim. Sci. 70:3922.

Van Ryssen, J.B.J., J.T. Deagen, M.A. Beilstein and P.D. Whemger. 1989. Comparative metabolism of organic and inorganic selenium by sheep. J. Agric. Food Chem 37: 1358.

Weiss, W.P., J.S. Hogan and K.L. Smith. 1990. Relationship among selenium, Vitamin E, and mammary gland health in commercial dairy herds. J. Dairy. Sci. 73:381.

Organic selenium: benefits to animals and humans, a biochemist's view

PETER F. SURAI

Department of Biochemistry and Nutrition, SAC, Auchincruive, Ayr., Scotland, UK

Introduction

Selenium (Se) as a chemical element was discovered by Swedish chemist Berzelius 180 years ago. Since then, many publications have appeared describing its chemical properties and biological activity. In the 1930s, it was found that selenium is a toxic element and can even be carcinogenic. Thus the next 20 years of research was devoted mainly to selenium toxicity; however, in 1957 it became clear that selenium was an essential nutrient in animal nutrition. This discovery was expanded by the knowledge that selenium is an integral part of an antioxidant enzyme, glutathione peroxidase (GSH-Px), as it was described in 1973 by Rotruck and coworkers. Nevertheless, it has been only recently that free radical production during physiological metabolism has been described and that the antioxidant system responsible for prevention of lipid peroxidation has been characterised.

Selenium exists in two chemical forms in nature, organic and inorganic. Inorganic selenium can be found in different minerals in the form of selenite, selenate and selenide as well as in the metallic form. In contrast, in vegetable feed ingredients selenium is an integral part of amino acids including methionine and cysteine where it substitutes for sulphur. Therefore, in nature animals receive selenium mainly in the organic form. On the other hand, selenium concentration in grains and forages varies widely and depends on ability of the plant to absorb this element from the soil. In acidic and poorly-aerated soils selenium has low availability for plants and as a result its concentration in plant materials is substantially lower.

Inorganic selenium (mainly in the form of selenite) has been widely used for the last 20 years to supplement diets of farm animals. The experience of using selenium in animal nutrition has given us today some important information necessary for further understanding of the biological role of this element. The limitations of using inorganic selenium are well known: toxicity, interactions with other minerals, poor retention, low efficiency of transfer to milk and meat and poor ability to maintain selenium reserves in the

205

body. Consequently, a high proportion of the element consumed is excreted. In addition, a prooxidant effect of the selenite ion is a great disadvantage (Spallholz, 1997). Thus, recently the use of sodium selenite in animal diets has been questioned (Pehrson, 1993). The development and commercialisation of organic selenium (Sel-Plex) opened a new era in animal nutrition providing new opportunities not only for improvement of animal health and productivity but also for production of selenium-enriched meat, milk, eggs and other foods. Since like other animals our diet is a major factor in determining susceptibility to different diseases, organic selenium can also have a great impact on human health.

Selenium as an integral part of the antioxidant system

For the majority of organisms on earth, life without oxygen is impossible. Animals, plants and many microorganisms rely on oxygen for the efficient production of energy. However, the high oxygen concentration in the atmosphere is potentially toxic for living organisms since free radicals derived from oxygen can damage all types of biological molecules. It is only the presence of natural antioxidants in living organisms that enable survival in an oxygen-rich environment (Halliwell, 1994).

Free radical formation is a pathobiochemical mechanism involved in the initiation or progression of various diseases including cardiovascular disease, some forms of cancer, cataracts, age-related macular degeneration, rheumatoid arthritis and a variety of neurodegenerative diseases (Hogg, 1998; Morrissey and O'Brien, 1998; Knight, 1998). In animal production free radial generation and lipid peroxidation are responsible for the development of various diseases, decreases in animal productivity and product quality (Hurley and Doane, 1989; Weiss, 1998; McDowell, 2000).

THREE LEVELS OF ANTIOXIDANT DEFENCE

Antioxidant systems of the living cell include three major levels of defence (Figure 1, Surai, 1999). The first level of defence is responsible for prevention of free radical formation and consists of three antioxidant enzymes, namely superoxide dismutase (SOD), glutathione peroxidase (GSH-Px) and catalase plus metal-binding proteins. It is generally accepted that the superoxide radical is the main free radical produced in living cells; and the electron transport chain in the mitochondria is responsible for its generation (Halliwell and Gutteridge, 1999). SOD dismutases this radical with formation of hydrogen peroxide (H_2O_2); but the latter is still toxic to the cell and must be quickly removed. This important step in antioxidant defence is provided by GSH-Px and catalase (Yu, 1994). GSH-Px is found in different parts of the cell, but catalase is located mainly in peroxisomes. As a result, the efficacy of hydrogen peroxide removal from the cell is higher in the case of GSH-Px

(Halliwell and Gutteridge, 1999). Therefore selenium, as an integral part of the antioxidant enzyme GSH-Px, belongs to the first line of antioxidant defence.

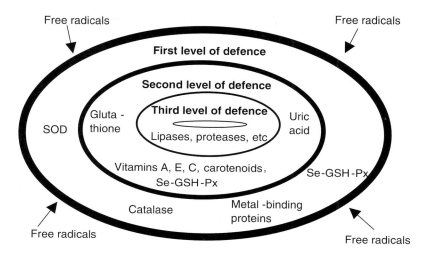

Figure 1. Three major levels of antioxidant defence in the cell.

Unfortunately the first line of antioxidant defence in the cell is not sufficiently powerful to completely prevent free radical formation and lipid peroxidation. Therefore a second level of antioxidant defence includes fat soluble (vitamins A, E, carotenoids, ubiquinols) and water soluble (ascorbic acid, glutathione, uric acid, etc.) antioxidants. These antioxidants are potent chain-breaking compounds that prevent free radical chain formation and propagation. Hydroperoxides can be formed during reactions of free radicals with these antioxidants as follows:

$$ROO* + Toc = Toc* + ROOH$$

Where ROO* is a peroxyl radical; Toc is tocopherol; Toc* is a tocopheroxyl radical, ROOH is a hydroperoxide.

Hydroperoxides are toxic, and if not removed impair membrane structure and function (Gutteridge and Halliwell, 1990). Lipid hydroperoxides are not stable and in the presence of transition metal ions can decompose to produce new free radicals and cytotoxic aldehydes (Diplock, 1994). Therefore, hydroperoxides must be removed from the cell in the same way as H_2O_2, but catalase is not able to react with these compunds. Only selenium-dependent GSH-Px can convert these radicals into non-reactive products (Brigelius-Flohe, 1999). Thus selenium, as an integral part of the GSH-Px, also belongs to the second line of antioxidant defence.

Even the second line of antioxidant defence is unable to prevent lipid peroxidation and some biological molecules are damaged. In this case the third level of antioxidant defence deals with the repair of damaged molecules and includes such specific enzymes as proteases, lipases and some others. Therefore, all the elements of the antioxidant system interact to form an efficient antioxidant defence. This interaction probably starts at the level of nutrient absorption and continues during nutrient metabolism.

The importance of selenium in animal nutrition comes from the knowledge that both the first and second lines of antioxidant defence in the cell rely on the activity of GSH-Px, which in turn depends on adequate selenium. Lipid peroxidation is accelerated in selenium deficiency and damage to biological molecules can be lethal for the cell (Halliwell and Gutteridge, 1999). For example, if H_2O_2 or ROOH are not removed from the cell, they can damage molecules such as enzymes. Even more importantly, H_2O_2 can take part in the formation of other more active free radicals including the hydroxyradical (OH^*), which is considered the most damaging radical in biological systems (Jaeschke, 1995).

A delicate and critical balance exists in the cell between free radical generation and antioxidant defence and repair systems (Figures 2a and 2b). Under physiological conditions, the right and left ends of the so-called 'balance' are in equilibrium, i.e. free radicals are neutralised by the antioxidant system. Exogenous dietary factors are among the most important elements affecting efficiency of the antioxidant system of the organism. Natural and synthetic antioxidants, along with optimal levels of selenium, manganese, copper and zinc in the diet, help to maintain efficient levels of endogenous antioxidants in the tissues. Optimal diet composition allows the antioxidants in food to be efficiently absorbed and metabolised. Optimal temperature, humidity and other environmental conditions are also required for effective protection against free radical production.

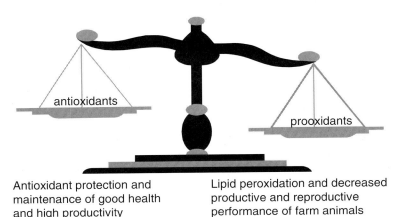

Antioxidant protection and maintenance of good health and high productivity

Lipid peroxidation and decreased productive and reproductive performance of farm animals

Figure 2a. Antioxidant-and pro-oxidant balance in the cell.

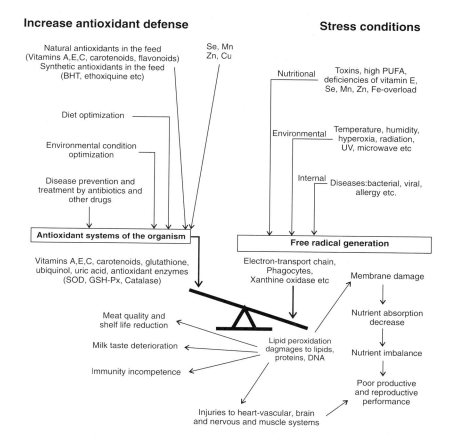

Figure 2b. Antioxidant and pro-oxidant balance in the organism.

STRESS INCREASES FREE RADICAL GENERATION

Different stress conditions are associated with over-production of free radicals and cause oxidative stress, i.e. a disturbance in the prooxidant-antioxidant balance leading to potential tissue damage (Jaeschke, 1995). Stress conditions can be generally divided into three main categories. The most important category is nutritional stress including high dietary levels of polyunsaturated fatty acids, deficiencies of vitamin E, selenium, zinc or manganese, iron overload, hypervitamintosis A and presence of different toxins and toxic compounds. A second group of stress factors are environmental conditions: increased temperature or humidity, hyperoxia, radiation, etc. Internal stress factors including various bacterial or viral diseases as well as allergic responses comprise a third group of stressors.

All the stress conditions mentioned above stimulate free radical generation by a decrease in the coupling of oxidation and phosphorylation in the mitochondria that results in an increased electron leakage and overproduction of superoxide radical (Dalton *et al.*, 1999). The activation of macrophages in stress conditions is another important source of free radical generation (Halliwell and Gutteridge, 1999). It should be emphasized that the intensive rearing conditions of commercial animal production and reproduction are often associated with various types of stress. For example, hatching is considered to be a stress condition for the chick (Surai, 1999). In accordance with commercial practice chicks stay in the incubator several hours after hatching (another stress), then chick delivery from incubator to a poultry house is an added stress. Vaccinations are another source of stress.

Once free radical production exceeds the capacity of antioxidant systems to neutralise, lipid peroxidation causes damage to unsaturated lipids in cell membranes, amino acids in proteins and nucleotides in DNA. As a result, membrane and cell integrity are disrupted. Membrane damage is associated with decreased efficiency of nutrient absorption (including water soluble vitamins, where active transport systems are necessary for effective absorption) and leads to an imbalance of vitamins, amino acids and inorganic elements. All these events result in decreased productive and reproductive performance. The situation is exacerbated by a reduction in immunocompetence and unfavourable changes in the cardiovascular, brain and neurons and muscle systems due to increased lipid peroxidation.

The redox state of the cell, which reflects antioxidant/prooxidant balance, can be considered an important element of gene regulation (Bowie and O'Neill, 2000). Therefore, the effect of antioxidant status on animal health is much more involved than one expected several years ago. To maintain natural antioxidant status in the animal, it is an important task of the nutritionist to assure inclusion of effective antioxidant nutrients in the diet. Antioxidant balance can be considered one way to maintain high productivity and reproductive efficiency of farm animals in intensive rearing commercial conditions.

The selenoproteins

Selenium is an essential component of a number of functional selenoproteins. The best characterised among them is the GSH-Px family. In mammals this family of selenoproteins includes four members. The first, the so-called classical GSH-Px, was described in 1973 (Rotruck *et al.*, 1973; Flohe *et al.*, 1973). The second selenoperoxidase, the phospholipid hydroperoxide glutathione peroxidase (PH-GSH-Px) was discovered nine years later (Ursini *et al.*, 1982). The next member of this family, plasma glutathione peroxidase (pGSH-Px), was described in 1987 (Maddipati and Marnett, 1987; Takahashi *et al.*, 1987). Recently the fourth selenoperoxidase, gastrointestinal glutathione peroxidase (GI-GSH-Px), has been described (Chu *et al.*, 1993; for review Wingler and Brigelius-Flohe, 1999). These enzymes differ in tissue-specificity and are expressed by different genes (Ursini *et al.*, 1997; Brigelius-Flohe, 1999). The major function of these peroxidases is removal and detoxification of hydrogen peroxide and lipid hydroperoxides (Ursini *et al.*, 1997; Mates and Sanchez-Jimenez, 1999). Since hydrogen peroxide is considered an intracellular messenger (Rhee, 1999) and redox status regulates activation of key transcription factors (Jackson *et al.*, 1998; Dalton *et al.*, 1999), it has been suggested that the regulation of the delicate regional redox balance is one of the main functions of the glutathione peroxidases (Brigelius-Flohe, 1999).

A range of other selenoproteins have been identified, however their functions are less obvious (Holben and Smith, 1999; Burk and Hill, 1999). The selenoproteins and their known or suspected functions are listed in Table 1.

Table 1. Selenoproteins and their functions.

Glutathione peroxidase	Four known types, all are involved in removal and detoxification of hydrogen peroxide and lipid hydroperoxides
Thioredoxin reductase	An enzyme taking part in the reduction of protein disulphides and different physiological compounds, including dehydro-ascorbic acid.
Selenoprotein P	Present in plasma with roles in Se transport, selenoprotein P also serves a redox function in the extracellular space (Burk and Hill, 1994). In human plasma selenoprotein P accounts for approximately 40% of total plasma selenium (Akessson *et al.*, 1994).
Thyroid hormone deiodinases	Found in three different forms (Type I, Type II and Type III), the deiodinases regulate the conversion of thyroxine (T4) to 3,3,5-triiodothyronine (T3), the active thyroid hormone.
Selenoprotein W	Purified from rat muscle and suggested to play a role in muscle metabolism.
Selenophosphate synthetase	An enzyme catalysing incorporation of the amino acid selenocysteine into selenoproteins
Sperm capsule selenoprotein	Localised in the midpiece of the spermatozoa and recently identified as PH-GSH-Px (Ursini *et al.*, 1999).

Tissue concentrations of selenoproteins are dependent on the dietary intake of selenium (Chen *et al.*, 1990; Behne *et al.*, 1991; Marchaluk *et al.*, 1995; Persson-Moschos *et al.*, 1998). In general, the selenoproteins discovered in mammalian cells may account for the essentiality of selenium in the body's antioxidant defence, thyroid hormone function, immune system function (particularly cellular immunity), formation and motility of sperm and function of the prostate gland (Badmaev *et al.*, 1996).

Selenium supplementation of poultry

PHYSIOLOGICAL ROLES AND DEFICIENCY SYNDROMES

Selenium is an important element in poultry nutrition, participating in maintaining the cellular antioxidant system. In the chicken, selenium deficiency, especially in combination with low vitamin E supply, is responsible for the development of a range of diseases including exudative diathesis (Noguchi *et al.*, 1973; Barthlomew *et al.*, 1998), nutritional encephalomalacia (Century and Hurwitt, 1964; Combs and Hady, 1991) and nutritional pancreatic atrophy (Thompson and Scott, 1969; 1970; Cantor *et al.*, 1975). It seems likely that lipid peroxidation is important in etiology of these diseases (Fraga *et al.*, 1987). For example, nutritional pancreatic atrophy in chicks may be overcome by feeding vitamin E at levels 15-20-fold higher than normally required (Whitacre *et al.*, 1987). Selenium supplementation can also decrease incidence of nutritional muscular dystrophy in the chick (Jonsson, 1993). Selenium deficiency is also associated with impaired immunodevelopment, reduced egg production and increased embryonic mortality (Combs and Combs, 1984). Moreover, selenium is required in turkey breeder diets for optimum hatchability and viability of offspring (Cantor *et al.*, 1978). In this respect, recent progress in understanding the importance of different selenoproteins as elements of antioxidant systems could aid in explaining at least some of clinical signs of the diseases. It is also interesting to note that exudative diathesis was observed at hatching, indicating that the deficiency lesions had developed during the embryonic period (Hassan *et al.*, 1990). Nevertheless, the role of selenium in embryo development has received limited attention.

PRACTICAL APPLICATIONS: BROILER BREEDERS

Chick embryo tissues contain a large proportion of highly-polyunsaturated fatty acids in the lipid fraction (Speake *et al.*, 1998), and therefore need effective antioxidant protection. Tissues of newly-hatched chicks express a range of antioxidant defences including natural antioxidants (vitamin E, carotenoids, glutathione, ascorbic acid) and antioxidant enzymes (superoxide dismutase, glutathione peroxidase and catalase) as well as antioxidant enzyme cofactors (selenium, zinc, manganese and iron) (Surai *et al.*, 1999a). Of these, vitamin E, carotenoids and metals, including selenium, are delivered from the maternal diet via the yolk while the others are synthesised in the tissues. Therefore, maternal diet composition is a major determinant of antioxidant system development in the chick during embryogenesis and in early postnatal development (Surai, 1999). Vitamin E (Surai *et al.*, 1998b) and carotenoids (Surai and Speake, 1998) are transferred from feed into egg yolk and subsequently to embryonic tissues. Our observations indicate that increased antioxidant supplementation of the maternal diet can substantially increase concentrations of antioxidants in the developing tissues of the chick and significantly decrease tissue susceptibility to lipid peroxidation (Surai *et al.*, 1999; Surai and Speake, 1998). The selenium content of the egg depends on its concentration in the hen's diet and also on the form of dietary selenium used, since organic selenium is more efficiently deposited in the egg yolk (Cantor, 1997). There is also an indication that selenium can be transferred to chick embryo tissues from the egg content (Hassan, 1986).

Effects of organic selenium and vitamin E supplementation of the breeder diet on antioxidant status during embryonic development and in newly hatched chicks

In the experiment conducted at SAC in Scotland, the effect of selenium and vitamin E supplementation of the maternal diet on transfer of these nutrients to the egg yolk and subsequent levels in tissues of newly hatched chicks was studied. The effect of increased selenium and vitamin E supply on the activity of Se-GSH-Px in the chick liver in early postnatal development was determined (Surai, 2000). In this experiment 100 Cobb broiler breeder hens were divided into ten equal groups and housed in pens at 25 weeks of age. Each hen received one of the treatment diets (Table 2). Selenium was supplemented in the organic form (Sel-Plex, Alltech, Inc). After six weeks, the hens were artificially inseminated once per week. Beginning at week 8 eggs were collected and placed in an incubator. Liver, yolk sac membrane, brain and blood plasma were collected from chicks for biochemical analysis.

Table 2. Selenium and vitamin E dietary treatments.

	Selenium	Vitamin E
	mg/kg	
Semi-synthetic diet	0.044*	
Commercial diet	0.17*	
Commercial diet + Sel-Plex 0.2	0.2	
Commercial diet + Sel-Plex 0.4	0.4	
Commercial diet + Vitamin E 40		40
Commercial diet + Vitamin E 100		100
Commercial diet + Vitamin E 200		200
Commercial diet + Vitamin E 40/Sel-Plex 0.2	0.2	40
Commercial diet + Vitamin E/Se/Sel-Plex 0.4	0.4	100

*Selenium derived from ingredients, no inorganic Se added.

Inclusion of organic selenium in the commercial diet increased the selenium concentration in the egg yolk and the albumen (P<0.01, Figure 3). During incubation selenium accumulated in the egg was transferred to the developing embryo. As a result, liver selenium concentration in day old chicks obtained

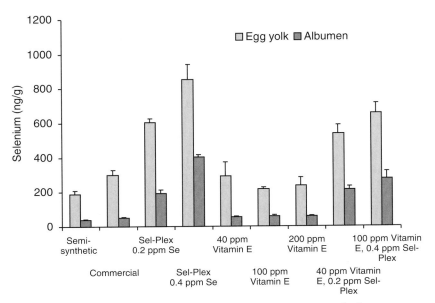

Figure 3. Effect of maternal diet vitamin E and selenium content on selenium concentration in eggs.

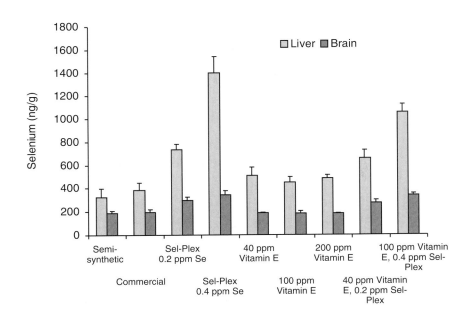

Figure 4. Effect of maternal diet vitamin E and selenium content on selenium concentration in the liver and brain of day old chicks.

from the selenium-enriched eggs was significantly higher compared to controls (P<0.05, Figure 4). Therefore, selenium concentration in the egg yolk and in the liver of newly hatched chicks depends on maternal dietary selenium content. However, there was large variation in yolk and albumen selenium content. This may account in part for the lack of a significant difference in selenium levels in yolk and albumen between the groups fed the semi-synthetic and commercial diets even though the level of selenium in the diet differed substantially. Selenium availability in feedstuffs depends on many factors and varies widely (Combs and Combs, 1986). These factors include the amount and chemical form of the element ingested with feed, solubilization within the intestine, the physiological state of the organism, interactions with other elements, diseases, drug administration and age (Wolffram, 1999). In this respect the form of selenium used in this study (Sel-Plex) is characterised by high bioavailability in different animal species (Mahan, 1999, Yoshida *et al.*, 1999).

There is tissue specificity in selenium transfer from egg to the embryo. For example, in contrast to the liver, there was only a trend toward higher selenium accumulation in the brain of chicks hatched from selenium-enriched eggs (Figure 4). In general, the brain is considered to be quite resistant to compositional manipulation (Meydani *et al.*, 1988; Vatssery *et al.*, 1984). There is a lack of information available indicating mechanisms of selenium delivery from the liver to peripheral tissues. Recently a selenium-binding protein has been isolated from chick embryo hepatic tissues with an approximate molecular mass of 56 kD and a high concentration of sulfhy-dryl groups (Padmaja *et al.*, 1996).

The effects of added organic selenium in the maternal diet were still apparent at 5 and 10 days of age. This finding suggests that selenium accumulated in the liver of newly hatched chicks is actively used during the first days post-hatch. It is possible to suggest that selenium absorption from the diet is not sufficient during the first few days of life and the chick must rely on reserves of the element accumulated during embryogenesis.

Vitamin E accumulation in the egg yolk reflected its level in the breeder diet and varied with selenium supplementation (Figure 5). Dietary organic selenium significantly increased vitamin E level in the yolk, but a combination of selenium and increased vitamin E supplementation did not further increase vitamin E accumulation. Vitamin E in the liver (Figure 6), yolk sac membrane (Figure 5), plasma and brain (data not shown) of day old chicks also reflected vitamin E levels in egg yolk. Again, there was a positive effect (P<0.05) of selenium supplementation of the maternal diet on the levels of vitamin E in the liver, brain and blood plasma of day old chicks. Over the first 10 days of age liver vitamin E rapidly decreased (Figure 6). A positive effect of selenium and vitamin E supplementation of the maternal diet was seen at day 5 and day 10 of age when vitamin E concentrations in the liver and plasma were elevated compared with those of the control group (P<0.05; Surai, 2000).

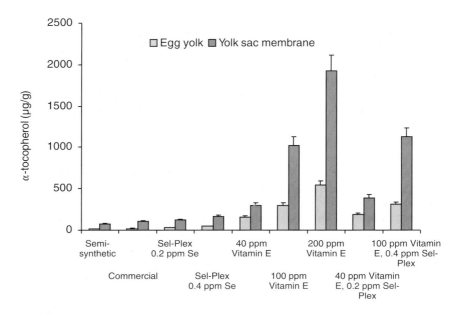

Figure 5. Vitamin E concentration in the egg yolk and yolk sac membrane of day old chicks.

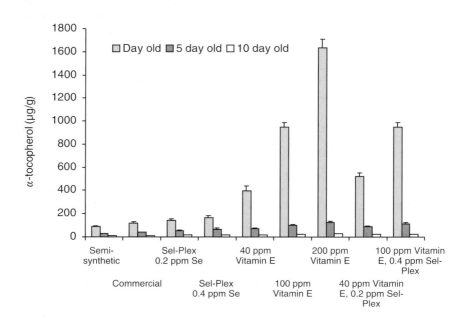

Figure 6. Vitamin E concentration in the chick liver.

In this study it has been shown that one of the important features of chick postnatal development is the depletion of vitamin E in the liver. Similar trends have been observed in chickens, goslings, ducklings (Surai *et al.,* 1998b) and with turkey poults (Soto-Salanova, 1998; Soto-Salanova and Sell, 1995;1996; Soto-Salanova *et al.,* 1993). Selenium supplementation of the maternal diet increased vitamin E levels in the liver and plasma of day old chicks; and this difference was maintained through 10 days of age. Increased vitamin E supplementation of the maternal diet was even more effective, delaying vitamin E depletion not only in the liver but in the brain as well. These data explain why it is difficult to produce symptoms of vitamin E and Se deficiency in chicks during postnatal development if the maternal diet contains sufficient levels of vitamin E (Hassan *et al.,* 1990).

In contrast to chicks, vitamin E in liver, kidney and heart tissues of rats rose after birth (Gunther *et al.,* 1993). In general, there is an age-related (from 8 to 32 months of age) accumulation of vitamin E in the rat liver (Matsuo, 1993; Matsuo *et al.,* 1992). It seems likely that in mammals there is a similar protective role for vitamin E following its accumulation in the neonatal liver. For example, Kelly *et al.* (1992) studied the α-tocopherol content of a number of different foetal, neonatal and maternal guinea pig tissues. They found that during gestation, the foetal liver appears to act as a storage site for α-tocopherol, most of which is released immediately after birth. In rats, during the first few days of life vitamin E is considered an important protective factor against lipid peroxidation (Yoshioka *et al.,* 1987).

The most striking finding of this work was the 'sparing' effect of selenium on vitamin E metabolism and transfer to the egg yolk and the developing tissues. Inclusion of organic selenium in the breeder diet significantly increased vitamin E concentration in egg yolk. This is in agreement with previous reports indicating an increased vitamin E level in the plasma of rats, chicken and ducklings as a result of selenium supplementation (Scott *et al.,* 1977; Thompson and Scott, 1970; Dean and Combs, 1981). The mechanism for this sparing is not clear. The effect could be related to selenium antioxidant properties. One can also speculate that selenium can have an effect on other aspects of vitamin E metabolism and transport to target tissues. For example, vitamin E is metabolised more rapidly in selenium-deficient rats than in supplemented rats (Fisher and Whanger, 1977).

An increased vitamin E concentration in the yolk was associated with its accumulation in the liver of the newly hatched chick, in agreement with our previous observations (Surai, 1999; Surai *et al.,* 1997; 1999). The efficiency of vitamin E transfer from egg yolk to the liver of the developing embryo depends on the initial vitamin E concentration in the egg. In the groups fed the low vitamin E diet, about 30% of total egg yolk vitamin E was found in the liver of the newly hatched chick. In contrast, dietary vitamin E supplementation (40-200 mg/kg) decreased this efficiency 2-fold (13.0-15.8%). These results indicate that in the developing embryo presumably there are metabolic mechanisms responsible for increased vitamin E mobilisation from the egg yolk in the case of low vitamin E provision.

The capacity for fat and probably fat-soluble vitamin E absorption is incompletely developed in the newly hatched chick, but matures rapidly in the first week of life (Freeman, 1976; Noy and Sklan, 1998). On the other hand, during this period tissues with incompletely developed antioxidant regulation require effective protection against lipid peroxidation, which is afforded mainly by vitamin E. The liver of newly-hatched chicks contains lipid droplets (Noble and Cocchi, 1990) that can serve as an ideal milieu for vitamin E accumulation and provide a means for the tissue to maintain very high levels of this vitamin (Surai *et al.*, 1996). In postnatal development, the chick liver becomes depleted of lipid droplets, thus limiting the capacity of this tissue to store high amounts of vitamin E. Further research is needed to understand the molecular mechanisms of such changes in vitamin E metabolism in newly hatched chicks and to find a way to improve their vitamin E status.

Another important finding in this study was the beneficial effect of organic selenium supplementation on the level of reduced glutathione in the liver of the newly hatched chick (P<0.01, Figure 7). The highest vitamin E dose in the maternal diet increased the concentration of glutathione in the liver of newly hatched chicks as well. Similar results were obtained with rats fed a high level of vitamin E (Scott *et al.*, 1977; Lii *et al.*, 1998).

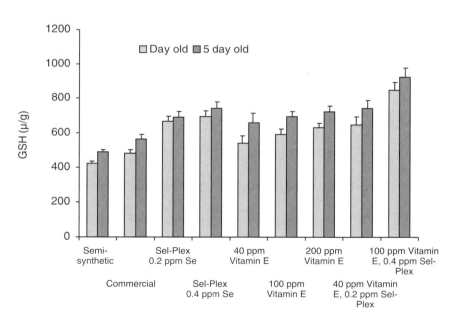

Figure 7. Effect of maternal diet on reduced glutathione concentrations of chick liver.

The relationship between dietary selenium provision and glutathione concentration in animal tissues has received some attention, but the results are not conclusive. It has been shown previously that glutathione metabolism in the chick can be affected by nutritional status with respect to vitamin E and selenium (Kim and Combs, 1993). In particular, in the mentioned work selenium deficiency in the chick was associated with increased glutathione concentration in plasma. On the other hand, freshly isolated hepatocytes from selenium or vitamin E deficient rats had the same glutathione concentration (Hill and Burk, 1982) and it has been suggested that increased GSH synthesis and release is an *in vivo* phenomenon associated with selenium deficiency. More than half of the increased plasma glutathione produced in selenium deficiency was removed by the kidney (Hill and Burk, 1985). Chicks fed excess selenium in diets had hepatic GSH concentration greater than those of selenium-adequate chicks (Kim and Combs, 1993). Similar results were obtained with rats (LeBoeuf *et al.*, 1985). It was also shown that hepatic GSH increased with dietary selenium content in a non-linear manner, but synthetic and degradation enzyme activities were not influenced by selenium (Davies *et al.*, 1985). In contrast, hepatic GSH level and GSH synthesis activity were about three times as much in selenium- and vitamin E deficient chicks (Yoshida *et al.*, 1984). In another study, increasing selenium supplementation up to 4 ppm did not change glutathione levels in rat liver (Scott *et al.*, 1977).

In our work, glutathione concentration in plasma and other tissues was not monitored, and it is difficult to clarify whether an increase in liver glutathione was a reflection of its enhanced synthesis, reduced use for metabolic purposes due to increased concentration of other antioxidants or inhibited release to plasma and delivery to other tissues. Again, mechanisms of such interactions among vitamin E, selenium and glutathione are not clear at present and more work is needed for their clarification. Nevertheless, the interaction between vitamin E and glutathione in the cell is very important in so far as glutathione was found to be specific for vitamin E-dependent inhibition of lipid peroxidation and could not be replaced by other sulf-hydryl compounds tested (Reddy *et al.*, 1982). In addition, glutathione is considered one of the most important water soluble antioxidants in the cell (Sastre *et al.*, 1996; Bains and Shaw, 1997); and its elevated level is an indication of increased antioxidant protection of the tissues.

By five days of age, the yolk sac membrane is usually resorbed (Noble and Cocchi, 1990) and the chick is subsequently dependent on nutrients obtained from the feed. These first days posthatch are extremely important for the chicks. Because of the active development of digestive, humoral, neural and other systems, free radical production at this stage could be very dangerous and antioxidant protection plays a vital role during this period. Thus, increased vitamin E and glutathione concentrations together with enhanced GSH-Px activity in the liver of 5-day old chicks could be considered an important improvement in the antioxidant defence of the chick. It is interesting to note that the amount of reduced glutathione in the chick liver further increased between week 3 and 5 of age (Enkvetchakul *et al.*, 1995). In the cell, GSH can be used to maintain vitamin E in reduced form, thereby lowering the concentration of vitamin E necessary to inhibit microsomal lipid peroxidation (Leedle and Aust, 1990). As such, glutathione metabolism lies at the core of the cellular antioxidant system (Christon *et al.*, 1995; Sastre *et al.*, 1996).

GSH-Px activity in the liver of day-old chicks depends on the selenium content of the maternal diet (Figure 8). Low dietary selenium content was associated with decreased GSH-Px in the egg yolk; and consequently liver Se-GSH-Px activity in newly hatched chicks significantly decreased. Similarly, chicks produced from hens fed a low selenium/low vitamin E diet had low activities of GSH-Px in plasma and pancreas at hatching (Bunk and Combs, 1981). On the other hand, dietary selenium supplementation increased Se-GSH-Px activity in the liver and pancreas (Bunk and Combs, 1981). An efficient carry-over of selenium and vitamin E from hens to their progeny was indicated by a significant increase in muscle selenium, liver GSH-Px activity and vitamin E content at hatching (Hassan *et al.*, 1990). There was no difference in Se-GSH-Px activity in chick liver in response to increasing dietary selenium from 0.2 to 0.4 mg/kg; which probably means that 0.2 mg/kg Se in the maternal diet provides enough selenium to the egg and embryonic tissues to meet the requirement for maximum Se-GSH-Px activity.

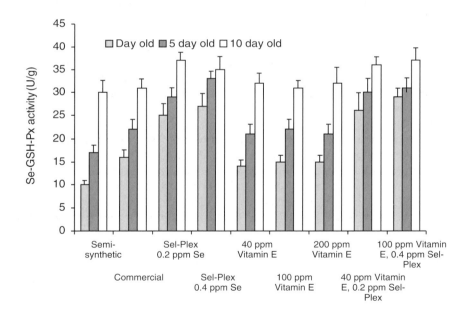

Figure 8. Glutathione peroxidase (Se-GSH-Px) activity in the chick liver.

Inclusion of 0.3 mg/kg Se from baker's yeast to chickens from hatching to day 35 significantly increased GSH-Px activity in erythrocytes, plasma and liver (Arai *et al.*, 1994). GSH-Px activity in the liver increased throughout embryonic development, reaching its maximum at time of hatching (Surai, 1999a). In the liver of the newly hatched chick, selenium-dependent GSH-Px is the major form of the enzyme comprising about 61% of total activity (Surai *et al.*, 1999a). In the majority of the tissues of the newly hatched chick there was a highly significant correlation between selenium level and the activity of Se-GSH-Px (Surai *et al.*, 1999a).

It is interesting that in chicken liver about 28% of GSH-Px activity is represented by the monomeric form of the enzyme (Miyazaki and Motoi, 1992). It has been suggested that the effect of selenium on the activity of GSH-Px is achieved through pretranslational mechanisms, including Se-GSH-Px gene expression and cytosolic mRNA stabilisation (Christinsen and Burgener, 1992). Further, dietary selenium can also regulate the level of GSH-Px mRNA in the post-transcriptional step (Toyoda *et al.*, 1990). Therefore, GSH-Px mRNA is a primary target of the selenium regulatory mechanism (Weiss *et al.*, 1997).

Increasing organic selenium content of the hen's diet from 0.2 to 0.4 ppm did not affect chick liver GSH-Px activity in day-old chicks; however 0.4 mg/kg Se gave more protection against peroxidation due to higher liver vitamin E and glutathione in day-old and 5 day-old chicks. Since the process of selenium transfer from feed to egg yolk and subsequently to embryonic tissues has received limited attention (Cantor, 1997), there is no clear answer as to which level of selenium supplementation is optimal for broiler breeders. Recently, it has been shown that 0.4 mg/kg Se in diets fed White Leghorn type chickens reduced death or lesions from *E. coli* or sheep erythrocyte antigen challenge from 86 to 21%; and dietary additions of selenium between 0.1 and 0.8 mg/kg resulted in a substantial (77%) antibody titre increase in chickens (Larsen *et al.*, 1997). Similarly, inclusion of increased dietary levels of selenium (0.6 mg/kg) decreased morbidity and mortality from Marek's disease, increased ability to remove oxygen free radicals and lipid peroxide, and alleviated the degree of tissue damage caused by oxygen free radicals (Huang and Chen, 1996). In another experiment, chicks were given basal diets containing 0.086, 0.3 or 0.6 mg/kg Se. They were infected with infectious bursal disease virus at 39 days of age. Ten days later the mortality rates were 33.3, 12.4 and 10.6%, respectively; and the infection-induced inhibition of T lymphocyte transformation was less in the selenium-supplemented birds (Bu *et al.*, 1996).

Postnatal development of the chick is associated with changes in antioxidant defence strategy. The level of fat soluble antioxidants, vitamin E and carotenoids decreases and antioxidant defence is compensated by increased activity of antioxidant enzymes and higher levels of ascorbic acid (Surai, 1999). Thus, in this experiment the previous suggestion (Surai, 1999a), that the antioxidant system is immature during embryonic development and its regulation is improved postnatally, has been substantiated. The activity of Se-GSH-Px in the chick liver significantly increased from hatching to day 10 of age. To date, age-related changes in antioxidant enzyme activities in chicken have received limited attention. It has been shown that in the chicken postnatal development activities of GSH-Px and catalase in the liver increased reaching a maximum at 20-30 days of age (Kalytka and Donchenko, 1995). In contrast, activities of antioxidant enzymes in muscle decreased from week 1 to 4 months after hatch (Mizuno, 1984; 1984a). In mammalian (mainly rat) liver, it has been shown that SOD and GSH-Px activities did not change; but that catalase activity decreased as a function of age (Matsuo *et al.*, 1992; Matsuo, 1993). In these studies, however, the perinatal period was not considered. In contrast, catalase, GSH-Px and SOD activities in rat liver increased after birth (Gonzalez *et al.*, 1995; Gunther *et al.*, 1993). Similarly, in rat brain GSH-Px activity increased by 70% from birth to adulthood (Brannan *et al.*, 1981).

Activities of antioxidant enzymes are regulated by gene expression (Storz and Tartaglia, 1992) and can respond to environmental changes, thereby making regulation of the antioxidant system more sophisticated and reliable. It is interesting to note that selenium supplementation of the maternal diet increased GSH-Px activity in the liver of newly hatched chicks to such an extent that during the next 10 days it remained at this plateau level with a further increase noted at day 20 of age (Surai, unpublished data).

Tissue susceptibility to peroxidation significantly decreased between days 1 and 5 of age (Figure 9). MDA accumulation in the liver of day-old and 5-day old chicks from antioxidant-supplemented hens was significantly reduced. When hens had been given either 200 ppm vitamin E or 40 ppm vitamin E plus 0.2 ppm Se, differences remained through 10 days of age. Therefore, liver susceptibility to lipid peroxidation substantially decreased despite decreasing vitamin E and carotenoid concentration. This can be explained as a result of increased concentration of glutathione (Figure 7) and GSH-Px activity (Figure 8) as well as of lipid composition changes (Noble and Cocchi, 1990). In fact, MDA accumulation in livers of chicks in treatments 3-6 was similar and significantly lower than the controls (commercial diet). This means that antioxidant protection afforded by increased GSH-Px activity is equal to dietary inclusion of 40-100 mg/kg vitamin E. Similarly, in another experiment dietary inclusion of 0.5 ppm Se or its combination with vitamin E for five weeks increased activities of GSH-Px and SOD and decreased MDA contents in tissues, confirming the antioxidant protective effect of selenium (Huang *et al.*,1998). In rats, an inverse linear correlation was found between lipid peroxide concentration and Se-GSH-Px activities in various tissues (Gromadzinska *et al.*, 1988).

The benefit of organic selenium in breeder diets lies in its efficient absorption, transport and accumulation in egg and embryonic tissues. This results in improved antioxidant status of the newly hatched chick. As the levels of major natural antioxidants (vitamin E and carotenoids) in tissues progressively decline after hatch, the antioxidant enzymes become a critical arm of antioxidant defence. Therefore, enhanced GSH-Px activity in tissues as a result of organic selenium supplementation of the maternal diet may have a positive impact on chick viability in the first few weeks posthatch. An improved antioxidant system of the chick may also enhance immune system function, which is extremely important at this point in physiological development. The sparing effect of organic selenium on vitamin E also presents the possibility of decreasing excess vitamin E supplementation.

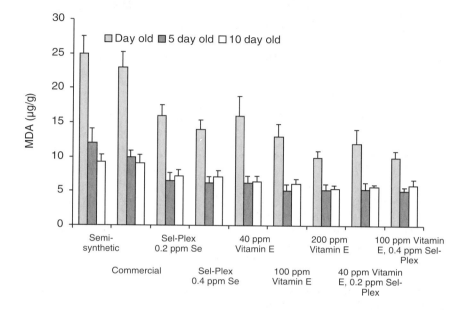

Figure 9. Malondialdehyde (MDA) accumulation in the chick liver.

The generalized scheme of selenium involvement in chick embryo development is shown in Figure 10.

SELENIUM AND MALE FERTILITY

Research conducted over the last 25 years has clearly shown that selenium is essential for male fertility (Behne *et al.*, 1982; Calvin *et al.*, 1987; Wu *et al.*, 1979; Hansen and Deguchi, 1996). It has been shown that in mild deficiency selenium is preferentially retained in rat testes (Behne *et al.*, 1982); and progressive selenium deficiency is associated with morphological alterations of spermatids and spermatozoa (Calvin *et al.*, 1987) with subsequent complete disappearance of mature germinal cells (Behne *et al.*, 1996). In selenium-deficient mice, the proportion of abnormal sperm was high, ranging from 6.8 to 49.6%, while in the control group it ranged from only 4.0 to 15.0%. The most frequently occurring abnormalities in sperm shape were in the sperm head. There was also a tendency toward increased abnormalities in other regions (neck, midpiece and tail) (Watanabe and Endo, 1991).

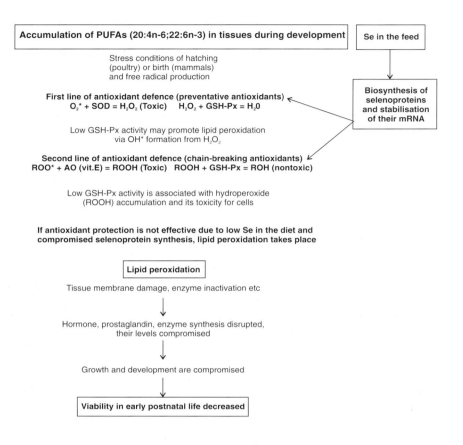

Figure 10. Relationship between selenium and embryonic postnatal development.

In addition, mammalian spermatozoa are among tissues with the highest selenium concentration (Behne *et al.*, 1986). More than 85% of total selenium was found in human seminal plasma and sperm motility was maximal at semen selenium levels ranging between 50 and 69 ng/ml. Above and below this range motility was decreased (Bleau *et al.*, 1984). Among the five species studied, the selenium content of seminal plasma was lowest in human males and stallions, higher in rams and boars, and the highest levels were encountered in the bull (Saaranen *et al.*, 1989). In humans, significant positive correlations in selenium concentrations were demonstrated between the different reproductive organs with the testis having the highest concentrations. No correlation was found between concentrations of selenium in the genital organs and liver, kidney or blood, suggesting that its uptake and/or biochemical activity in the reproductive organs may be controlled by similar mechanisms not shared by the other organs (Oldereid *et al.*, 1998).

A specific sperm capsule selenoprotein was identified in 1978 in rats (Calvin, 1978). Since then this protein has been intensively studied and it has been suggested that selenium may thus affect function of spermatozoa. Hansen and Deguchi (1996) reviewed recent research and suggested that selenium is essential for normal sperm development in experimental animals, livestock and in humans. Recently it has been shown that PH-GSH-Px protein represents at least 50% of the capsule material that embeds the helix of mitochondria (Ursini *et al.*, 1999). Therefore, the structural role of PH-GSH-Px in mature spermatozoa has been suggested.

The biological function of selenium in male reproduction is not restricted to mitochondria selenoprotein, as GSH-Px plays an important role in antioxidant defence in spermatozoa. Mammalian (Kelso *et al.*, 1997; Lenzi *et al.*, 1996) and avian (Surai *et al.*, 1997a, 1998; 2000) spermatozoa are characterised by high concentrations of polyunsaturated fatty acids (PUFA) within the phospholipids. This is an important risk factor for peroxidative damage to spermatozoa membranes and is considered a cause of male subfertility (Wishart, 1984; Aitken, 1994). Consequently, an efficient antioxidant system is required to protect sperm membranes against peroxidative damage (Aitken, 1995; Surai *et al.*, 1997a).

The antioxidant system of avian semen is poorly understood. Chicken semen contains the natural antioxidants vitamin E (Surai, 1989, Surai and Ionov, 1992; Surai *et al.*, 1997a), vitamin C and glutathione (Surai *et al.*, 1998a) as well as antioxidant enzymes GSH-Px (Kelso *et al.*, 1996; Surai *et al.*, 1998a) and SOD (Manella and Jones, 1980; Froman and Thurston , 1980; Surai *et al.*, 1998a). Of these, vitamin E in conjunction with Se-GSH-Px plays an essential role in the protection of spermatozoan lipids against peroxidation.

In addition, GSH-Px activity has been found in the semen of several other species besides humans including canine, ovine, caprine and bovine (Li, 1975; Kantola *et al.*, 1988; Kelso *et al.*, 1997). Seminal plasma GSH-Px activity was low in human males and rams, absent in boars and stallions but very high in the bull (Saaranen, 1989). It was concluded that this selenium-dependent enzyme may be important in protecting bovine spermatozoa against damage caused by oxygen radicals, while in man such a mechanism is not functional (Kantola *et al.*, 1988). In some species, for example mice, it is considered the major protective system against oxidative damage (Ghyselinck *et al.*, 1991) as a result of its action against decomposing lipid hydroperoxides - the key intermediates in spontaneous lipid peroxidation in mammalian sperm (Hansen and Deguchi, 1996).

It has been shown that approximately two thirds of GSH-Px activity in bull semen was non-Se-GSH-Px (Slaweta *et al.*, 1988). In the same experiment it was noted that MDA level was negatively correlated with Se-GSH-Px activity and it was suggested that Se-GSH-Px plays a role in protecting against disruption of the acrosomal membrane.

There are also differences among avian species in activities and distribution of GSH-Px in semen. For example, total GSH-Px activity in seminal plasma was highest for turkeys and lowest in ducks and geese (Surai *et al.*, 1998). In contrast, the highest GSH-Px activities in spermatozoa were found in geese and ducks and much lower activities were noted in guinea fowl, turkeys or chicken (Figure 11). Recently, it has been shown that despite a high proportion of PUFAs and low levels of vitamin E, duck spermatozoa have the same susceptibility to lipid peroxidation as chicken spermatozoa (Surai *et al.*, 2000), emphasising the importance of increased Se-GSH-Px activity in duck semen. In the five avian species studied, the Se-dependent form of GSH-Px in spermatozoa comprised from 77.7 % (chicken) to 87.4% (guinea fowl) (Figure 12). In cocks, about 60% of Se-GSH-Px was found in seminal plasma and 40% in the spermatozoa (Surai *et al.*, 1998).

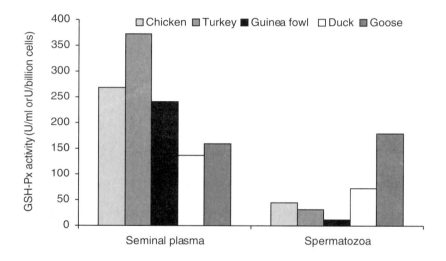

Figure 11. Total GSH-Px activity in avian semen.

Evidence has been provided from studies in cattle and humans (Julien and Murray, 1977; Pratt, 1978; Vezina *et al.*, 1996) indicating that selenium supplementation enhances *in vitro* motility and oxygen uptake of sperm and has a positive effect on motility of human sperm in subfertile males (MacPherson *et al*, 1994; Scott *et al.*, 1998). In order to verify the hypothesis that selenium and vitamin E could improve male fertility, nine men with low semen quality were supplemented for a period of 6 months with selenium and vitamin E. Compared to the baseline (pre-supplementation) period of four months, statistically significant increases were observed for selenium and vitamin E levels, sperm motility, percent live and percent normal spermatozoa. These improvements are likely to be 'supplementation-dependent' since all of the parameters returned to baseline values during the post-treatment period (Vezina *et al.*, 1996).

Selenium can affect spermatozoa *in vitro*. Incubation of ram spermato-zoa with selenite, selenocystine or selenomethionine ranging from 10^{-6} to

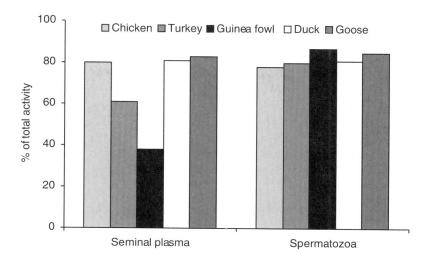

Figure 12. Se-GSH-Px activity in avian semen as a percentage of total GSH-Px activity.

2.5×10^{-5}M significantly improved sperm motility and oxygen consumption (Alabi *et al.*, 1985).

On the other hand, the male reproductive system is quite sensitive to selenium excess. Ingestion of 2 or 4 ppm Se in the diet by the house rat, *Rattus rattus*, for five weeks caused a dose-dependent reduction in body weight, testicular and cauda epididymidis weights. Concentration, motility and percentage of live spermatozoa also decreased with a simultaneous increase in the percentage of abnormal sperm (Kaur and Parshad, 1994).

Enhancement of the antioxidant capacity of semen could present a major opportunity for improving male fertility. The beneficial consequences of effective protection against lipid peroxidation are likely to result from two related mechanisms. Firstly, defence against peroxidative damage is essential to prevent any reduction in functionally important C_{20-22} polyunsaturated fatty acid levels of spermatozoan phospholipids and to maintain the structural integrity of the spermatozoa. Secondly, minimisation of lipid peroxidation will prevent accumulation of the toxic products of peroxidation. Additional possibilities may also be envisaged for the use of antioxidants in improving the viability of semen during cryopreservation.

The proportion of PUFA in sperm phospholipids decreased as a result of peroxidation during chicken sperm storage. The main PUFA affected was 22:4n-6 (Surai *et al.*, 1998a). This contrasts with mammalian spermatozoa where 22:6n-3 and 20:4n-6 were preferentially oxidised during sperm storage (Jones and Mann, 1976; Griveau *et al.*, 1995). Stimulated peroxidation of the spermatozoa in the presence of Fe^{2+} was associated with the loss of 22:6n-3, 22:5n-3, 20:4n-6 and 20:3n-6. At the same time MDA production significantly increased (Surai *et al.*, 1998a). The mechanisms by which oyxgen radicals disrupt sperm function is believed to involve the peroxidation of PUFA in the sperm plasma membrane (Aitken, 1994); and this process plays an important role in the pathophysiology of male infertility (Aitken *et al.*, 1993).

Lipid peroxidation has also been shown to affect the activities of cytochrome oxidase, lactate dehydrogenase and glucose-6-phosphate dehydrogenase, with the seminal plasma affording a measure of protection against such deleterious effects *in vivo* (Ferrandi *et al.*, 1992) and during sperm storage (Cecil and Bakst, 1993). During spontaneous lipid peroxidation, the spermatozoa chromatin has been shown to undergo destabilisation associated with marked alterations in the physico-chemical state of the DNA-protein complex (Ferrandi *et al.*, 1992a).

Reactive oxygen species increase DNA fragmentation (Lopes *et al.*, 1998; Twigg *et al.*, 1998), modify the cytoskeleton (Hindshaw *et al.*, 1986), affect the sperm axoneme (De Lamirande and Gagnon, 1992) and inhibit sperm-oocyte fusion (Aitken *et al.*, 1993a). A negative correlation between sperm motility and lipid peroxidation in cryopreserved semen has also been recorded (Bell *et al.*, 1993). Alvarez and Storey (1992) demonstrated that cryopreservation enhanced lipid peroxidation and this enhancement was mediated at least in part by the loss of SOD activity during the freezing process. Excessive generation of reactive oxygen species and increased peroxidation of membrane phospholipids was proposed as a biochemical basis for reduced activity of spermatozoa in cryopreserved semen (Askari *et al.*, 1994). The toxic effects of hydrogen peroxide and organic hydroperoxide on sperm motility have also been demonstrated (Surai *et al.*, 1998a).

In an experiment conducted jointly at SAC (Scotland) and the Poultry Research Institute (Ukraine), the effect of dietary selenium supplementation (0.3 mg/kg) and two levels of vitamin E (20 and 200 mg/kg) on chicken semen quality was evaluated (Surai *et al.*, 1998c). Inclusion of selenium in the male diet significantly increased Se-GSH-Px activity in the liver, testes, spermatozoa and seminal plasma (Figure 13). This resulted in significantly decreased sperm susceptibility to lipid peroxidation as indicated by lower MDA accumulation (Figure 14). In addition, the increased activity of Se-GSH-Px in sperm obtained from birds fed the selenium-supplemented diet was associated with greater protection against lipid peroxidation in stored semen. As GSH-Px in the sperm is considered the main enzyme which removes peroxides and thereby protects cells against damage caused by free radicals and the products of lipid peroxidation *in vivo* (Griveau *et al.*, 1995), its protective effect during sperm storage is also probably associated with this function. The results indicate the importance of GSH-Px in the protection of spermatozoa against lipid peroxidation during storage.

GSH-Px is expressed in both seminal plasma and spermatozoa of cockerels (Surai *et al.*, 1998; 1998a). This is in contrast to bulls where GSH-Px is exclusively associated with the seminal plasma and not spermatozoa (Brown *et al.*, 1977; Smith *et al.*, 1979). Given the specificity of Se-GSH-Px to hydrogen peroxide and the low activity of catalase in seminal plasma, it

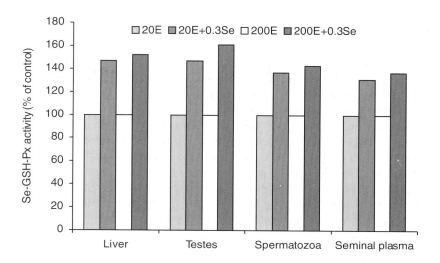

Figure 13. Effect of selenium and vitamin E supplementation (0.3 ppm) on Se-GSH-Px activity.

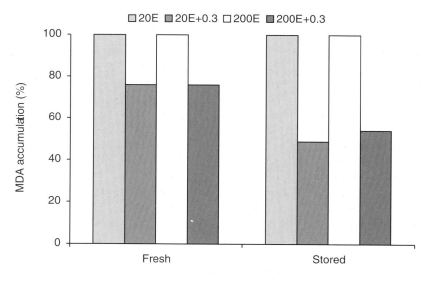

Figure 14. Effect of selenium supplementation on MDA formation in fresh and stored semen.

is reasonable to suggest that this form of the enzyme has the major role in hydrogen peroxide detoxification in spermatozoa.

Since hydrogen peroxide and lipid peroxides are toxic to spermatozoa (Alvarez *et al.*, 1987; Delamirande and Gagnon, 1992); GSH-Px plays an important role in protecting cell membrane lipids from peroxidation, thus maintaining the integrity of the cell (Flohe and Zimmermann, 1970). In this respect, it is important to note that an inducable form of the enzyme (Se-GSH-Px) represents more than 75% of the total enzymatic activity in the spermatozoa and more than 60% in the testes and liver of cockerels. In addition, GSH-Px activity in the testis was less than half that in the liver. Similarly, testis GSH-Px activity in rats was found to be lower than in liver, heart, kidney or lung (Lei *et al.*, 1995); but the PH-GSH-Px is considered to be of greater relevance in rat testis than liver (Cockell *et al.*, 1996).

The general relationship between selenium and male fertility is shown in Figure 15. Recent data indicate that the antioxidant/prooxidant balance in avian semen is an important element in maintaining membrane integrity and function including sperm viability and fertilising capacity. Therefore, the antioxidant system is a crucial element in male reproduction; and dietary selenium has a unique role via antioxidant mechanisms.

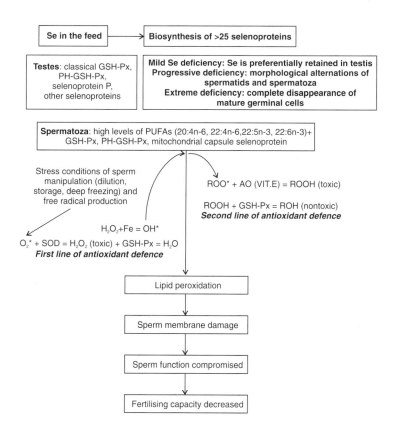

Figure 15. Selenium and male fertility.

SELENIUM STATUS AND MYCOTOXICOSIS

Selenium has a protective effect against different toxicoses. Selenium supplementation significantly decreased cadmium (Zasadowski *et al.*, 1997), monensin (Yarsan, 1998), salinomycin (Zarski *et al.*, 1995) and mercury (Maretta *et al.*, 1995) toxicity in chickens or arsenic cytotoxic effects in mice (Biswas *et al.*, 1999). Moreover, selenium protection against mycotoxins has received considerable attention.

Burguera *et al.* (1983) indicated that selenium had a protective effect against aflatoxin B_1 toxicity in turkey poults. To investigate the biochemical mechanism of this protective effect, hepatic metabolism of aflatoxin B_1 in turkey poults was examined at various dietary selenium concentrations (0.2, 2.0 or 4.0 ppm). The experimental results provided clear evidence of selenium-induced enhancement of aflatoxin detoxification (Gregory and Edds, 1984); and it was suggested that the protective action of selenium was not mediated by an increase in glutathione availability for aflatoxin conjugation or by effects on the activities of these enzymes as measured *in vitro*. Therefore nutrients such as selenium are considered effective in the reduction of aflatoxicosis in poultry (Dalvi, 1986). Recently the protective effect of organic selenium in combination with vitamin E has been shown in broilers exposed to aflatoxin-contaminated feed (Stanley *et al.*, 1998).

Similar protective effects of selenium against aflatoxicosis have been shown with mammalian species. In pigs a diet containing 2.5 mg/kg Se was protective against the toxic effects of aflatoxin B_1; and the protection was demonstrated by alteration of clinical responses and hematologic (prothrombin times), electrophoretic and clinical chemistry values (Davila *et al.*, 1983). Effects of a single intramuscular injection of selenium-vitamin E (5 mg Se + 68 IU α-tocopherol/60 kg of body weight) 14 days before an oral dose of aflatoxin B_1 (1.0 mg/kg) were evaluated in 24 dairy calves. Although aflatoxin exposure significantly decreased body weight and feed intake, selenium increased feed intake in calves fed diets containing aflatoxin (Brucato *et al.*, 1986).

Milks *et al.* (1985) showed that selenium is able to protect against the hepatocarcinogenic effects of aflatoxin B_1 in the rat. Morover, inhibitory activity of selenium on mutagenesis induced by aflatoxin B_1 in the presence of a rat liver microsomal activation system has been shown using *Salmonella typhimurium* tests (Francis *et al.*, 1988). The results of another experiment showed that selenium could protect cultured cells from aflatoxin B_1 cytotoxicity, but had no effect on aflatoxin B_1-DNA adduct formation or mutagenesis (Shi *et al.*, 1995). In a different study, the same authors reported that selenium could inhibit aflatoxin B_1-induced DNA damage (Shi *et al.*, 1994).

It has been revealed that selenium can inhibit formation of hyperplastic and enzyme-altered foci as well as hepatocarcinogenesis induced by aflatoxin B_1; but selenium can neither prevent the enlargement nor accelerate the regression of foci already developed after administration of carcinogens (Wang, 1990). Therefore Lei *et al.* (1990) concluded that selenium had an inhibitory effect on initiation and promotion stages of aflatoxin B_1-induced preneoplastic foci and nodules. Selenium also prevented progression of these nodules to hepatocellular carcinoma even after cessation of aflatoxin B_1 administration.

Additional experiments were conducted to verify the effect of selenium on the mutagenic activity of aflatoxin B_1. After 14 days of selenium administration to Chinese hamsters, the incidence of chromosomal aberrations in bone marrow cells due to a single administration of 5 mg aflatoxin B_1 per kg body weight was significantly reduced (Petr *et al.*, 1990). A significant decrease in the frequency of aberrant cells, breaks and gaps was observed at almost any time during the investigation.

A protective effect of selenium is not restricted to aflatoxins, but is obvious with T-2 toxin as well. When male Wistar rats were fed diets supplemented with selenium (0.5 and 2.5 mg/kg) for six weeks, toxicity symptoms were less distinct and mortality was two (Kravchenko *et al.*, 1990) or 3-5 (Tutelyan *et al.*, 1990) times lower compared to the unsupplemented group. The acute lethal toxicity of T-2 toxin was reduced by administration of sodium selenite (Yazdanpanah *et al.*, 1997).

Other antioxidant compounds have shown similar protective effects against mycotoxicosis symptoms. Rizzo *et al.* (1994) demonstrated that trichothecenes stimulate lipid peroxidation with a consequent decrease in GSH content and that dietary inclusion of selenium, α-tocopherol and ascorbic acid provided protection against acute toxicosis caused by deoxynivalenol or T-2 toxin. T-2 toxin plus carotenoid lycopene added to chicken diets at an approximate ratio of 1:17 diminished some toxic effects including protection of cellular GSH level (Leal *et al.*, 1999). The efficiency of carotenoids as anti-toxicants varies considerably. Okotie-Eboh *et al.* (1997) showed that ß-carotene was not effective at ameliorating aflatoxicosis in broiler chickens; but canthaxanthin was somewhat effective with respect to certain clinical blood chemistry indicators.

Ascorbic acid given to guinea pigs via gavage had protective effects against acute toxicity of aflatoxin B_1 (Netke *et al.*, 1997). The effects of such antioxidants as retinol, ascorbic acid and α-tocopherol were tested on ochratoxin A genotoxicity. Pretreatment of mice by vitamin E, vitamin A or vitamin C decreased DNA adduct formation in kidney by 80, 70 and 90%, respectively (Grosse *et al.*, 1997). In the same experiment, pretreatment of female mice with α-tocopherol before administration of zearalenone inhibited DNA adduct formation in liver and in kidney.

Oxidative damage caused by T-2 toxin may be one of the underlying mechanisms for T-2-induced cell injury and DNA damage, which eventually lead to tumorigenesis. Two antioxidants, coenzyme Q10 and vitamin E, showed some protection against toxic cell death and glutathione depletion caused by T-2 toxin in mouse liver (Atroshi *et al.*, 1997). It was found that T-2 toxin inclusion in the diet stimulated lipid peroxidation in the tissues.

The most sensitive species was the goose followed by ducks and chickens; and the most sensitive tissue was the liver followed by blood plasma and red blood cells (Mezes *et al.*, 1999). Similarly, in rat liver T-2 toxin has been shown to be involved in the generation of free radicals which cause the observed increase in lipid peroxidation (Suneja *et al.*, 1989).

Dietary fumonisin B_1 levels of 250 and 500 mg/kg ($P < 0.05$) increased the level of thiobarbituric acid reactive substances (TBARS) in the liver of rats fed the mycotoxin over 21 days (Abel and Gelderblom, 1998). *In vitro* investigations in primary rat hepatocytes by the same authors indicated that the level of TBARS was increased in a dose dependent manner and associated with an increase in cytotoxicity. Addition of α-tocopherol decreased the cytotoxicity; and TBARS content was decreased to basal levels, suggesting that lipid peroxidation is likely to contribute to the cytotoxic effect of fumonisin B_1 (Abel and Gelderblom, 1998).

These data indicate that stimulation of lipid peroxidation and DNA adduct formation are important mechanisms of mycotoxin action. In this respect various antioxidants (vitamin E, carotenoids, vitamin A and coenzyme Q10) provide a considerable protective effect; and the protective effect of selenium is even more pronounced. Positive responses were recorded in different mammalian and avian species and with different mycotoxins tested. However, doses of selenium used for such protection were quite high and considerably in excess of physiological requirements. In some cases selenium levels used were almost toxic.

SELENIUM AND MAINTENANCE OF EGG FRESHNESS

The ability to sustain egg freshness during storage and transport is economically important. Egg freshness decreases during storage, a process associated with biochemical changes in composition and structure of egg yolk and albumin. Oxidation most probably has a role in decreasing egg freshness. As shown previously, selenium can be transferred from the feed into the egg. In the experiments conducted in Japan (Wakebe, 1998) it was shown that inclusion of Sel-Plex organic selenium in the hen diet at 0.3 ppm Se increased GSH-Px activity in the egg yolk and albumin (Figure 16). The Haugh units were used as an indicator of egg freshness. The value was high on day 1 in both treatment and control groups with no difference due to selenium supplementation. As time progressed, Haugh units of the control group declined sharply while the declination was more moderate in the treatment group. By day 7, it was evident that the Haugh unit measurement was significantly higher in the treatment group (Figure 17).

These data have a commercial application as they indicate longer maintenance of egg quality during storage. There may also be an application for incubated eggs since long egg storage times are associated with decreased hatchability.

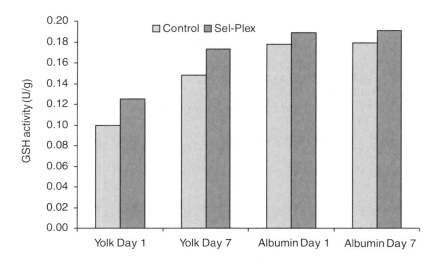

Figure 16. Effect of storage time and selenium form on GSH-Px activity in eggs.

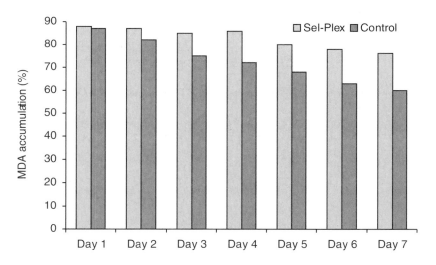

Figure 17. Effect of storage time and selenium form on Haugh unit measurements.

SELENIUM STATUS, BROILER PERFORMANCE AND MEAT QUALITY

One of the main challenges to the food animal industry is to enhance the image of meat and its appearance on supermarket shelves. There are many meat quality characteristics that attract consumer attention. They include appearance, texture and flavour (Liu *et al.*, 1995) as well as tenderness, juiciness, aroma (Janssens, 1998) and some other subjective characteristics. Among these characteristics, appearance has the major impact on the initial decision of the customer to purchase or reject the product (Sheehy *et al.*, 1997). The consumer prefers to have fresh meat with a minimum loss of water during handling and cooking. Therefore water-holding capacity of the meat (Mahan and Kim, 1999) as well as colour (Froning, 1995) and the absence of off-flavours (Sheehy *et al.*, 1997) are important characteristics of meat quality.

It has been shown that sensory qualities of meat are affected by muscle biochemistry and modern processing technologies (Ouali, 1991). Grinding meat increases oxygen incorporation into muscle and cooking releases protein-bound iron into the intracellular pool (Chan and Decker, 1994). In this process free radical production and lipid peroxidation disrupt membrane structure and quality and lead ultimately to off-flavours, off colours and poor texture etc. (Stanley, 1991).

One of the most common approaches to increasing the oxidative stability of meat is to utilize antioxidants both as dietary supplements and during processing (Decker, 1998). An increasing body of evidence indicates that vitamin E supplementation (at levels in excess of requirements) is an effective means of improving meat quality in chickens, turkeys, cattle, pigs and lambs (Sheehy *et al.*, 1997; Wulf *et al.*, 1995; Buckley *et al.*, 1995; Liu *et al.*, 1995). Based on the data in these reports and taking into account antioxidant interactions, it is reasonable to suggest that synergistic relationships between selenium level and form and vitamin E could be used to advantage in meat quality improvement.

GSH-Px activity in muscle did not change significantly during eight days storage of beef (Renerre *et al.*, 1996). This suggests that once GSH-Px activity is established, it is maintained during meat storage and therefore a stabilizing effect of selenium supplementation might be expected. Supplementing a broiler diet with 0.25 ppm Se substantially increased GSH-Px activity in breast (2.1-fold) and leg muscles (4.1-fold). Consequently, decreased lipid peroxidation was detected in the muscles (2.5-fold in breast muscle and 3.3-fold in leg muscle) after four days storage at 4 ^{0}C (DeVore *et al.*, 1983). Edens (1996) showed that drip loss was lower when organic selenium was fed to broilers. Edens (1997) also found an interaction between vitamin E and organic selenium in improving yield in growing chickens. In a trial during the spring season, organic selenium improved feather development and reduced drop loss. Additional conclusive results have been obtained recently in the University of New England in Australia (Naylor *et al.*, 2000). In this experiment, birds receiving dietary organic selenium had reduced (P<0.01) drip loss (Figure 18). In addition, organic selenium improved eviscerated weight (P<0.05) and breast yield (P<0.05) and also had a positive effect on feathering. These data indicate that meat quality during storage can be improved by inclusion of organic selenium. It is also obvious that increased selenium supplementation (0.25 ppm) in the form of Sel-Plex

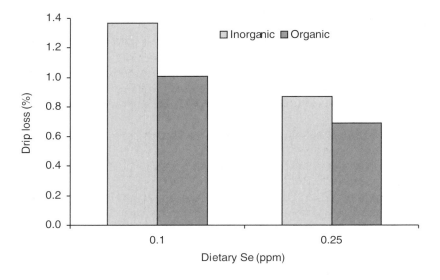

Figure 18. Effect of selenium source and level on 24-h drip loss in male broilers (Naylor *et al.*, 2000).

had an additional positive effect (compared to 0.1 ppm) on prevention of drip loss. Inorganic selenium added to pig diets had a detrimental effect on loin quality as indicated by higher drip loss and a paler colour (Mahan *et al.*, 1999). Species-specific differences in the effect of selenium and other antioxidants on meat quality probably reflect differences in the levels of PUFA as well as some other antioxidants (vitamin E, vitamin C, glutathione) and prooxidants.

Since lipid manipulation and enrichment of meat by n-3 fatty acids are considered an important step in improving the human diet (Wood and Enser, 1997), antioxidant supplementation in such cases could also be of great importance. In particular, use of organic selenium in combination with other antioxidants (vitamin E and ascorbic acid) awaits investigation.

Selenium status and human health

A great body of evidence indicates that European intakes of selenium are falling (Rayman, 1997). In 1978 selenium intake in Britain was 60 µg/day (Thorn *et al.*, 1978) and seven years later it was only 43 µg/day. By 1990 it had fallen to 30 µg/day (MacPherson *et al.*, 1993). Even in 1997 the average reported selenium intake was only 43 µg/d (Shortt *et al.*, 1997). Dietary intakes of selenium across the world vary, but are low in many countries including Egypt (29 µg/day); Belgium (30 µg/day); Turkey (32 µg/day), Sweden (38 µg/day), Slovak Republic (38.2 µg/day) France and Germany (47 µg/day) and Italy (49 µg/day) (Reilly, 1996; Kadrabova *et al.*, 1998).

The British government's defined reference nutrient intake is 75 µg/day for men and 60 µg/day for women (Rayman, 1997). Recommended daily intake (RDI) in the US is very similar at 70 and 55 µg/day for men and women, respectively (NRC, 1989). An intake of 40 µg/day was suggested as the minimum selenium amount required for humans (Whanger, 1998). The decline in selenium intake is associated with decreased serum and whole blood selenium concentrations (Alfthan and Neve, 1996; MacPherson and Barclay, 1997).

Low selenium concentration in blood is associated with increased risk of spontaneous abortions (Barrington *et al.*, 1996), male subfertility (Bleau *et al.*, 1984), increased risk of cancer (Clark *et al.*, 1984, Willett *et al.*, 1983) and higher cancer mortality rates (Clark *et al.*, 1991; Schrauzer *et al*, 1977). An inverse relationship between blood selenium concentrations and cardiovascular disease has been also reported (Kok *et al.*, 1989). Epidemiological studies indicate an association between low nutritional selenium status and increased risks of cardiomyopathy, cardiovascular disease, and carcinogenesis in various tissues (Badmaev *et al.*, 1996).

It has long been known that nutritional deficiency of the host leads to increased susceptibility to infectious diseases. Additionally, relatively harmless viruses can become virulent by passing through a selenium-deficient host due to specific mutations (Beck *et al.*, 1995). It has been suggested that increased oxidative stress of the host leads to increased mutations in the viral genome with following change in virulence (Beck, 1999).

On the other hand, selenium supplementation of the human diet (200 µg daily) significantly decreased cancer mortality (by 50%) (Clark *et al.*, 1996). The selenium-treated group had substantial reductions in the incidence of prostate cancer and total cancer incidence and mortality (Clark *et al.*, 1998). Of all the human cancer intervention studies completed in recent years, the selenium trial by Clark and co-workers is the most successful (Ip, 1998).

In animal models selenium is an active anticarcinogen. Dietary supplementation of selenomethionine (2.5 or 5 ppm) decreased tumour cross-sectional area and tumour volume in mice (Yan *et al.*, 1999). These results demonstrate that dietary supplementation of selenomethionine reduced experimental metastasis of melanoma cells in mice and inhibited the growth of metastatic tumours in the lungs. The molecular mechanisms of anticancer activity of selenium need further elucidation; but recently it has been shown that direct exposure of cultured human umbilical vein endothelial cells to selenium induced cell death predominantly through apoptosis, decreased gelatinolytic activities of matrix metalloproteinase-2, or both (Jiang *et al.*, 1999). Therefore selenium metabolites can inhibit important attributes (proliferation, survival, and matrix degradation) of endothelial cells critical for angiogenic sprouting. Together these data suggest that adequate selenium intake is essential for cancer prevention (Fleet, 1997).

Administration of selenium to subfertile patients (100 µg/day) significantly increased sperm motility (MacPherson *et al.*, 1993) and chance of successful conception (Scott *et al.*, 1998). Selenium also had a protective effect against age-related immunosuppression (Turner and Francis, 1991). Selenium supplementation provides significant improvement in elderly patients by increasing the humoral response after vaccination and could have considerable public health importance by reducing morbidity from respiratory tract infections (Girodon *et al.*, 1999). Utilizing a mouse model system and healthy human volunteers, it has been shown that selenium enhances the capacity of lymphocytes to respond to stimulation with mitogen or alloantigen, to proliferate and to differentiate into cytotoxic effector cells. Supplementation with selenium resulted in a significant increase in the tumour cytotoxicity of mouse cytotoxic lymphocytes, lymphokine activated killer cells and macrophages, and human cytotoxic lymphocytes and natural killer cells (Kiremidjian-Schumacher and Roy, 1998).

Selenium supplementation boosts cellular immunity by three main mechanisms (McKenzie *et al.*, 1998): by upregulating the expression of T-cell high affinity IL-2 receptors and providing a vehicle for enhanced T-cell responses; by preventing oxidative stress-induced damages to immune cells and by altering platelet aggregation and decreasing the ratio of tromboxane:leukotriene produced. Therefore antioxidant properties of selenoproteins are responsible only partly for immune-stimulating properties of selenium although oxygen species scavenging was proposed as an important mechanism for selenium to promote immunity (Sun *et al.*, 1995).

The possibility that a subclinical deficiency of selenium might exist in a sample of the British population was examined by giving a selenium supplement for five weeks (Benton and Cook, 1990). Using a double-blind crossover design 50 subjects received either a placebo or 100 µg Se on a daily basis. On three occasions, they completed the Profile of Moods questionnaire. Mood did not change when taking the placebo, whereas when taking the selenium the subjects reported a substantial improvement after both 2.5 and 5 weeks. The lower the level of selenium in the diet prior to supplementation, the higher the reduction in reports of anxiety, depression and tiredness following selenium therapy (Benton and Cook, 1991). More recent results suggest that persons with low selenium status might experience relatively depressed moods and support the idea that selenium plays a special role in the brain (Hawkes and Hornbostel, 1996).

Another advantage of optimal selenium supplementation of humans is its effect on fatty acid profiles of human plasma and milk. In China linoleic acid (18:2n-6) concentration, the primary PUFA in human plasma and milk, was higher in women with adequate selenium intake compared to those with extremely low or extremely high selenium consumption (Dodge *et al.*, 1999). Similarly, in New Zealand women selenium concentration of breast milk was significantly increased by supplementation, which was associated with increased concentrations of polyunsaturated fatty acids, especially linoleic acid, and decreased proportions of saturated fatty acids (Dodge *et al.*, 1999a). Since PUFA in human milk are important determinants of neonatal development, the health effects of these findings need further study.

It has also been shown that selenium, and more effectively combined selenium and vitamin E supplementation, has a role in controlling oxidative status and altered lipid metabolism in the liver during experimental diabetes. The antioxidants maintained favourable fatty acid distribution in the major tissues affected by diabetic complications (Douillet *et al.*, 1998). An effect of selenium on PUFA level and metabolism has wide-ranging consequences since long chain PUFA are precursors of prostaglandins and leucotrienes, important regulators of cell metabolism and function.

Reilly (1998) mentioned more than 40 human health conditions having a link with selenium that included aging, arthritis, cancer, cardiovascular disease, cataracts, cholestasis, cystyc fibrosis, diabetis, immunodeficiency, Kaschin-Beck disease, Keshan disease, lymphoblastic anemia, macular degeneration, muscular dystrophy, stroke and some others. The mechanisms of selenium participation in such conditions needs further elucidation; however in many cases the antioxidant role of selenoproteins appears to be the driving force. The results clearly indicate that selenium plays an important role in human health and disease prevention. Since selenium content of food depends on its availability from soil, the level of this element in food substantially varies.

It becomes increasingly clear that the issue of improving human selenium intake needs to be addressed. At present a number of alternatives exist.

- Use of daily organic selenium supplements.

- Addition of selenium to soils: some countries (eg. Finland) with low soil selenium add sodium selenate to fertilizers (Alfthan, 1993).

- Addition of selenium to bread flour (Rayman, 1997) or to produce bread using selenium-enriched yeast (Rumi *et al.*, 1994).

- Production of so-called functional foods enriched with selenium (Reilly, 1998).

SELENIUM AND FUNCTIONAL FOOD

A number of selenium-fortified foods are available in different countries (Reilly, 1998) including infant formulae, sports food supplements and drinks.

Beale *et al.* (1990) stated in a comprehensive review that there is no evidence that selenium supplementation of livestock produces potentially hazardous residues in meat, milk or eggs. In the same review, it was shown that selenium accumulation in muscle is comparatively low. These data were mainly based on usage of inorganic selenium, which is characterised by low accumulation in meat tissues. On the other hand, recently it has been shown that organic selenium has a much higher potential for accumulation in tissues.

Meat products account for varying proportions of human selenium intake in countries around the world. In Germany, where daily selenium intakes by men and women are 47 and 38 µg, respectively, meat is the primary source, providing 65.5% of total selenium intake. Pork contributes 25.1% (Oster and Prellwitz, 1989). Similar selenium concentrations in meat products were found in the Slovak Republic (Kadrabova *et al.*, 1997) and the main contributors of selenium to daily intake were eggs, pork, and poultry (Kadrabova *et al.*, 1998). In other countries selenium consumption in meat is somewhat lower. For example in Spain, pork and chicken provide 4.7 and 2.7 µg/day, respectively (Diaz-Alarcon *et al.*, 1996).

The bioavailability of selenium from natural sources in the human diet must be considered. In a nine week repletion experiment with rats, it was shown that relative selenium availability (based on liver GSH-Px) was as follows: pork, 86%; sodium selenite, 81%; selenomethionine, 80%; beef, 80%; chicken, 77%; veal, 77% and lamb, 58% (Wen *et al.*, 1997). Similarly it has been shown that beef is a highly bioavailable source of dietary selenium when compared with selenite or selenomethionine (Shi and Spallholz, 1994; 1994a). Using similar tests the authors have found that after selenium depletion the order of recovery of liver GSH-Px activity compared to the control animals (set at 100%) were selenite (98%), selenate (117%), raw beef (127%) and cooked ground beef (139%). The data suggest that bioavailability of selenium from ground beef is greater than that from either selenite or selenate.

The high bioavailability of selenium in meat suggests the value of functional foods based on meat for increasing human selenium intake. Supplementation of pig diets with organic selenium more than doubled loin selenium content compared to pigs given the same amount of inorganic selenium (Mahan, 1999). Lamb meat can also be substantially enriched in selenium (MacPherson *et al.*, 1994; Molnar *et al.*, 1997). Shoulder and thigh meat selenium content exhibited a dose-response relationship to dietary supplementation (Molnar *et al.*, 1996). Therefore, meat enriched with selenium could be an additional source of selenium in the diet.

Milk selenium content can also be substantially enriched by using organic selenium in dairy diets (Mahan, 1999). Given the selenium level in milk from cows supplemented with Sel-Plex (>0.1 ppm), 200 ml of milk can provide more than 20 µg of selenium, which can be a reasonable addition to the daily selenium intake. Therefore, milk from cows given organic selenium can be considered a functional food and can be used for improvement of the selenium status of humans.

Eggs from hens given Sel-Plex organic selenium can deliver up to 20-25 µg Se (based on the data in Figure 3), which is more than 30% of the daily requirement. Clearly such designer eggs can be placed in the functional food category and can substantially improve human selenium status. The enrichment of eggs with a combination of selenium and other antioxidants and n-3 PUFA could be an additional advantage for the improvement of the human diet (Surai *et al.*, 2000a).

Conclusion

A substantial body of evidence over the past few years has accumulated indicating that organic selenium is characterised by higher bioavailability for meat, milk and egg-producing species. This advantage provides an important tool for feed manufacturers and nutritionists to effectively use selenium to enhance antioxidant balance, a beneficial response in intensively-reared animals and poultry. Appropriate use of natural antioxidants in the diet is a logical approach to fighting the effects of stress. Moreover natural antioxidants, especially organic selenium, added to the diet can help to maintain animal health and productivity as well as to produce designer or functional foods enriched in this element.

Discussions concerning factors affecting our health started long ago and will continue. In the last decade it has become clear that lifestyle, including diet, stress, smoking, medical attention and exercise is a major determinant of health status and resistance to different diseases. In this contest, diet plays a critical role. Traditionally, food products were developed for taste, appearance, value and convenience for the consumer. Nevertheless, observations on the relationship between food choices and health have been made since ancient times and Hippocrates observed such a relationship in the fourth century BC. Since then many different nutritional guidelines have been issued and strong associations between diet and health have been shown (Truswell, 1998). Consumers increasingly use vitamin and mineral supplements. In this respect, functional foods enriched in selenium and other antioxidants may be useful for groups at risk for marginal antioxidant deficiencies, such as the chronically ill (e.g. diabetics), people using medicaments, older people and pregnant women. These foods could also substantially contribute to the diets of children, smokers, those eating unbalanced diets, people on slimming diets, vegetarians and people engaged in intensive sports, etc. Selenium has a number of roles in physiology; and there are advantages to be gained by using organic selenium to improve selenium status in tissues and assure optimum physiological function. Higher selenium content of meat, milk and eggs could bring about an improvement in human selenium status.

References

Abel, S. and W.C. Gelderblom. 1998. Oxidative damage and fumonisin B$_1$-induced toxicity in primary rat hepatocytes and rat liver *in vivo*. Toxicology 131:121-131.

Aitken, R.J. 1994. A free radical theory of male infertility. Reprod. Fert. Dev. 6:19-24.

Aitken, R.J. 1995. Free radicals, lipid peroxidation and sperm function. Reprod. Fert. Dev. 7:659-668.

Aitken, R.J., D. Harkiss and D. Buckingham. 1993. Relationship between iron-catalysed lipid peroxidation potential and human sperm function. J. Reprod. Fert. 98:257-265.

Aitken, R.J., D.W. Buckingham and D. Harkiss. 1993a. Use of xanthine oxidase free radical generating system to investigate the cytotoxic effects of reactive oxygen species on human spermatozoa. J. Reprod. Fert. 97:441-450.

Akesson, B., N. Bellew and R.F. Burk. 1994. Purification of selenoprotein P from human plasma. Biochim. Biophys. Acta. 1204:243-249.

Alabi, N.S., P.D. Whanger and A.S. Wu. 1985. Interactive effects of organic and inorganic selenium with cadmium and mercury on spermatozoal oxygen consumption and motility *in vitro*. Biol. Reprod. 33:911-919.

Alfthan, G. 1993. Effects of selenium fertilization on the human selenium status and the environment. Norwegian J. Agr. Sci. Suppl.11:175-181.

Alfthan, G. and J. Neve. 1996. Reference values for serum selenium in various areas evaluated according to the TRACY protocol. J. Trace Elem. Med. Biol. 10:77-87.

Alvarez, J.G. and B.T. Storey. 1992. Evidence for increased lipid peroxidative damage and loss of superoxide dismutase activity as a mode of sublethal cryodamage to human sperm during cryopreservation. J. Androl. 13:232-241.

Alvarez, J.G., J.C. Touchstone, L. Blasco and B.T. Storey. 1987. Spontaneous lipid peroxidation and production of hydrogen peroxide and superoxide in human spermatozoa. J. Androl. 8:338-348.

Arai, T., M. Sugawara, N. Sako, S. Motoyoshi, T. Shimura, N. Tsutsui and T. Konno. 1994. Glutathione peroxidase activity in tissues of chicken supplemented with dietary selenium. Comp. Biochem. Physiol. 107A:245-248.

Askari, H.A., J.H. Check, N. Peymer and A. Bollendorf. 1994. Effect of natural antioxidants tocopherol and ascorbic acid in maintenance of sperm activity during freeze-thaw process. Arch. Androl. 33:11-15.

Atroshi, F, A. Rizzo, I. Biese, P. Veijalainen, E. Antila and T. Westermarck. 1997. T-2 toxin-induced DNA damage in mouse livers: the effect of pretreatment with coenzyme Q10 and alpha-tocopherol. Mol. Aspects Med. 18 Suppl:S255-S258.

Badmaev, V., M. Majeed and R.A. Passwater. 1996. Selenium: a quest for better understanding. Altern. Ther. Health Med. 2:59-62, 65-67.

Bains, J.S. and C.A. Shaw. 1997. Neurodegenerative disorders in humans: the role of glutathione in oxidative stress-mediated neuronal death. Brain Res. Rev. 25:335-358.

Barrington, J.W., P. Lindsay, D. James, S. Smith and A. Roberts. 1996. Selenium deficiency and miscarrige: a possible link? Br. J. Obs. Gynaecol. 103:130-132.

Bartholomew, A., D. Latshaw and D.E. Swayne. 1998. Changes in blood chemistry, hematology, and histology caused by a selenium/vitamin E deficiency and recovery in chicks. Biol. Trace Elem. Res. 62:7-16.

Beale, A.M., D.A. Fasulo and A.L. Craigmill. 1990. Effects of oral and parenteral selenium supplements on residues in meat, milk and eggs. Rev. Environ. Contamin. Toxicol. 115:125-150.

Beck, M.A. 1999. Selenium and host defence towards viruses. Proc. Nutr. Soc. 58: 707-711.

Beck, M.A, P.C. Kolbeck, Q. Shi, L.H. Rohr, V.C. Morris and O.A. Levander. 1994. Increased virulence of a human enterovirus (coxsackievirus B3) in selenium-deficient mice. J. Infect. Dis. 170:351-357.

Beck, M.A., S. Quing, V.C. Morris and O.A. Levander. 1995. Rapid genomic evolution of a non-virulent Coxsackievirus B3 in selenium-deficient mice results in selection of identical virulent isolates. Nature Med. 1:433-436.

Behne, D., M. Duk and W. Elger. 1986. Selenium content and glutathione peroxidase activity in the testis of the maturing rat. J. Nutr. 116:1442-1447.

Behne, D., H. Weiler and A. Kyriakopoulos. 1996. Effects of selenium deficiency on testicular morphology and function in rats. J. Reprod. Fertil. 106:291-297.

Behne, D., T. Hofer, R. von Berswordt-Wallrabe and W. Elger. 1982. Selenium in the testis of the rat: studies on its regulation and its importance for the organism. J. Nutr. 112:1682-1687.

Behne, D., A. Kyriakopoulos, S. Scheid and H.Gessner. 1991. Effects of chemical form and dosage on the incorporation of selenium into tissue proteins in rats. J. Nutr. 121:806-814.

Bell, M., R. Wang, W.J.G. Hellstrom, and S.C. Sikka. 1993. Effect of cryoprotective additives and cryopreservation protocol on sperm membrane lipid peroxidation and recovery of motile human sperm. J. Androl. 14:472-478.

Benton, D. and R. Cook. 1990. Selenium supplementation improves mood in a double-blind crossover trial. Psychopharmacology (Berl).102:549-550.

Benton, D. and R. Cook. 1991. The impact of selenium supplementation on mood. Biol. Psychiatr. 29:1092-1098.

Biswas, S., G. Talukder and A. Sharma. 1999. Prevention of cytotoxic effects of arsenic by short-term dietary supplementation with selenium in mice *in vivo*. Mutat. Res. 441:155-160.

Bleau, G., J. Lemarbre, G. Faucher, K.D. Roberts and A. Chapdelaine. 1984. Semen selenium and human fertility. Fertil. Steril. 42:890-894.

Bowie, A. and L.A.J. O'Neill. 2000. Oxidative stress and nuclear factor-kB activation. A reassessment of the evidence in the light of recent descoveries. Biochem. Pharmacol. 59:13-23.

Brannan, T.S., H.S. Maker and C. Weiss. 1981. Developmental study of rat brain glutathione peroxidase and glutathione reductase. Neurochem. Res. 61:41-45.

Brigelius-Flohe, R. 1999. Tissue-specific functions of individual glutathione peroxidases. Free Rad. Biol. Med. 27:951-965.

Brown, D.V., P.L. Senger, S.L. Stone, J.A. Froseth and W.C. Becker. 1977. Glutathione peroxidase in bovine semen. J. Reprod. Fert. 50:117-118.

Brucato, M., S.F. Sundlof, J.U. Bell and G.T. Edds. 1986. Aflatoxin B_1 toxicosis in dairy calves pretreated with selenium-vitamin E. Am. J. Vet. Res. 47:179-83.

Bu, Z.G., K.H. Huang and W.F. Chen.1996. Study on the cell mediated immunity mechanism in the selenium-enhanced resistance of chicks to infectious bursal disease. Chinese J. Vet. Sci. 16:273-276.

Buckley, D.J., P.A. Morrissey and J.I. Gray. 1995. Influence of dietary vitamin E on the oxidative stability and quality of pig meat. J. Anim. Sci. 73:3122-3130.

Bunk, M.J. and G.F. Combs. 1981. Relationship of selenium-dependent glutathione peroxidase activity and nutritional pancreatic atrophy in selenium-deficient chicks. J. Nutr. 111:1611-1620.

Burguera, J.A., G.T. Edds and O. Osuna. 1983. Influence of selenium on aflatoxin B_1 or crotalaria toxicity in turkey poults. Am. J. Vet. Res. 44:1714-1717.

Burk, R.F. and K.E. Hill. 1994. Selenoprotein P. A selenium-rich extracellular glycoprotein. J. Nutr. 124:1891-1897.

Burk, R.F. and K.E. Hill. 1999. Orphan selenoproteins. Bioessays 21:231-237.

Calvin, H.I. 1978. Selective incorporation of selenium-75 into a polypeptide of the rat sperm tail. J. Exp. Zool. 204:445-452.

Calvin, H.I., K. Grosshans, S.R. Musicant-Shikora and S.I. Turner. 1987. A developmental study of rat sperm and testis selenoproteins. J. Reprod. Fertil. 81:1-11.

Cantor, A.H. 1997. The role of selenium in poultry nutrition. In: Biotechnology in the Feed industry. Proc. Of the 13th Annual Symposium (T.P. Lyons and K.A. Jacques, eds.). Nottingham University Press, Nottingham, UK, pp. 155-164.

Cantor, A.H., M.L. Langevin, T. Noguchi and M.L. Scott. 1975. Efficiency of selenium compounds and feedstuffs for prevention of pancreatic fibrosis in chicks. J. Nutr. 105:106-111.

Cantor, A.H., P.D. Moorhead and K.I. Brown. 1978. Influence of dietary selenium upon reproductive performance of male and female breeder turkey. Poultry Sci. 57:1337-1345.

Cecil, H.C. and M.R. Bakst. 1993. *In vitro* lipid peroxidation of turkey spermatozoa. Poultry Sci. 72:1370-1378.

Century, B. and M.K. Hurwitt. 1964. Effect of dietary selenium on incidence of nutritional encephalomalacia in chicks. Proc. Soc. Exp. Biol. Med. 117: 320.

Chan, K.M. and E.A. Decker. 1994. Endogenous skeletal muscle antioxidants. Crit. Rev. Food. Sci. Nutr. 34:403-426.

Chen, J., T.C. Campbell, J. Li and R. Peto. 1990. Diet, life-style and mortality in China. A study of the characteristics of 65 Chinese counties. Oxford: Oxford University Press.

Christinsen, M.J. and K.W. Burgener. 1992. Dietary selenium stabilises glutathione peroxidase mRNA in rat liver. J. Nutr. 122:1620-1626.

Christon, R., R.B. Haloui and G. Durand, G. 1995. Dietary polyunsaturated fatty acids and aging modulate glutathione-related antioxidants in rat liver. J. Nutr. 125:3062-3070.

Chu, F.F., J.H. Doroshow and R.S. Esworthy. 1993. Expression, characterization, and tissue distribution of a new cellular selenium-dependent glutathione peroxidase, GSHPx-GI. J. Biol. Chem. 268:2571-2576.

Clark, L.C., K.P. Cantor and W.H. Allaway. 1991. Selenium in forage crops and cancer mortality in U.S. counties. Arch. Environ. Health. 46:37-42.

Clark, L.C., G.F. Combs, B.W. Turnbull, E.H. Slate, D.Chalker, J. Chow, L.S. Davis, R.A. Glover, G.F. Graham, E.G. Gross, A. Krongrad, J.L. Lesher, H.K. Park, B.B. Sanders, C.L. Smith CL and J.R. Taylor. 1996. Effects of Se supplementation for cancer prevention in patients with carcinoma of the skin. JAMA. 276:1957-1963.

Clark, L.C., B. Dalkin, A. Krongrad, G.F. Combs, B.W. Turnbull, E.H. Slate, R. Witherington, J.H. Herlong, E. Janosko, D. Carpenter, C. Borosso, S. Falk and J. Rounder. 1998. Decreased incidence of prostate cancer with selenium supplementation: results of a double-blind cancer prevention trial. Brit. J. Urol. 81:730-734.

Clark, L.C., G.F. Graham, R.G. Crounse, R. Grimson, B. Hulka and C.M. Shy. 1984. Plasma selenium and skin neoplasms: a case-control study. Nutr. Cancer. 6:13-21.

Cockell, K.A., A.R. Brash and R.F. Burk. 1996. Influence of selenium status on activity of phospholipid hydroperoxide glutathione peroxidase in rat liver and testis in comparison with other selenoproteins. J. Nutr. Biochim. 7:333-338.

Combs, G.F. and S.B. Combs. 1984. The nutritional biochemistry of selenium. Annu. Rev. Nutr. 4:257-280.

Combs, G.F., Jr. and S.B. Combs. 1986. The role of selenium in nutrition. Academic Press, Orlando.

Combs, G.F. and M.M. Hady. 1991. Selenium involved with vitamin E in preventing encephalomalacia in the chick. FASEB J. 5:A714.

Dalton, T.P., H.G. Shertzer and A. Puga. 1999. Regulation of gene expression by reactive oxygen. Annu. Rev. Pharmacol.Toxicol. 39:67-101.

Dalvi, R.R. 1986. An overview of aflatoxicosis of poultry: its characteristics, prevention and reduction. Vet. Res. Commun.10:429-443.

Davies, M.H., B.A. Merrick, D.F. Birt and R.C. Schmell. 1985. Differential effects of dietary selenium on hepatic and renal glutathione metabolism in the rat. Drug Nutr. Interact. 3:229-238.

Davila, J.C., G.T. Edds, O. Osuna and C.F. Simpson. 1983. Modification of the effects of aflatoxin B_1 and warfarin in young pigs given selenium. Am. J. Vet. Res. 44:1877-1883.

Dean, W.F. and G.F. Combs. 1981. Influence of dietary selenium on performance, tissue selenium content, and plasma concentrations of selenium-dependent glutathione peroxidase, vitamin E, and ascorbic acid in ducklings. Poultry Sci. 60:2555-2663.

Decker, E.A. 1998. Strategies for manipulating the prooxidative/antioxidative balance of foods to maximize oxidative stability. Trends Food. Sci. Technol. 9:241-248.

De Lamirande, E. and C. Gagnon. 1992. Reactive oxygen species and human spermatozoa. 1. Effect on the motility of intact spermatozoa and on sperm axonemes. J. Androl. 13:368-378.

DeVore, V.R., G.L. Colnago, L.S. Jensen and B.E. Greene. 1983. Thiobarbituric acid values and glutathione peroxidase activity in meat from chickens fed a selenium-supplemented diet. J. Food Sci. 48:300-301.

Diaz-Alarcon, M., H. Lopez-Garcia de la Serrana and M.C. Lopez-Martinez. 1996. Determination of selenium in meat products by hydride generation atomic absorption spectrometry - selenium levels in meat, organ meats, and sausages in Spain. J. Agric. Food Chem. 44:1494-1497.

Diplock, A.T. 1994. Antioxidants and disease prevention. Mol. Asp. Med. 15:295-376.

Dodge, M.L., R.C. Wander, J.A. Butler, S.H. Du, C.D. Thompson and P.D. Whanger. 1999. Selenium supplementation increases the polyunsaturated fatty acid content of human breast milk. J. Trace Elem. Exp. Med. 12:37-44.

Dodge, M.L., R.C. Wander, Y. Xia, J.A. Butler and P.D. Whanger. 1999a. Glutathione peroxidase activity modulates fatty acid profiles of plasma and breast milk in Chinese women. J. Trace Elem. Med. Biol.12:221-230.

Douillet, C., M. Bost, M. Accominotti, F. Borson-Chazot and M. Ciavatti. 1998. Effect of selenium and vitamin E supplements on tissue lipids, peroxides, and fatty acid distribution in experimental diabetes. Lipids 33:393-399.

Edens, F.W. 1996. Organic selenium: from feathers to muscle integrity to drip loss. Five years onward: no more selenite! In: Biotechology in the Feed industry. Proc. Of the 12th Annual Symposium (T.P.Lyons and K.A. Jacques, eds.). Nottingham University Press, Nottingham, UK, pp. 165-185.

Edens, F.W. 1997. Potential for organic selenium to replace selenite in poultry diets. Zootec. Internat. 20:28-31.

Enkvetchakul, B., N.B. Anthony and W.G. Bottje. 1995. Liver and blood glutathione in male broiler chickens, turkeys and quail. Poultry Sci. 74:885-889.

Ferrandi, B., A.L. Consiglio, A. Carnevali and F. Porcelli. 1992a. Effects of lipid peroxidation on chromatin in rabbit and mouse spermatozoa- a cytochemical approach. Anim. Reprod. Sci. 29:89-98.

Ferrandi, B., F. Cremonesi, A.L. Consiglio, A. Carnevali and F. Porcelli. 1992. Cytophotometric assay of cytochrome oxidase, lactate dehydrogenase and glucose-6-phosphate-dehydrogenase activities in human peroxidized spermatozoa. Acta Histochem. 93:363-370.

Fisher, W.C. and P.D. Whanger. 1977. Effects of selenium deficiency on vitamin E metabolism in rats. J. Nutr. Sci. Vitam. 23:273-280.

Fleet, J.C. 1997. Dietary selenium repletion may reduce cancer incidence in people at high risk who live in areas with low soil selenium. Nutr. Rev. 55:277-279.

Flohe, I. and R. Zimmermann. 1970. The role of GSH peroxidase in protecting the membrane of rat liver mitochondria. Biochim. Biophys. Acta. 223:210-213.

Flohe, L., W.A. Gunzler and H.H. Schock. 1973. Glutathione peroxidase: a selenoenzyme. FEBS Lett. 32:132-134.

Fraga, C.G., R.F. Arias, S.F. Llesui, O.R. Koch and A. Boveris. 1987. Effect of vitamin E and selenium deficiency on rat liver chemiluminescence. Biochem. J. 242:383-386.

Francis, A.R., T.K. Shetty and R.K. Bhattacharya. 1988. Modifying role of dietary factors on the mutagenicity of aflatoxin B_1: *in vitro* effect of trace elements. Mutat. Res.199:85-93.

Freeman, C.P. 1976. Digestion and absorption of fat. In: Digestion in the fowl (K.N. Boorman and C.P. Freeman, eds) British Poultry Science Ltd., Edinburgh. pp. 117-142.

Froman, D.P. and R.J. Thurston. 1981. Chicken and turkey spermatozoal superoxide dismutase: a comparative study. Biol. Reprod. 24:193-200.

Froning, G.W. 1995. Colour of poultry meat. Poult. Avian Biol. Rev. 6: 83-93.

Ghyselinck, N.B., C. Jimenez and J.P. Dufaure. 1991. Sequence homology of androgen- regulated epididymal proteins with glutathione peroxidase in mice. J. Reprod. Fert. 93:461-466.

Girodon, F., P. Galan, A.L. Monget, M.C. Boutron-Ruault, P. Brunet-Lecomte, P. Preziosi, J. Arnaud, J.C. Manuguerra and S. Herchberg. 1999. Impact of trace elements and vitamin supplementation on immunity and infections in institutionalized elderly patients: a randomized controlled trial. MIN. VIT. AOX. geriatric network. Arch. Intern. Med. 159:748-754.

Gonzalez, M.M., R. Nadrid, R. and R.M. Arahuetes. 1995. Physiological changes in antioxidant defences in fetal and neonatal rat liver. Reprod. Fert. Dev. 7:1375-80.

Gregory, J.F., and G.T. Edds. 1984. Effect of dietary selenium on the metabolism of aflatoxin B$_1$ in turkeys. Food Chem. Toxicol. 22:637-642.

Griveau, J.F., E. Dumont, P. Renard, J.P. Callegari and D. LeLannou. 1995. Reactive oxygen species, lipid peroxidation and enzymatic defence systems in human spermatozoa. J. Reprod. Fert. 103:17-26.

Gromadzinska, J., M. Sklodowska and W. Wasowicz. 1988. Glutathione peroxidase activity, lipid peroxides and selenium concentration in various rat organs. Biomed. Biochim. Acta. 47:19-24.

Grosse, Y., L. Chekir-Ghedira, A. Huc, S. Obrecht-Pflumio, G. Dirheimer, H. Bacha and A. Pfohl-Leszkowicz. 1997. Retinol, ascorbic acid and alpha-tocopherol prevent DNA adduct formation in mice treated with the mycotoxins ochratoxin A and zearalenone. Cancer Lett. 114:225-229.

Gunther, T., V. Hollriegl and J. Vormann. 1993. Perinatal development of iron and antioxidant defence system. J. Trace Elem. Electrolyt. Health Dis. 7:47-52.

Gutteridge, J.M.C. and B. Halliwell. 1990. The measurement and metabolism of lipid peroxidation in biological systems. Trends Biochem. Sci. 15:129-135.

Halliwell, B. 1994. Free radicals and antioxidants: A personal view. Nutr. Rev. 52:253-265.

Halliwell, B. and J.M.C. Gutteridge. 1999. Free radicals in biology and medicine. Third edition, Oxford University Press, Oxford.

Hansen, J.C. and Y. Deguchi. 1996. Selenium and fertility in animals and man - A review. Acta Vet. Scand. 37:19-30.

Hassan, S. 1986. Effect of dietary selenium on the prevention of exudative diathesis in chicks, with special reference to selenium transfer via eggs. J. Vet. Med. A. 33:689-697.

Hassan, S., J. Hakkarainen, M.L. Jonsson and J. Tyopponen. 1990. Histopathological and biochemical changes associated with selenium and vitamin E deficiency in chicks. J. Vet. Med. A. 37: 708-720.

Hawkes, W.C. and L. Hornbostel. 1996. Effects of dietary selenium on mood in healthy men living in a metabolic research unit. Biol. Psychiatr. 39:121-128.

Hill, K.E. and R.F. Burk. 1982. Effect of selenium deficiency and vitamin E deficiency on glutathione metabolism in isolated hepatocytes. J. Biol. Chem. 257:10668-10672.

Hill, K.E. and R.F. Burk. 1985. Effect of selenium deficiency on the disposition of plasma glutathione. Arch. Biochem. Biophys. 240:166-171.

Hindshaw, D.B., L.A. Sklar and B. Bohl. 1986. Cytoskeletal and morphologic impact of cellular oxidant injury. Am. J. Pathol. 123:454-464.

Hogg, N. 1998. Free radicals in disease. Semin. Reprod. Endocrinol.16:241-248.

Holben, D.H. and A.M. Smith. 1999. The diverse role of selenium within selenoproteins: A review. J. Am. Diet. Assoc. 99:836-843.

Huang, K.H. and W.F. Chen. 1996. Effect of selenium on the resistance of chickens to Marek's disease and its mode of action. Acta Vet. Zootechn. Sinica. 27:448-455.

Huang, S.Z., X.Y. Meng, S.P. Gu, Y.W. Zhou and L.Y. Peng. 1998. Effect of vitamin E and selenium on lipid peroxidation in chickens. Chinese J.Vet. Sci. 18:191-192.

Hurley, M.L. and R.M. Doane. 1989. Recent developments in the roles of vitamins and minerals in reproduction. J. Dairy Sci. 72:784-804.

Ip, C. 1998. Lessons from basic research in selenium and cancer prevention. J. Nutr. 128:1845-1854.

Jackson, M.J., A. McArdle and F. McArdle. 1998. Antioxidant micronutrients and gene expression. Proc. Nutr. Soc. 57:301-305.

Jaeschke, H. 1995. Mechanisms of oxidant stress-induced acute tissue injury. Proc. Soc. Exp. Biol. Med. 209:104-111.

Janssens, G. 1998. Vitamin E improves chicken meat quality. Meat Processing: Intern. Edittion. September/October. 42:44-46.

Jiang, C., W. Jiang, C. Ip, H. Ganther and J. Lu.1999. Selenium-induced inhibition of angiogenesis in mammary cancer at chemopreventive levels of intake. Mol. Carcinog. 26:213-225.

Jones, R. and T. Mann. T. 1976. Lipid peroxides in spermatozoa; formation, role of plasmalogen and physiological significance. Proc. R. Soc. Lond. 193: 317-333.

Jonsson, L. 1993. The pathology of diseases and diffuse disorders due to selenium deficiency in non-ruminants. Norwegian J. Agr. Sci. Suppl. 11:95-103.

Julien, W.E. and F.A. Murray. 1977. Effect of selenium and selenium with vitamin E on *in vitro* motility of bovine spermatozoa. In: Proc. Am. Soc. Anim. Sci., 69th Annual Meeting, University of Wisconsin, Madison. page 174.

Kadrabova, J, A. Madaric and E. Ginter. 1997. The selenium content of selected food from the Slovak Republic. Food Chem. 58:29-32.

Kadrabova, J., A. Madaric and E. Ginter. 1998. Determination of the daily selenium intake in Slovakia. Biol. Trace Elem. Res. 61:277-286.

Kalytka, V.V. and H.V. Donchenko. 1995. The antioxidant system and lipid peroxidation in chickens during postnatal ontogenesis. Ukr. Biochem. J. 67:80-85.

Kantola, M., M. Saaranen and T. Vanha-Perttula. 1988. Selenium and glutathione peroxidase in seminal plasma of men and bulls. J. Reprod. Fert. 83:785-794.

Kaur, R., and V.R. Parshad. 1994. Effects of dietary selenium on differentiation, morphology and functions of spermatozoa of the house rat, *Rattus rattus* L. Mutat. Res. 309:29-35.

Kelly, F.J., M. Safavi and K.H. Cheeseman. 1992. Tissue α-tocopherol status during late fetal and early neonatal life of the guinea pig. Brit. J. Nutr. 67:457-462.

Kelso, K.A., S. Cerolini, R.C. Noble, N.H.C. Sparks and B.K. Speake. 1996. Lipid and antioxidant changes in semen of broiler fowl from 25 to 60 weeks of age. J. Reprod. Fert. 106:201-206.

Kelso, KA, A. Redpath, R.C. Noble and B.K. Speake. 1997. Lipid and antioxidant changes in spermatozoa and seminal plasma throughout the reproductive period of bulls. J. Reprod. Fertil. 109:1-6.

Kim, Y.S. and G.F. Combs. 1993. Effect of aurothioglucose and dietary Se on glutathione S-transferase activities and glutathione concentrations in chick tissues. Biol. Trace Elem. Res. 37:165-177.

Kiremidjian-Schumacher, L. and M. Roy. 1998. Selenium and immune function. Z. Ernahrungswiss. 37(Suppl 1):50-56.

Knight, J.A. 1998. Free radicals: Their history and current status in aging and disease. Ann. Clin. Lab. Sci. 28:331-346.

Kok, F., A. Hofman and J.C.M. Witterman. 1989. Decreased Se levels in acute myocardial infarction. JAMA 261:1161-1164.

Kravchenko, L.V., E.E. Kuzmina, L.I. Avreneva and V.A.Tutelyan. 1990. Protective effect of selenium in acute T-2 mycotoxicosis. Vopr. Med. Khim. 36:36-38.

Larsen, C.T., Pierson, F.W. and W.B. Gross. 1997. Effect of dietary selenium on the response of stressed and unstressed chickens to *Escherichia coli* challenge and antigen. Biol. Trace Elem. Res. 58:169-176.

Leal, M., A. Shimada, F. Ruiz and E. Gonzalez de Mejia. 1999. Effect of lycopene on lipid peroxidation and glutathione-dependent enzymes induced by T-2 toxin *in vivo*. Toxicol. Lett. 109:1-10.

Leboeuf, R.A., K.L. Zenter and W.G. Hoekstra. 1985. Effect of dietary selenium concentration and duration of selenium feeding on hepatic glutathione concentrations in rats. Proc. Soc. Exp. Biol. Med. 180:348-352.

Leedle, R.A. and S.D. Aust. 1990. The effect of glutathione on the vitamin E requirement for inhibition of liver microsomal lipid peroxidation. Lipids. 25:241-245.

Lei, X.G., J.K. Evenson, K.M. Thompson and R.A. Sunde. 1995. Glutathione peroxidase and phospholipid hydroperoxide glutathione peroxidase are differentially regulated in rats by dietary selenium. J. Nutr. 125:1438-1446.

Lei, D.N., L.Q. Wang, B.H. Ruebner, D.P. Hsieh, B.U. Wu, C.R. Zhu and M.J. Du. 1990. Effect of selenium on aflatoxin hepatocarcinogenesis in the rat. Biomed. Environ. Sci. 3:65-80.

Lenzi, A., M. Picardo, L. Gandini and F. Dondero. 1996. Lipids of the sperm plasma membrane: from polyunsaturated fatty acids considered as markers of sperm function to possible scavenger therapy. Hum. Reprod. Update 2:246-256.

Li, K.T. 1975. The glutathione and thiol content of mammalian spermatozoa and seminal plasma Biol. Reprod. 12:641-646.

Lii, C.K., Y.J. Ko, M.T. Chiang, W.C. Sung and H.W. Chen. 1998. Effect of dietary vitamin E on antioxidant status and antioxidant enzyme activities in Sprague-Dawley rats. Nutrit. Cancer. 32:95-100.

Liu, Q., M.C. Lanari and D.M. Schaefer. 1995. A review of dietary vitamin E supplementation for improvement of beef quality. J. Anim. Sci. 73:3131-3140.

Lopes, S., A. Jurisicova, J.G. Sun and R.F. Casper. 1998. Reactive oxygen species: potential cause for DNA fragmentation in human spermatozoa. Hum. Reprod. 13:896-900.

MacPherson A. and M.N.I. Barclay. 1997. Loss of Canadian wheat imports lowers selenium intake and status of the Scottish population. In: Trace elements in man and animals (TEMA 9) (P.W.F. Fisher, M.R. L'alabbe, K.A. Cockell and R.S. Gibson, eds.) Ottawa, NRC Research Press, p.203-205.

MacPherson, A., S. Drusch, J. Dixon and J. Dunsmuir. 1994. Effect of chemical form of supplementary selenium on lamb carcass selenium concentration as a means of increasing human dietary selenium intake in the UK. In: Deficient and Excessive Levels of Macroelements and Trace Elements in Nutrition. Proc. 14th Conference on Macroelements and Trace Elements (M. Anke, D. Meissner, H. Bergmann, R. Bitsch, W. Dorn, G. Flachowsky, B. Groppel, H. Gurtler and I. Lombeck, eds), Friedrich Schiller Univ, Jena, Germany, pp. 171-178.

MacPherson A., R.Scott and R. Yates. 1993. The effect of selenium supplementation in subfertile males. In: Proc. 8th Int. Symp. On Trace Elements in Man and Animals. (M. Anke, D. Meissner and C.F. Mills, eds.) Jena, Germany: Verlag Media Touristik. pp. 566-569.

Maddipati, K.R. and L.J. Marnett. 1987. Characterization of the major hydroperoxide-reducing activity of human plasma. Purification and properties of a selenium-dependent glutathione peroxidase. J. Biol. Chem. 262:17398-17403.

Mahan, D. 1999. Organic selenium: using nature's model to redefine selenium supplementation for animals. In: Biotechnology in the Feed industry. Proc. of the 15th Annual Symposium (T.P.Lyons and K.A. Jacques, eds.). Nottingham University Press, Nottingham, UK, pp. 523-535.

Mahan, D.C. and Y.Y. Kim. 1999. The role of vitamins and minerals in the production of high quality pork. Review. Asian-Australian J. Anim. Sci. 12:287-294.

Mahan, D.C., T.R. Cline and B. Richert. 1999. Effects of dietary levels of selenium-enriched yeast and sodium selenite as selenium sources fed to growing-finishing pigs on performance, tissue selenium, serum glutathione peroxidase activity, carcass characteristics, and loin quality. J. Anim. Sci. 77:2172-2179.

Mannella, M.R.T. and R. Jones. 1980. Properties of spermatozoal superoxide dismutase and lack of involvement of superoxides in metal-ion-catalysed lipid peroxidation reactions in semen. Biochem. J. 191:289-297.

Marchaluk E, M. Persson-Moschos, E.B. Thorling and B. Akesson. 1995. Variation in selenoprotein P concentration in serum from different European regions. Eur. J. Clin. Nutr. 49:42-48.

Maretta, M., E. Marettova, P. Skrobanek and M. Ledec. 1995. Effect of mercury on the seminiferous epithelium of the fowl testis. Acta Vet. Hung. 43:153-161.

Mates, J.M. and F. Sanchez-Jimenez. 1999. Antioxidant enzymes and their implications in pathophysiologic processes. Front Biosci. 4:D339-D345.

Matsuo, M. 1993. Age-related alterations in antioxidant defence. In: Free Radicals in Ageing. (B.P.Yu, ed.) CRC Press, Boca Raton, London, Tokyo, pp. 143-181.

Matsuo, M., F. Gomi and M.M. Dooley. 1992. Age-related alterations in antioxidant capacity and lipid peroxidation in brain, liver, and lung homogenates of normal and vitamin E-deficient rats. Mech. Age. Dev. 64: 273-292.

McDowell, L.R. 2000. Reevaluation of the metabolic essentiality of the vitamins. Review. Asian-Australian J. Anim. Sci. 13:115-125.

McKenzie, R.C., T.S. Rafferty and G.J. Beckett. 1998. Selenium: an essential element for immune function. 19:342-345.

Meydani, M., J.B. Macauley and J.B. Blumberg. 1988. Effect of dietary vitamin E and selenium on susceptibility of brain regions to lipid peroxidation. Lipids. 23:405-409.

Mezes, M., M. Barta and G. Nagy.1999. Comparative investigation on the effect of T-2 mycotoxin on lipid peroxidation and antioxidant status in different poultry species. Res. Vet. Sci. 66:19-23.

Milks, M.M., S.R. Wilt, I.I. Ali and D. Couri. 1985. The effects of selenium on the emergence of aflatoxin B_1-induced enzyme-altered foci in rat liver. Fundam. Appl. Toxicol. 5:320-326.

Mizuno, Y. 1984. Changes in superoxide dismutase, catalase, glutathione peroxidase, and glutathione reductase activities and thiobarbituric acid-reactive products levels in early stages of development in dystrophic chickens. Exp. Neur. 84:58-73.

Mizuno, Y. 1984a. Superoxide dismutase activity in early stages of development in normal and dystrophic chickens. Life Sci. 34:909-914.

Miyazaki, S. and Y. Motoi. 1992. Tissue distribution of monomeric glutathione peroxidase in broiler chicks. Res.Vet. Sci. 53: 47-51.

Morrissey, P.A. and N.M. O'Brien. 1998. Dietary antioxidants in human health and disease. Int. Dairy J. 8:463-472.

Molnar, J, S. Drusch and A. MacPherson. 1997. The effect of level and form of supplementary selenium on tissue concentrations in lambs and their importance in raising human dietary selenium intake. In: Trace Elements in Man and Animals. 9th International Symposium on Trace Elements in Man and Animals (TEMA 9) (P.W.F. Fischer, M.R. Labbe, K.A. Cockell K.A. and R.S. Gibson, eds.) BANFF, Canada, pp. 468-470.

Molnar, J., A. MacPherson and J. Dixon. 1996. Effect of supplementation with selenium on whole blood glutathione peroxidase activities and on plasma and tissue selenium concentrations in lambs. Biol. Trace Elem. Res. 55: 253-262.

National Research Council. 1989. Recommended Dietary Allowances, 10th ed. National Academy of Sciences, Washington, DC.

Naylor, A.J., M. Choct and K.A. Jacques. 2000. Effects of selenium sources and level on performance, mortality and meat quality in male broilers. Poster presented at Southern Poultry Science Conference, Atlanta, GA.

Netke, S.P., M.W. Roomi, C. Tsao and A. Niedzwiecki. 1997. Ascorbic acid protects guinea pigs from acute aflatoxin toxicity. Toxicol. Appl. Pharmacol.143:429-435.

Neumann, U.F. and K. Bronsch. 1988. Studies on the optimum supplementation of non-gravid and gravid sows. J. Vet. Med. Ser. A. 35:673-682.

Noble, R.C. and M. Cocchi. 1990. Lipid metabolism in the neonatal chicken. Prog. Lipid Res. 29:107-140.

Noguchi, T., A.H. Cantor and M.L. Scott. 1973. Mode of action of selenium and vitamin E in prevention of exudative diathesis in chicks. J. Nutr. 103:1502-1511.

Noy, Y. and D. Sklan. 1998. Yolk utilization in hatching birds. Proc. 10th European Poultry Conference, Jerusalem, Israel, pp. 435-438.

Okotie-Eboh, G.O, L.F. Kubena, A.D. Chinnah and C.A. Bailey. 1997. Effects of ß-carotene and canthaxanthin on aflatoxicosis in broilers. Poult. Sci. 76:1337-1341.

Oldereid, N.B., Y. Thomassen and K. Purvis. 1998. Selenium in human male reproductive organs. Hum. Reprod.13:2172-2176.

Oster, O. and W. Prellwitz. 1989. The daily dietary selenium intake of West German adults. Biol. Trace Elem. Res. 20:1-14.

Ouali, A. 1991. Sensory quality of meat as affected by muscle biochemistry and modern technologies. In: Animal Biotechnology and the Quality of Meat Production (L.O. Fiems, B.G. Cottyn and D.I. Demeyer, eds.). Elsevier Science Publishers B.V. Amsterdam, pp. 85-105.

Padmaja, K., R. Ramamurthi, K. Thyagaraju and A.R. Prasad. 1996. Isolation of ^{75}Se binding protein from hepatic tissues of chick embryos. Indian J. Exp. Biol. 34:678-682.

Pehrson, B. 1993. Selenium in nutrition with special reference to the biopotency of organic and inorganic selenium compounds. In: Biotechnology in the Feed industry. Proc. of the 9th Annual Symposium (T.P. Lyons and K.A. Jacques, eds.). Nottingham University Press, Nottingham, UK, pp. 71-89.

Persson-Moschos, M., G. Alfthan and B. Akesson. 1998. Plasma selenoprotein P levels of healthy males in different selenium status after oral supplementation with different forms of selenium. Eur. J. Clin. Nutr. 52:363-367.

Petr, T., I. Barta and B.Turek. 1990. *In vivo* effect of selenium on the mutagenic activity of aflatoxin B_1. J. Hyg. Epidemiol. Microbiol. Immunol. 34:123-128.

Pratt, W. 1978. A study of the effect of *in vitro* supplementation of sodium selenite on the metabolism of bovine sperm, M.S. Thesis, Ohio State University, Columbus, Ohio.

Rayman, M.P. 1997. Dietary selemium: time to act. Br. Med. J. 314: 387-388.

Reddy, C.C., R.W. Scholz, C.E. Thomas and E.J. Massaro. 1982. Vitamin E dependent reduced glutathione inhibition of rat liver microsomal lipid peroxidation. Life Sci.31: 571-576.

Reilly, C. 1996. Selenium in food and health. Blackie Academic & Professional, an imprint of Chapman & Hall, London.

Reilly, C. 1998. Selenium: A new entrant into the functional food arena. Trends Food Sci. Technol. 9:114-118.

Renerre, M., F. Dumont and Ph. Gatellier. 1996. Antioxidant enzyme activities in beef in relation to oxidation of lipid and myoglobin. Meat Sci. 43:111-121.

Rhee, S.G. 1999. Redox signaling: hydrogen peroxide as intracellular messenger. Experim. Mol. Med. 31:53-59.

Rizzo, A.F., F. Atroshi, M. Ahotupa, S. Sankari and E. Elovaara. 1994. Protective effect of antioxidants against free radical-mediated lipid peroxidation induced by DON or T-2 toxin. Zentralbl. Veterinarmed [A] 41:81-90.

Rotruck, J.T., A.L. Pope, H.E. Ganther, A.B. Swanson, D.G. Hafeman and W.G. Hoekstra. 1973. Selenium: biochemical role as a component of glutathione peroxidase. Science 179:588-590.

Rumi, G, L. Imre, C. Sulle, M.Z. Lassune, I. Sarudi and J. Kelemen. 1994. Selenium supplementation with bread. Orv. Hetil. (Hungary) 135:2371-2372.

Saaranen, M., U. Suistomaa and T. Vanha-Perttula. 1989. Semen selenium content and sperm mitochondrial volume in human and some animal species. Hum. Reprod. 4:304-308.

Sastre, J., F.V. Pallardo and J. Vina. 1996. Glutathione, oxidative stress and aging. Age. 19:129-139.

Schrauzer, G.N., D.A. White and C.J. Schneider. 1977. Cancer mortality correlation studies. III. Statistical associations with dietary selenium intakes. Bioinorg. Chem. 7:23-31.

Scott, D.L., J. Kelleher and M.S. Losowsky. 1977. The influence of dietary selenium and vitamin E on glutathione peroxidase and glutathione in the rat. Biochim. Biophys. Acta. 497:218-224.

Scott R., A. MacPherson, R.W.S. Yates, B.Hussain and J.Dixon. 1998. The effect of oral selenium supplementation on human sperm motility. Br. J. Urol. 82:76-80.

Sheehy, P.J.A., P.A. Morrissey, D.J. Buckley and J. Wen. 1997. Effects of vitamins in the feed on meat quality in farm animals: Vitamin E. In: Recent advances in animal nutrition. (P.C. Garnsworthy and J. Wiseman, eds.) Nottingham University Press, Nottingham, pp. 3-27.

Shi, B. and J.E. Spallholz. 1994. Selenium from beef is highly bioavailable as assessed by liver glutathione peroxidase (EC 1.11.1.9) activity and tissue selenium. Br. J. Nutr. 72:873-881.

Shi, B. and J.E. Spallholz. 1994a. Bioavailability of selenium from raw and cooked ground beef assessed in selenium-deficient Fischer rats. J. Am. Coll. Nutr.13:95-101 .

Shi, C.Y., S.C. Chua, H.P. Lee and C.N. Ong. 1994. Inhibition of aflatoxin B_1-DNA binding and adduct formation by selenium in rats. Cancer Lett. 82:203-208.

Shi, C.Y., Y.C. Hew and C.N. Ong. 1995. Inhibition of aflatoxin B_1-induced cell injury by selenium: an *in vitro* study. Hum. Exp. Toxicol. 14:55-60.

Shortt, C.T., G.G. Duthie, J.D. Robertson, P.C. Morrice, F. Nicol and J.R. Arthur. 1997. Selenium status of a group of Scottish adults. Eur. J. Clin. Nutr. 51:400-404.

Slaweta, R., T. Laskowska and E. Szymanska. 1988. Lipid peroxides, spermatozoa quality and activity of glutathione peroxidase in bull semen. Acta. Physiol. Pol. 39:207-214.

Smith, D.G., P.L. Senger, J.F. McCutchan and C.A. Landa. 1979. Selenium and glutathione peroxidase distribution in bovine semen and selenium-75 retention by the tissues of the reproductive tract in the bull. Biol. Reprod. 20:377-383.

Soto-Salanova, M.F. 1998. Vitamin E in young turkeys: A reassessment of the requirement. Turkeys. 45:18-20.

Soto-Salanova, M.F. and J.L. Sell. 1995. Influence of supplemental dietary fat on changes in vitamin E concentration in livers of poults. Poultry Sci. 74:201-204.

Soto-Salanova, M.F. and J.L. Sell. 1996. Efficacy of dietary and injected vitamin E for poults. Poultry Sci. 75:1393-1403.

Soto-Salanova, M.F., J.L. Sell, E.G. Mallarino, F.J. Piquer, D.L. Barker, P.E. Palo and R.C. Ewan. 1993. Research note: Vitamin E status of turkey poults as influenced by different dietary vitamin E sources, a bile salt, and an antioxidant. Poultry Sci. 72:1184-1188.

Spallholz, J.E. 1997. Free radical generation by selenium compounds and their prooxidant toxicity. Biomed. Environ. Sci. 10:260-270.

Speake, B.K., A.M.B. Murray and R.C. Noble. 1998. Transport and transformation of yolk lipids during development of the avian embryo. Progr. Lipid Res. 37:1-32.

Stanley, D.W. 1991. Biological membrane deterioration and associated quality losses in food tissues. Crit. Rev. Food. Sci. Technol. 30:487-553.

Stanley, G.V., H. Chakwu and D. Thompson. 1998. Single and combined effects of organic selenium (Se-Yeast) and vitamin E on ascites reduction in broilers. PSSA, 1998, abst.111.

Storz, G. and L.A. Tartaglia. 1992. OxyR: A regulator of antioxidant genes. J. Nutr. 122:627-630.

Sun, E., H. Xu, Q. Liu, J. Zhou, P. Zuo and J. Wang. 1995. The mechanism for the effect of selenium supplementation on immunity. Biol. Trace Elem. Res. 48:231-238.

Suneja, S.K., D.S.Wagle and G.C. Ram. 1989. Effect of oral administration of T-2 toxin on glutathione shuttle enzymes, microsomal reductases and lipid peroxidation in rat liver. Toxicon 27:995-1001.

Surai, P.F. 1989. Relations between vitamin E concentration in poultry sper-matozoa and some semen biochemical and physiological characteristics. Proc. 8th International Symposium on Current Problems of Avian Genet-ics, Smolenice, Czechoslovakia, pp. 171-173.

Surai, P.F. 1999. Vitamin E in avian reproduction. Poultry Avian Biol. Rev. 10:1-60.

Surai, P.F. 1999a. Tissue-specific changes in the activities of antioxidant enzymes during the development of the chicken embryo. Brit. Poultry Sci. 40:397-405.

Surai, P.F. 2000. Effect of the selenium and vitamin E content of the mater-nal diet on the antioxidant system of the yolk and the developing chick. Brit. Poultry Sci. (In press).

Surai, P.F. and I. Ionov. 1992. Vitamin E in fowl sperm. Proc. 12th Interna-tional Congress on Animal Reproduction, The Hague, The Netherlands, Vol. 1, pp. 535-537.

Surai, P.F. and B.K. Speake. 1998. Distribution of carotenoids from the yolk to the tissues of the chick embryo. J. Nutr. Biochem. 9:645-651.

Surai, P.F., E. Blesbois, I. Grasseau, T. Chalah, J.P. Brillard, G.J. Wishart, S. Cerolini and N.H. Sparks. 1998. Fatty acid composition, glutathione peroxidase and superoxide dismutase activity and total antioxidant activ-ity of avian semen. Comp. Biochem. Physiol. B. Biochem. Mol. Biol. 120:527-533.

Surai, P.F., J.P. Brillard, B.K. Speake, E. Blesbois, F. Seigneurin and N.H.C. Sparks. 2000. Phospholipid fatty acid composition, vitamin E content and susceptibility to lipid peroxidation of duck semen. Theriogenology (In press).

Surai. P.F., S. Cerolini, G.J. Wishart, B.K. Speake, R.C. Noble and N.H.C. Sparks. 1998a. Lipid and antioxidant composition of chicken semen and its susceptibility to peroxidation. Poultry Avian Biol. Rev. 9:11-23.

Surai, P.F., T. Gaal, R.C. Noble and B.K. Speake. 1997. The relationship between α-tocopherol content of the yolk and its accumulation in the tissues of the newly hatched chick. J. Sci. Food Agric. 75:212-216.

Surai, P.F., I. Ionov, E. Kuchmistova, R.C. Noble and B.K. Speake. 1998b. The relationship between the levels of α-tocopherol and carotenoids in the maternal feed, yolk and neonatal tissues: Comparison between the chicken, turkey, duck and goose. J. Sci. Food Agric. 76:593-598.

Surai, P.F., I.A. Kostjuk, G.J. Wishart, A. MacPherson, B.K. Speake, R.C. Noble, I.A. Ionov and E. Kutz. 1998c. Effect of vitamin E and selenium of cockerel diets on glutathione peroxidase activity and lipid peroxidation susceptibility in sperm, testes and liver. Biol. Trace Elem. Res. 64:119-132.

Surai, P.F., E. Kutz, G.J. Wishart , R.C. Noble and B.K. Speake. 1997a. The relationship between the dietary provision of alpha-tocopherol and the concentration of this vitamin in the semen of chicken: effects on lipid composition and susceptibility to peroxidation. J. Reprod. Fertil. 110:47-51.

Surai P.F., A. MacPherson, B.K. Speake and N.H.C. Sparks. 2000a. Designer egg evaluation in a controlled trial. European J. Clin. Nutr. (In press).

Surai, P.F., R.C. Noble and B.K. Speake. 1999. Relationship between vitamin E content and susceptibility to lipid peroxidation in tissues of the newly hatched chick. Brit. Poultry Sci. 40:406-410.

Surai, P.F., R.C. Noble and B.K. Speake. 1996. Tissue-specific differences in antioxidant distribution and susceptibility to lipid peroxidation during development of the chick embryo. Biochim. Biophys. Acta. 1304:1-10.

Surai, P.F., B.K. Speake, R.C. Noble and N.H.C. Sparks. 1999a. Tissue-specific antioxidant profiles and susceptibility to lipid peroxidation of the newly hatched chick. Biol. Trace Elem. Res. 68:63-78.

Takahashi, K., N. Avissar, J. Whitin and H. Cohen. 1987. Purification and characterization of human plasma glutathione peroxidase: a selenoglycoprotein distinct from the known cellular enzyme. Arch Biochem. Biophys. 256:677-686.

Thompson, J.N. and M.L. Scott. 1969. Role of selenium in the nutrition of the chick. J. Nutr. 97:335-342.

Thompson, J.N. and M.L. Scott. 1970. Impaired lipid and vitamin E absorption related to atrophy of the pancreas in selenium-deficient chicks. J. Nutr. 100:797-809.

Thorn, J., J. Robertson, D.H. Buss and N.G. Bunton. 1978. Trace nutrients. Selenium in British food. Br. J. Nutr. 39:391-396.

Toyoda, H., S. Himeno and N. Imura. 1990. Regulation of glutathione peroxidase mRNA level by dietary selenium manipulation. Biochim. Biophys. Acta. 1049:213-215.

Truswell, A.S. 1998. Practical and realistic approaches to healthier diet modifications. Am. J. Clin. Nutr. 67(Suppl.):583S-590S.

Turner, R.J. and J.E. Francis. 1991. Selenium and the immune response. Proc. Nutr. Soc. 50:275-285.

Tutelyan, V.A., L.V. Kravchenko, E.E. Kuzmina, L.I. Avrenieva and J.T. Kumpulainen. 1990. Dietary selenium protects against acute toxicity of T-2 toxin in rats. Food Addit. Contam. 7:821-827.

Twigg, J., N. Fulton, E. Gomez, D.S. Irvine and R.J. Aitken. 1998. Analysis of the impact of intracellular reactive oxygen species generation on the structural and functional integrity of human spermatozoa: lipid peroxidation, DNA fragmentation and effectiveness of antioxidants. Hum. Reprod. 13:1429-1436.

Ursini, F, S. Heim, M. Kiess, M. Maiorino, A. Roveri, J. Wissing and L. Flohe. 1999. Dual function of the selenoprotein PHGPx during sperm maturation. Science. 285:1393-1396.

Ursini, F., M. Maiorino and A. Roveri. 1997. Phospholipid hydroperoxide glutathione peroxidase (PHGPx): more than an antioxidant enzyme? Biomed. Environ. Sci. 10:327-332.

Ursini, F., M. Maiorino, M. Valente, L. Ferri and C. Gregolin. 1982. Purification from pig liver of a protein which protects liposomes and biomembranes from peroxidative degradation and exhibits glutathione peroxidase activity on phosphatidylcholine hydroperoxides. Biochim. Biophys. Acta 710:197-211.

Vatassery, G.T., C.K. Angerhofer, C.A. Knox and D.S. Deshmukh. 1984. Concentrations of vitamin E in various neuroanatomocal regions and subcellular fractions, and the uptake of vitamin E by specific areas, of rat brain. Biochim. Biophys. Acta. 792:118-122.

Vezina, D., F. Mauffette, K.D. Roberts and G. Bleau. 1996. Selenium-Vitamin E supplementation in infertile men - effects on semen parameters and micronutrient levels and distribution. Biol. Trace Element Res. 53:65-83.

Wakebe, M. 1998. Feed for meat chickens and feed for laying hens. Japanese Patent Office, Application Heisei 8-179629. Jan 27.

Wang, L.Q. 1990. The effect of selenium on hepatocarcinogenesis of rats induced by aflatoxin B_1. Chung Hua Ping Li Hsueh Tsa Chih 19:46-49.

Watanabe, T. and A. Endo. 1991. Effects of selenium deficiency on sperm morphology and spermatocyte chromosomes in mice. Mutat. Res. 262:93-99.

Weiss, S.L., J.K. Evenson, K.M. Thompson and R.A. Sunder. 1997. Dietary selenium regulation of glutathione peroxidase mRNA and other selenium-dependent parameters in male rats. J. Nutr. Biochem. 8:85-91.

Weiss, W.P. 1998. Requirements of fat soluble vitamins for dairy cows: A review. J. Dairy Sci. 81:2493-2501.

Wen, H.Y., R.L. Davis, B. Shi, J.J. Chen , L. Chen, M. Boylan and J.E. Spallholz. 1997. Bioavailability of selenium from veal, chicken, beef, pork, lamb, flounder, tuna, selenomethionine, and sodium selenite assessed in selenium-deficient rats. Biol. Trace Elem. Res. 58:43-53.

Whanger, P.D. 1998. Metabolism of selenium in humans. J. Trace Elem. Exp. Med. 11:227-240.

Whitacre, M.E., G.F. Combs, S.B. Combs and R.S. Parker. 1987. Influence of dietary vitamin E on nutritional pancreatic atrophy in selenium-deficient chicks. J. Nutr. 117:460-467.

Willett, W.C., B.F. Polk, J.S. Morris, M.J. Stampfer, S. Pressel, B. Rosner, J.O. Taylor, K. Schneider and C.G. Hames. 1983. Prediagnostic serum selenium and risk of cancer. Lancet 2:130-134.

Wingler, K. and R. Brigelius-Flohe. 1999. Gastrointestinal glutathione peroxidase. BioFactors. 10:245-249.

Wishart, G.J. 1984. Effects of lipid peroxide formation in fowl semen on sperm motility, ATP content and fertilising ability. J. Reprod. Fert. 71:113-118.

Wolffram, S. 1999. Absorption and metabolism of selenium: difference between inorganic and organic sources. In: Biotechnology in the Feed industry. Proc. o+f the 15th Annual Symposium (T.P.Lyons and K.A. Jacques, eds.). Nottingham University Press, Nottingham, UK, pp. 547-566.

Wood, J.D. and M. Enser. 1997. Factors influencing fatty acids in meat and the role of antioxidants in improving meat quality. 78:S49-S60.

Wu, A.S., J.E. Oldfield, L.R. Shull and P. Cheeke. 1979. Specific effect of selenium deficiency on rat sperm. Biol. Reprod. 20:793-798.

Wulf, D.M., J.B. Morgan, S.K. Sanders, J.D. Tatum, G.C. Smith and S. Williams. 1995. Effects of dietary supplementation of vitamin E on storage and caselife properties of lamb retail cuts. J. Anim. Sci. 73:399-405.

Yan, L., J.A.Yee, D. Li, M.H. McGuire and G.L. Graef. 1999. Dietary supplementation of selenomethionine reduces metastasis of melanoma cells in mice. Anticancer Res.19:1337-1342.

Yarsan, E. 1998. Effects of giving vitamin E and/or selenium on monensin poisoning in broilers. Turk. Veterinerlik ve Hayvancilik Dergisi. 22:53-63.

Yazdanpanah, H, F. Roshanzamir, B. Shafaghi, M. Faizi, M. Elhami and H.R.Rasekh. 1997. Assessment of possible protective roles of selenium, zinc, and cis-stilbene oxide against acute T-2 toxin poisoning: a preliminary report. Nat. Toxins 5:133-135.

Yoshida, M., T. Fukunaga, K. Iwami and K.Yasumoto. 1984. Variation of glutathione level and synthesis activity in chick liver due to selenium and vitamin E deficiencies. J. Biochem. (Tokyo) 96:1391-1397.

Yoshida, M, K. Fukunaga, H. Tsuchita and K. Yasumoto. 1999. An evaluation of the bioavailability of selenium in high-selenium yeast. J. Nutr. Vitaminol. 45:119-128.

Yoshioka, T, H. Motoyama, F. Yamasaki, M. Ando, M. Yamasaki and Y. Takehara. 1987. Protective effect of vitamin E against lipoperoxides in developing rats. Biol. Neonate, 51:170-176.

Yu, B.P. 1994. Cellular defences against damage from reactive oxygen species. Physiol. Reviews. 74:139-162.

Zasadowski, A, F. Przala, T. Rotkiewicz, B. Kupis-Froyn and I. Wladyka. 1997. Cadmium, selenium and fenitrothion influence on the vitamin A (retinal) and carotene concentration in chicks liver. Acta Academiae Agriculturae ac Technicae Olstenensis, Veterinaria (Poland). 25:3-13.

Zarski, T.P., H. Zarska and B. Debski. 1995. The effect of selenium supplementation in case of salinomycin overdose in broilers. Annals of Warsaw Agricultural University, Animal Science. 31:69-73.

Effect of dietary antioxidants on the incidence of pulmonary hypertension syndrome in broilers

GHISLAINE ROCH, MARTINE BOULIANNE AND LASZLO DE ROTH

University of Montreal, St. Hyacinthe, Quebec, Canada

Summary

Pulmonary hypertension syndrome (PHS) followed by ascites is a major cause of economic loss in the broiler industry. The main mechanism responsible for ascites in broiler chickens is an increase in intravascular hydrostatic pressure occurring secondary to right ventricular failure. Development of cardiac failure in an apparently healthy young broiler chicken is affected by a range of factors including genetic selection for rapid growth rate, high feed efficiency and a large pectoral muscle mass; all of which increase oxygen demand.

The low ratio between lung volume and body weight in the modern chicken is responsible for the inability of the respiratory system to respond to elevated oxygen needs, which leads to hypoxia and respiratory acidosis. During hypoxia, various mechanisms increase free radical production. The objective of this study was to verify the effects of antioxidants (dietary vitamin E, organic and inorganic selenium (Se)) on the incidence of pulmonary hypertension syndrome (PHS), serum glutathione peroxidase (GSH-Px), blood gases, electrolytes and growth performance in cold-stressed broilers.

The experimental design was a 2x3x4 factorial; with a starter feed containing either 50 or 250 IU vitamin E per kg, 0.3 ppm Se (organic selenium yeast, Sel-Plex), and 0.3 ppm or 0.6 ppm Se from sodium selenite. Vitamin E levels were decreased to 30 and 150 IU/kg, and 20 and 100 IU/kg for the grower and finisher diets, respectively. Broilers were fed *ad libitum* and subjected to cold stress beginning at 21 days of age with temperatures decreasing to 19, 14 and 11.5°C over a two week period. Weekly body weights, daily feed consumption and mortality were recorded and right ventricular/total ventricular weight ratios (RV/TV), blood gases, electrolytes and GSH-Px at 47 days of age were measured. The combination of high vitamin E and organic selenium (Sel-Plex) reduced mortality associated with PHS in cold stressed broilers from 10 to 0.90%. Protective effects of antioxidants on cellular membranes were demonstrated by higher hemoglobin concentration, increased GSH-Px activity, improved blood gas parameters, bicarbonate, pH and normal acid-base status in birds given the high vitamin E level and Sel-Plex organic selenium. Lower mortality and better feed conversion appeared to be the result of improved antioxidant status in the birds.

Introduction: the pulmonary hypertension syndrome

Pulmonary hypertension syndrome (PHS), also called ascites, is a major source of economic loss in the broiler industry. Olkowski *et al.* (1996) showed that PHS was responsible for 2% of the death loss and 0.35% of condemnations in Canada. In 1994, economic losses due to ascites were estimated at USD$12 million and USD$100 million for Canadian and American industries, respectively (Odom, 1993; Olkowski *et al.*, 1996). Conservative estimates of yearly economic cost of PHS worldwide would approach USD$500 million.

The main mechanism responsible for ascites in broiler chickens is an increase in intravascular hydrostatic pressure occurring secondary to right ventricular failure. In response to increased pressure, the transudate leaks out of blood vessels and accumulates in the abdominal cavity, hence the ascites. Development of cardiac failure in an apparently healthy young broiler chicken is explained by a series of factors such as genetic selection for a rapid growth rate, high feed efficiency and a large pectoral muscle mass, all requiring high oxygen levels (Chabot, 1992; Boulianne, 1993; Julian, 1993; Julian *et al.*, 1995; Maxwell *et al.*, 1986a; 1986b; Maxwell and Robertson, 1997; 1998).

The modern chicken has small lung volume:body weight ratio, causing an inability of the respiratory system to respond to the broiler's elevated oxygen needs, which leads to hypoxia and respiratory acidosis (Table 1) (Vidyadaran *et al.*, 1990; Peacock *et al.*, 1990; Reeves *et al.*, 1991; Chabot, 1992; Julian, 1989; 1993).

Table 1. Blood parameters of broilers with and without PHS syndrome.*

	Normal	PHS
pH	7.282	7.163
Hematocrit, %	0.29	0.43**
Protein, g/l	34.2	27.5**
PCO$_2$, kPa	6.4	12.3**
Potassium, mM/l	6.03	7.35
Sodium, mM/l	151.0	146.8**
Chlorine, mM/l	115.0	102.9**
Base excess, meq/l	42.01	51.29**

*Chabot, 1992.
*P<0.05
**P<0.01

Impact of hypoxia on free radical production

During hypoxia, various mechanisms increase free radical production including lipid peroxide, hydrogen peroxide and superoxide (Figure 1). Tissue damage secondary to hypoxia attracts white blood cells, which in turn release more free radicals, causing further damage (McCord, 1985; Halliwell and Gutteridge, 1990; Bottje *et al.*, 1995a). Maxwell *et al.* (1986a) and Enkvetchakul *et al.* (1993) have observed inflammatory cell infiltration in various tissues of PHS chickens. Acidosis will also affect cellular membrane integrity and reduce free radical elimination, hence exacerbating the negative effect of free radicals.

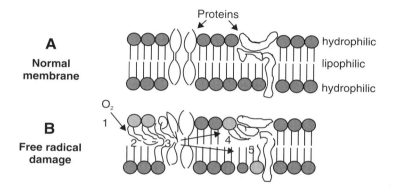

Figure 1. Lipid peroxidation (adapted from Bottje *et al.*, 1995a).

Higher plasma lipid peroxide values have been reported in PHS broilers (Bottje *et al.*, 1995a). Maxwell *et al.* (1986a) have hypothesized that autogenous antioxidant levels were lower in PHS broiler chickens. This theory is supported by the findings of Enkvetchakul *et al.* (1993), who demonstrated lower pulmonary and hepatic tocopherol and glutathione levels in PHS broilers (Figure 2).

The role of these antioxidants is to transform free radicals into harmless compounds, stopping the lipid peroxidation process. Vitamin E (tocopherol) and GSH-Px are excellent antioxidants. First, vitamin E reduces the peroxyl radical to an oxidized lipid. These lipids are then converted by GSH-Px to a lipid alcohol, which contributes to lipid repair (Figure 3) (Maddaiah, 1990; Machlin, 1991; Yu, 1994; Bottje *et al.*, 1995a). Formation of one type of GSH-Px is dependent upon the presence of selenium. This is why selenium and vitamin E work in synergy to protect cellular membranes.

Vitamin E in prevention of PHS

Subcutaneous vitamin E implants have been shown to reduce mortality in PHS chickens (Bottje *et al.*, 1995b). In this study control broilers were

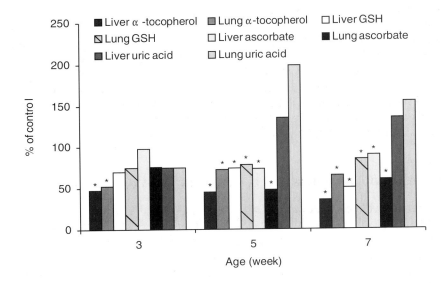

Figure 2. Liver and lung α-tocopherol, GSH, ascorbate and uric acid in PHS broilers. (* means differ, p<0.05; Enkvetchakul *et al.*, 1993).

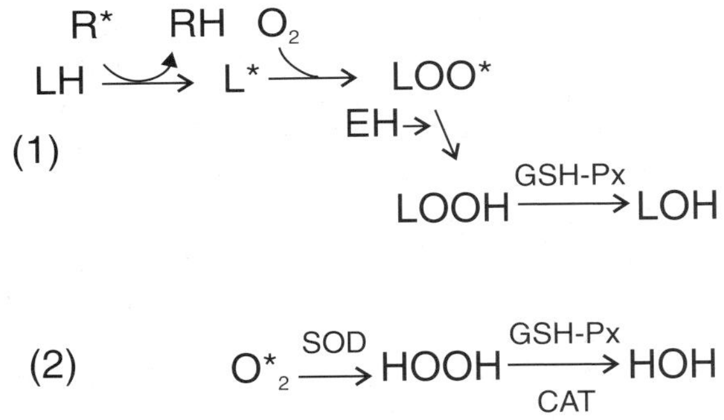

$$(1) \quad LH \xrightarrow[R^*]{RH} L^* \xrightarrow{O_2} LOO^*$$

$$EH \rightarrow \searrow$$

$$LOOH \xrightarrow{GSH\text{-}Px} LOH$$

$$(2) \quad O^*_2 \xrightarrow{SOD} HOOH \xrightarrow[CAT]{GSH\text{-}Px} HOH$$

Figure 3. Protection of membranes by antioxidants (Bottje *et al.*, 1995a).

provided normal ventilation but others maintained under low ventilation conditions to induce PHS were randomly assigned to nonimplanted, placebo, or vitamin E-implanted groups. The vitamin E implant released a total 15 mg α-tocopherol over the first three weeks of age. Tissues and blood samples were obtained at 3 and 5 weeks of age from birds with and without PHS. Cumulative mortality at 5 weeks was lowered by α-tocopherol with mortality rates of 3.6, 4.2, 11.9 and 11.8% for controls (maintained under normal ventilation conditions), vitamin E, non-implanted and placebo treatments, respectively. The PHS birds had lower body weights, higher hematocrit, lower α-tocopherol and glutathione (GSH) concentrations in liver and lung tissue. Oxidative stress was indicated by elevated plasma lipid peroxides and lower oxidized GSH in liver and erythrocytes. These results indicate that the vitamin E implant was effective in reducing PHS mortality in broilers.

In contrast, vitamin E supplementation of the diet had no effects on performance and mortality (Bottje *et al.*, 1997). The maximum vitamin E dose used for this study was 87 IU/kg, a dose similar to recommended commercial levels. We hypothesized that this level was too low to have a significant impact and that it would be necessary to test higher vitamin E doses.

Selenium in prevention of free radical production

One major role of selenium is as a part of the GSH-Px structure. Inorganic selenium (sodium selenite) is the most common form of selenium added to animal feed. Inorganic selenium is passively absorbed in the intestine then reduced to selenide form in the liver where it undergoes an enzymatic process with cysteine to form selenocysteine. GSH-Px, along with the other selenoproteins, is composed of selenocysteine molecules. This mechanism of selenocysteine formation in liver is rapidly saturated when dietary inorganic selenium is increased above 0.3 ppm (Meyer *et al.*, 1981; NRC, 1983; Pehsron, 1993; Mahan, 1995). Animals can store a small quantity of inorganic selenium in different tissues (muscle, liver, etc.,) as a source of non-functional selenium that may eventually be diverted to form biologically important compounds. Because metabolic mechanisms to convert inorganic selenium into organic compounds are rapidly exhausted and body storage is limited, excess inorganic selenium is eliminated in urine and feces.

While inorganic selenium is capable of providing selenium for GSH-Px synthesis, its potential prooxidative effects may be a disadvantage. Several authors have pointed out this disadvantage on noting an increase in lipofuscin pigments in mouse liver tissue after supplementation of the diet with inorganic selenium. Lipofuscin is a metabolic end product of lipid peroxidation (Csallany and Menken, 1986; Pehsron, 1993).

Selenomethionine is the major form of organic selenium in grains and vegetable protein sources. Selenium concentration in plants is dependent on selenium content in soils and on soil conditions. Some soils of North America are deficient in selenium, so plants grown in these areas are also low in selenium. When fed without supplementation, symptoms of selenium deficiency can be observed. It is generally accepted that dietary organic selenium is more effectively retained than inorganic selenium (Mutanen, 1986; Pehrson, 1993; Arai *et al.*, 1994; Mahan, 1995). It is suggested that organic selenium (primarily in selenoamino acid form) is absorbed across the intestinal wall by active transport mechanisms rather than the passive diffusion process used for selenium ions derived from inorganic sources. As mentioned above, the ability of organic and inorganic selenium compounds to supply selenium for GSH-Px synthesis is about the same. However retention of selenium is significantly higher for organic compounds (Perhson, 1993; Mahan, 1995; Edens, 1996; Mahan and Kim, 1996). The magnitude of the difference has been found to be more pronounced with increasing levels of dietary selenium and in certain tissues, particularly brain and muscle (Whanger and Butler, 1988). This higher retention of organic selenium could be used for GSH-Px synthesis when animals are under stress conditions. It could also explain why animals raised under adverse conditions perform better when organic selenium is present in feed (Ku *et al.*, 1973; Mahan, 1995; Edens, 1996).

A new source of selenium, selenium yeast (Sel-Plex, Alltech Inc., Nicholasville, Kentucky), has recently been commercialized. Organic selenium in Sel-Plex is more extensively assimilated and thus dietary levels needed to support animal performance are potentially decreased. Many studies have shown improved animal performance (eg. Table 2), tissue selenium levels (blood, milk, eggs, meat) and reduced selenium excretion in urine and feces in response to organic selenium (Marsh *et al.*, 1981; 1986; Mahan, 1995; Edens, 1996; Mahan and Kim, 1996).

Table 2. Effect of selenium source on mortality and carcass quality in broilers.

Trial	Treatment	Mortality (%)	Drip loss (%)
1	Selenite	10.2	5.3
	Sel-Plex	7.9	4.6
2	Selenite	4.0	3.9
	Sel-Plex	2.0	1.9

Edens, 1996.

Effects of vitamin E level and selenium level and form on incidence of ascites and blood chemistry of broilers

The hypothesis of the present study was that higher dietary vitamin E in synergy with selenium supplementation might protect membranes against oxidation caused by hypoxia and acidosis and help maintain performance of fast growing broilers while protecting against development of PHS. Consequently the objectives were to determine the effects of higher levels of vitamin E and two forms of selenium, organic and inorganic, on the incidence of PHS, serum GSH-Px, blood gases, electrolytes and growth performance in cold-stressed broiler chickens.

MATERIALS AND METHODS

Broiler chickens (1,368) of the Ross 308 x Ross 308 strain were vaccinated at one day of age against Marek's disease and infectious bronchitis and given *ad libitum* access to feed and water during a 49 day trial. Birds were wing-tagged at seven days of age and divided into six groups of four replicate

266

pens each. Each pen contained 57 birds to achieve a final floor density of 0.085 m² per bird. Birds received three types of pelleted feeds: a crumbled starter feed for the first 18 days, a crumbled grower feed for the next 17 days and a pelleted finisher feed during the last two weeks of the grow-out period (Table 3). To predispose birds to PHS, a cold stress temperature protocol modified from Julian *et al.* (1989) was employed (Table 4).

Table 3. Formula and composition of basal diets.

Ingredients [1]	Starter	Grower % of diet	Finisher
Corn yellow	43.00	50.00	55.00
Wheat	20.00	15.00	13.00
Soybean meal, 48%	27.00	21.50	17.00
Meat and bone meal, 52%	5.00	6.00	8.00
Animal fats	1.50	4.50	5.50
Dicalcium phosphate	1.10	0.73	0.25
Limestone	1.00	0.55	0.34
Salt	0.30	0.30	0.27
Premix[2]	1.00	1.30	0.55
Lysine HCl	0.09	0.175	0.14
Dl-methionine	0.23	0.20	0.175
Virginiamycin 44	0.025	0.025	0.025
Coccidiostat	0.05	0.10	0.10
Total	**100**	**100**	**100**
Calculated values			
ME, kcal/kg	3000	3200	3275
Crude protein	22	20	18.5
TSAA	0.92	0.84	0.78
Methionine	0.55	0.5	0.45
Lysine	1.15	1.07	1.00
Calcium	1.05	0.9	0.85
Phosphorus	0.8	0.7	0.65
Sodium	0.16	0.16	0.16
Chlorine	0.25	0.25	0.25

[1] As-fed basis
[2] Per kg of diet: vitamin A, 12,000 IU; cholecalciferol, 3,000 IU; menadione, 3 mg; thiamin HCl, 2 mg; riboflavin, 6 mg; pyridoxine HCl, 4 mg; vitamin B_{12}, 16 mg; niacin, 35 mg; Ca pantothenate, 12 mg; choline Cl, 400 mg; folic acid, 1 mg; D-biotin, 0.1 mg; Mn, 80 mg; Cu, 15 mg; I, 1 mg; Fe, 15 mg; Zn, 60 mg.

Table 4. Cold stress temperature protocol.

	Regular program							Cold stress		
Age, days	0-2	3	5	7	10	14	18	21	28	35-49
Temperature,° C	30	29	27.5	26	25	24	22.5	19	14	11.5

Vitamin E levels used in the trial were the recommended commercial level (50 IU/kg) and five times that recommendation (250 IU/kg). The experimental design was a 2x3x4 factorial with starter feed containing either 50 or 250 IU vitamin E per kg fed with either 0.3 ppm Se from organic selenium yeast (Sel-Plex, Alltech Inc), or 0.3 ppm or 0.6 ppm Se from sodium selenite. Vitamin E levels were decreased to 30 and 150 IU/kg, and 20 and 100 IU/kg for the grower and finisher diets, respectively (Table 5).

Table 5. Antioxidant-supplemented dietary treatments.

	Starter (22% CP)			Grower (20% CP)			Finisher (18% CP)		
	Vit. E[1]	Selenite	Sel-Plex[2]	Vit. E[1]	Selenite	Sel-Plex[2]	Vit. E[1]	Selenite	Sel-Plex[2]
	IU/kg	Se, ppm		IU/kg	Se, ppm		IU/kg	Se, ppm	
Control (Low vit. E/selenite)	50	0.3	–	30	0.3	–	20	0.3	–
High vit. E/selenite	250	0.3	–	150	0.3	–	100	0.3	–
Low vit. E/high selenite	50	0.6	–	30	0.6	–	20	0.6	–
Low vit. E/Sel-Plex	50	–	0.3	30	–	0.3	20	–	0.3
High vit. E/high selenite	250	0.6	–	150	0.6	–	100	0.6	–
High vit. E/Sel-Plex	250	–	0.3	150	–	0.3	100	–	0.3

[1] Vitamin E From BASF, Georgetown Ontario Canada
Organic selenium yeast from Sel-Plex, Alltech Inc., Nicholasville, Kentucky

All birds were individually weighed at 7, 18, 35, 40, 47 days of age. Feed consumption and feed conversion were evaluated for each pen and each group at weighing time. Every broiler dying during the study was necropsied to determine the cause of death. Diagnosis of PHS was confirmed when there was presence of fluid in the abdominal cavity, right ventricular dilation, hydropericardium and generalized vascular congestion. At 47 days, venous blood samples were drawn from one third of the birds (16 broilers per pen). Bicarbonate, pH and hemoglobin were measured with a blood gas apparatus (ABL-300). Hematocrit was determined by centrifugation. Plasma electrolytes (Na, K, Cl) and GSH-Px were measured from frozen samples by HPLC. Birds were slaughtered at 49 days of age. Hearts of blood-sampled birds were collected at the slaughterhouse and dissected to measure the right ventricle/total ventricle (RV/TV) ratio (Julian, 1986; Julian *et al.*, 1989).

Statistical analysis was carried out using General Linear models procedures of SAS® software (SAS Institute, 1966). Growth performance, consumption and feed conversion data, were subjected to repeated measures ANOVA with treatment as fixed effects factors and time as repeated factors. Logarithmic transformation was used to normalize the GSH-Px data. First-order auto-regressive structure to model covariance was performed to provide the best description of covariance structure (Littel *et al.*, 1998). At each time period GLM was used with Tukey's post-hoc test to determine which treatments were statistically different (P<0.05). Chi-square tests to establish mortality rate were performed to examine association with treatment. Sequential contrasts were then applied to determine which treatments were different (P<0.05). For blood parameters and RV TV heart ratio analysis, a GLM with Tukey's post-hoc test was used to determine statistical differences between treatments (P<0.05). Statistical analysis was carried out using General Linear models procedures of SAS (1996).

RESULTS

Ascites mortality

Cumulative mortality rate of the control group was 16.3%, while mortality caused by ascites was 10% (Figure 4). Mortality attributed to ascites decreased in birds given 250 IU vitamin E (4.98%), 0.6 ppm Se from selenite (3.76%), or high vitamin E plus 0.06 ppm Se from selenite (3.24%). The greatest reduction in ascites mortality was observed in birds given 0.3 ppm Se from Sel-Plex with either low vitamin E (2.82%) or high vitamin E (0.90%) (P<0.05).

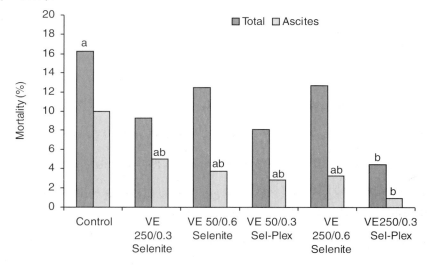

Figure 4. Effect of antioxidant supplementation on mortality in broilers ([ab]Means differ, p<0.05).

Bottje *et al.* (1995b) showed decreased ascites mortality rate in chickens implanted with subcutaneous vitamin E pellets. Boren and Pond (1996) also observed a reduction in total mortality and condemnations due to ascites in commercial flocks supplemented with 260 IU/kg of feed during the first two weeks of age. Similarly, Stanley *et al.* (1998) showed that chicks exposed to cold stress and aflatoxin-contaminated feed had lower ascites mortality when treated with high levels of vitamin E (500 IU/kg) and Sel-Plex organic selenium (0.1 ppm). However, when Bottje *et al.* (1997) tested vitamin E feed supplementation (87 IU/kg), no effects on performance and mortality were observed. Results of the present study and those of Stanley *et al.* (1998) suggest that in order to prevent mortality caused by ascites, higher levels of vitamin E and selenium are required. Furthermore, it appears that organic selenium was more effective than the inorganic source.

Ventricular weight ratio

Addition of any antioxidant in feed improved the RV/TV ratio (P<0.05), decreasing it from 0.30 in the controls to below 0.24 in all other treatment groups (Table 6). Similarly to ascites mortality rate, the smallest ratio was obtained with the combination of high dietary vitamin E and organic selenium (0.215).

Table 6. Ratio between right ventricular and total ventricular volume.[1]

Treatments	RV/TV
Control (Vitamin E 50/0.3 selenite)	0.300[a] ± 0.105
Vitamin E 250/0.3 Selenite	0.232[b] ± 0.077
Vitamin E 50/0.6 Selenite	0.241[b] ± 0.075
Vitamin E 50/0.3 Sel-Plex	0.234[b] ± 0.071
Vitamin E 250/0.6 Selenite	0.230[b] ± 0.052
Vitamin E 250/0.3 Sel-Plex	0.215[b] ± 0.049

[1]Values are mean ± standard deviation.
[a,b]Means with no common superscripts differ (P<0.05).

Ventricular weight ratios (RV/TV) above 0.25 have been associated with the clinical appearance of PHS. A positive linear relationship between PHS incidence and RV/TV ratio has previously been demonstrated (Maxwell *et al.*, 1986a; Julian, 1986; Huchzermeyer *et al.*, 1988; Chabot, 1992). The results of the present study are in concordance with these findings.

Blood chemistry responses, GSH-Px

Analysis of blood samples revealed that GSH-Px, hemoglobin (Hb), pH and bicarbonate (HCO_3) values were significantly different in the antioxidant-treated groups when compared to controls (Table 7). There were no significant differences in hematocrit values, sodium or potassium levels due to treatment. Serum GSH-Px increased with addition of organic selenium alone (4796 U/l) or when combined with the high vitamin E level (5489 U/l) (Figure 5). Hemoglobin was significantly higher in birds given 250 ppm vitamin E with either 0.6 ppm Se from selenite (10.11 g/dl) or 0.3 ppm Se from Sel-Plex (10.44 g/dl) (Figure 6).

Blood pH in the control group revealed metabolic acidosis with a value of 7.29. All antioxidant treatments prevented acidosis and kept blood pH in the normal range (7.34 to 7.39) (Table 7). Since pH and bicarbonate are positively correlated; a similar effect on blood bicarbonate values was observed with the control group having significantly lower values than those of antioxidant groups.

In the present study, GSH-Px activities in the high vitamin E/high selenite, 0.3 ppm Sel-Plex Se and high vitamin E plus Sel-Plex treatments were 136, 155 and 178% higher, respectively, when compared to controls (P<0.05). A positive correlation between selenium addition to feed and GSH-Px activity

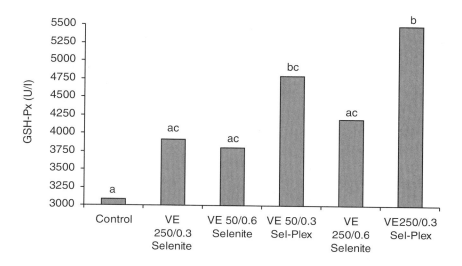

Figure 5. Effect of antioxidant supplementation on plasma GSH-Px in broilers ([abc]Means differ, P<0.05).

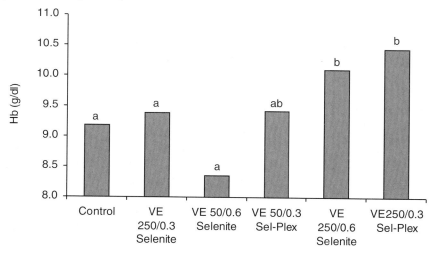

Figure 6. Effect of antioxidant supplementation on hemoglobin levels in broilers ([ab]Means differ, P<0.05).

has been noted in many species when dietary selenium content was less than 0.3 ppm (Chavez, 1979; Arai *et al.*, 1994; Mahan, 1995; Mahan and Kim, 1996). The difference in GSH-Px activity noted between the two types of selenium in this study is proably due to the nature of the selenium in each form. Since higher GSH-Px levels are desirable in order to better protect various tissues against the deleterious effects of oxidative stress

271

Table 7. Effect of antioxidant supplementation on blood parameters[1].

Samples	Control	Vitamin E 250 0.3 Selenite	Vitamin E 50 0.6 Selenite	Vitamin E 50 0.3 Sel-Plex	Vitamin E 250 0.6 Selenite	Vitamin E 250 0.3 Sel-Plex
	28	28	29	15	31	32
Hemoglobin, g/dl	9.18[a]	9.38[a]	8.35[a]	9.41[ab]	10.11[b]	10.44[b]
pH	7.29[a]	7.35[b]	7.39[c]	7.34[b]	7.37[c]	7.38[c]
Hematocrit, %	28.15[a]	29.09[a]	28.52[a]	28.56[a]	26.69[a]	25.27[a]
GSH-Px, U/l	3083[a]	3914[ac]	3805[ac]	4796[cb]	4200[ac]	5489[b]
HCO$_3$, mM/l	22.11[a]	27.54[b]	26.11[b]	27.01[b]	27.47[b]	27.01[b]
Na, mM/l	147.83[a]	147.85[a]	148.86[a]	148.73[a]	147.68[a]	147.94[a]
K, mM/l	8.66[a]	7.41[a]	8.01[a]	9.39[a]	7.32[a]	9.08[a]
Cl, mM/l	109.19[a]	108.31[b]	112.39[a]	108.2[b]	107.97[b]	108.49[b]

[1] Data are uncorrected for mortality.
[abcd] Means in rows with no common superscript differ (P<0.05).

(Bottje *et al.*, 1995b), it is not surprising that lower ascites mortality rates were observed with the more bioavailable organic selenium alone or in combination with higher dietary vitamin E.

The increase in hemoglobin concentrations observed in the high vitamin E/high selenite or Sel-Plex groups likely reflected improved integrity of the erythrocyte cellular membranes and thus potentially better tissue oxygenation. The present results, along with higher hemoglobin concentrations, pH and bicarbonate levels, are compatible with normal acid-base status also reported elsewhere (Chabot, 1992).

Body weight and feed efficiency

Addition of antioxidants did not affect final body weight. However, feed conversion was significantly improved in birds given 250 IU vitamin E plus 0.3 ppm Se from Sel-Plex diet (Table 8).

Reduction of ascites mortality during the last two weeks of the grow-out period, better feed conversion, improved GSH-Px and blood gas values showed that birds with normal acid-base status both perform better and are better protected against the deleterious effects of oxidative stress. Boren and Bond (1996) were the first to demonstrate the potential of vitamin E to improve broiler performance using 260 IU vitamin E per kg in a starter diet for commercially-reared broilers. Total mortality and condemnation rates were lower in the supplemented group. High levels of vitamin E also proved effective in improving performance under stress conditions. Stanley *et al.* (1998) submitted broiler chickens to cold stress and fed aflatoxin-contaminated feed supplemented with 500 IU/kg vitamin E and 0.1 ppm Se from Sel-Plex. Incidence of PHS, mortality and hematocrit values were reduced and better hemoglobin values and tissue protection demonstrated.

In the present study 250 IU/kg vitamin E and 0.3 ppm Se from Sel-Plex in cold stressed broilers gave similar improvements in performance. Together

Table 8. Influence of antioxidants on body weights and feed conversion of broilers.[1]

	Control	Vitamin E 250 0.3 Selenite	Vitamin E 50 0.6 Selenite	Vitamin E 50 0.3 Sel-Plex	Vitamin E 250 0.6 Selenite	Vitamin E 250 0.3 Sel-Plex
Time (days)	28	28	29	15	31	32
Body weight, kg						
7	0.201[a]	0.193 [b]	0.192[b]	0.190[b]	0.190[b]	0.196[ab]
18	0.692[a]	0.696[a]	0.687[a]	0.661[ab]	0.647[b]	0.677[ab]
35	2.229[a]	2.220[a]	2.190[a]	2.169[ab]	2.119[b]	2.160[ab]
40	2.753[a]	2.719[a]	2.703[a]	2.692[a]	2.638[a]	2.680[a]
47	3.526[a]	3.434[a]	3.529[a]	3.517[a]	3.431[a]	3.474[a]
Feed conversion						
0-7	1.050[a]	1.146[b]	1.108[ab]	1.09[ab]	1.080[ab]	1.055[a]
8-18	1.421[a]	1.434[a]	1.388[a]	1.462[a]	1.444[a]	1.385[a]
19-35	1.753[a]	1.767[a]	1.713[a]	1.641[a]	1.648[a]	1.618[a]
36-40	1.973[a]	1.875[a]	1.785[a]	1.945[a]	1.714[a]	1.709[a]
41-47	2.912[a]	2.910[a]	2.512[ab]	2.379[ab]	2.748[ab]	2.272[b]
0-47	1.892[a]	1.915[a]	1.806[ab]	1.793[ab]	1.792[ab]	1.717[b]

[1] Data are uncorrected for mortality.

[ab] Means in rows with no common superscript differ ($P<0.05$).

these three studies demonstrate that higher levels of vitamin E and Sel-Plex could help prevent PHS and maintain performance of broiler chickens.

Conclusions

Results of this study provide evidence that increased vitamin E in the diet and organic selenium (Sel-Plex) reduce mortality associated with PHS in cold stressed broiler chickens. Low mortality and better feed conversion appear to be the result of improved antioxidant status in birds. Protective effects of antioxidants on the erythrocyte cellular membrane were demonstrated by higher hemoglobin concentration, increased GSH-Px activity, improved blood gas parameters, HCO_3, pH and normal acid-base status.

Acknowledgments

We would like to thank Ms. Avila Croisetière and Dr Guy Beauchamps for their technical support in this project. This study was made possible by the financial support of Probiotech Inc., Alltech, Inc., BASF Canada and CORPAQ.

References

Arai, T., M. Sugawara, T. Sako, S. Motoyoshi, T. Shimura, N. Tsutsui and T. Konno. 1994. Glutathione peroxidase activity in tissues of chickens supplemented with dietary selenium. Comp. Biochem. Physiol. 107A (1):245-248.

Boren B. and P. Bond. 1996. Vitamin E and immunocompetence. Broiler Industry, November 1996. pp. 26-33.

Bottje, W., B. Enkvetchakul and R. Wideman. 1995a. Antioxidants, hypoxia and lipid peroxidation involvement in pulmonary hypertension syndrome (Ascite). In: Novus, Nutrition Update 5(2). pp. 1-11.

Bottje, W., B. Enkvetchakul, R. Moore and R. McNew. 1995b. Effect of α-tocopherols on antioxidants, lipid peroxidation and the incidence of pulmonary hypertension syndrome (ascites) in broilers. Poultry Sci. 74:1356-1369.

Bottje, W., G.F. Erf, T.K. Bersi, D. Wang, D. Barnes and K.W. Beers. 1997. Effect of dietary dl-α-tocopherols on tissue α-and γ-tocopherol and pulmonary hypertension syndrome (ascites) in broilers. Poultry Sci. 76:1506-1512.

Boulianne, M. 1993. Cas d'aspergillose précoce suivi d'une forte incidence d'ascite. Le Médecin Vétérinaire du Québec, 23(1):28-31.

Chabot, R. 1992. Le syndrome de l'ascite chez les poulets à chair. Mémoire de Maîtrise, Faculté de Médecine vétérinaire de l'Université de Montréal à St-Hyacinthe. pp. 50.

Chavez, E.R. 1979. Effect of dietary selenium depletion and repletion on plasma glutathione peroxidase activity and selenium concentration in blood and body tissues of growing pigs. Can. J. Anim. Sci. 59:761-771.

Coelho, M.B. and J.L. McNaughton. 1995. Effect of composite vitamin supplementation on broilers. J. Appl. Poultry Res. 4:219.

Csallany, A.S. and B.Z. Menken. 1986. Effect of dietary selenite on hepatic organic solvent-soluble lipofuscin pigments. J. Am. Coll. Toxic 5:79.

Edens, F.W. 1996. Organic selenium: From feathers to muscle integrity to drip loss. Five years onward: No more selenite. In: Biotechnology in the Feed Industry, Proceedings of the 12th Annual Symposium (T.P. Lyons and K.A. Jacques, eds), Nottingham University Press, UK. pp. 165-185.

Enkvetchakul, B., W. Bottje, R. Moore and W. Huff. 1993. Compromised antioxidant status associated with ascites in broilers. Poultry Sci. 72:2272-2280.

Halliwel, B. and J.M.C. Gutteridge. 1990. Role of free radicals and catalytic metal ion in human disease: An overview. Methods Enzymol. 186:1-85.

Huchzermeyer, F.W., R.J. Julian and J.K. Barker. 1988. Lesions of right heart failure and ascites in broiler chickens. Avian Dis.32:246-261.

Julian, R.J. 1986. Right ventricular failure as a cause of ascites in broiler and roaster chickens. In: Proceedings IVth International Symposium Veterinary Laboratory Diagnosticians, Amsterdam. pp. 608-611.

Julian, R.J. 1989. Lung volume in meat-type chickens. Avian Dis. 33:174-176.

Julian, R.J. 1993. Review article; Ascites in poultry. Avian Pathol. 22:419-454.

Julian, R.J., M. Boulianne and J.P. Vaillancourt. 1995. Prévention de la défaillance ventriculaire droite secondaire à l'hypertension pulmonaire et de l'ascite chez le poulet à griller. Le Médecin Vétérinaire du Québec 25(2):73-76.

Julian, R.J., I. McMillan and M. Quinton. 1989. The effect of cold and dietary energy on right ventricular hypertrophy, right ventricular failure and ascites in meat-type chickens. Avian Pathol. 18:730-732.

Ku, P.K., E.R. Miller, R.C. Wallstram, A.W. Grace, J.P. Hichcock and D.E. Ullrey. 1973. Selenium supplementation of naturally high selenium diets for swine. J. Anim. Sci. 37:501.

Machlin, L. 1991. Vitamin E. In: Handbook of vitamins (L.J. Machlin, ed). Marcel Dekker, Inc. New York, NY. pp. 100-144.

Maddaiah, V.T. 1990. Glutathione correlates with lipid peroxidation in liver mitochondria of triiodothyronine injected hypophysectomized rats. FASEB J. 4:1513-1518

Mahan D.C. 1995. Selenium metabolism in animals: What role does selenium yeast have? In: Biotechnology in the Feed Industry, Proceedings of the 11th Annual Symposium (T.P. Lyons and K.A. Jacques, eds), Nottingham University Press, UK. pp. 257-266.

Mahan, D.C. and Y.Y. Kim. 1996. Effect on inorganic or organic selenium at two levels on reproductive performance and tissue selenium concentrations in first parity gilts and their progeny. J. Anim. Sci. 74:2711-2718.

Marsh, J.A., R.R. Dietert and G.F. Combs Jr. 1981. Influence of dietary selenium and vitamin E on the humoral immune response of chick. Proc. Soc. Exp. Biol. Med. 166:228.

Marsh, J.A., G.F. Combs, Jr., M.E. Whitacre and R.R. Dietert. 1986. Effect of selenium and vitamin E dietary deficiencies on chick lymphoid organ development. Proc. Soc. Exp. Biol. Med. 182:425.

Maxwell, M.H., G.W. Robertson and S. Spence. 1986a. Studies on an ascitic syndrome in young broilers. 1. Haematology and pathology. Avian Pathol. 15:511-524.

Maxwell, M.H., G.W. Robertson and S. Spence. 1986b. Studies on an ascitic syndrome in young broilers. 2. Ultrastructure. Avian Pathol. 15:525-538.

Maxwell, M.H. and G.W. Robertson. 1997. World broiler ascites survey 1996. Poultry International, April. pp. 16-30.

Maxwell, M.H. and G.W. Robertson. 1998. UK survey of broiler ascites and sudden death syndromes in 1993. Br. Poult. Sci. 39:203-215.

McCord, J.M. 1985. Oxygen-derived free radicals in post-ischemic tissue injury. N. Engl. J. Med. 312:159-163.

Meyer, W.R., D.C. Mahan and A.L. Moxon. 1981. Value of dietary selenium and vitamin E for weanling swine as measured by performance and tissue selenium and glutathione peroxidase activities. J. Anim. Sci. 52:302-311.

Mutanen, M. 1986. Bioavailability of selenium. Ann. Clin. Res. 18:48.

National Research Council. 1983. Subcommitee on selenium. Selenium in Nutrition. Revised Ed. Nutrient of Poultry 8th rev. Ed. National Academy Press Washington, DC.

Odom, T.W. 1993. Ascites syndrome: Overview and update. Poultry Sci. 50:14-22.

Olkowski, A.A., L. Kumor and L. Classen. 1996. Changing epidemiology of ascites in broiler chickens. Can. J. Anim. Sci. 76:135-140.

Peacock, A.J., C.K. Pickett, K.G. Morris and J.T. Reeves. 1990. Spontaneous hypoxaemia and right ventricular hypertrophy in fast growing broiler chickens reared at sea level. Comp. Biochem. Physiol. 97A:537-541.

Pehrson, B.G. 1993. Selenium in nutrition with special reference to the biopotency of organic and inorganic selenium compounds. In: Biotechnology in the Feed Industry, Proceedings of the 9th Annual Symposium (T.P. Lyons and K.A. Jacques, eds), Alltech Technical Publications, Nicholasville, Ky. pp. 71-89.

Reeves, J.T., G. Ballam, S. Hofmeister, C. Pickett, K. Morris and A. Peacock. 1991. Improved arterial oxygenation with feed restriction in rapidly growing broiler chickens. Comp. Biochem. Physiol. 99A:481-495.

SAS Institute. 1996. SAS/STAT User's Guide, Version 6, 4th ed., SAS Institute Inc., Cary, NC

Stanley G.V., H. Chukwu and D. Thompson. 1998. Singly and combined effects of organic selenium (Se-Yeast) and vitamin E on ascites reduction in broilers. PSSA, 1998 abst: 111.

Vidyadaran, M.K., A.S. King and H. Kassin. 1990. Quantitative comparisons of lung structure of adult domestic fowl and red jungle fowl, with to broiler ascites. Avian Pathol. 19:51-58.

Whanger, P.D. and J.A. Butler. 1988. Effects of various dietary levels of selenium as selenite or selenomethionine on tissue selenium levels and glutathione peroxidase activity in rats. J. Nutr. 118:846.

Yu, B.P. 1994. Cellular defenses against damage from reactive oxygen species. Physiol. Rev. 74:139-162.

Biological chemistry and absorption of inorganic and organic trace metals

RONAN POWER AND KARINA HORGAN

European Bioscience Centre, Alltech Inc., Dunboyne, Co. Meath, Ireland.

Introduction

Trace elements may be generally defined as those which occur or are required at relatively low concentrations in living tissues. Classically, they have been subdivided into two categories: those which have been established as essential for life or health, and those for which proof of essentiality does not (yet) exist. Although the essentiality of some trace elements is still a matter for debate, it is widely accepted that the trace elements now considered to be essential or beneficial to mammalian and avian species are: arsenic (As), boron (B), chromium (Cr), cobalt (Co), copper (Cu), fluorine (F), iodine (I), iron (Fe), manganese (Mn), molybdenum (Mo), nickel (Ni), selenium (Se), silicon (Si), vanadium (V) and zinc (Zn). Trace element supplementation of animal diets has traditionally been achieved through the use of inorganic salts such as copper (II) sulphate. However, since a host of intrinsic and extrinsic factors are known to affect the bioavailability of dietary inorganic trace elements, continuous efforts have been made over the years to improve their utilization by humans and animals. It is now well established that metal chelates of, for example, Cu^{2+}, Zn^{2+} and Mn^{2+} with amino acids and peptides can enhance the bioavailability of these trace elements, thereby leading to improvements in parameters such as growth, reproduction and general health status when they are otherwise unavailable in sufficient amounts to meet animal needs. Today there are many such forms of metal complexes available in the marketplace for use in animal nutrition; and these have (perhaps unfortunately) been generically entitled 'organic trace minerals' by virtue of the fact that the trace elements in question are complexed or otherwise associated with organic molecules.

In view of the increasing use of these products by the animal feed industry, it is of interest to briefly review the essential biochemical functions of at least some of the essential trace elements to establish why it is so desirable to increase their biological availability and to explore some of the possible mechanisms by which the aforementioned organic trace elements can achieve this.

The role of trace metals in biological systems

Even a cursory inspection of the available literature reveals that the involvement of trace metals in key biochemical processes is immense and quite beyond the scope of this particular text (for review see Fenton, 1995). A broad classification of metallobiomolecues (Figure 1) shows the association of trace elements with easily recognisable key enzymes, transport proteins and other systems which are essential for life. A summary of trace mineral biological functions is in Table 1.

Table 1. Nutritional aspects of zinc, copper, iron and manganese.

Element	Functions	Deficiency
Zinc	Enzymes in most major metabolic pathways, hormone interactions, nucleic acid and protein synthesis, immune system.	Dermal disorders, emaciation, impaired sexual function, retarded growth.
Copper	Cellular respiration, enzymes in synthesis of cartilage, bone, myelin, carbohydrate and lipid metabolism. Immune function.	Retarded growth, ataxia, anaemia, bone disorders, cardiovascular disorders, achromotrichia, keratinization failure.
Iron	Heme respiratory carrier, essential component of catalases, cytochromes and peroxidases.	Anaemia, fatigue, abnormalities in epithelial tissues.
Manganese	Metalloenzymes in protein, carbohydrate and lipid metabolism. Bone development, reproductive function.	Skeletal abnormalities, impaired growth, decreased egg production and shell quality, pancreatic abnormalities.

Iron has a vital role in many biochemical reactions. It plays an active part in oxidation/reduction reactions and electron transport associated with cellular respiration. It is found in complexes bound to proteins such as haem, in enzymes such as microsomal cytochromes, catalase, etc., and in non-haem compounds such as transferrin, ferritin and flavin iron-enzymes. Haemoglobin occurs in erythrocytes while transferrin is found in plasma. The latter is the principal carrier of iron in blood. In general terms, iron is essential to cellular and whole body energy and protein metabolism and is vital for good health and the prevention of anaemia (Kaim and Schwederski, 1993).

Copper is very important for animals as it is an essential component of physiologically important metalloenzymes such as cytochrome oxidase, superoxide dismutase, lysyl oxidase, dopamine hydroxylase and tyrosinase. Overall, this metal is involved in cellular respiration, cardiac function, bone formation, connective tissue development, keratinisation and pigmentation of tissue, as well as myelination of the spinal cord (McDowell, 1992). Copper has a direct effect on iron metabolism and thus indirectly affects

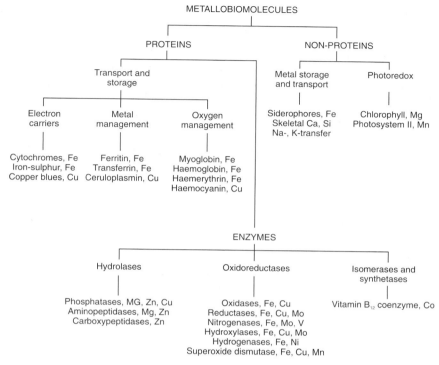

Figure 1. A classification of some metallobiomolecules.

haemoglobin biosynthesis. The first sign of copper deficiency experimentally observed was anaemia in rats. In those early studies haemoglobin regeneration was used to estimate the bioavailability of various copper compounds (Schultze *et al.*, 1934; 1936) and in later years to assess copper-amino acid and copper-peptide complexes (Kirchgessner and Grassman, 1970). The overall growth-promoting effects of copper are well established and are amply reviewed elsewhere (Underwood, 1977; McDowell, 1992).

Manganese, like other essential trace elements, can function both as an enzyme activator and as a constituent of metalloenzymes. Manganese-containing enzymes include arginase, pyruvate carboxylase and Mn-superoxide dismutase. Although the number of Mn-metalloenzymes is limited, a large number of enzymes can be activated by manganese. These include hydrolases, kinases, decarboxylases and transferases. Manganese is a vital element for correct bone growth, carbohydrate and lipid metabolism, immune and nervous system function and reproduction. Indeed, effects on reproduction were among the first signs of Mn deficiency to be noted.

Zinc is the second most abundant trace element in mammals and is required as a component of over 300 enzymes in different species of all phyla, (Vallee and Falchuk, 1993). These include carbonic anhydrase, alcohol dehydrogenase and alkaline phosphatase. In its association with enzymes, zinc plays an active catalytic role, generally as a strong Lewis acid, or acts in a regulatory or structural role. Biologically, it is a trace element of immense importance having significant effects on the production and secretion of steroid and peptide hormones which, of course, may offer an explanation for some of the well documented effects of zinc deficiency such as growth retardation, impaired reproductive development/function, aberrant water and cation balance and parakeratosis.

Apart from its well established structural role in key metalloenzymes, zinc performs unique structural functions at a nucleic acid level. The transcription of DNA to RNA and the ultimate translation of the latter to protein is initiated by regulatory proteins called transcription factors. Certain transcription factors such as steroid hormone receptors possess strikingly similar structural organisation. In particular, they contain a distinctive structural motif; the zinc finger, which allows the transcription factor to bind to the corresponding recognition sequence of the target gene thereby regulating its expression. The highly conserved amino acid sequence for zinc fingers contains nine cysteine residues. For each zinc finger formed, zinc is enfolded in tetrahedral co-ordination via donor atoms from cysteine and histidine (Evans and Hollenberg, 1988). Computer-assisted searches for related sequences have revealed potential zinc finger sequences in several classes of proteins involved in nucleic acid recognition. Such findings underline the essentiality of zinc in many critical biological processes.

Increasing the bioavailability of dietary trace metals

From the foregoing very brief overview of the broad functions of some essential trace elements, it is obvious why efforts have been made to increase their biological availability through the use of metal complexes or chelates. The various categories of organic trace metals used in agricultural practice have been defined by the Association of American Feed Control Officials (AAFCO, 1998). These are shown in Table 2. Chelation refers to a specific type of complex formation between a metal ion and a ligand. A ligand in this case may be defined as a molecule containing an atom which has a lone pair of electrons. Metal ions in complexes are bonded to the ligand through donor atoms such as oxygen, nitrogen or sulphur. Chelation occurs where such ligands bond to a metal ion via two or more donor atoms to form a complex containing one or more heterocyclic rings containing the metal atom. Amino acids are examples of 'bidentate' ligands, which bond to metal ions via an oxygen of the carboxylic acid group and the nitrogen of the amino group (Hynes and Kelly, 1995). Obviously, not all metal complexes are chelates.

In view of the space which would be required to review all of the available literature on the categories of organic trace minerals listed in Table 2, considerations will be restricted to the most commonly used organic trace mineral supplements, namely; proteinates/chelates of zinc, copper, iron and manganese.

Table 2. AAFCO definitions for organic mineral complexes.

Metal Amino Acid Complex – is the product resulting from complexing of a soluble metal salt with an amino acid(s).

Metal Amino Acid Chelate – is the product resulting from the reaction of a metal ion from a soluble metal salt with amino acids with a mole ratio of one mole of metal to one to three (preferably two) moles of amino acids to form coordinate covalent bonds. The average weight of the hydrolyzed amino acids must be approximately 150 and the resulting molecular weight of the chelate must not exceed 800.

Metal Polysaccharide Complex – is the product resulting from complexing of a soluble salt with a polysaccharide solution.

Metal Proteinate – is the product resulting from the chelation of a soluble salt with amino acids and / or partially hydrolyzed protein.

The term 'bioavailability' has been the source of considerable debate and is not explained similarly by all investigators. It has been defined as the proportion of the total mineral/nutrient in a food utilized for normal body functions (Fairweather – Tait, 1992). Others have defined bioavailability as the efficiency with which a natural or manufactured source of an element delivers the element to storage or supplies it to metabolically active tissue or to a protein (Wapnir, 1998). It is also considered to reflect the efficiency with which consumed nutrients are absorbed from the alimentary tract and are thus available for storage or use (Forbes and Erdman, 1983; Bender, 1989). Similarly, Ammerman *et al.* (1995) defined bioavailability as the degree to which an ingested nutrient in a particular source is absorbed in a form that can be utilized in metabolism by the animal. Bioavailability encompasses the sum of impacts that may reduce or promote the metabolic utilization of a nutrient (Schumann *et al.*, 1997). If agreement can be reached, therefore, it is that bioavailability involves both the absorption and the ultimate metabolic utilization of nutrients within the cell.

Physiochemical factors affect nutrient uptake from the intestinal lumen and the incorporation of nutrients into complex biochemical pathways within the cellular environment. On balance, however, impaired intracellular utilization of absorbed inorganic nutrients may not be the major component when considering their overall bioavailability. The aforementioned physiochemical factors that reduce uptake of mineral nutrients from the intestine are the predominant influence on this parameter (Dreosti, 1993). Some of these factors relate obviously to the chemical form of the element or to the presence of other inorganic ions that compete for the same uptake mechanism. Others are caused by the interaction of mineral nutrients with carrier molecules that enhance absorption via specific mucosal receptors or with other organic molecules that reduce it (Table 3). Examples of the latter include phytate, certain sugars, fibre sources and polyphenols. The overall complexity of these interactions is further compounded by the fact that host-related variables also influence mineral availability. These include age, sex, stage of growth, pregnancy, lactation, nutritional status, disease, gastrointestinal secretions and microflora as well as gastrointestinal transit time (Johnson, 1989; Fairweather-Tait, 1996).

Table 3. Examples of dietary factors that increase or decrease absorption, excretion or utilization of certain trace elements.

Dietary constituent	Effect	Element
Phytate	Decrease absorption	Zn, Fe, Mn,
	Increase excretion	Cu
Phosphate	Decrease absorption	Fe, Mn
Polyphenols	Decrease absorption	Fe
Ascorbic acid	Increase absorption	Fe
	Decrease utilization	Cu
Some protein sources	Decrease excretion	Cu
	Increase absorption	Zn, Fe, Mn
Casein	Decrease absorption	Fe
Some amino acids	Increase absorption	Zn, Cu, Fe, Mn
Certain sugars	Decrease absorption	Cu
Fructose	Decrease absorption	Cu
	Increase absorption	Zn, Fe, Mn
Other metals	Decrease absorption	Zn + Fe / Sn
		Cr + Zn / Fe / V / Ca
		Fe + Ca / Mn / Zn
		Cu + Zn
		Mn + Ca / Fe
	Increase excretion	Cu + Mo
	Decrease utilization	Cu + Fe / Cd

In view of all of these factors, it is not surprising that much remains to be learned in terms of specific uptake mechanisms and utilization of natural and manufactured sources of trace elements, despite the intensive research attention which the area has received over the years.

BIOAVAILABILITY OF TRACE METAL CHELATES AND PROTEINATES

Several investigators have looked at the bioavailability of metal chelates and proteinates relative to inorganic sources. It will be recalled (Table 2) that proteinates are defined as trace metals chelated to amino acids and/or partially hydrolyzed protein. Studies in poultry have revealed notable differences in the bioavailability of zinc from different sources. For example, it has been reported that the bioavailability of zinc from zinc methionine was

206% relative to that of zinc sulphate (Wedekind *et al.*, 1992). Other indicators of the improved bioavailability of organic zinc versus inorganic sources in poultry include studies which document significantly positive effects on gonad development in breeding cocks receiving zinc proteinate versus zinc sulphate (Suchy *et al.*, 1998). In addition, recent studies have demonstrated that the replacement of inorganic zinc and manganese sources with zinc and manganese proteinate improved eggshell quality (Miles, 1998). Indeed, many studies on the relative bioavailability of manganese have been conducted with poultry for which there is a critical supplemental need for the element. Early studies with poultry, in which growth or leg deformities were measured, were not sufficiently sensitive to detect differences in bioavailability among supplemental sources. However, over the last two decades, tissue deposition of the element has been used to estimate manganese bioavailability. Such studies have revealed that the most available sources of manganese are manganese-methionine and manganese proteinate (Henry, 1995).

In ruminants, copper proteinate has been reported to be more bioavailable than cupric sulphate in studies involving beef cattle (Hemken *et al*, 1993). Further studies by the same group in dairy cows demonstrated an increased hepatic iron content in copper proteinate versus cupric sulphate-supplemented animals, suggesting that copper proteinate did not interfere with iron uptake and storage as might be expected with inorganic copper sources. In addition, it was found that copper proteinate–supplemented cows had lower plasma ceruloplasmin activity than cows fed cupric sulphate even though plasma copper was essentially the same for both groups (Du *et al.*, 1995). These data suggested that copper proteinate was absorbed via a different mechanism (perhaps even in an intact form) to cupric sulphate and was transported in the blood without binding to ceruloplasmin. In relation to plasma copper levels arising from the use of different copper sources, it is interesting to note that the bioavailability of copper proteinate relative to cupric sulphate has been calculated to be either 147% or 112% depending on whether liver copper or plasma copper is used as the response criterion (Baker and Ammerman, 1995; Kincaid *et al.*; 1986). Such findings are in agreement with recommendations that liver copper levels, not plasma copper levels, are a better indicator of copper status and relative bioavailability between sources (Lee *et al.*, 1988; Xin *et al.*, 1991).

A number of other studies have compared proteinates with inorganic forms of Cu, Zn, Fe and Mn. Unfortunately, many of these studies have used a combination of organic supplements, which makes it difficult to ascribe specific effects to individual metals. Nevertheless, these studies have demonstrated benefits versus inorganic supplements in reducing somatic cell counts and the incidence of clinical mastitis (Boland *et al.*, 1996). Similarly, Spain (1993) noted fewer (P<0.05) new mammary infections in cows fed zinc proteinate compared to cows fed zinc oxide.

In pigs, a major goal has been to improve the iron status of the newborn piglet through the use of more bioavailable iron sources. For example, iron chelated to amino acids has been reported to lead to increased transfer of iron across the placenta and into the foetus (Ashmead and Graff, 1982). When provided at 200 ppm in the gestation diet, greater quantities of Fe were incorporated into the foetuses resulting in significantly reduced mortality and heavier piglets at birth and weaning (Ashmead, 1996). When employed over eight parities, there were fewer stillborn piglets and more piglets weaned in each parity as well as a shorter interval between weaning and oestrus. Similar effects have been reported for iron proteinate incorporated in a normal late gestation/lactation diet fed from seven days pre-farrowing and throughout a 26 day lactation. This led to improved feed intake of the sows and increased weaning weight of the piglets (Close, 1999). In other recent studies, piglets from sows whose diets were supplemented with iron proteinate 21 days pre-farrowing had a higher erythrocyte count ($P<0.05$) and haemoglobin level ($P<0.01$) than piglets from sows receiving inorganic iron sources. In addition, liver iron levels were notably higher in piglets from the proteinate supplemented group (Egeli *et al.*, 1998).

Mineral uptake in the gastrointestinal tract

It is evident from the literature that clear differences in bioavailability exist between sources of the same trace metal, with metal proteinates and chelates proving superior to inorganic sources in many cases. As discussed earlier, if it can be accepted that uptake of metals from the intestine is the predominant factor influencing their bioavailability, then differences in uptake mechanisms or in the general presentation of the metal in organic versus inorganic form in the intestinal lumen are likely explanations for the differences noted.

The theory that metal amino acid chelates and proteinates utilise peptide and amino acid uptake mechanisms rather than normal metal ion uptake mechanisms in the intestine has become widely accepted (Ashmead *et al.*, 1985; Ashmead, 1993). The basic concept of this theory is that the metal in question is 'protected' within the complex in a chemically inert form due to the co-ordinate covalent and ionic bonding by the amino acid ligands. Consequently, the metal is not susceptible to the range of physicochemical factors which can adversely affect the efficient uptake of 'unprotected' metal ions. Furthermore, it is believed that the metal chelate is absorbed intact through the intestinal mucosa, effectively pulling the metal along with it. The metal chelate traverses the mucosal cell membrane, the mucosal cell and basement membrane surviving, still intact, into the plasma. It is very tempting to accept this suggested uptake mechanism, even in part, because it explains numerous practical observations from studies on the relative bioavailability of organic versus inorganic trace metal sources. The reductions noted in negative interactions between elements such as copper, iron and zinc when organic supplements are used agree well with this theory (Hemken *et al.*, 1996). For example, if copper in a proteinated form utilises a peptide uptake mechanism, it is rendered unavailable to compete with iron for regular metal ion uptake mechanisms. This readily explains results such as those reported by Du *et al*. (1995) which were discussed earlier. Chemically inert metal complexes would also be protected from negative interactions with dietary constituents such as phytate, which binds cations making them unavailable for absorption (Fairweather-Tait, 1996). Furthermore, transmucosal passage of intact peptides and the existence of peptide carriers in brush-border membranes which utilise a proton-gradient transport mechanism is now firmly established (Gardner, 1998). Indeed, there is good evidence that amino acid absorption in the form of peptides is as important or perhaps even more important than absorption of free amino acids in both ruminants and monogastric animals (Webb *et al*., 1992; 1993; Rerat and Nunes, 1988). Metals using either amino acid or peptide uptake mechanisms would therefore be expected to be absorbed and circulated to target tissues very efficiently. Nevertheless, while considerable circumstantial evidence exists to support such a metal uptake mechanism, direct experimental evidence has failed to identify it. In many respects, this is not surprising given the difficulties of establishing even semi-quantitative models *in vitro* to study such mechanisms. Simulated studies of mineral availability to animals and humans involve closed systems, which theoretically can be described by a set of equations describing the interactions of the chemical components in that system. *In vivo* systems are not closed, and nutrients neither enter nor leave at a steady state. Because of the non-steady state nature of mammalian digestion and the fact that major parameters such as luminal pH and rates of passage are in a state of flux following meal ingestion makes the design of meaningful *in vitro* systems with which to study mineral uptake mechanisms very difficult. Our current state of knowledge is that there is no conclusive evidence to support the uptake of trace metal chelates or proteinates in intact form through the utilization of amino acid or peptide uptake mechanisms. Indeed, a number of publications suggest that complexes such as zinc methionine are not, in fact, absorbed as intact entities (Hill *et al*., 1987; Hempe and Cousins, 1989; House, 1999).

Although there is strong evidence to suggest that selenium in the form of selenomethionine enters the enterocyte via the electrogenic Na^+-dependent neutral amino acid transport system in a manner kinetically indistinguishable from that of methionine (Wolffram *et al*., 1989; Vendeland *et al*., 1994), selenomethionine cannot be directly compared to the metal amino acid chelates and proteinates which are under consideration here. In selenomethionine, selenium replaces sulphur as an intrinsic part of the amino acid. It would be inaccurate therefore to extrapolate findings on uptake mechanisms for selenomethionine to complexes such as zinc methionine, other metal amino acid chelates or proteinates.

Any consideration of uptake mechanisms for metal complexes cannot ignore the possible effects of gastrointestinal pH on the stability or dissociation of such complexes. This topic has been reviewed in a concise and informative manner by Hynes and Kelly (1995), who demonstrated the species distribution of a number of copper-glycine and zinc-glycine complexes as a function of pH. While the authors concluded that chelates of amino acids and peptides have stability constants of such magnitude as to allow the metal ions to be transferred to the recipient biological system, they presented several important findings in relation to the popularly held theory that metals in complexes are absorbed in a chemically inert form as part of the intact complex. Their findings were as follows:-

1. The distribution of metal species present at given concentrations of metal and amino acids depends on the pH of the solution.

2. Complexed forms (chelates) of dispositive metal ions are not necessarily neutral.

3. Different metal ions have different stability constants and thus the percentage of a metal present as a particular species will depend not only on the pH of the solution but also on the stability constant of the complex.

Taking all such factors into account, it cannot be assumed that metal amino acid chelates and proteinates owe their superior metal bioavailability to uptake mechanisms which allow them to be absorbed as amino acids or peptides in disguise. In the event that such mechanisms do not exist, it is of obvious interest to investigate alternative explanations for the improvements in bioavailability noted for these complexes.

ALTERNATIVE MECHANISMS

Although much effort has been directed towards the identification of metal ion and chelate transport mechanisms, the initial handling of metal ions in the intestinal lumen has received relatively little attention. In this respect, ingested metals may be considered in two categories: those soluble throughout the potential pH range of the gastrointestinal lumen such as Na, Mg and Ca and those susceptible to hydroxy-polymerisation such as Cu, Fe, Mn and Zn. The latter group, termed 'hydrolytic metals' also includes potentially toxic metals such as Al. They are acid-soluble but as the pH is raised in the absence of soluble binding ligands, they readily hydroxy-polymerise to form insoluble precipitates.

Recent work strongly suggests that normal metal ion uptake requires both endogenous soluble ligands and mucosally associated ligands to be present in the gut. The former prevent hydroxy-polymerisation of cations such as copper, iron and zinc, while the latter allows some specificity of absorption between toxic and essential metals (Whitehead *et al.*, 1996). The predominant mucosally-associated ligand is thought to be the large glycoprotein mucin, which was once termed 'gastroferrin'. Mucin is secreted throughout the gastrointestingal tract and provides both the mucosally-adherent gelatinous layer and a soluble luminal form. The role of mucin in metal binding has been well documented (Crowther and Marriott, 1984; Conrad *et al.*, 1991). The affinity of gastrointestinal mucin for metals follows the pattern $M^{3+} > M^{2+} > M^+$ and binding may occur at more than one binding site on mucin since the molecule contains sulphated groups (sulphated mucins) and carboxylate groups (sialomucins). In addition, it has been reported that Zn has two pH-dependent binding sites on mucin (Powell *et al.*, 1999a) and this could be true for other metals. In such a complex binding system it is obvious that there may be competition between different metals for mucin and between mucin and different ligands for metals. This would obviously affect how mucin promotes the availability of dietary metals to the mucosally-adherent mucus layer for the next phase of absorption.

In the mucosally-adherent mucus layer, metal binding to mucus also follows the pattern $M^{3+} > M^{2+} > M^+$ and for metal absorption the pattern is $M^+ > M^{2+} > M^{3+}$ (Whitehead *et al.*, 1996). Thus the mucus layer acts as a filter in regulating metal uptake and the strength of binding to and rate of passage across the mucosally-adherent mucus layer could be important in determining the overall absorption of a metal (Powell *et al.*, 1999b). For example, Al^{3+} will be tightly bound by mucus, has kinetically slow rates of ligand exchange and is therefore unlikely to pass quickly through this layer. In summary, metal absorption from the gastrointestinal lumen for Cu, Fe, Mn and Zn depends on a number of factors including the extent of prevention of luminal hydroxy- polymerisation, the rates of metal ligand exchange and the rate of passage across the mucosally-adherent mucus layer.

Superior absorption/bioavailability of metal amino acid chelates and proteinates versus inorganic sources could therefore be explained in a number of ways. For example, even if a complex is dissociatively labile in the gastrointestinal tract it may still, at least transiently, interfere with metal hydrolysis to allow a more effective presentation of the metal to mucin. As explained by Hynes and Kelly (1995), the extent of this 'protection' will be dictated by factors such as pH and the stability constant of the complex itself. Alternatively, as suggested by Powell *et al.* (1999b), if a ligand is present in significant quantities and is sufficiently strong to compete with mucus for binding of the metal, it may facilitate the rate of passage of the metal through this barrier. Such a mechanism would readily explain many of the reported observations on mineral bioavailability, including the variation in absorption of different elements, the effects of different ligands on mineral uptake and the competition for absorption between different metals.

Conclusions

Significant evidence indicates that amino acid and peptide complexes of metals such as Fe, Zn, Cu and Mn are more bioavailable than inorganic salts. This has led to the belief that these metal complexes are absorbed intact in a chemically inert form using peptide or amino acid transport mechanisms. While such a mechanism for metal uptake may exist, it has not been directly demonstrated to date. Furthermore, conditions in the gastrointestinal tract make it likely that some dissociation of such complexes will occur. Nevertheless, it is not necessary for amino acid chelates or proteinates to be present in an intact, electrically neutral form in order to be absorbed efficiently. The superior uptake of metals contained in such complexes may be explained by an alternative mechanism. For example, their constituent ligands may slow the rate of hydroxy-polymerisation of the metal and allow its effective donation to higher molecular weight binding ligands such as mucin, thereby maintaining them soluble and available to the mucosa for effective absorption.

References

AAFCO. 1998. Official Publication of the Association of American Feed Control Officials Incorporated (Paul. M. Bachman, ed). page 237-238.

Ammerman, C.B., D.B. Baker and A.J. Lewis. 1995. Bioavailability of nutrients for animals. Academic Press, New York. p. 441.

Ashmead, H.D. 1993. Comparative intestinal absorption and subsequent metabolism of metal amino acid chelates and inorganic metal salts. In: The Roles of Amino Acid Chelates in Animal Nutrition. (H.D. Ashmead, ed). Noyes Publishers, New Jersey, pp 306-319.

Ashmead, H.D. and D.J. Graff. 1982. Placental transfer of chelated iron. Proceedings of the International Pig Veterinary Society Congress, Mexico. p. 207.

Ashmead, H.D., D.J. Graff and H.H. Ashmead. 1985. Intestinal Absorption of Metal Ions and Chelates. Charles C. Thomas, Springfield, Illinois.

Ashmead, H.D. 1996. Nutrition of the high-producing first parity sow. Proceedings of the XVII ANAPORC Symposium, Santiago de Compostela, Spain.

Baker, D.H. and C.B. Ammerman. 1995. Copper bioavailability. In: Bioavailability of Nutrients for Animals. (C.B. Ammerman, D.H. Baker and A.J. Lewis, eds). Academic Press, San Diego, pp. 127-156.

Bender, A.E. 1989. Nutritional significance of bioavailability. In: Nutrient Availability: Chemical and Biological Aspects. (D.A.T. Southgate, I.T Johnson and G.R. Fenwick, eds). Special Publication No. 72, Royal Society of Chemistry, Cambridge, pp 3–9.

Boland, M.P., G. O'Donnell and D. O'Callaghan. 1996. The contribution of mineral proteinates to production and reproduction in dairy cattle. In: Biotechnology in the Feed Industry. (T.P. Lyons and K.A. Jacques, eds). Nottingham University Press, Nottingham, United Kingdom, pp. 95–103.

Close, B. 1999. Organic minerals for pigs: an update. In: Biotechnology in the Feed Industry. (T.P. Lyons and K.A. Jacques, eds). Nottingham University Press, Nottingham, UK, pp. 51–60.

Conrad, M.E., J.N. Umbreit and E.G. Moore. 1991. A role for mucin in the absorption of inorganic iron and other metal cations: A study in rats. Gastroenterology 100:129–136.

Crowther, R.S. and C. Marriott. 1984. Counter-ion binding to mucus glycoproteins. J. Pharm. Pharmacol 36:21–26.

Dreosti, I.E. 1993. Recommended dietary intakes of iron, zinc and other inorganic nutrients and their chemical form and identity. Nutrition 9:542–545.

Du, Z., R.W. Hemken and T.W. Clark. 1995. Copper proteinate may be absorbed in chelated form by lactating holstein cows. In: Biotechnology in the Feed Industry. (T.P. Lyons and K.A. Jacques, eds). Nottingham University Press, Nottingham, UK, pp. 315–319.

Egeli, A.K., T. Framstad and D. Greeningen. 1998. The effect of peroral administration of amino acid-chelated iron to pregnant sows in preventing sow and piglet anaemia. Acta Vet. Scand. 39:77–87.

Evans, R.M. and S. M. Hollenberg. 1988. Zinc fingers: gilt by association. Cell 52:1–3.

Fairweather-Tait, S.J. 1992. Bioavailability of trace elements. Food Chem. 43:213-217.

Fairweather-Tait, S.J. 1996. Bioavailability of dietary minerals. Biochem. Soc. Trans. 24:775–780.

Fenton, D.E. 1995. Biocoordination Chemistry. Oxford University Press, Oxford, UK, pp. 1-92.

Forbes, R.M. and J.W. Erdman. 1983. Bioavailability of trace mineral elements. Ann. Rev. Nutr. 3:213-231.

Gardner, M.L.G. 1998. Transmucosal passage of intact peptides. In: Peptides in Mammalian Protein Metabolism. (G.K. Grimble and F.R.C. Blackwell, eds). Portland Press, London, pp. 11-29.

Hemken, R.W., T.W. Clark and Z. Du. 1993. Copper: Its role in animal nutrition. In: Biotechnology in the Feed Industry. (T.P. Lyons, ed). Alltech Technical Publications, Nicholasville, Kentucky, USA, pp. 35–39.

Hemken, R.W., Z. Du and W. Shi. 1996. Use of proteinates to reduce competition from other trace minerals. In: Biotechnology in the Feed Industry. (T.P. Lyons and K.A. Jacques, eds). Nottingham University Press, Nottingham, UK, pp. 91–94.

Hempe, J.M. and R.J. Cousins. 1989. Effect of EDTA and zinc-methionine complex on zinc absorption by rat intestine. J. Nutr. 119:1179–1187.

Henry, P.R. 1995 Manganese bioavailability. In: Bioavailability of Nutrients for Animals (C.B. Ammerman, D.H. Baker and A.J. Lewis, eds). Academic Press, New York, pp. 239–256.

Hill, D.A., E.R. Peo and A.J. Lewis. 1987. Influence of picolinic acid on the uptake of ^{65}Zn-amino acid complexes by the everfed rat gut. J. Anim. Sci. 65:173–178.

289

House, W.A. 1999. Trace element bioavailability as exemplified by iron and zinc. Field Crops Research 60:115-141.

Hynes, M.J. and M.P. Kelly. 1995. Metal ions, chelates and proteinates. In: Biotechnology in the Feed Industry (T.P. Lyons and K.A. Jacques, eds). Nottingham University Press, Nottingham, UK pp. 233–248.

Johnson, P.E. 1989. What can *in vitro* methods tell us about mineral availability? Biological Trace Element Research 19:3–10.

Kaim, W. and B. Schwederski. 1993. Uptake, transport and storage of an essential element as exemplified by iron. In: Bioinorganic Chemistry: Inorganic elements in the Chemistry of Life. (W. Kaim and B. Schwederski, eds). John Wiley and Sons, London, pp. 150–171.

Kincaid, R.L., R.M. Blauwiekel and J.D. Conrath. 1986. Supplementation of copper as copper sulfate or copper proteinate for growing calves fed forages containing molybdenum. J. Dairy Sci. 69:160–163.

Kirchgessner, M. and E. Grassman. 1970. Dynamics of copper absorption. In: Trace Element Metabolism in Animals (C.F. Mills, ed). Livingston, Edinburgh, pp. 227–242.

Lee, D–Y., J. Schroder and P.T. Gordon. 1988. Enhancement of copper bioavailability in the rat by phytic acid. J. Nutr. 118:712-716.

McDowell, L.R. 1992. Copper and molybdenum. In: Minerals in Animal and Human Nutrition (T.J. Cunha. ed). Academic Press, San Diego, pp. 176–204.

Miles, R.D. 1998. The influence of Eggshell 49 on shell quality of hens grouped by their shell quality. Poultry Sci. 77(Suppl. 1):43.

Powell, J.D., R. Jugdaohsingh and R.P.H. Thompson. 1999a. The regulation of mineral absorption in the gastrointestingal tract. Proc. Nutr. Soc. 58:147–153.

Powell, J.D., M.W. Whitehead, C.C. Ainley, M.D. Kendall, J.K. Nicholson and R.P.H. Thompson. 1999b. Dietary minerals in the gastrointestinal tract: hydroxypolymerisation of aluminium in regulated by luminal mucins. J. Inorg. Biochem. 75:167–180.

Rerat, A. and C. Simoes-Nunes. 1988. Amino acid absorption and production of pancreatic hormones in non-anaesthetized pigs after duodenal infusions of a milk enzymic hydrolysate or of free amino acids. Br.J. Nutr. 60:121–136.

Schultze, M.O., C.A. Elvehjem and E.B. Hart. 1934. The availability of copper in various compounds as a supplement to iron in haemoglobin formation. J. Biol. Chem. 106:735–740.

Schultze, M.O., C.A. Elvehjem and E.B. Hart. 1936. Further studies on the availability of copper from various sources as a supplement to iron in haemoglobin formation. J. Biol. Chem. 115:453-457.

Schumann, K., H.G. Classen, M. Hages, R. Prinz-Langenohl, K. Pietrzik and H.K. Biesalski. 1997. Bioavailability of oral vitamins, minerals and trace elements in perspective. Drug Res. 47:369–380.

Spain, J. 1993. Tissue integrity: a key defence against mastitis infection: the role of zinc proteinates and a theory for mode of action. In: Biotechnology in the Feed Industry (T.P. Lyons, ed). Alltech Technical Publications, Nicholasville, Kentucky, USA, pp. 53–60.

Suchy, P.E., Strakova and M. Simon. 1998. Effect of applications of various forms of zinc on gonad development in breeding cocks. Czech J. Anim. Sci. 43:343–348.

Underwood, E.J. 1997. Trace elements in human and animal nutrition. Academic Press, New York.

Vallee, B.L. and K.H. Falchuk. 1993. The biological basis of zinc physiology. Physiol. Rev. 73:79-118.

Vendeland, S.C., J.T. Deagen, J.A. Butler and P.D. Whanger. 1994. Uptake of selenite, selenomethionine and selenate by brush border membrane vesicles isolated from rate small intestine. BioMetals 7:305-312.

Wapnir, R.A. 1998. Copper absorption and bioavailability. AM. J. Clin. Nutr. 67(Suppl):1054S-1060S.

Webb, K.E., J.C. Matthews and D.B. DiRienzo. 1992. Peptide absorption: A review of current concepts and future perspectives. J. Anim. Sci. 70:3248-3257.

Webb, K.E., D.B. DiRienzo and J.C. Matthews. 1993. Symposium: nitrogen metabolism and amino acid nutrition in dairy cattle. J. Dairy. Sci. 76:351-361.

Wedekind, K.J., A.E. Hortin and D.H. Baker. 1992. Methodology for assessing zinc bioavailability: efficacy estimates for zinc methionine, zinc sulphate and zinc oxide. J. Anim. Sci. 70:178-184.

Whitehead, M.W., R.P.H. Thompson and J.J. Powell. 1996. Regulation of metal absorption in the gastrointestinal tract. Gut 39:625-628.

Wolffram, S., B. Berger., B. Grenacher and E. Scharrer. 1989. Transport of selenoamino acids and their sulfur analogues across the intestinal brush border membrane of pigs. J. Nutr. 119:706-712.

Xin, Z., D.F. Waterman, R.W. Hemken and R.J. Harmon. 1991. Effects of copper status on neutrophil function, superoxide dismutase and copper distribution in steers. J.Dairy Sci. 74:3078-3082.

Practical experiences with Bioplexes in intensive pig production

R.J. SMITS AND D.J. HENMAN

Bunge Meat Industries, Corowa, New South Wales, Australia

Introduction

Since the end of 1998, pig production around the world has been subject to a global cycle of supply and demand. Those producers left standing have done so by smart management, making the most of marketing opportunities and reeling in costs. The crash in the market price for pig meat led to a short-term focus on immediate production costs in an effort to maintain cash flow. However, for future viability producers must rely on decisions based on improving the cost-effectiveness of more long-term production strategies. The production of pigs in the 21st century will, more than ever before, need to accommodate the consumer acceptability of pork products and the processes involved in pig meat production.

Bunge Meat Industries (BMI) is the largest piggery in Australasia, producing 900,000 carcasses per year from a population of 50,000 sows. The company is fully integrated with a feed mill, abattoir and boning room located at Corowa on the border of New South Wales and Victoria. The company has a fully funded Research and Development facility and Technical Services group, which allows us to evaluate new products and technologies using our own pigs and tailoring research and development for our specific production systems. In this paper, we provide a summary of our results using Bioplexes and examples as to how we have adopted these outcomes within the BMI production system.

The 'bio-' in mineral supplements

Research in mineral metabolism has shown that the uptake of trace elements can be improved by binding them to organic ligands. The amount of essential micronutrients absorbed across the gut wall largely determines the effectiveness of nutrient supplementation. Trace elements occur naturally in most ingredients. However, the amount and bioavailability varies considerably due to 1) their existence as parts of complex molecules which are not fully broken down during digestion; and 2) the degree to which minerals are absorbed from the small intestine and hence available at the cell level. An example of the former is phosphorus from plant sources, which is sequestered in phytate (Stahl *et al.*, 1999). Formulating diets for adequate mineral content has typically taken the form of supplementing the ration with a premix of inorganic salts such as sulphates, chlorides, carbonates and oxides. During digestion the mineral ions are released and can re-combine with other digesta components in the intestine to form insoluble compounds, thereby reducing their absorption across the small intestine. Thus the degree to which minerals supplemented as inorganic salts are available for absorption depends on the extent to which they form complex molecules in the gut.

Use of Bioplexes can increase the amount of mineral absorbed from the small intestine. By complexing the element with an organic molecule of amino acids or peptides, the Bioplex mineral, or proteinate, is prevented from breaking down into reactive ions during digestion. The mode of uptake across the intestine is altered as the chelated mineral is transported via amino acid uptake pathways rather than competing for ion transport pathways (Close, 1998). A summary of experimental reports reviewed by Close in 1998 and updated in 1999 on the relative performance of growing and breeding pigs when using organic sources of minerals is provided in Table 1.

Table 1. Summary of research data on performance improvement from the use of organic minerals in pigs.

Author	Mineral	Stage	Performance parameter	Indicator
Close, 1998; 1999	Iron	Gestation	Embryo survival, Litter size	↑
		Lactation	Lactation intake	↑
			Piglet growth	↑
			Weaning weight	↑
Ashmead, 1996	Iron	Lactation	Pre-weaning mortality	↓
Zhou *et al.*, 1994; Coffey *et al.*, 1994; Close, 1998	Copper	Weaners	Weaning to oestrus interval	↓
			Feed intake	↑
			Growth rate	↑
			Feed efficiency	↑
			Variability	↓
Spears *et al.*, 1999	Copper	Finishers	Cu excretion	↓
Cheng *et al.*, 1998	Zinc	Weaners	Feed efficiency	↑
Spears *et al.*, 1999	Zinc	Finishers	Zn excretion	↓
Swinkles *et al.*, 1996	Zinc	Weaners	Fe absorption	↑
Mahan and Kim, 1996	Selenium	Sows	Stillbirths	↓
			Pre-weaning mortality	↓
Close, 1998	Selenium	Finishers	Meat quality	↑
Campbell, 1998	Chromium	Sows	Farrowing rate	↑
Lindemann, 1996	Chromium	Sows	Litter size	↑
			Number weaned	↑
Bortolozzo *et al.*, 1998	Chromium	Sows	Embyro survival	↑

Close, 1998; 1999.

The performance indicators listed in Table 1 are all production traits that we wish to influence when making the decision to include organic Bioplexes as part of the nutrition strategy at BMI. The list in Table 1 is not an exhaustive review of all recent experiments conducted on mineral metabolism in pigs. There are many reports in the literature showing that supplementation with either organic or inorganic minerals had little or no effect on pig performance. There are numerous factors reported that explain the lack of responsiveness to supplementation. These include rate of inclusion, immunological status, dietary protein, dietary energy, age, presence of disease and the structure of the Bioplex. As in all experiments, results are heavily influenced by experimental numbers, and as such may not be enough to demonstrate a benefit which may well be commercially profitable.

Work with Bioplexes and Sel-Plex at BMI

The pig production business is driven by the weight of pig meat sold. As part of the BMI business, the effects of variation from week to week and throughout the year have consequences for the sales division and the feed mill, as well as the pig production sector. Customers require a reasonably consistent supply of high quality carcasses from the abattoir or pig meat from the boning room. Variation occurs in production volume and in weight within a population sold. There will be some variation due to market shifts (eg. development of the Singapore market in 1999), special events and festivities (eg. Christmas, Chinese New Year), and product promotion. These are generally planned and the production division and feed mill can adjust for increased production needs. It is the unforeseen sudden shifts in volume that must be minimised to allow maximum production efficiency.

RESEARCH AND DEVELOPMENT AT BMI

The research and development program at BMI is constantly evaluating new technologies to reduce the low points of supply caused by reproductive failure, disease of the progeny or variation in dietary nutrient supply from the major ingredients. The key to the practical implementation of experimental technologies is the extent of the response under commercial production scenarios, and the cost-effectiveness of the outcome. When new technologies become available, we conduct a comprehensive series of experiments at our own Research and Development Unit (RDU), using our genetics and diets in a small (1500 sow herd equivalent) commercial production unit. The unit is equipped with weigh stations, electronic feeders, single pen feeders and silo capacity for testing many different dietary treatments. Technologies that show benefits in RDU protocols are then monitored when implemented in the commercial production modules. In this way, BMI have evaluated the use of Bioplex minerals in our diets.

Campbell (1998) reported an experiment conducted at BMI where organic chromium was supplemented at 200 ppb during gestation and lactation. The experiment was conducted at two commercial modules of 5000 and 6000 sows, respectively. The trends recorded in this the experiment confirmed earlier studies overseas and showed that supplementing the diet fed during lactation and gestation can improve fertility (Table 2). However, the number of animals used in experiments often limits the level of statistical significance. This is particularly the case when looking at the effect of a treatment on reproductive performance.

Table 2. The effect of supplementing the breeder diet with 200 ppb chromium picolinate on reproductive perfomance.

	Performance trait	Chromium (ppb)		Significance (P value)
		0	200	
Site 1	Sow number	831	775	
	Farrowing rate, %	82.0	86.3	0.125
	Born alive	12.3	12.4	0.325
	Still births, %	7.2	7.1	0.584
Site 2	Sow number	197	222	
	Farrowing rate, %	85	84	0.905
	Born alive	10.9	11.1	0.345
	Stillbirths, %	9.1	8.3	0.885

MONITORING COMMERCIAL PERFORMANCE

Over the last year, BMI have worked alongside the developers of a statistical analysis program as part of our data monitoring system. PigPulse is a software program that uses historical data to predict significant changes in the parameter being measured. Cook *et al.* (1993) describes the different ways the program can be used in the pig industry. At BMI we are using it to monitor whether a change in a production process has had an effect on performance traits. Whilst there are many changes and factors which influence any one trait, we can use PigPulse to account for the season and normal variation that typically occurs within production units.

At the start of 1999, BMI introduced the use of the Alltech products Sel-Plex and Bioplex Iron into the breeder premix for diets used in the gilt pool and the sow and boar diets. The breeder premix already contained 200 ppb chromium picolinate.

Figure 1 is a graph derived from PigPulse of pigs born alive for all five sites at BMI Corowa (26,000 sows). PigPulse calculates the historical seasonal cyclical effect, a de-seasonalised trend line and the weekly data of the whole population. The figure demonstrates a number of points. Firstly, there is a seasonal cycle in which litter size increases in the June quarter each year and decreases in the December quarter. The Sel-Plex/Bioplex Iron was introduced in the matings starting in February 1999, hence those farrowing in June. The weekly average data are well above the seasonal cycle line for the June 1999 quarter and the December 1999 quarter. In other words, we are observing a better litter size than we expected given the seasonal pattern over the last three years. This is highlighted in the de-seasonalised trend line, which is going up.

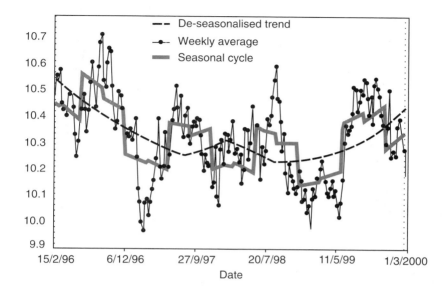

Figure 1. The litter size born alive from a population of 26,000 sows at BMI, Corowa. (Marbles indicate weekly averages; box line is the quarterly seasonal cycle with a forecast seasonal cycle; dashed line is the de-seasonalised trend line).

Through the continued use of statistical monitoring programs such as PigPulse, along with our herd recording systems, BMI are in a much better position to determine the commercial cost-benefit of introducing new technologies to our production system.

GROWER-FINISHER PERFORMANCE FROM ORGANIC COPPER

Copper is widely used in the pig industry to promote growth. The development of the Bioplex copper sources with a higher bioavailability has been shown to improve growth performance and reduce the excretion of copper into the effluent (Table 1). Table 3 summarises experimental results from BMI to evaluate the performance of growers and finishers supplemented with either copper as copper sulphate ($CuSO_4$) or as an organic Bioplex. Copper supplementation improved growth rate in the grower stage by increasing feed intake. The pigs fed diets supplemented with organic copper recorded similar levels of performance whilst reducing the amount of copper excretion substantially.

Table 3. The growth performance of entire male pigs individually housed and offered diets *ad libitum* **containing either no added copper (Control:basal diet containing 20 ppm Cu), copper sulphate (CuSO₄ 150 ppm Cu) or organic copper complex (40 ppm Cu).**

		Control	CuSO$_4$	Bioplex Cu	Significance (P)
Growers	Growth rate, kg/d	0.902	0.957	0.942	0.077
(30-60 kg)	Feed intake, kg/d	1.94	2.05	2.08	0.044
	FCR, feed:gain	2.15	2.16	2.21	0.470
	Faeces Cu, ppm DM	130	853	275	NA
Finishers	Growth rate, kg/d	0.845	0.871	0.836	0.660
(60-90 kg)	Feed intake, kg/d	2.39	2.59	2.65	0.073
	FCR, feed:gain	2.84	2.98	3.02	0.002
	Faecal Cu, ppm DM	108	776	199	NA

In a more recent experiment, we have repeated the response of copper supplementation and the effect of copper source on faecal excretion. There was little growth promotion effect of copper (Table 4). The reduction in faecal copper by using the organic Bioplex Copper was highly significant. These results indicate that we can use Bioplexes to decrease the environmental impact of pig manure. By replacing inorganic copper sources with more environmentally-friendly Bioplex Copper, BMI can maintain the use of copper as a proven growth promoter in a more responsible way.

Table 4. The growth performance of entire male pigs individually housed and offered diets *ad libitum* **containing no added copper (Control basal diet with 15 ppm Cu), copper sulphate (CuSO₄ 160 ppm Cu) or Bioplex Copper (50 ppm Cu).**

		Control	CuSO$_4$	Organic Cu	Significance (P)
(Growers	Growth rate, kg/d	0.800	0.773	0.744	0.106
(28-63 kg)	Feed intake, kg/d	1.82	1.73	1.68	0.822
	FCR, feed:gain	2.28	2.24	2.26	0.788
	Faecal Cu, ppm DM	173	372	199	0.001

It is hoped that the technological developments of other Bioplexes in the future will facilitate the aim of intensive livestock production to be environmentally sustainable. Examples could include replacing chromium and zinc oxide with a more bioavailable product.

Bioplexes and disease

Nutrient deficiencies can affect immunological responses in a number of complex ways. Kubena and McMurray (1996) reviewed the literature on the effect of vitamin and mineral nutrition on various aspects of the immune system. Certain minerals serve as cofactors for enzymes in cellular function of macrophages and lymphocytes. For example, copper deficiency in cattle is reported to reduce lymphocyte function, whilst the authors also cite studies showing that zinc interacts with vitamin A to enhance immune response in humans. The combination of a complex mix of organic Bioplexes, minerals and possibly vitamins may, in the future, be where we see more benefits in our production systems by enhancing the immunological status of all classes of pigs. Preventative disease strategies that reduce the use of antibiotics in the production of pigs are seen as a high priority at BMI. Not only will the issue of antibiotic residues in meat continue to be a regulatory concern, the degree of disease control may also be enhanced by the development of more bioavailable micronutrients.

Conclusion

The practical use of more available trace minerals will depend on the commercial performance response demonstrated in piggeries. The tools are now available to determine the magnitude of response whilst accounting for historical variation and seasonal impact. The magnitude of the response measured will determine the cost-effectiveness of commercial nutritional strategies. As producers, we are much more aware of the impact we have in pig meat production on the environment and the acceptance of pork by the public. The development of new technologies, particularly in nutrition, which improve the efficiency of growth and feed utilisation, must be adopted when they are proven to be effective in commercial production.

References

Ashmead, H.D. 1996. Nutrition of the high producing first-parity sow. Proceedings of the XVII ANAPORC Symposium, Santiago de Compostela, Spain. November.

Bortolozzo, I., I. Pinheiro Machado, R. Wentz, R. Nague and A.M. Perze. 1998. Effect of chromium picolinate on swine reproduction. In: Proceedings of the 15th International Pig Veterinary Society Congress 3:79 (S. Done, J. Thomson and M. Varley, eds.). Nottingham University Press, Nottingham, UK.

Campbell, R.G. 1998. Chromium and its role in pig production. In: Proceedings of Alltech's 14th Annual Symposium (T.P. Lyons and K.A. Jacques, eds.). Nottingham University Press Nottingham, UK, pp. 229-237.

Cheng, J., E.T. Kornegay and T. Scell. 1998. Influence of dietary lysine on the utilization of zinc from zinc sulphate and zinc-lysine complex by young pigs. J. Anim. Sci. 76:1064.

Close, W.H. 1998. The role of trace mineral proteinates in pig production. In Biotechnology in the Feed Industry. Proceedings of Alltech's 14th Annual Symposium (T.P. Lyons and K.A. Jacques, eds.). Nottingham University Press, Nottingham, UK, pp. 469-483.

Close, W.H. 1999. Organic minerals for pigs: an update. In: Biotechnology in the Feed Industry. Proceedings of Alltech's 15th Annual Symposium (T.P. Lyons and K.A. Jacques). Nottingham University Press, Nottingham, UK, pp. 51-60.

Coffey, R.D., G.L. Cromwell and H.J. Monegue. 1994. Efficacy of a copper-lysine complex as a growth promotant for weanling pigs. J. Anim. Sci. 72:2880-2886.

Cook, P.W., D.B. Preston and R.A. Spencer. 1993. PigPulse: A conceptual development in pig information technology. In: Manipulating Pig Production IV (E.S. Batterham, ed.). Australian Pig Science Association, Canberra, pp. 22-33.

Kubena, K.S and D.N. McMurray. 1996. Nutrition and the immune system: A review of nutrient-nutrient interactions. J. American Dietetic Assoc. 96:1156-1164.

Lindemann, M.D. 1996. Organic chromium: The missing link in farm animal nutrition. In: Biotechnology in the Feed Industry. Proceedings of Alltech's 12th Annual Symposium (T.P. Lyons and K.A. Jacques, eds.). Nottingham University Press, Nottingham, UK, pp. 299-314.

Mahan, D.C. and Y.Y. Kim. 1996. Effect of inorganic and organic selenium at two dietary levels on reproductive performance and tissue selenium concentrations in first-parity gilts and their progeny. J. Anim. Sci. 74:2711-2718.

Spears, J.W., B.A. Creech and W.L. Flowers. 1999. Reducing copper and zinc in swine waste through dietary manipulation. In: Proceedings of the North Carolina Waste Management Symposium. North Carolina State University, Raleigh, p. 179.

Stahl, C. H., Y.M. Han, K.R. Roneker, W.A. House and X.G. Lei. 1999. Phytase improves iron bioavailability for hemoglobin synthesis in young pigs. J. Anim. Sci. Vol. 77(8):2135-2142.

Swinkles, J.W.G.M, E.T. Kornegay, W. Zhou, M.D. Lindemann, K.E. Webb and M.W.A. Verstegan. 1996. Effectiveness of a zinc amino acid chelate and zinc sulphate in restoring serum and soft tissue zinc concentrations when fed to zinc-depleted pigs. J. Anim. Sci. 74:2420-2430.

Zhou, W., E.T. Kornegay, H. van Laar, J.W.G.M. Swinkles, E.A. Wong and M.D. Lindemann. 1994. The role of feed consumption and feed efficiency in copper-stimulated growth. J. Anim. Sci. 72:2385-2394.

A closer look at inorganic and organic copper and zinc supplementation in nursery pig diets

MARCIA S. CARLSON

University of Missouri, Columbia, Missouri, USA

The use of pharmacological concentrations of zinc (Zn) and (or) copper (Cu) in nursery pig diets to enhance growth has been widely accepted in the swine industry. A routine recommendation is to add 2,000 to 3,000 ppm Zn in the form of zinc oxide and (or) to add 250 ppm Cu as copper sulfate to the growing swine diet. Swine producers may use these high concentrations of inorganic zinc and copper sources for the entire nursery period of up to eight weeks and into the grower period. The effects of these high trace mineral concentrations in swine diets on the environment are of concern. Therefore, the development of more bioavailable organic trace mineral sources may allow lower inclusion rates of copper and zinc and still enhance growth performance. The major problem is that a majority of the research in this area has been inconclusive.

While the cumulative effects of long-term use of pharmacological concentrations of zinc and copper on soil nutrient management are not known, intuitively the suspicion is that the effects will be negative and utilization of manure nutrients on cropland may come under further regulation. This is particularly important in situations where a swine nursery production system is the main source of nutrients for a landmass.

Reasons and responses to high dietary copper

Copper has been acknowledged for many years as an essential nutrient needed for the immune system and normal growth and development of humans and animals. Pigs require copper to maintain basic systems such as synthesis of regulatory peptides, enzyme activity and iron metabolism. A copper deficiency is known to cause microcytic hypochromic anemia due to poor iron mobilization, diarrhea, bone disorders such as bowing of the legs and fractures, neonatal ataxia, hair depigmentation, poor keratinization, decreased synthesis of collagen, elastin and myelin, infertility, cardiovascular disorders, impaired glucose and lipid metabolism and depressed immune function.

301

In 1955, Barber *et al.* reported an enhancement in growth performance when growing pigs were fed 250 ppm Cu in the form of copper sulfate. Subsequent copper research (Bunch *et al.*, 1961; Cromwell *et al.*, 1989) has shown a similar response over a wider range of supplementation, 125 to 250 ppm Cu, even though the copper requirement is 5-6 ppm for the weanling pig (NRC, 1998). In general, copper supplementation at 125 to 250 ppm improves average daily gain and feed intake by 8 to 10%, which subsequently improves feed efficiency because the extra nutrients can be used for growth instead of maintenance. The improvement in growth in the weanling pig fed high copper is independent of source.

The mechanism behind the growth promotant effect of feeding 250 ppm Cu as copper sulfate remains unknown. It has long been hypothesized that this inorganic source of copper acts as an antimicrobial agent (enterically) on the intestinal microflora, thus reducing turnover of the intestinal cells and leaving more nutrients available for absorption by the pig (Fuller *et al.*, 1960). Other researchers have reported that copper enhances growth through a systemic effect rather than an antimicrobial effect in the intestinal tract (Zhou *et al.*, 1994ab). The idea that supplemental copper may be acting systemically is supported by the wide variety of biological systemic functions of copper that are related to growth. If a systemic effect is the more likely mode of action, then nutritionists and the feed industry need to develop ways to improve the efficacy of delivering copper into the circulation. This may be accomplished by using organic trace minerals.

Research has shown that pigs fed organic forms of copper have similar growth and feed intake responses to pigs fed 250 ppm Cu as copper sulfate. Recently, a nursery pig study was conducted to evaluate lower concentrations of an organic source of copper (proteinate source, Bioplex Cu, Alltech, Inc.) compared to 250 ppm Cu as copper sulfate, with pig growth performance for 28 days post-weaning as the criteria. The 28 day growth performance is shown in Figure 1. These results demonstrated that feeding 50 ppm Cu as Bioplex Cu improved pig growth performance during the first four weeks post-weaning (Carlson *et al.*, 2000a).

Future research is planned to evaluate trace mineral balance (copper and zinc) and excretion from nursery pigs fed either organic or inorganic sources. The bilary system is the major pathway of copper excretion; therefore, feces contain most of the unabsorbed copper with very little being excreted via the urine. Nursery pigs fed either 150 or 3000 ppm Zn with 125 ppm Cu excrete approximately 50 mg Cu/kg fecal DM (Hoover *et al.*, 1997). Copper concentration in both feces and urine are higher in pigs fed elevated copper from either inorganic or organic sources.

Reasons and responses to high dietary zinc

Zinc is an essential trace mineral required for numerous biological and physiological processes in all livestock species throughout the life cycle.

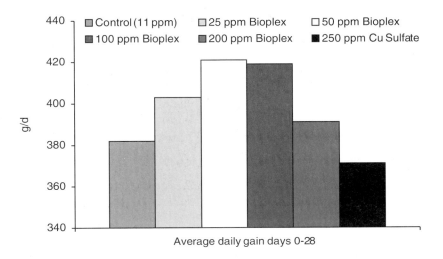

Figure 1. Effect of supplementing Bioplex Copper to nursery pigs on average daily gain.

In general, zinc plays a major role in protein synthesis, carbohydrate metabolism, and basic functions in growth and development, reproduction and healing of wounds. Zinc is involved in boosting the immune system in response to disease outbreaks. In 1955, Tucker and Salmon first reported zinc to be an essential nutrient and a zinc deficiency in swine resulted in parakeratosis (a skin disorder) and growth retardation. Due to the detrimental effects of zinc deficiency, the inclusion of this trace mineral in the diets of livestock is a common practice and has been for decades.

In recent years the inclusion of supplemental zinc above the requirement of 100 mg/kg for nursery pigs (NRC, 1998) has been studied. The investigation of feeding pharmacological concentrations of zinc to nursery pigs began following reports from Europe (Poulsen, 1995) that suggested supplemental zinc oxide decreased the incidence of non-specific post-weaning scours, and more importantly *Escherichia coli* proliferation. In addition, several reports from the United States have shown that the addition of pharmacological concentrations of zinc as zinc oxide can promote growth performance of the newly weaned pig (Hahn and Baker, 1993; Hill *et al.*, 1996; Smith *et al.*, 1997). The improvement in growth performance is observed in either early or traditionally weaned pigs fed pharmacological concentrations of zinc provided as zinc oxide for a minimum of two weeks immediately post-weaning (Carlson *et al.*, 1999). An average from these reports shows that nursery pigs fed 3,000 ppm Zn as zinc oxide have approximately 14% greater daily gains and 7% greater daily feed intakes. A North Central Region Swine Nutrition study (Hill *et al.*, 1999) has shown that 2,000 ppm Zn as zinc oxide is just as efficacious as 3,000 ppm Zn as zinc oxide in increasing daily gain, feed intake, and feed efficiency for four weeks post-weaning.

These results demonstrate the potential for nursery pigs fed high concentrations of zinc for the first two weeks post-weaning to be approximately 2 lb. heavier going into the grower-finisher period. This provides a huge economical advantage since each additional pound leaving the nursery results in three days less needed to reach market weight in most cases. It has become routine in the swine industry to add high concentrations (2,000 to 3,000 ppm) of inorganic zinc to nursery diets for improved growth performance. However, the biological mechanism behind the enhanced growth performance of nursery pigs fed 3,000 ppm Zn as zinc oxide is unknown.

The mode of action behind feeding 3,000 ppm Zn as zinc oxide in stimulating growth would appear to be similar to that of feeding 125-250 ppm Cu as copper sulfate. Carlson *et al.* (1998) reported that feeding pharmacological concentrations of zinc (3,000 ppm Zn as zinc oxide) altered duodenal morphology (deeper crypts and greater total thickness) and increased intestinal metallothionein concentrations, which indicates that high amounts of zinc have an enteric effect on the nursery pig. The interest in using lower concentrations of organic trace minerals in place of pharmacological concentrations of inorganic trace minerals has increased. Organic trace minerals have higher bioavailability than inorganic trace mineral sources and possibly exhibit greater metabolic activity, which could result in better responses in performance and less nutrient excretion (Wedekind *et al.*, 1994).

It has been reported that zinc retention is affected by zinc status of the pig as well as dietary zinc concentration. Fecal zinc excretion (major route) increases while percent retention decreases with increasing dietary zinc content (Poulsen and Larsen, 1995). Balance studies have reported that by the third week post-weaning, pigs are excreting 110-170 mg Zn/kg fecal DM when fed the traditional concentration of 150 ppm Zn; and excreting almost ten times more (1,022 mg Zn/kg fecal DM) when fed 3,000 ppm Zn from zinc oxide. However, when nursery pigs are fed a combination of 250 ppm Zn from sulfate and 250 ppm Zn from zinc methionine (organic form) for a total of 500 ppm Zn, fecal Zn excretion is approximately 250 mg Zn/kg DM (Hoover *et al.*, 1997). Urinary zinc excretion follows the pattern of dietary zinc concentration and fecal zinc excretion, but accounts for less than 1% of total zinc excreted (Poulsen and Larsen, 1995). Pigs fed 3,000 ppm Zn as zinc oxide excrete approximately 3 mg/l Zn via urine while pigs fed either 150 ppm Zn as zinc oxide or 500 ppm Zn from organic and inorganic sources excreted 1 mg/l Zn in urine.

A common recommendation is to feed supplemental zinc to nursery pigs only during the first two weeks post-weaning. This is because by the third week, pigs fed diets at or above 500 ppm from inorganic and (or) organic sources of zinc are in negative zinc balance. Negative zinc balance can be defined as more zinc being excreted than consumed on a daily basis. One can conclude that accumulation of zinc in plasma and tissues reached a threshold after two weeks and the ability to absorb zinc decreased, resulting in a negative balance. This may occur because fecal zinc contains not only unabsorbed zinc, but also endogenous zinc, i.e. absorbed zinc that is re-excreted into the gut via biological secretions.

Additional research has shown that pigs fed lower concentrations of organic zinc forms have similar growth response as pigs fed 3,000 ppm Zn as zinc oxide (Ward *et al.*, 1996). Recently, a nursery pig study was conducted to evaluate lower concentrations of an organic source of zinc (proteinate source, Bioplex Zn, Alltech, Inc.) compared to 2,000 ppm Zn as Zn oxide, with pig growth performance for 28 days post-weaning as the criteria. Over the entire 28 day nursery study, dietary zinc treatment had no effect on growth performance, feed intake or feed efficiency (Table 1). During week 1 and Phase 1 (weeks 1–2), nursery pigs fed either 50 or 100 ppm Zn as Bioplex Zn had the greatest average daily gain (P < 0.1) compared to the other dietary zinc treatments (Figure 2). It was concluded that feeding 50 to 100 ppm Zn as Bioplex Zn may replace 2,000 ppm Zn as zinc oxide based on 28 day post-weaning growth performance (Carlson *et al.*, 2000b). However, more research is needed to further evaluate the efficacy of organic trace minerals in swine nutrition.

Table 1. Effect of supplementing nursery pig diets with Bioplex Zn on growth performance during the first 4 weeks post-weaning.

Source	Bioplex Zn, ppm						Zn Oxide	P value
	0	50	100	200	400	800	2000	
ADG	348	354	369	319	348	332	374	0.28
ADFI	500	518	554	476	511	484	556	0.11
G/F	697	680	669	672	681	686	678	0.98

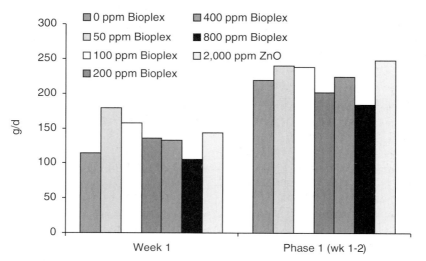

Figure 2. Effect of supplemental Bioplex Zn on nursery pig growth performance during the first two weeks post-weaning.

The bottom line is that as zinc concentrations increase in the diet regardless of form, urinary and fecal zinc excretion increases. Pigs fed nursery diets containing 3,000 ppm Zn as oxide had increased urinary and fecal zinc concentrations compared to pigs fed diets containing 150 ppm or 250 ppm Zn from an organic zinc source.

Why move away from high concentrations of inorganic trace minerals?

It has been generally accepted that nutrients in swine manure should be used to fertilize cropland at agronomic rates. In other words the application of manure should be restricted to the amount of nutrients taken up by crops. Most attention has been paid to macronutrients such as nitrogen, phosphorus and potassium, but it is useful to be aware of the agronomic rates of the micronutrients including zinc and copper as well. A corn crop of 150 bushels/acre has been reported to take up about 200 g Zn and about 50 g Cu per acre while a soybean crop of 40 bushels/acre takes up the same 50 g Cu, but only about 100 g Zn per acre. It is not clear what the long-term effects of micronutrient accumulation might be. We have no direct evidence of detrimental effects. Some countries (e.g. Canada, Japan, Denmark and the European Union) have taken the cautious approach and restricted the concentration of these minerals in swine diets (Table 2). Other countries may follow this path in the future.

Table 2. Recommended and allowed dietary levels of copper and zinc in Denmark.*

mg/kg diet	Recommended		Allowed	
	Copper	Zinc	Copper	Zinc
Nursery	6	100	175	250
Grow/finish	6	100	35	250
Sows	6	100	35	250

*Poulsen, 1998.

Conclusions

The feeding of pharmacological concentrations of inorganic copper and (or) zinc post-weaning results in improved growth performance and subsequently heavier pigs entering the grower-finisher period. However, there is a very realistic concern about potential mineral buildup in manure and subsequently in the soil when feeding high concentrations of copper and zinc to nursery pigs. Cropland acres needed per nursery pig space per year calculated from figures presented herein would be very rough estimates, but provide a reasonable impression of the magnitude of land required.

Farm practices will continue to apply swine excreta to soils, but when these manures are enriched in both copper and zinc, they will require an enormous increase in land mass in order to avoid mineral accumulation in the soil. Today, there is no documentation of any detrimental environmental impact. In the future, regulations on feed copper and zinc concentrations may be applied, similar to those concerning selenium.

References

Barber, R.S., R. Braude and K.G. Mitchell. 1955. Antibiotic and copper supplements for fattening pigs. Brit. J. Nutr. 9:378-382.

Bunch, R.J., V.C. Speer, V.W. Hays, J.H. Hawbaker and D.V. Catron. 1961. Effects of copper sulfate, copper oxide and chlortetracycline on baby pig performance. J. Anim. Sci. 20:723-728.

Carlson, M.S., S.L. Hoover, G.M. Hill, J.E. Link and J.R. Turk. 1998. Effect of pharmacological zinc on intestinal metallothionein concentration and morphology in nursery pigs. J. Anim. Sci. 76 (Suppl. 1):57 (Abstr.).

Carlson, M.S., G.M. Hill and J.E. Link. 1999. Early- and traditionally weaned nursery pigs benefit from phase-feeding pharmacological concentrations of zinc oxide: Effect on metallothionein and mineral concentrations. J. Anim. Sci. 77:1199-1207.

Carlson, M.S., C. Wu, A. Tsunoda, D.W. Bollinger, T.L. Veum and G.W. Tibbetts. 2000a. Effect of lower concentrations of copper proteinate compared to copper sulfate on nursery pig performance. J. Anim. Sci. 78 (Suppl. 1):(Abstr.).

Carlson, M.S., C. Wu, A. Tsunoda, D.W. Bollinger, T.L. Veum and G.W. Tibbetts. 2000b. Effect of lower concentrations of zinc proteinate compared to zinc oxide on nursery pig performance. J. Anim. Sci. 78(Suppl. 1):(Abstr.).

Cromwell, G.L., T.S. Stahly and H.J. Monegue. 1989. Effects of source and level of copper on performance and liver copper stores in weanling pigs. J. Anim. Sci. 67:2996-3002.

Fuller, R.L., G.M. Newland, C.A.E. Briggs, R. Braude and K.G. Mitchell. 1960. The normal intestinal flora of the pig. IV. The effect of dietary supplementation of penicillin, chlortetracycline or copper sulfate on fecal flora. J. Appl. Bacteriol. 23:195-202.

Hahn, J.D. and D.H. Baker. 1993. Growth and plasma zinc responses of young pigs fed pharmacological levels of zinc. J. Anim. Sci. 71:3020-3024.

Hill, G.M., G.L. Cromwell, T.D. Crenshaw, R.C. Ewan, D.A. Knabe, A.J. Lewis, D.C. Mahan, G.C. Shurson, L.L. Southern and T.L. Veum. 1996. Impact of pharmacological intakes of zinc and (or) copper on performance of weanling pigs. J. Anim. Sci. 74(Suppl. 1):181(Abstr.).

Hill, G.M., S.D. Carter, R.C. Ewan, D.C. Mahan, P.S. Miller, G.C. Shurson and T.L. Veum. 1999. Titration of pharmacological doses of zinc in the nursery pig. J. Anim. Sci. 77(Suppl. 1):177(Abstr.).

Hoover, S.L., M.S. Carlson, G.M. Hill, J.E. Link, T.L. Ward and T.M. Fakler. 1997. Evaluation of excretion and retention of zinc from inorganic and organic sources in diets fed to weanling pigs. J. Anim. Sci. 75 (Suppl. 1):189 (Abstr.).

NRC. 1998. Nutrient Requirements of Swine (10th Ed.). National Academy Press, Washington D.C.

Poulsen, H.D. 1995. Zinc oxide for weanling piglets. Acta Agri. Scand. Sect. A , Anim. Sci. 45:159-167.

Poulsen, H.D. 1998. Zinc and copper as feed additives, growth factors or unwanted environmental factors. J. Anim. Feed Sci. 7:135-142.

Poulsen, H.D. and T. Larsen. 1995. Zinc excretion and retention in growing pigs fed increasing levels of zinc oxide. Livestock Prod. Sci. 43:235-241.

Smith, J.W. II, M.D. Tokach, R.D. Goodband, J.L. Nelssen and B.T. Richert. 1997. Effects of the interrelationships between zinc oxide and copper sulfate on growth performance of early-weaned pigs. J. Anim. Sci. 75:1861-1866.

Tucker, H.F. and W.D. Salmon. 1955. Parakeratosis or zinc deficiency disease in the pig. Proc. Soc. Exp. Biol. Med. 88:613-616.

Ward, T.L., G.A. Asche, G.F. Louis and D.S. Pollmann. 1996. Zinc-methionine improves growth performance of starter pigs. J. Anim. Sci. 74(Suppl. 1):303(Abstr.).

Wedekind, K.J., A.J. Lewis, M.A. Giesemann and P.S. Miller. 1994. Bioavailability of zinc from inorganic and organic sources for pigs fed corn-soybean meal diets. J. Anim. Sci. 72:2681-2689.

Zhou, W., E.T. Kornegay, H. Laarvan, J.W.G.M. Swinkels, E.A. Wong and M.D. Lindeman. 1994a. The role of feed consumption and feed efficiency in copper-stimulated growth. J. Anim. Sci. 72:2385-2394.

Zhou, W., E.T. Kornegay, M.D. Lindeman, J.W.G.M. Swinkels, M.K. Welten and E.A. Wong. 1994b. Stimulation of growth by intravenous injection of copper in weanling pigs. J. Anim. Sci. 72:2395-2403.

The effect of the addition of organic trace elements on the performance of a hyper-prolific sow herd

ROBERT FEHSE[1] AND WILLIAM H. CLOSE[2]

[1]*Fehse Consultancy, Berg, Switzerland*
[2]*Close Consultancy, Wokingham, United Kingdom*

Introduction

For sows to remain hyper-prolific throughout their lives and to maintain a high level of production it is important that their nutritional and metabolic needs are met at all stages of reproduction. It is known that nutrition, by influencing the endocrine and physiological status of the sow, affects both short- and long-term reproductive capacity.

In terms of nutrition, major emphasis has been directed towards meeting energy, protein and amino acid requirements. Macrominerals, such as calcium and phosphorus and some vitamins are also taken into account. A very important source of nutrients, the trace minerals, are often neglected and their role in reproduction is often underestimated. A deficiency of these trace elements can cause a considerable reduction in performance. The potential role of some trace minerals in influencing sow productivity is suggested in Figure 1.

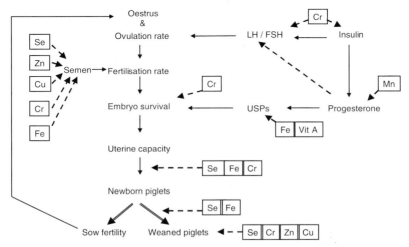

Figure 1. The role of trace elements in sow reproduction (Close, 1999).

309

Mineral requirements are dependent upon the level of production and in the modern animal with its high level of performance, it may well be that the requirements are higher than current recommendations, including ARC (1981) and NRC (1998). For example, Mahan and Newton (1995) have shown that the body mineral content of sows at the end of their third lactation was considerably lower when the mean litter weight at 21 days was above 60 kg than below 55 kg and well below that of non-breeding animals of similar age (Table 1). This suggests that significant de-mineralisation of the sow skeletal structure occurred to meet the needs of the higher performing animals. Although the animals were fed to normal recommendations, the losses from all body tissues were substantial when compared with non-breeding sows of similar age. This raises questions about the mineral requirements of the modern hyper-prolific sows, the actual forms and amounts needed in the feed, and availability of these mineral sources to the animal. This has prompted interest in the use of organic minerals, which are more bioavailable and bioactive within the animal than the corresponding inorganic sources normally provided.

Table 1. Mineral content in the body of the sow.

Mineral	Non-pregnant	Litter weight (kg)	
		< 55	> 60
Ca, g	1569	1480	1262
P, g	935	816	770
Mg, g	51	46	44
Fe, g	82	74	76
Zn, g	4.4	4.2	3.7
Cu, mg	516	488	468
Se, mg	22	21	18

Mahan and Newton, 1995.

Indeed, several recent commercial trials have shown that inclusion of organic minerals in sow diets has improved overall sow and piglet performance in terms of litter size, with less piglet mortality pre-weaning, higher sow feed intake and higher piglet weaning weights.

The objective of the present trial was therefore to establish whether a special supplement of organic minerals provided in addition to the normal inorganic sources of minerals in the diet of the gestating and lactating sow influenced sow and piglet performance. This special supplement contained several organic (Bioplex) minerals manufactured by Alltech Inc., (Nicholasville, Kentucky, USA) and was called 'Sow Pak'.

The trial was carried out on a research farm in Switzerland and therefore some information on pig production in Switzerland is provided.

Pig production in Switzerland

Pig production in Switzerland is very intensive and sophisticated. Feed costs are high; and as a consequence the use of by-products, in combination with computerised wet-feeding, is widespread. There are strict regulations on pollution control and animal welfare, which increase production costs. Dietary antibiotic growth promoters have been prohibited since July 1999. The main swine diseases are enzootic pneumonia, APP, rhinitis etc.; and these should be eradicated with the help of a national health care programme (SPF system) within the coming years. Currently about 50% of all piglets are produced in this high health system.

Economically, pig production contributes 14% to the Swiss agricultural output. The national herd has been decreasing since 1980 and the same trends can be observed in the consumption of pig meat, although there was a slight improvement in 1998 (Table 2).

Table 2. Swiss pig production: some key figures.

	1995	1998
Number of sows	163,000	152,000
Number of slaughter pigs	3,000,000	2,740,000
Pig meat, tonnes	251,000	232,000
Consumption per person/year, kg	27.3	26.3
Pig meat import, tonnes	5,498	14,434

The live weight at slaughter is between 100 and 105 kg. There are premiums and deductions for weight range, lean percentage, pH and fat quality (free fatty acids).

Prices and costs are roughly double those in the rest of Europe; and for a long time the market had been protected. However, because of WTO regulations, imports must now be accepted and these are increasing each year (Table 2). This means that Switzerland must adopt European prices within the next 5 to 10 years and it is therefore imperative to reduce production costs and to increase productivity, especially in piglet production, if the Swiss pig industry is to remain competitive.

Response to Sow Pak in a hyper-prolific herd

COMPOSITION AND ANALYSIS OF MINERALS IN THE FEEDS

It is normal practice to add a mineral supplement to the diet of the breeding sow. However, as indicated in Figure 1 and Table 3, specific elements play significant roles in reproduction, such as chromium, selenium, iron, zinc, manganese and copper. A special supplement of these minerals in organic form was therefore prepared and added to the regular inorganic mineral supplement. The composition of the regular inorganic supplement and the proposed added levels of the organic elements are shown in Table 4.

Table 3. The role of specific trace elements in sow reproduction.

Fe	Enzymes, haemoglobin, placenta, uteroferrin, immunoglobulin
Se	Prolonged farrowing, milk let-down, MMA, weak piglets, irontoxicosis
Cr	Insulin, LH/FSH, progesterone, litter size, stress
Cu	Enzymes, fertility in many species, iron mobilisation
Zn	Enzymes, LH/FSH, uterine involution, milk synthesis, testicular and sperm development
Mn	Enzymes, CL, anoestrus, abortion, still-births

Table 4. The contribution of the regular inorganic and proposed Bioplex mineral supplements (Sow Pak) to total diet mineral content.

	Inorganic (Control)	Bioplex: Sow Pak	Total
Zinc, mg/kg	80	26.2	106.2
Manganese, mg/kg	40	15	55
Iron, mg/kg	80	22.5	102.5
Copper, mg/kg	15	7.5	22.5
Chromium, ppb	-	200	200
Selenium, mg/kg	0.25	0.175	0.425
De-Odorase, mg/kg	-	120	120

De-Odorase was added as there was evidence to suggest that the action of the Yucca plant extract in improving air quality also enhances oxygen-carrying capacity and therefore reduces the number of stillborn piglets.

Samples of both the gestation and lactation feed, with and without the Sow Pak, were taken regularly throughout the study and analysed for mineral content. Since the Sow Pak was added to both the gestation and lactation feed, the values have been combined to show the actual quantities provided in the diets (Table 5) together with the actual and intended inclusion levels of the Sow Pak supplement.

Table 5. The mineral content (mg/kg) of the diets (Mean ±SD).

	Control diet	Sow Pak diets	Increased level with Sow Pak	
			Actual	Intended
Zn	120 ±21	143 ±31	+23	+25
Fe	216 ±39	255 ±82	+39	+23
Mn	113 ±20	120 ±27	+7	+15
Cu	25 ± 6	32 ± 7	+7	+7

The increase in the zinc and copper level was exactly as intended, but that for iron was higher and that for manganese lower. However, iron is likely to be a more limiting element in terms of reproduction and normally provokes a more positive and greater response than manganese. Indeed, the actual analysed level of iron in the diet was much higher than intended and the reasons for this are unknown. Nevertheless, the mineral content in all diets adequately covered the accepted recommended requirements.

Analysis of the Sow Pak showed that it also contained 0.151 ppm Se and 220 ppb Cr and when added to the diets these levels were close to the levels intended of 0.175 ppm Se from Sel-Plex and 200 ppb Cr from Bio-Chrome.

These data show that the difference in the mineral composition between the control diet and that supplemented with Sow Pak was as intended and any changes in the performance of the sows can be attributed to the higher levels of organic minerals in the diets augmented with Sow Pak.

MATERIALS, METHODS AND ROUTINE MANAGEMENT ON FARM

The trial started in March 1997 and ended in March 1999. Beginning at lactation, the sows were allocated to the two treatments (control and Sow Pak), farrowing room by farrowing room, until half of the herd was on the Sow Pak diet and half on the control diet. These were then fed until the end of the experiment. The trial therefore spanned a range of sow parities from parity 2 to parity 12.

The trial was carried out on the experimental farm of Rüti AG, a subsidiary of the feed company Haefliger AG, one of the most important in Switzerland. It is a commercial farm with 150 sows (the legal maximum), which are housed in groups during pregnancy and confined in individual pens during farrowing and lactation. Weaning is carried out at four weeks of age.

The Large White herd has been selected for the past 20 years as a female line with maximum priority on prolificacy. A sophisticated vaccination programme, professional management and the use of medicated feed for a two week period after weaning guarantee maximum health status.

The feeding strategy of the sows is based on a two phase feeding regime with a higher fibre diet in gestation and a more nutrient-dense diet in lactation. The chemical composition of the diets used in the trial is presented in Table 6.

Table 6. Chemical analysis of the diets.

	Gestation	Lactation
VES, MJ/kg	11.8	13.0
Digestible energy, MJ/kg	12.0	13.2
Crude protein, g/kg	13.5	18.0
Lysine, g/kg	6.5	10.0

VES = Swiss energy system for swine (Verdauliche Energie, Schwein)

A basic feeding regime of 1% of body weight per day is provided during pregnancy. This ration is fine-tuned at weaning when body condition score is taken into account. The gestation diet has a high fibre content, which allows higher feed levels so that the sows feel more satiated and content, resulting in better welfare.

During lactation, a semi-*ad libitum* feeding regime is used. At farrowing, the lactation diet is provided initially at about 2 kg/day and this is gradually increased until a defined quantity is reached and thereafter it is kept constant to the end of lactation. The quantity provided depends on the condition of the sow and the number of suckling piglets, as indicated in Table 7. These dietary guidelines are modified depending on body condition. The ration is weighed daily into a special *ad libitum* feeder. The sow is then able to eat as often as she likes and to consume the feed in small portions with minimal wastage.

Table 7. Daily feeding regime in lactation from week 2 of lactation to weaning.

Number of piglets in the litter	Feed (kg/day)*
< 8	4 - 5
8 and 9	5 – 6
10	6 – 7
11	6.5 – 7.5
> 11	*Ad libitum*

*depending on the litter performance

The following data were routinely recorded during the trial:

• Condition of the sow throughout the cycle

• Weight, backfat thickness (P_2) measurements, body score condition
  -At mating
  -Before farrowing (on entering the farrowing room)
  -At weaning

  (The weight of the sows after farrowing was calculated from the litter weight at birth.)

• Feed consumption
  -In gestation: group, daily
  -In lactation: individually, daily

• Performance of the sow
  -Pedigree, birth date, on-farm testing
  -Reproduction data, including total piglets born, born alive and weaned, piglet weight at birth and weaning and pre-weaning mortality

More details on management and husbandry on the farm are provided by Fehse (1999).

RESULTS

General comments

In all, the trial involved 742 litters of piglets from sows ranging between parities 2 and 12; 386 on the control and 356 on the Sow Pak diets. However, despite this large data set, there was considerable variation in many of the parameters measured and although there were numerical differences between treatments, few of these were statistically different at P<0.05. This is not surprising, since it is well known that it takes very large sow and piglet numbers to establish significant differences in reproductive traits. Indeed, there was very little difference in many of the parameters measured at the different parities between the treatments. Results have therefore been presented in relation to the early (parities 1 and 2), the most prolific mid parities (parities 3-6) and the later parities (parities >6). Statistical differences were determined using Students t test.

Sow performance and litter size

Table 8 shows the total number of piglets born, born alive and numbers weaned (exclusive of fostered piglets) for the different parities and different treatments throughout the duration of the trial. This information is also presented graphically in Figure 2 for the total number of piglets born alive. In the first parity there was no difference in performance between the two groups of sows. This is not unexpected, since the Sow Pak was not introduced until the first lactation. In the second parity, the control sows had higher litter sizes than those fed the Sow Pak. This effect is difficult to explain and there appears to be no logical explanation other than the natural variation associated with reproductive traits in sows. However, from parity 3 onwards, the sows fed the Sow Pak generally had higher litter sizes than the control sows.

As expected, litter size increased up to parities 3-6 and then generally decreased. However, the performance of the sows fed the Sow Pak diet was generally better than performance of those fed the control diet. Across all parities, the sows given Sow Pak produced 0.2-0.3 more piglets for the total number of piglets born, born alive and weaned, compared with the controls. However, when the peak parities (parities 3-6) were considered, the sows given the Sow Pak had 0.4 more piglets born or born alive and weaned 0.5 more piglets compared with the controls (Table 9).

The number of fully developed piglets that were born dead and the pre-weaning mortality is also shown in Table 8 and Figure 3, respectively. Although there was no statistically significant difference (P>0.05) in mortality between the control and Sow Pak treatments, the latter generally had fewer fully developed piglets born dead than the control sows. A greater proportion of piglets of low birthweight (<1 kg body weight) from the Sow Pak fed

Table 8. The effect of treatment on reproductive performance.

Parity	Total born		Born alive		Weaned (excl. fostered)		Pre-weaning piglet deaths	
	Sow Pak	Control	Sow Pak	Control	Sow Pak	Control	Sow Pak	Control
1	10.52	10.55	9.69	9.60	8.26	8.58	1.43	1.02
2	11.25	12.42	10.50	11.58	9.75	10.76	0.75	0.82
3	13.00	13.25	12.29	11.99	11.54	11.06	0.75	0.93
4	13.54	13.83	12.49	12.74	11.14	11.24	1.35	1.50
5	14.52	13.81	13.55	12.85	11.90	11.15	1.65	1.70
6	14.73	13.33	13.15	12.33	11.82	10.72	1.33	1.61
7	14.14	13.19	12.63	11.48	11.51	10.62	1.12	0.86
8	14.06	14.60	12.71	13.53	11.50	12.07	1.21	1.46
9	13.30	13.20	12.00	12.13	10.95	11.13	1.05	1.00
>9	14.50	12.09	11.64	11.55	10.00	10.36	1.64	1.19
Overall N	373	394	373	394	371	391		
Mean	12.9	12.6	11.79	11.52	10.57	10.42		

Table 9. The effect of treatment and parity on reproductive performance.

Parity	Total born		Born alive		Weaned (excl. fostered)	
	Sow Pak	Control	Sow Pak	Control	Sow Pak	Control
1	10.52	10.55	9.69	9.60	8.26	8.58
2	11.25	12.42	10.50	11.58	9.75	10.76
3-6	13.88	13.52	12.80	12.39	11.58	11.09
>6	13.77	13.04	12.30	11.86	10.97	10.77

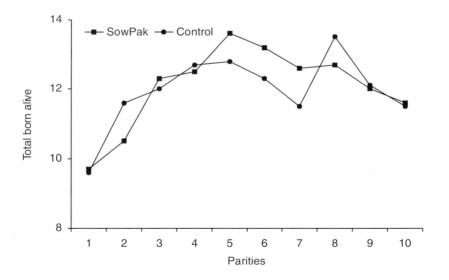

Figure 2. The effect of treatment on the number of piglets born alive.

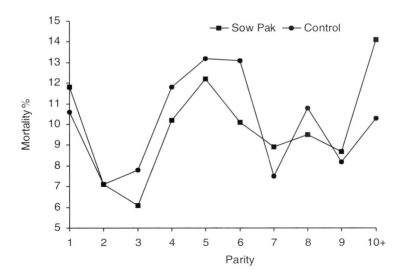

Figure 3. The effect of treatment on pre-weaning mortality (%).

sows died relative to the controls. However, when overall mortality at farrowing was considered, including mummified piglets, there was no difference between the treatments.

Generally, the mortality of the piglets pre-weaning was lower in the Sow Pak fed sows than the controls, and especially so in the most productive parities (parities 3-6) (Figure 3). In many parities, pre-weaning mortality was below the generally accepted level of 10%, indicating the high level of management and stockmanship on the farm.

Piglet weight and performance

The litter and mean weight of the piglets at birth and at weaning are presented in Table 10. There was little difference in weights between the two treatments at any of the parities investigated. Litter weaning weights of ~80 kg were achieved in the peak parities at around 26 days of lactation. This is excellent performance and resulted in 28-day corrected piglet weaning weights of ~7.6-7.8 kg. However, there were variations in both litter size and lactation length, which can be accounted for by calculating mean litter growth rate. This increased with parity and was highest at 2.4 kg/day in the mid parities, with little difference between treatments. Such daily growth rates are well above those commonly achieved in commercial practice.

Table 10. Piglet performance during lactation.

	Parity 1		Parity 2		Parity 3 - 6		Parity > 6	
	Sow Pak	Control	Sow Pak	Control	Sow Pak	Control	Sow Pak	Control
Birthweight (kg/litter)	12.2	12.2	14.2	14.8	16.7	16.3	16.0	15.3
Birthweight (kg/piglet)	1.3	1.3	1.3	1.3	1.3	1.3	1.3	1.3
Lactation (days)	26.5	27.9	26.1	25.6	26.5	26.1	25.7	26.0
Weaning weight (kg/litter)	56.3	61.4	75.2	74.2	80.7	78.9	72.7	73.0
Piglet weight (kg) 28-day corr.	6.4	6.5	7.6	7.4	7.6	7.8	7.7	7.6
Litter growth rate (kg/d)	1.66	1.76	2.34	2.32	2.42	2.4	2.21	2.22

Sow body weight and body weight gain

The trends in the body weight and body weight gain of the sows during the various parities are presented in Tables 11 and 12. At first mating, the gilts weighed 118 kg on both the control and the Sow Pak treatments. The body weights at the end of the trial were also similar at 255 kg for both groups. Thus, the weight gain of the sows throughout the study was similar and unaffected by treatment.

Table 11. Comparison of sow weight (kg) during the various parities.

Parity	Previous weaning		Mating		Pre-farrowing		Post-farrowing		Weaning	
	Sow Pak	Control	Sow Pak	Control	Sow Pak	Control	Sow Pak	Control	Sow Pak	Control
1	-	-	118	118	182	180	165	164	154	153
2	155	153	148	146	212	211	193	191	179	176
3-6	201	194	192	186	253	250	231	228	218	211
> 6	239	243	229	235	279	284	257	263	247	250

Table 12. Comparison of the change in sow bodyweight (kg) during the various parities.

Parity	Total gain in gestation		Net gain in gestation		Loss in lactation		Change in weight wean-mating		Overall	
	Sow Pak	Control	Sow Pak	Control	Sow Pak	Control	Sow Pak	Control	Sow Pak	Control
1	64	62	47	46	-11	-11	-7	-7	29	28
2	64	65	45	45	-14	-15	-9	-7	22	23
3-6	61	64	39	42	-15	-17	-10	-10	14	15
>6	40	49	28	28	-10	-13	-	-	18	15

In terms of the weight gain of the animals within each parity and overall, there was no obvious effect of treatment. The sows gained weight during pregnancy and lost weight during both lactation and in the wean-to-mating period. The overall net weight gain decreased with parity from approximately 30 kg in parity 1 to 23 kg in parity 2 and 14-18 kg in the following parities.

Backfat thickness of the sows

As indicated in Table 13, there was little difference in the backfat thickness (P_2 value) of the sows during the trial. There was a tendency for the sows fed the Sow Pak diet to lose less backfat thickness during lactation than those fed the control diet; and this had an effect on the overall change in P_2 at the different parities (Figure 4). There was a general increase in P_2 with parity and, with the exception of parities 3–6 where the response was similar, sows fed the Sow Pak diet always gained more than the control animals (Figure 4).

Table 13. The backfat thickness of the sows.

Parity	Previous weaning		Mating		Farrowing		Weaning	
	Sow Pak	Control	Sow Pak	Control	Sow Pak	Control	Sow Pak	Control
1			11.5	11.9	14.9	15.1	12.0	11.9
2	12.1	11.6	12.0	11.6	16.1	15.4	12.4	11.9
3- 6	13.4	12.3	13.3	12.1	16.9	16.5	13.9	12.8
>6	14.3	14.4	13.7	14.4	16.9	18.1	15.1	15.1

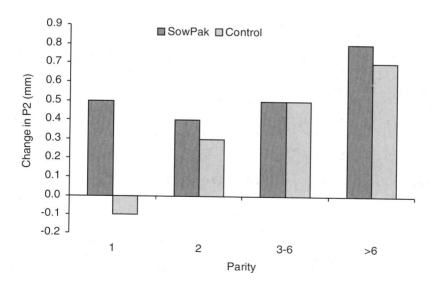

Figure 4. Comparison of the change in backfat (mm) at the different parities.

Body condition scoring

The body condition score of the sows was assessed on a scale of 1–5, as follows:

1   thin
2   below optimum
3   optimum
4   above optimum
5   fat

There was little difference in body condition score of the sows between treatments or at the different parities (Table 14). Generally, the sows gained body condition during gestation, but this was lost during suckling so that the condition score of the sows at mating was constant. The values were close to 3, which is the optimum required for good reproductive performance. This indicated that the nutritional regime offered to the sows maintained a good body condition.

Table 14. Comparison of the body condition score of the sows during the trial.

Parity	Mating		Farrowing		Weaning	
	Sow Pak	Control	Sow Pak	Control	Sow Pak	Control
1	2.9	2.9	3.0	2.9	2.5	2.6
2	2.6	2.5	2.8	2.8	2.5	2.6
3- 6	2.8	2.7	3.0	3.0	2.9	2.7
> 6	2.9	3.0	3.0	3.3	3.0	3.1

Feed consumption

The total and daily quantities of feed consumed by the animals during gestation and lactation at the different parities is presented in Table 15. With the exception of parity 1, feed intake in later parities remained constant during pregnancy. The small variation in consumption during gestation is the result of the feeding strategy during the previous lactation. A sow with minimum loss of condition during lactation is easy to feed in the following pregnancy and this simplifies rationing.

Table 15. Comparison of feed consumption over the different parities.

| Parity | Gestation | | | | Lactation | | | | Total | |
| | Total (kg) | | (kg/day) | | Total (kg) | | (kg/day) | | (kg) | |
	Sow Pak	Control	Sow Pak	Control	Sow Pak	Control	Sow Pak	Control	Sow Pak	Control
1	272.5	264.8	2.3	2.3	110.4	124.3	4.1	4.4	382.9	389.1
2	342.1	340.6	2.9	2.9	137.6	136.9	5.2	5.3	479.7	477.5
3- 6	336.9	335.7	2.9	2.9	155.1	148.6	5.8	5.7	492.0	484.3
>6	336.1	335.5	2.9	2.9	145.5	142.9	5.6	5.5	481.6	478.4

In lactation, there was a tendency for feed intake to increase with parity until parities 3-6 and then to remain constant. However, within each parity, there was no difference in feed intake between the sows fed the Sow Pak or the control diet. The feed required per kg of piglet weaned was also similar between treatments.

Duration of cycle and annual sow productivity

The weaning-to-mating interval varied between five and eight days, indicating that the sows returned to oestrus promptly after weaning and there was no significant difference between treatments (Table 16). In parity 2, the sows fed the Sow Pak returned to oestrus 1 day earlier than the control sows, but there was no difference in subsequent parities. There was no difference in either the duration of the cycle or the number of parities per sow per year (~2.4 litters per sow per year).

Table 16. Details of sow reproductive cycles.

Parity	Weaning-mating interval (days)		Gestation* (days)		Lactation (days)		Duration of cycle (days)		Parities/sow/year	
	Sow Pak	Control	Sow Pak	Control	Sow Pak	Control	Sow Pak	Control	Sow Pak	Control
1			121.8	118.3	26.5	27.9	148.3	146.2		
2	6.6	7.6	119.2	117.0	26.1	25.6	151.9	150.2	2.40	2.43
3-6	6.1	6.3	117.9	117.4	26.6	26.1	150.6	149.8	2.42	2.43
>6	5.8	5.6	117.7	117.6	25.6	26.0	149.1	149.2	2.45	2.45

*including returns to heat

Since both the litter size and the number of potential litters per sow per year are known, it is possible to calculate the annual sow productivity (Table 17). With the exception of parities 1 and 2 when the Sow Pak treatment was introduced, the sows on both treatments produced more than 30 live-born piglets per year. In parities 3-6, the difference between the sows fed the Sow Pak and those fed the control diets was 0.8 extra piglets born alive and 1.0 extra piglets weaned. In later parities, the difference was an extra 1.1 piglet born alive and 0.5 extra piglets weaned per year. There was little difference between treatments in overall pre-weaning piglet mortality.

Table 17. Calculated annual sow productivity.

Parity	Piglets/sow/year total born		Piglets/sow/year born alive		Piglets/sow/year weaned	
	Sow Pak	Control	Sow Pak	Control	Sow Pak	Control
1 + 2	26.12	27.73	24.22	25.54	21.55	23.40
3 - 6	33.64	32.94	31.02	30.18	28.05	27.02
>6	33.71	31.91	30.11	29.01	26.86	26.35

Sow longevity and lifetime performance

Sows were of differing parities when they were introduced onto the trial at weaning of their respective litters. The trial was carried out over a 24-month period and the data base represented some 742 observations; 356 observations were made on sows on the Sow Pak treatment and 386 observations on control sows and included sows between their 2nd and 12th parity.

Analysis of the data suggested that when the proportion of sows at the different parities was compared, there was little difference between the control and Sow Pak groups over the first four parities (Figure 5). The proportion of sows decreased from 100% in parity 1 to 52-57% in parity 4. Thereafter there was a difference between the two treatments. The proportion of sows fed the Sow Pak diet was maintained at 50-57% between parities 4 to 8, whereas for the control sows it decreased from 52% in parity 4 to about 20% in parities 6 to 8. Thus, a larger proportion of sows fed the Sow Pak diet were retained and were better able to maintain good productivity in these most productive parities compared with the control sows. It may well be that the provision of the additional organic mineral better met the needs of the animal, enhancing its metabolic, physiological and endocrine status and thus optimising sow productivity.

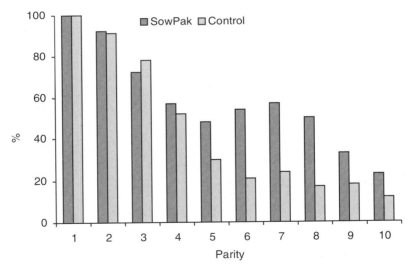

Figure 5. Proportion of litters during the trial.

DISCUSSION

Adding Sow Pak to the diet of sows during gestation and lactation resulted in improved sow productivity compared with that of the controls, although none of the results were significant at P <0.05. However, the performance of the control sows was exceptionally high (29-31 piglets born alive per sow per year from parity 2 onwards) and this was further improved with the addition of Sow Pak. Across all parities, there were 0.2–0.3 extra piglets born alive and weaned in sows fed the diet containing Sow Pak compared with the controls. However, when the peak parities (parities 3-6) were considered, 0.4 more piglets were born or born alive and 0.5 more piglets were weaned from the sows fed Sow Pak than from the controls. Pre-weaning mortality, especially in parities 3-6, was also reduced. When the annual sow productivity was calculated (excluding parities 1 and 2 when all sows may not have received Sow Pak) there were 0.8 extra piglets born alive and 1.0 extra piglet weaned in parities 3–6 and 1.1 extra piglets born alive and 0.5 extra piglets weaned per year in the later parities. There was no difference between the two treatments in either the growth rate of the piglets during lactation or their weaning weights; or in the change in body weight or body condition of the sows throughout the trial, or the feed consumption of the animals.

An interesting feature of the results was the greater number of litters produced by the sows fed the Sow Pak and the reduced removal rate, especially between parities 5 and 9. Overall, the sows fed the Sow Pak produced on average 0.9 more litter per sow lifetime, indicating that these sows were better able to maintain productivity, especially in the most productive parities.

It is interesting to speculate on why the improvements in sow productivity occurred on addition of the Bioplex minerals:

1. The control diet contained the recommended mineral allowances, although in the inorganic form. There is concern about the availability of some of these compounds and it may be that they do not meet the animals' increased requirement for normal reproduction. However, compared with general commercial production, the performance of all the animals in this trial, including those on the control diet, was exceptionally high, suggesting that their mineral requirements were met.

2. It has been suggested that the inclusion of organic minerals better meets the needs of the animal and allows it to express its true genetic potential. Ammerman *et al.* (1998) have suggested that organic minerals provide the animal with a 'metabolic benefit' beyond the usual concept of bioavailability that often results in improved performance.

3. Minerals, such as iron, copper, zinc, manganese, chromium and selenium play specific roles in reproduction (Figures 1 and 2); and if for any reason there is a deficiency in the diet or in the body, then high levels of performance cannot be achieved. In the current trial it

is not known whether the effect was due to one element in particular or to the combination of elements.

4.   The modern sow is expected to be hyperprolific and her nutritional requirements are therefore high, especially in lactation. On the other hand, the selection for lean tissue growth and feed efficiency has resulted in animals with reduced appetite. Even when fed to appetite in lactation, many sows must mobilise considerable body reserves to meet their metabolic needs. Indeed, Mahan and Newton (1995) have shown that considerable quantities of minerals were mobilised from skeletal structures in sows by the end of their third lactation compared with non-breeding animals; and that the higher the level of performance, the greater the loss of minerals from the body. It may well be that the sow has sufficient mineral reserves in her body to sustain high productivity for 2-3 parities; but while there will be some replenishment of reserves during pregnancy, there may be a gradual depletion over time. This may become apparent in reduced productivity and higher culling rates in later parities. Organic minerals with their high bioavailability may help to redress any imbalance or deficit in the animal and therefore maintain high levels of performance. This could explain the much higher reproductive performance of the sows fed Sow Pak from parity 3 onwards, as well as the much greater proportion of productive animals in the herd and lower removal rates. This suggests that the inclusion of the Sow Pak provides the sow with a greater 'biosecurity' throughout her reproductive life, as well as benefiting the piglets.

There are therefore a number of possible mechanisms by which the addition of Bioplex minerals to standard sow diets in the current trial enhanced sow performance and longevity in an already highly productive herd. Indeed, it may well be that the response to the addition of Bioplex minerals during gestation, lactation and post-weaning is even greater in sow herds where performance is limited and below accepted levels of productivity.

Overall conclusions

The provision of a special package of organic minerals, including iron, copper, zinc and manganese, as well as chromium yeast and Sel-Plex, to a standard sow diet further improved the performance of a hyper-prolific herd. The lifetime performance of the animals was also increased, since sow disposal rate was reduced.

The Sow Pak was also provided in the diet of sows on a commercial farm, which was not part of this trial, but which had problems of MMA in sows and piglets scouring in early lactation. There was an improvement in the health status of both the sows and the piglets and an observed reduction in stress in the sows. The beneficial effects of such a package of elements on the quality of the colostrum and the health status of the sows should therefore be further evaluated under a range of commercial farm conditions.

References

Agricultural Research Council. 1981. The nutritional requirements of pigs. CAB Slough, UK.

Ammerman, C.B., P.R. Henry and R.D. Miles. 1998. Supplemental organically-bound mineral compounds in livestock nutrition. In:Recent Advances in Animal Nutrition - 1998. (P.C. Garnsworthy and J. Wiseman eds.). Nottingham University Press, Loughborough, Leics. UK. pp 67-91.

Close, W.H. 1999. Organic minerals for pigs: an update. In: Biotechnology in the Feed Industry, Proceedings of the 15th Annual Symposium (T.P Lyons and K.A. Jacques, eds). Nottingham University Press, Nottingham, Leics. UK. pp. 51-60.

Fehse, R. 1999. 30 Ferkel pro Sau und Jahr? Interne Publikation, Haefliger AG. Herzogenbuchsee, Switzerland.

Mahan, D. and Newton, C.A. 1995. Effect of initial breeding weight on macro- and micromineral composition over a three-parity period using a high-producing sow genotype. J. Anim. Sci. 73:151-158.

National Research Council. 1998. Nutritional requirements of swine. National Academy Press, Washington, USA.

The egg shell: a case study in improving quality by altering mineral metabolism – naturally

VLADIMIR SISKE[1], LADISLAV ZEMAN[2] AND DALIBOR KLECKER[2]

[1]*Alltech Czech Republic*
[2]*Mendel University of Agriculture and Forestry, Brno, Czech Republic*

Introduction

It is in the best interest of poultry breeders to obtain as many top quality eggs as possible from each hen. Egg quality can be influenced by nutritional variables such as diet composition, electrolyte ratio and the content and composition of amino acids in the diet. Similarly, egg shell quality is of great interest to egg producers and poultry breeders. Reductions in egg shell quality are associated with economic losses. It is estimated that losses caused by poor shell quality range from 6 to 8%. However, this estimate does not involve shell-less eggs that fall through the cages into the litter. On some farms the proportion of eggs lost in this way may be as high as 7%.

Our research has focused on finding ways to reduce the proportion of cracked eggs, primarily by increasing egg shell strength. The egg shell is *de facto* a porous structure with approximately 7 to 17 thousand pores. The density of these pores is greater on the pointed end of the egg. The number and size of these pores can have a negative effect on egg quality, e.g., lower hatchability. In addition, the egg shell represents the first line of defense against microbial contamination of egg white.

The number of cracked eggs is influenced by many factors; and it is important to remember that the occurrence of cracked eggs is due to more than one reason. Such factors involve nutritional status, health condition of the flock, microclimate, management, housing and egg handling. In spite of our extensive knowledge about the factors contributing to the incidence of cracked eggs, it remains impossible to eliminate all problems associated with egg shell quality. The following paper reports work from our group on the effects of altering trace mineral form on aspects of egg shell quality and the consequent effects on egg production and fertility.

The egg shell

STRUCTURE AND COMPOSITION

The egg shell is comprised of five layers: an inner egg shell membrane, an outer egg shell membrane, the mammillary layer, spongy layer and cuticle. The egg shell membranes are also called the 'organic matrix'; and their importance and effect on egg shell quality are often neglected. This matrix is comprised of a combination of proteins and mucopolysaccharides. Most of the protein is made up of keratin with a high concentration of sulfur (70-75%) while about 10% of the protein is collagen. The amino acid ratio of matrix proteins changes as the hen ages and these changes are reflected in the quality of egg shell.

Changes in synthesis and secretion of egg shell membranes may have negative effects on shell formation and ultimately on quality. Adequate amounts of certain trace minerals, particularly manganese and zinc, are very important for the synthesis of these membranes, which form the basis of the calcified part of egg shell. Deficiencies in either mineral have negative effects on formation of membranes, egg shell morphology and egg production. These problems result very probably from the role that manganese plays in the process of synthesis of mucopolysaccharides. It seems that this glucoprotein structure influences calcification of egg shell. Moreover, zinc is indispensable for proper formation of keratin.

The mammillary layer is formed by cells of irregular conical shape forming irregular conical structures on the outer egg shell membrane. They form approximately one third of egg shell thickness. The so-called spongy layer is very firm; and its firmness increases in the direction of the egg shell surface. This layer forms approximately two thirds of egg shell thickness. The cuticle is an organic layer on the egg shell surface that prevents penetration of microorganisms into the egg. It contains a high proportion of surface pigments.

From the chemical point of view, the egg shell consists of water (2%) and dry matter (98%). The dry matter is composed of 5% crude protein and 93% ash. Average values of mineral contents in different parts of the egg and egg shell, as found in our experiments, are presented in Table 1.

FACTORS AFFECTING EGG SHELL QUALITY

Obtaining an egg with a smooth and strong egg shell is desirable. Shells from eggs collected immediately after lay as well as those of big eggs are more susceptible to cracking. The hen is able to deposit only a certain amount of calcium into the egg shell and this amount is influenced by genotype. This means that increasing the level of calcium in the diet will not necessarily improve the quality of egg shell (Ceylan and Scheideler, 1999). As hens age, egg size increases such that a constant amount of calcium is distributed over a larger surface. This means that changes in egg weight and the

Table 1. Egg composition as analyzed in our experiments.

		Egg yolk	Egg white	Egg shell	Whole egg
Weight	g	16.72	40.92	6.17	63.81
Ash	g	0.2900	0.2100	5.8677	6.3677
Ca	g	0.0249	0.0022	2.2466	2.2736
P	g	0.0876	0.0043	0.0063	0.0982
Na	g	0.0173	0.0519	0.0043	0.0735
Zn	mg	0.562	0.032	0.148	0.743
Mn	mg	0.012	0.001	0.044	0.057
Cl	mg	29.309	64.892		
K	mg	17.304	51.913		
Mg	mg	1.082	4.326		
Cu	mg	0.004	0.002		
Fe	mg	0.638	0.119		
I	mg	0.024	0.002		

age of layers influence the quality of egg shell. Changes in temperature inside the laying house influence feed intake and therefore egg size. The fact that the egg shell is thick does not necessarily mean that it is also strong. Sometimes a thin egg shell may be stronger than a thick shell.

Calcium and the egg shell

It is obvious that in order to maintain good egg shell quality it is necessary to assure adequate nutrition. Hens producing approximately 300 eggs per year must deposit 24 times more calcium into egg shells than the amount contained in their bones. For that reason, the requirements for calcium supply in the diet are enormous. During the 20 hr period in which the egg shell is formed, the hen must deposit 25 mg of calcium on the egg surface every 15 minutes. As the hen can only obtain 30-50% of total dietary calcium (depending on its source, size of particles, health condition of birds, etc.), the amount of dietary calcium that must be supplied daily ranges from 3.2 to 4.5 g (depending on production level, daily feed intake, environmental temperature and other factors).

Availability of calcium from various sources differs. Ground shells of marine animals are the best source of calcium followed by egg shells. These organic sources are followed by aragonite and then by common limestone. The most sensitive response to calcium deficiency can be observed in hens at the age of 150-180 days. Toward the end of the laying period, the utilization of calcium generally decreases. This can be partly improved by a change of calcium source.

Important also is the particle size in which calcium is supplied to hens. The coarser the particles, the longer the residence time in the upper gastrointestinal tract. The release of calcium from coarser particles is slower; and this fact may be important given that shell formation is continuous and proceeds during the non-daylight hours when layers do not eat. This is demonstrated by the fact that shells of eggs laid in the afternoon are usually thicker. The presence of adequate amounts of vitamin D_3 in relation to calcium is obviously also important. However, increased doses of this vitamin do not affect the quality of egg shell.

Zinc and the egg shell

Along with calcium, carbonate ions are needed in formation of calcium carbonate. However, they are usually neglected as a potential cause of problems associated with egg shell quality. Carbon dioxide, which is present in the oviduct as a common product of cell metabolism or as a gaseous compound in blood, is the main source of carbonate ions. The carbonic anhydrase enzyme requires the presence of zinc and catalyses formation of carbonic acid from water and carbon dioxide. In non-laying hens, activity of carbonic anhydrase is lower than in laying hens. Ceylan and Scheideler (1999) demonstrated that organic zinc was associated with higher activity of carbonic anhydrase and in turn with improved shell quality. The fact that zinc is a co-factor of this enzyme makes both activity and proper function of this enzyme potentially sensitive to trace elements, their interactions and availability. The dietary concentration of zinc needed to meet daily zinc requirements ranges from 40 to 60 mg/kg of feed dry matter. Zinc oxide and zinc sulfate have been the most commonly-used sources of zinc.

Manganese and the egg shell

The presence of manganese (Mn) has an activating effect on alkaline phosphatase; explaining the importance of this element in proper formation of bone tissue and egg shell. Ochrimenko *et al.* (1992) noted a positive effect of manganese supplements on calcification and egg shell strength. In experiments carried out by Sazzad *et al.* (1994), no effects of increased amounts of manganese in the diet on production and weight of eggs were observed. However, egg shell thickness increased significantly. These authors recommended that laying hens receive 105 mg/kg Mn in the diet. Manganese deficiency decreases egg shell weight; which may support the hypothesis regarding the importance of manganese as a enzyme co-factor in controlling synthesis of mucopolysaccharides.

Phosphorus and the egg shell

A surplus of phosphorus in the diet has a negative effect on egg shell quality. For that reason it is important to maintain an optimum ratio of phosphorus and calcium, which widens as the hen ages. If calcium is supplied in powder form, the optimum phosphorus/calcium ratios from week 19 to 50 and after week 50 of age are 1:9-10 and 1:11-12, respectively. However, if calcium is supplied in the form of coarse particles (65%, 2-4 mm), the optimum phosphorus/calcium ratios are 1:10-11 and 1:12-13 for weeks 19-50 and after week 50 of age, respectively. The phosphorus requirement of hens increases in a hot environment.

Magnesium and the egg shell

Magnesium deficiency reduces egg production, calcium deposition and formation of egg shell. In practice, however, it is not necessary to supplement diets with special amounts of magnesium because its content in vegetable-based feed ingredients and common (dolomitic) sources of limestone is sufficient.

Research at Mendel University: applications for organic sources of trace elements in poultry nutrition

Mineral proteinates are obtained by means of hydrolysis of a protein source such that the resulting hydrolysate contains a mixture of amino acids and small peptides with chains of different lengths. This hydrolysate is then reacted with metal salts to form complexes containing chelated metallic ions (Hynes and Kelly, 1995). In this way stable chelates are formed which protect trace elements against chemical reactions taking place in the course of digestion. This protection maintains the solubility of these substances during their passage through the gastrointestinal tract to the sites of absorption. In the small intestine, chelates are thought to be absorbed via peptide and amino acid routes as opposed to the passive absorption mechanisms of ions derived from inorganic mineral sources (Close, 1998). Such absorption would explain the apparent decrease in interaction between mineral forms shown in various reports as well as allowing inorganic and organic forms to be used together to advantage. Greater stability during digestion, along with absorption and transport via peptide and amino acid routes, results in higher biological availability.

Differences in the bioavailability of various trace mineral sources for layers have been demonstrated in numerous studies in cattle and pigs, however there are fewer experiments with organic mineral forms in poultry. In the case of manganese, the two sources primarily used for supplementation of animal diets are manganous oxide and manganous sulfate. Using manganous sulfate as a basis for comparison, (i.e. 100 %), the relative biological availabilities of manganous oxide, manganese dioxide and manganese carbonate are 60-80%, 30-40% and 25-40%, respectively (McDowell, 1992). However, it was found that the availability of organic forms of this element was higher than that of manganous sulfate (Henry, 1995). Gomez-Basauri (1997) summarized the responses to mineral proteinates in layers both in research and commercial trials.

The topic of organic trace elements in diets for laying hens has been studied at the Mendel University of Agriculture and Forestry in Brno (Czech Republic) over the past five years (Klecker and Zeman, 1996; Klecker *et al.*, 1996; 1997a; 1997b; Svobodova-Cizkova, 1998; Bunesova, 2000). The following presents a summary of the experiments done in this period and details new results in applications of organic forms of trace minerals in laying hens and cockerels.

MATERIAL AND METHODS: EXPERIMENTS 1-5

Experiments 1, 2 and 3 were carried out in cages in the experimental poultry house at Mendel University of Agriculture and Forestry (MUAF) in Brno using 640 laying hens (hybrid ISA Brown obtained from Integra Zabcice, Czech Republic). Experiment 4 was done in large-scale commercial conditions using 12,000 parent stock ISA Brown birds. Experiment 5 was carried out on ISA Brown cockerels also in the experimental poultry house at MUAF. For all experiments, diets were formulated and fed according to age. Basal diets were formulated as per NRC (1994) and Zelenka *et al.*, 1999. Formulations, nutrient and mineral contents are listed in Table 2. Egg production, egg weight and feed consumption were measured daily. At four week intervals two eggs from each hen were analysed for the following parameters: egg shell weight, egg shell thickness, egg shell strength, standard egg yolk and egg white measurements. Strength of the egg shell was measured by the destruction method with the use of an egg crusher (Veit Electronics CZ). In Experiment 2 egg shell quality was observed by scanning electron microscope using methods described by Jelinek and Lhotecky (1996).

Experiment 1: Effects of substituting 20 or 40% of the inorganic zinc and manganese with Bioplex proteinates

The basal diet contained inorganic forms of zinc and manganese. In the treatment diets either 20 or 40% of the inorganic zinc and manganese was replaced by organic forms (Bioplex Zinc and Bioplex Manganese) from week 17 to week 67 of age.

Experiment 2: Effects of replacing 50% of the inorganic zinc and manganese with Bioplex proteinates

The basal diet contained inorganic forms of zinc and manganese. The treatment diets consisted of replacing 50% of the inorganic zinc and manganese either together or separately by organic forms (Bioplex Zinc and Bioplex Manganese). This experiment lasted from week 17 to week 72 of age.

Table 2. Feed mixture formulation, nutrient and mineral contents of feed mixtures for layers.

	to 42 weeks	after 42 weeks
Ingredient	%	
Wheat	30	29
Corn	41	41
Soybean meal	15	15
Fish meal	3.1	3.1
Premix AA (methionine 20%)	0.4	0.4
Premix ISA (vitamins)	0.5	0.5
Premix Mikrop (macroelements)	9.8	10.8
Premix MD II (trace elements)	0.2	0.2
Total	100	100
Premix MD II (trace elements)	mg/kg	
Mn	60	60
Zn	50	50
Fe	50	50
I	1	1
Cu	5	5
Co	0.2	0.2
Se	0.15	0.15
Calculated analysis		
AME, MJ/kg	11.24	11.11
	g/kg	
Crude protein	157.92	156.64
Lysine	7.5	7.47
Met+Cys	6.14	6.1
Linoleic acid	13.02	12.94
Ca	38.18	41.77
P	3.33	3.48
Na	1.48	1.57

Experiment 3: Effects of Eggshell 49 added to the basal diet under controlled conditions

The control group received the basal diet and the experimental group received the same diet with the addition of Eggshell 49 (Alltech Inc.) in the amount of 2 kg/tonne of feed. The experiment lasted from week 53 to week 72 of age.

Experiment 4: Effects of Eggshell 49 on performance of parent stock under commercial conditions

The experiment was conducted on a commercial farm with 12,000 parent stock birds. In this experiment, the effect of Eggshell 49 supplementation on the percentage of selected hatching eggs was observed. The experiment was conducted on receiving a request from the poultry breeder who complained that his selection of hatching eggs was too low.

Experiment 5: Effect of organic zinc, manganese and selenium fed to cockerels on fertilization of hatching eggs

In this experiment, which lasted from week 25 to week 40, ISA Brown cockerels were divided into two groups. The control group was given a diet containing the mineral premix MD II (Table 2), which contained only inorganic forms of trace minerals. In the experimental group 50% of the zinc, manganese and selenium was substituted with proteinates (Bioplex Zinc, Bioplex Manganese) and by organic selenium (Sel-Plex). The objective of this experiment was to determine whether the organic mineral substitution would effect fertilization of hatching eggs.

RESULTS

Experiment 1: Effects of substituting 20 or 40% of the inorganic zinc and manganese with Bioplex proteinates

Bioplex Zinc and Bioplex Manganese significantly increased egg shell strength (Table 3, Figure 1). Detailed statistical analysis demonstrated a significant improvement of egg shell strength as early as week 24, i.e. 28 days after the onset of lay. A positive improvement was also observed in egg mass and in daily egg production (Table 3, Figure 3). In all cases, both daily egg production and production of egg mass were higher than model data presented by the ISA company for hybrid ISA Brown hens (ISA Brown, 1993a; 1993b). Means were not significant owing to the relatively small number of hens in the study.

Table 3. The effect of substituting 20 or 40% of the inorganic zinc and manganese with Bioplexes on performance and egg shell parameters (Experiment 1).

	Control		20% Bioplex Zn, Mn		40% Bioplex Zn, Mn	
	Mean	SE	Mean	SE	Mean	SE
Egg production, %	90.915	0.203	92.613	0.157	92.095	0.143
Percentage of cracked eggs, %	1.4		1.2		0.9	
Egg weight, g	63.91	0.433	62.08	0.401	63.94	0.391
Egg shell thickness, mm	0.388	0.001	0.394	0.001	0.403	0.002
Egg shell strength, Newtons	32.357	0.463	34.812	0.448	34.948	0.437

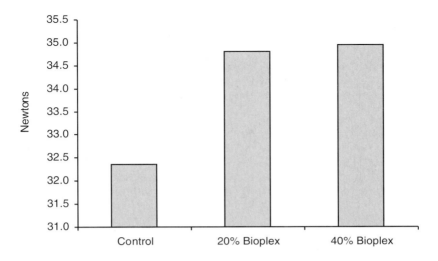

Figure 1. Effects of substituting 20 or 40% of the inorganic zinc and manganese with Bioplexes on egg shell strength (Newtons) (Experiment 1).

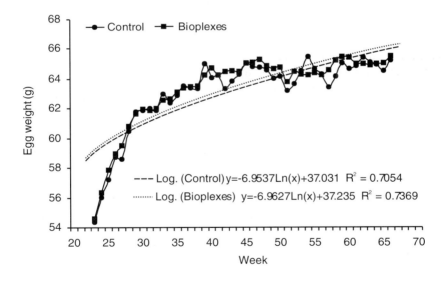

Figure 2. Effects of substituting 20 or 40% of the inorganic zinc and manganese with Bioplexes on egg weight (g) (Experiment 1).

The relationships between hen age and weekly egg production and egg mass were determined using biometric analysis. For evaluation, analysis of variance and orthogonal polynomials were used and results compared

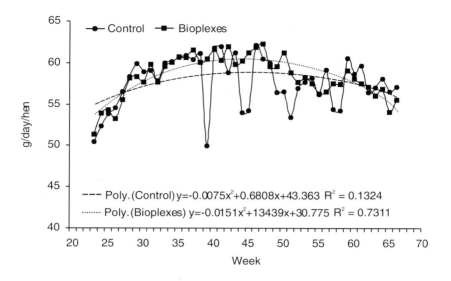

Figure 3. Effects of substituting 20 or 40% of the inorganic zinc and manganese with Bioplexes on egg mass produced (g/day/hen) (Experiment 1).

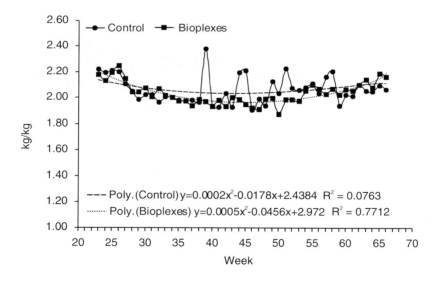

Figure 4. Effects of substituting 20 or 40% of the zinc and manganese by Bioplexes on feed consumption per egg mass produced (kg/kg) (Experiment 1).

with the ideal laying curve for model production determined by the breeder company (ISA Brown, 1993). This comparison revealed a number of significant differences in response to Bioplex substitution. Equations and

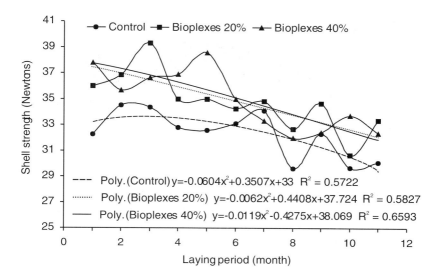

Figure 5. Effects of substituting 20 or 40% of the inorganic zinc and manganese by Bioplexes on egg shell strength (Newtons) (Experiment 1).

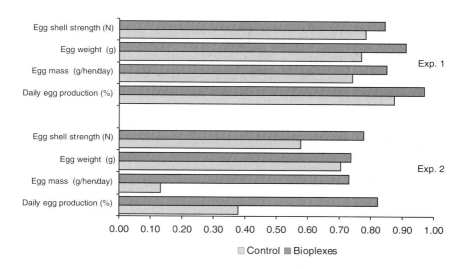

Figure 6. Correlation coefficients for performance and egg shell parameters (Experiments 1 and 2).

correlation coefficients are presented in Figures 2, 3 and 4. These equations indicated that supplementing the laying diet with Bioplexes slightly improved egg weight, daily production of egg mass and feed consumption per egg

337

mass produced. In Figure 3 it can be seen that hens given Bioplexes had higher egg mass production. Reviewing the variation in weekly values, it was found that hens fed Bioplexes had a more uniform course of egg production. From the correlation coefficient (R^2) it can be seen that where Bioplexes were administered 73% of values lie on the theoretically calculated curve. On the other hand, in the control group only 13% of measured values lie on the theoretically calculated curve. In addition, higher uniformity was demonstrated for egg weight, feed consumption per egg mass produced and egg shell strength in the group given the organic minerals (Figures 2, 4 and 5).

Figure 6 demonstrates that for all main parameters (daily egg production, egg mass production, egg weight, egg shell strength) correlation coefficients were higher in the groups given Bioplexes compared to the groups with inorganic minerals, indicating higher uniformity. A similar trend was noted in Experiment 2 (Figure 6).

Experiment 2: Effects of replacing 50% of the inorganic zinc and manganese with Bioplex proteinates

Substitution of both zinc and manganese produced the best performance (Table 4), indicating an additive effect in this experimental design. Egg shell thickness was increased significantly in response to all experimental diets (Figure 7). In addition, all treatments reduced the percentage of cracked eggs. In all treatment groups (controls and experimental groups) laying performance and production of egg mass were higher than model values recommended by the ISA company for hybrid combination ISA Brown layers.

Results of a mathematical evaluation of the egg production curve, egg weight and egg mass production from week 23 to 72 of age are presented in Figures 8, 9 and 10. Equations and correlation coefficients are presented as a part of these graphs.

The most interesting response to 50% substitution with Bioplexes in this experiment occurred in egg weight (Figure 9). Using logarithmic transformation it was observed that the group given both organic zinc and manganese had higher egg weights. Uniformity was also improved as indicated by higher correlation coefficients.

Egg shells were examined by scanning electron microscopy (Jelinek and Lhotecky, 1996) and results are illustrated in Figure 11 (A-D). The upper two (Figures A and B) show differences of crystallization centers of the mammillary layer between experimental and control groups at 120X enlargement. At present this is the subject of further research at MUAF. Photographs C and D show egg shell fracture at the same enlargement and demonstrate the thicker egg shell when hens were given the Bioplex-supplemented diets.

Table 4. The effect of substituting 50% of inorganic zinc and manganese with Bioplexes separately and in combination on performance and egg shell parameters (Experiment 2).

	Control		50% Bioplex Mn		50% Bioplex Zn		50% Bioplex Zn, Mn	
	Mean	SE	Mean	SE	Mean	SE	Mean	SE
Egg production, %	89.839	5.683	90.179	5.448	88.496	6.438	91.161	5.328
Percentage of cracked eggs, %	2.98		2.85		2.90		2.10	
Egg weight, g	64.225	0.233	65.41	0.19	65.191	0.182	64.402	0.249
Egg shell weight, g	6.023	0.028	6.082	0.022	6.128	0.023	6.204	0.026
Egg shell thickness, mm	0.388	0.002	0.391	0.001	0.393	0.001	0.400	0.001
Egg shell strength, Newtons	31.745	0.385	31.025	0.279	31.965	0.270	32.154	0.371

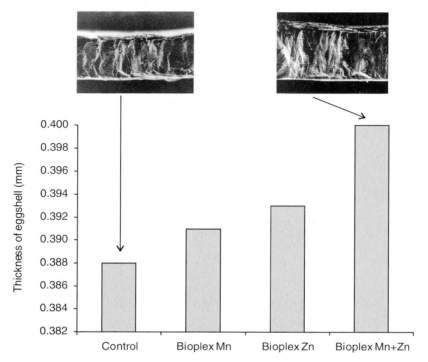

Figure 7. Effect of substituting 50% of the inorganic zinc and manganese with Bioplexes separately and in combination on thickness (mm) of egg shell (enlargement 120X) (Experiment 2).

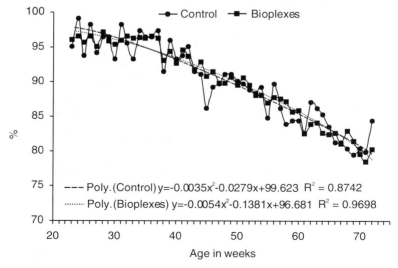

Figure 8. The effect of substituting 50% of the inorganic zinc and manganese with Bioplexes on egg production (%) (Experiment 2).

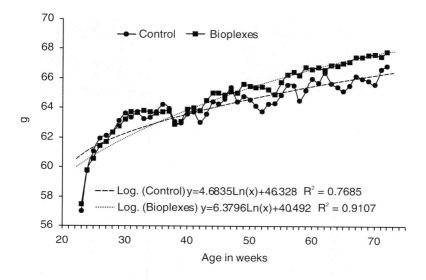

Figure 9. The effect of substituting 50% of the inorganic zinc and manganese with Bioplexes on egg weight (g) (Experiment 2).

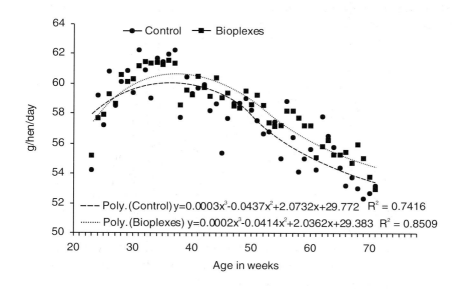

Figure 10. The effect of substituting 50% of the inorganic zinc and manganese with Bioplexes on egg mass production (g/hen/day) (Experiment 2).

(A) Control   (B) Bioplexes

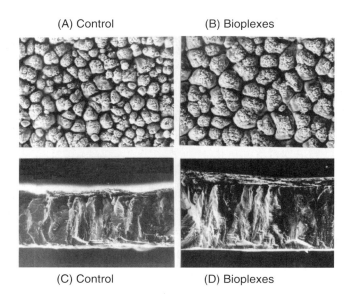

(C) Control   (D) Bioplexes

Figure 11. The effects of Bioplexes on mamillary layer cells in egg shell (A, B) and on thickness of egg shell (C,D) (Experiment 2).

Experiment 3: Effects of Eggshell 49 added to the basal diet under controlled conditions

Hens given Eggshell 49 had higher egg production (+2.47%) after 19 weeks (Table 5). Egg weight increased from 65.05 to 66.20 g, eggshell thickness was increased (P< 0.05) from 0.386 to 0.403 mm, shell weight increased from 5.990 to 6.270 g and egg shell strength increased from 28.05 to 29.76 Newtons.

Table 5. The effect of Eggshell 49 from week 53 to week 72 of age on performance of laying hens and egg parameters (Experiment 3).

	Control		Eggshell 49	
	Mean	SE	Mean	SE
Egg production, %	73.07	1.035	75.54	0.987
Percentage of cracked eggs, %	3.85		2.91	
Egg weight, g	65.05	0.613	66.20	0.516
Egg shell weight, g	5.990	0.097	6.270	0.090
Egg shell thickness, mm	0.386	0.005	0.403	0.005
Egg shell strength, Newtons	28.050	1.003	29.760	1.034
Haugh units	79.510	1.930	81.510	1.947
Feed intake per hen, g/day	120.080	0.997	120.088	1.022

Quality of the egg white also improved in response to Eggshell 49 as indicated by the increase in Haugh units. The percentage of cracked eggs decreased from 3.85 to 2.91%.

Experiment 4: Effects of Eggshell 49 on performance of parent stock birds under commercial conditions

On this poultry farm, the percentage of selection of hatching eggs was initially low (71.5%). After three weeks, Eggshell 49 supplementation was interrupted for a period of four weeks and thereafter the application was resumed for another four weeks. Results are presented in Figure 12. Eggshell 49 increased the selection of hatching eggs by 4-5%, an effect that lasted for the 3-week supplementation period. When supplementation was interrupted, hatching egg percentage decline to previous values. Performance again increased during the second period of supplementation after week 54 of age and this positive effect persisted till the end of this experiment.

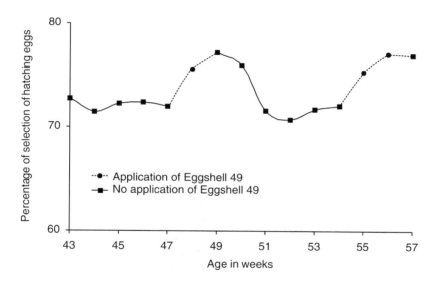

Figure 12. The effect of Eggshell 49 in layer diets during two periods on selections of hatching eggs (Experiment 4).

Experiment 5: Effect of organic zinc, manganese and selenium fed to cockerels on fertilization of hatching eggs

Substitution of 50% of the inorganic manganese, zinc and selenium with Bioplex Zinc, Bioplex Manganese and Sel-Plex in diets for cockerels increased fertilization of hatching eggs (Figure 13). At the first collection of eggs at week 27, an increase of 4.85% in fertilization of hatching eggs was noted while at the second collection at week 38, there was in increase of 3.76% for the group given Bioplexes and Sel-Plex. This increase could be explained in part through effects on spermatogenesis.

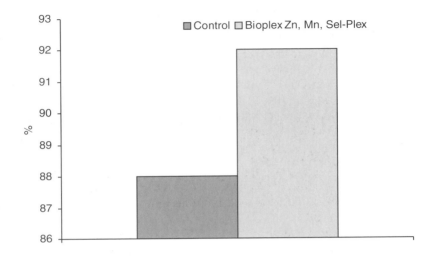

Figure 13. The effect of substituting 50% of the inorganic zinc, manganese and selenium with Bioplexes and Sel-Plex addition in diets fed cockerels on fertilization of hatching eggs (Experiment 5).

Conclusions

Based on these data, the organic sources were of greater value in providing nutrients limiting in egg production and fertility. Substitution with proteinates had a beneficial effect on egg shell quality and total egg production which translated to a larger percentage of hatching eggs, hatchability and consequently to improved economics for the egg producer.

In summary, use of mineral proteinates (Bioplex Zinc and Bioplex Manganese) and Eggshell 49 in diets for poultry in our experiments resulted in:

- A significant increase in egg shell strength. This response was observed as early as six weeks after beginning supplementation (after week 23 of age) and persisted for the whole period of administration.

- Improved laying performance, egg weight and egg mass.

- Significant improvement in uniformity of the laying curve, egg weight and egg mass production. Higher uniformity is very favourable for egg producers because it indicates more eggs that can be sold in the higher quality grades.

- Alterations in the crystallization centers of the mammillary layer and increased percentage of hatching eggs. The increase in percentage of hatching eggs was observed as early as one week after beginning supplementation.

- In cockerels with reduced fertility, the application of Bioplex Zinc, Bioplex Manganese and Sel-Plex increased fertilization of hatching eggs.

References

Bunesova, A. 2000. Analysis of performance of laying hens in dependence on application of various form of minerals. Ph.D. disertation, Mendel University of Agriculture and Forestry, Brno, Czech Republic, p. 103.

Close, W.H. 1998. New developments in the use of trace mineral proteinates to improve pig performance and reduce environmental impact. In: European Lecture Tour, Alltech Inc. Technical Publications, Nicholasville, KY, USA, p. 51–68.

Ceylan, N. and S.E. Scheideler. 1999. Effects of Eggshell 49, dietary calcium level and hen age on performance and egg shell quality. In: Biotechnology in the Feed Industry, Proceedings of the 15th Annual Symposium (T.P. Lyons and K.A. Jacques, eds), Nottingham University Press, Nottingham, UK. p. 61–73.

Gomez-Basauri, J. 1997. Eggshell quality and economic losses: The potential for improvement with dietary trace mineral proteinates. In: Biotechnology in the Feed Industry, Proceedings of the 13th Annual Symposium (T.P. Lyons and K.A. Jacques, eds), Nottingham University Press, Nottingham, UK., p. 381–388.

Henry, P.R. 1995. Manganese bioavailability. In: Bioavailability of Nutrients for Animals. (C.B. Ammerman, D.H. Baker and A.J Lewis, eds). Academic Press, San Diego-New York-Boston-London-Sydney-Tokyo-Toronto. p. 239–256.

Hynes, M.J. and M.P. Kelly. 1995. Metal ions, chelates and proteinates. In: Biotechnology in the Feed Industry, Proceedings of the 11th Annual Symposium (T.P. Lyons and K.A. Jacques, eds), Nottingham University Press, Nottingham, UK. p. 233–248.

ISA Brown. 1993a. Management Guide, Commercial Layers. ISA, Lyon, France. p. 24.

ISA Brown. 1993b. Annex Management Guide, Commercial Layers. ISA, Lyon, France. p. 12.

Jelinek, K. And J. Lhotecky. 1996. Changes in egg shell ultrastructure in hens' cracked eggs. Zivocisna vyroba. 41(9):413–421.

Klecker, D. and L. Zeman. 1996. Organic trace minerals in Eggshell 49 improve egg shell quality. Poster presented at the 12th Annual Symposium

Biotechnology in the Feed Industry, April 22–24th, Lexington, Kentucky.

Klecker, D., L. Zeman and A. Bunesova. 1996. Effect of Mn and Zn chelates on production of eggs. 47th Annual Meeting of the European Association for Animal Production. Lillehammer, Norway. 25-29, p. 91.

Klecker, D., L. Zeman and A. Bunesova. 1997a. Effect of organic selenium on the qualitative parameters of eggs. 48th Annual Meeting of the European Association for Animal Production. Wien. 25-28, p. 295.

Klecker, D., L. Zeman, V. Siske, J. Gomez Basauri. 1997b. Influence of trace mineral proteinate supplementation on egg shell quality. Poultry Sci. 76(Suppl. 1)131.

McDowell, L.R. 1992. Minerals in Animal and Human Nutrition. Academic Press. San Diego.

NRC. 1994. Nutrient Requirements of Poultry, Ninth Revised Edition, National Academy Press, Washington, D.C., p. 19–34.

Ochrimenko, C., A. Lemser, G. Richter, U. Krause and H. Bonsak. 1992. Effect of the manganese content in laying hen feed with different Ca and mineral levels on the egg shell quality and bone mineralization of hens. Arch Tierernahr, 42(1):25–45.

Sazzad, H.M., A.G. Bertechini, P.T.C. Nobre. 1994. Egg production, tissue deposition and mineral metabolism in two strains of commercial layers with various level of manganese in diet. Anim. Feed Sci. and Tech. 46:3–4, pp. 271–275.

Svobodova-Cizkova, J. 1998. Effects of manganese, zinc and chromium chelates on blood parameters, egg shell quality and mineral profile of bones in young and laying hens. Ph.D. dissertation, Mendel University of Agriculture and Forestry in Brno, Czech Republic, p. 122.

Wedekind, K.J., A.J. Lewis, M.A. Giesemann and P.S. Miller. 1994. Bioavailability of zinc from inorganic and organic sources for pigs fed corn–soybean meal diets. J. Anim. Sci. 72(2681–2689).

Zelenka, J., J. Heger and L. Zeman. 1999. Nutrient Requirements and Nutritional Value of Feed for Poultry, Czech Academy of Agricultural Science, Mendel University of Agriculture and Forestry, Brno, p. 63.

Biopeptides in post-weaning diets for pigs: results to date

G. WALTER TIBBETTS

Alltech Inc., Nicholasville, Kentucky, USA

Introduction: options for protein supplementation

Where once we considered feed protein to be strictly a means of supplying essential amino acids, we now know that certain peptides produced during gastrointestinal hydolysis of protein have nutritional and physiological roles. The potential attributes of biological peptides have been documented in recent reviews (Power and Murphy, 1999) and include sensory, hormonal, anti-microbial, palatability enhancing, anti-carcinogenic, immunoactivity, antioxidant, mineral binding and nutritive functions. A common feature associated with these activities is that only a relatively minute quantity of peptide is required to effect the response.

The livestock industry and their feed suppliers are perhaps as sensitive to nutritional advances as any commercial group. Since rate of gain and efficiency of feed utilization are directly linked to profit, potential improvements in these areas are generally scrutinized for return on investment. Ration formulation technology has advanced dramatically in the last 25 years with the advent of complex nursery rations, a better understanding of amino acid interactions leading to the development of ideal protein patterns and a host of products inlcuding synthetic amino acids, and now peptides, along with an ever increasing list of by-products from other industries.

Besides a direct impact on profitability, external influences such as environmental concerns, animal welfare and human health risks from food contamination also drive the search for new and improved methods of feeding livestock. Nitrogen, typically in the form of protein-rich oilseed meals, is one of the most expensive items to adequately supply in rations. Excess nitrogen may also be quite putrefactive or volatile in the environment, causing odor and pollution problems. Nitrogen tends to leach rapidly from soils leading to ground water pollution when applied to land either outside the growing season or in quantities beyond what actively growing plants can utilize. Therefore improving nitrogen metabolism in the body holds great appeal to the livestock industry and its suppliers.

Synthetic amino acid availability has provided both nutritional and environmental advantages. Requirements for specific limiting amino acids can be met without adding protein-rich feed ingredients in excess. Judicious use of synthetic amino acids can reduce total ration costs while limiting nitrogen excretion. Although the use of synthetic amino acids is relatively widespread, they unfortunately may be used only at relatively low addition rates. That free amino acids may not replace intact protein altogether is well understood.

Although research with both ruminants and monogastrics is beginning to unravel the potential of peptides to the animal feed industry (Webb *et al.*, 1992; Webb and Matthews, 1998; Gardner, 1994; 1995), much of the nutritional research with peptides has stemmed from investigations into human applications. Siemensma *et al.* (1993), investigating peptide applications in human infant formula, outlined several important reasons why peptides have nutritional advantages that differ from amino acids and intact proteins. These include:

a. Transport of short peptides across the intestinal wall is facilitated by diffusion, in contrast to free amino acids.

b. Peptides are more hypertonic than free amino acids with the net effect of increasing efficiency of absorption and reducing osmotic problems.

c. Short peptides, in many cases, are less antigenic than larger polypeptides or the native protein from which they are derived.

d. Shorter peptides often possess beneficial sensory characteristics.

Webb (2000) summarized other information regarding the nutritional advantages of peptides compared to free amino acids in a presentation to the Virginia State Feed Association:

a. There is a lower energy cost to the body for absorbing peptides. Carrier proteins are involved in moving peptides from the intestine via facilitated diffusion with little or no energy expenditure. On the other hand, individual amino acids are moved via active transport, an energy-requiring action.

b. Peptides are absorbed more rapidly from the gastrointestinal tract as measured by peptide appearance in the blood.

c. Peptides are more stable than free amino acids in the gut as well as within the circulatory system.

Biopeptides, a practical approach

The purpose of this discussion is to present recent results from both field trials and controlled studies, giving an overview of practical responses to a product (Biopeptides) designed to supply dietary nitrogen primarily in peptide form. The focus of the work to date has been on early weaning nutrition. The peptide supplement used in these studies was produced with microbially derived proteases in a tightly controlled enzymatic process involving several hydrolysis steps. Power and Murphy (1999) have previously discussed the advantages of enzymatic hydrolysis to produce peptides for animal feeding purposes as compared to the use of chemical or DNA recombinant methods.

One important difference between this product and other peptide products in the marketplace for livestock is that the Biopeptide product is based on non-animal protein. Such a product is necessary in the industry owing to prevailing concerns, real or otherwise, about animal proteins in food animal diets. Consumer perception of blood and meat meals has suffered from the BSE and salmonella crises. In addition, export hurdles and expense for blood-based products preclude use of these high quality proteins in many markets. Others are concerned that use of animal proteins represents a biosecurity risk to otherwise closed herds. Consequently, several of the following trials examine the potential for replacing spray-dried blood plasma with Biopeptides. The data presented herein will hopefully not only offer alternative solutions, but possibly bring to the forefront a new product capable of improving digestion, absorption and utilization.

Response in commercial studies

TRIAL 1: REPLACEMENT OF ALL OR PART OF THE PLASMA PROTEIN IN DIETS FED WEEKS 1-3

A large Midwestern feed company examined the potential of Biopeptides to replace all or a portion of the plasma protein in the first three weeks of the nursery phase. Biopeptides were substituted for 1/3 of the standard plasma regimen (6%) in week one (Phase 1), resulting in a combination of 4% spray-dried plasma protein/2% Biopeptides. In weeks 2 and 3 (Phase 2), pigs were fed diets with either 3% plasma protein or 3% Biopeptides. Two hundred hybrid pigs weaned at an average age of 17 days and average weight of 10.45 lb were divided into treatment groups. Although this trial was conducted as a field experiment, it took place in a modern research facility under controlled conditions.

In Phase 1, similar gains and feed conversions were observed, with an advantage shown for the Biopeptides in cost per pound of gain (Table 1; Ferrell, 1999; personal communication). There were numerical improvements for gain, efficiency and cost of gain during weeks 2 and 3. Overall results (weeks 1-3) showed an improvement in daily gain, efficiency and cost of gain for pigs fed the diet containing Biopeptides.

In an interesting side development, pigs at the research facility where the trial was conducted contracted an unidentified virus during the second week of the trial. Pigs fed the Biopeptides showed a dramatic improvement (-0.52 lb feed/lb gain) in feed conversion efficiency during this week compared to pigs given plasma protein while maintaining higher daily gains, thereby producing a greater difference in cost of gain. These results are significant because many nutritionists consider plasma protein the additive of choice because of its potential to promote feed intake, especially during a time when intake could be expected to dip below normal due to health problems. The pigs on the plasma protein diets did consume 0.4 lb more feed per head during this week. However, the pigs fed the diets containing Biopeptides continued to improve growth rate relative to the first week. Pigs on the plasma protein diet did not show improved growth rate, possibly indicating a much greater utilization of the feed consumed when Biopeptides were included.

Table 1. Commercial performance: effect of substituting 1/3 of the spray-dried plasma protein in Phase 1 and complete replacement in Phase 2 (Trial 1).

Week 1 Treatments	6% Plasma protein	4% Plasma protein + 2% Biopeptides
No. pigs	99	97
Daily gain, lbs	0.312	0.307
Feed intake, lbs	222.5	210.5
Feed efficiency	1.03	1.02
Cost, $/lb gain	0.329	0.259
Week 2 Treatments	**3% Plasma protein**	**3% Biopeptides**
Daily gain, lbs	0.31	0.36
Feed efficiency	2.45	1.93
Cost/lb gain, USD	0.594	0.417
Week 3		
Daily gain, lbs	0.78	0.79
Feed efficiency	1.59	1.45
Cost/lb gain, USD	0.386	0.314
Week 2-3		
Daily gain, lbs	0.54	0.58
Feed efficiency	1.84	1.60
Cost/lb gain, USD	0.445	0.346
Weeks 1-3		
Daily gain, lbs	0.47	0.50
Total gain, lbs	9.93	10.45
Feed efficiency	1.63	1.46
Feed/head/day, lbs	0.77	0.73
Cost/lb gain, USD	0.402	0.316

Ferrell, 1999.

TRIAL 2: EFFECTS OF 5, 3.75 AND 2.75% PLASMA PROTEIN OR
BIOPEPTIDES IN PHASES 1-3

A second midwest feed company evaluated Biopeptides in an on-farm setting
utilizing 4000 commercial pigs. Pigs received a three diet sequence containing
either plasma or Biopeptides at 5, 3.75 and 2.5%, respectively, in Phases 1-
3 (Table 2, Robbins, 1999; personal communication). Pigs were placed on
test at an average weight of 12 lb and fed until reaching approximately 20 lb
on these diets, then were switched to a common diet containing neither
plasma nor Biopeptides, and fed to approximately 55 lb of body weight.
Pigs were only weighed at the beginning and end of the nursery phase.

Table 2. Dietary treatments in Trial 2.

	Biopeptides	Plasma protein
	(%)	
Prestarter	5	5
Starter 2	3.75	3.75
Starter 3	2.50	2.50
Phase 4+	0	0

Average daily gains were the same for both treatments; however, pigs fed
diets with Biopeptides consumed less feed resulting in improved feed
efficiency and lower cost of gain (Table 3). This study was not able to
separate treatment effects for the individual phases owing to weighing
procedures; however, the final summary demonstrated the potential of
biopeptides to provide equal or better performance when compared with
plasma under standard commercial conditions for the entire nursery period.

**Table 3. Commercial performance: effect of including either plasma protein or
Biopeptides on performance of pigs between 12 and 20 lbs (Trial 2).**

	Biopeptides	Plasma protein
Daily gain, lbs	0.89	0.89
Daily intake, lbs	0.58	1.65
Feed efficiency	1.77	1.85
Cost/100 lbs gain, USD	16.97	20.72

Robbins, 1999.

Controlled studies in research settings

TRIAL 1. REPLACEMENT OF PLASMA PROTEIN WITH BIOPEPTIDES IN
PHASES 1 AND 2

A 21 day evaluation of Biopeptides in nursery pigs was conducted at the
University of Manitoba. The trial utilized 144 Cotswold pigs weaned at an
average age of 16 days with average weight of 5.5 kg (12.1 lb). Dietary

351

treatments included either 6% spray-dried plasma protein or 6% Biopeptides in Phase 1 (days 16-23) with the test ingredients reduced to 3% during Phase 2 (days 23-27). Pigs fed diets containing Biopeptides consumed more feed, had higher rates of gain and lower feed conversion ratios in both phases of the trial (Table 4, Baidoo, 1999; personal communication). Pigs fed Biopeptides were 0.55 kg (1.2 lb) heavier after at the end of the three week period.

Table 4. Effects of plasma protein and Biopeptides on pig performance during Phases 1 and 2.

	Plasma protein	Biopeptides
Phase 1		
Intake, g/day	219	237
Gain, g/day	201	231
FCR	1.09	1.03
Phase 2		
Intake, g/day	435	443
Gain, g/day	340	364
FCR	1.28	1.22
Overall		
Intake, g/day	363	374
Total intake, kg	7.623	7.854
Gain, g/day	293.5	320.0
Total gain, kg	6.164	6.720
FCR	1.24	1.17

Baidoo, 1999

TRIAL 2. GRADED LEVELS OF BIOPEPTIDES AND PLASMA PROTEIN IN DIETS FED WEEKS 1-3 POST-WEANING

A trial conducted at the Ohio State University by Don Mahan investigated whether some combination of spray-dried plasma protein and Biopeptides would give better performance than either would individually. Eighty crossbred pigs weaned at an average age of 21 days (average weight of 12.9 lb) were used to evaluate several combinations of plasma protein and Biopeptides. Pigs were divided into four treatment groups for a 10 day Phase 1 period followed by a 14 day Phase 2 period. Treatments consisted of a positive control containing 6% plasma protein, 4% plasma protein plus 2% Biopeptides, 2% plasma protein plus 4% Biopeptides, and 6% Biopeptides. The basal diet contained 41.5 and 13.5% corn and soybean meal (48%) during Phase 1 and 42.5 and 21.0% corn and soybean meal in Phase 2. Dried whey and lactose were included at 20 and 10%, respectively, in Phase 1 and 15 and 10% during Phase 2. Phase 1 diets were formulated to contain 1.6% lysine. Phase 2 diets contained 1.45% lysine.

No significant differences were noted for daily gain, feed intake or feed efficiency between the protein sources during the initial two phases of the

352

post-weaning period (Table 5). Weaned pigs apparently utilized the protein sources equally well. In Phase 3 pigs were fed a common diet containing neither of the test protein sources for 14 days. No differences were noted for gain, intake or feed efficiency during this phase.

Table 5. Effect of protein source on pig performance.

Item	Biopeptides/spray-dried plasma protein (%)*				SEM	P
	100/0	66/33	33/66	0/100		
No. pigs	20	20	20	20		
Daily gain, g						
0 to 10 days post-weaning	220	213	187	217	16	.27
10 to 24 days	495	522	495	504	13	.51
Daily feed intake, g						
0 to 10 days post-weaning	310	297	270	303	20	.26
10 to 24 days	711	725	708	690	38	.65
Gain:feed, g/kg						
0 to 10 days post-weaning	732	729	693	716	23	.41
10 to 24 days	697	720	699	730	34	.42

*80 pigs in 5 replicates weaned at 21 days with 5.83 kg average initial weight.
Mahan, 1999.

TRIAL 3. GRADED LEVELS OF BIOPEPTIDES AND PLASMA PROTEIN IN DIETS FED WEEKS 1-3 POST-WEANING

An experiment with the same dietary treatments as the Ohio State study was conducted at Michigan State University by Trottier and co-workers. Ninety-six crossbred pigs were allotted in five replicates per treatment. Pigs in this trial were weaned between 14 and 24 days at an average initial weight of 6.12 kg (13.5 lb). No differences in performance were found at the end of the first two phases or for the three phases combined (Table 6). Average daily gains and gain to feed ratios were similar among all treatments.

Table 6. Effect of protein source on pig performance, overall summary.

Item	Biopeptides/plasma protein (%)*				SEM
	100/0	66/33	33/66	0/100	
No. pigs	24	24	24	24	
Daily gain, g	468	487	502	499	0.019
Daily feed intake, g	724	722	752	772	4.93
Gain:feed, g/kg	647	678	668	650	0.024

*96 pigs in 5 replicates weaned between 14 and 24 days with 6.12 average start wt.
Trottier *et al.*, 1999.

TRIAL 4. EFFECT OF BIOPEPTIDES IN BASAL DIETS WITHOUT PLASMA PROTEIN

A trial was conducted at Harper Adams University College in the UK to evaluate the effectiveness of Biopeptides in a basal diets that did not include plasma protein (Stewart, 1999). A total of 320 Cotswold pigs with an average age of 28 days and an average weight of 8.9 kg (19.6 lb) were used for this trial. Prior to weaning, all pigs had free access to a common creep diet. During Phase 1 (days 29-35) pigs received diets containing either 0 or 5% Biopeptides. The Phase 2 diet contained either 0 or 2.5% Biopeptides. Diets contained equal amounts of amino acids and energy. In this study, Biopeptides replaced portions of the fish meal and full fat soy protein.

Although differences were not statistically significant, numerical trends were evident (Table 7). In Phase 1, feed intake was increased by 25 g/day with the inclusion of Biopeptides; however, gain was 8 g/day less, resulting in a difference in feed conversion ratio. Feed intakes remained higher in phase 2, with gains also increasing for pigs fed diets containing Biopeptides. In the overall summary, pigs had higher intakes, increased gain and improved feed conversion ratios with the inclusion of Biopeptides.

Table 7. Effects of Biopeptides on pig performance during Phases 1 and 2.

	Control	Biopeptides
Phase 1		
Intake, g/day	249.5	274.7
Gain, g/day	173.3	165.5
FCR	1.44	1.66
Phase 2		
Intake, g/day	426.6	446.4
Gain, g/day	292.2	328.2
FCR	1.46	1.36
Overall (days 1-21)		
Intake, g/day	358.7	372.6
Total intake, kg	7.533	7.825
Gain, g/day	252.6	274.0
Total gain, kg	5.305	5.754
FCR	1.42	1.36

Stewart, 1999.

Summary

Following a year of testing the Biopeptides in commercial and research conditions, the data indicate that this product can not only replace some important traditional protein sources, including those of animal origin, but may in many cases be superior to these proteins for young pigs. Even in complex diets where nutritionists typically try to use a variety of animal-based proteins, the Biopeptides appear to be performing as well as or better than the animal-based counterparts. Biopeptides did not appear to enhance feed intake to the degree noted for plasma protein; however in the absence of plasma or using restricted amounts of plasma, Biopeptides may serve to boost intake. Since vegetable-based proteins do not have the same amino acid profile as animal products, it appears that supplying nitrogen to animal species in a peptide form offers exciting potential. Additional research is needed to better delineate the physiological mechanisms by which peptides enhance performance. The possibility that peptides may offer an even greater performance response during periods of health challenge also merits further investigation. In situations where certain animal proteins are deemed unsuitable for inclusion, this product would certainly seem to hold even greater promise for improving performance.

References

Baidoo, S.K. 1999. Evaluation of UP 1672 for early weaned pigs. Research report to Alltech. University of Manitoba, Canada.

Gardner, M.L.G. 1994. In: The Physiology of the Gastrointestinal Tract. (L.R. Johnson, ed.). Raven Press, New York, pp. 1795-1820.

Gardner, M.L.G. 1995. In: Absorption of Orally Administered Enzymes. (M.L.G. Gardner and K.J. Steffens, eds.). Springer-Verlag, Berlin, pp. 1-7.

Mahan, D.C. 1999. Comparison of plasma protein and ultimate protein in the diets of starter pigs. Report to Alltech. Ohio State University.

Power, R. and R. Murphy. 1999. Biologically active peptides: sources, production and nutritional importance. In: Biotechnology in the Feed Industry, Proceedings of Alltech's 15th Annual Symposium (T.P. Lyons and K.A. Jacques, eds.). Nottingham University Press, Nottingham, pp. 435-447.

Siemensma, A.D., W.J. Weijer and H.J. Bak. 1993. The importance of peptide lengths in hypoallergenic infant formulae. Trends Food Sci. Technol. 4:16-21.

Stewart, A. 1999. Biological peptides for weanling pigs. Research report to Alltech. Harper Adams University College, UK.

Trottier, N., E. Otto and J. Perez-Laspiur. 1999. Tri State Weanling Pig Project. Replacement of starter protein source. Unpublished. Michigan State University.

Webb, K.E. 2000. Peptide absorption. Presented at the Virginia State Feed Association Meeting. Feb.16-17. Hot Springs, VA.

Webb, K.E. and J.C. Matthews. 1998. Peptide absorption and its significance in ruminant protein metabolism. In: Peptides in Mammalian Protein Metabolism. (G.K. Grimble and F.R.C. Backwell, eds.). Portland Press, London, pp. 1-10.

Webb, K.E., J.C. Matthews and D.B. DiRenzo. 1992. Peptide absorption: A review of current concepts and future perspectives. J. Anim. Sci. 70:3248-3257.

Peptide absorption: where peptides fit in protein nutrition and metabolism

JAMES C. MATTHEWS

University of Kentucky, Lexington, Kentucky, USA

Introduction

Research over the last 30 years has demonstrated that the absorption of amino acids in the form of oligopeptides (principally di- to tri-peptides) constitutes the most quantitatively important form of amino acid uptake from digesta by gut epithelia (Matthews and Adibi, 1976; Steinhardt and Adibi, 1986; Matthews, 1991; Seal and Parker 1991; Webb *et al.*, 1992; Koeln *et al.*, 1993; Gardner, 1994) and physiologically important amounts from glomerular filtrate by renal epithelia (Daniel *et al.*, 1992; Adibi, 1997). In contrast, quantitatively important amounts of intact oligopeptide absorption by liver and skeletal muscle is thought not to occur (Adibi, 1997), whereas the physiological significance and form of circulating peptides to support the function of other peripheral tissues is under investigation (Kee *et al.*, 1994; Backwell, 1998; Webb and Matthews, 1998; Dieck *et al.*, 1999; Power and Murphy, 1999). Given the significance of peptide absorption to whole-animal protein nutrition, an understanding of the mechanisms by which peptides are absorbed, where they are expressed, and the potential to regulate these events, is of fundamental importance to nutritionists.

Peptide absorption mechanisms

The expression of proteins that are capable of recognizing and transporting peptide-bound amino acids across cellular membranes appears to be a universal phenomenon; Gram-negative and Gram-positive bacteria, fungi, the seeds of many cereal grains, round worms, fruit flies, and many types of animal cells have been shown to be capable of intact peptide absorption. From the pioneering work of David Matthews (Matthews, 1991), Siamak Adibi (Adibi, 1997), and Fredrick Leibach and Vadivel Ganapathy (Ganapathy *et al.*, 1994; Leibach and Ganapathy, 1996) we now understand that digesta and plasma proteins do not need to be completely hydrolyzed to their constituent amino acids for absorption to occur by discrete transport proteins. Owing to the work of these and many other researchers, three peptide transport activities have been biochemically characterized in mammals: 1) a low-affinity transport system that is highly expressed in the apical membranes of differentiated enterocytes, which also is weakly expressed in the microvillus membrane of kidney tubule epithelia, 2) a high-affinity transport capacity primarily expressed in the apical membranes of kidney proximal tubules epithelia, and 3) a low-affinity system on the basolateral membranes of polarized cell types that displays a more limited range of transport capacity than the low-affinity apical transporters.

From this understanding, a generalized model (Ganapathy *et al.*, 1994) has emerged to account for how peptide-bound amino acids are absorbed across mammalian polarized epithelia: 1) peptides are recognized and trans-located through the apical membrane into the cell cytosol by a H^+-coupled, concentrative, low-affinity, high-capacity transporter, 2) hydrolysis of the peptide to free amino acids occurs, followed by transport into the blood by amino acid transporters, or 3) passage of intact peptides across the basolateral membrane into the blood is achieved by a high-affinity, low-capacity membrane transporter (Ganapathy *et al.*, 1994; Adibi, 1997; Steel *et al.*, 1997). Currently under investigation is whether the basolateral transporter is H^+-dependent (Thwaites *et al.*, 1993) or a facilitative (Terada *et al.*, 1999) transporter. The proportion of peptides that actually survive transepithelial passage from the lumen into the blood is typically estimated as 10 to 20% for enterocytes (Ganapathy *et al.*, 1994) and virtually 0% for renal absorptive cells (Adibi, 1997). In ruminant forestomach tissue, a single report for one peptide (methionylglycine) suggests that omasal tissue has a greater ability to hydrolyze absorbed peptides (95%) than does ruminal epithelium (64%) (Matthews and Webb, 1995). In terms of energy expenditure, the H^+/peptide cotransport is classified as a tertiary transporter (Ganapathy *et al.*, 1994). That is, after H^+ are cotransported with small peptides across the apical membranes of enterocytes and released into the cytoplasm by the H^+/peptide cotransporter, H^+ are then pumped out of the cell by the apical membrane-bound Na^+/H^+ exchanger (driven by the extracellular-to-intracellular Na^+ gradient), thereby reestablishing the extracellular-to-intracellular H^+ gradient. The activity of the basalateral Na^+/K^+ ATPase then reestablishes the high extracellular-to-intracellular Na^+ gradient with the expenditure of ATP.

The cloning of nucleic acid sequences that encode peptide transporters has clarified several apparent anomalies that existed between the low-affinity, high-capacity transport activity that predominates in the intestinal epithelia and the high-affinity/lower-capacity activity that predominates in renal tissue. PepT1 (<u>Pep</u>tide <u>T</u>ransporter <u>1</u>; 707 amino acid polypeptide for rabbit and 708 amino acids for human) complementary (c) DNA encodes a low-affinity, high-capacity transporter that is predicted to contain one relatively large cytosolic domain and twelve alpha-helical membrane-spanning domains (Fei *et al.*, 1994). PepT2 (Liu *et al.*, 1995) cDNA encodes for a high-affinity, low-capacity transporter that is predicted to consist of 729 amino acids and possess 12 membrane-spanning domains (Leibach and

Ganapathy, 1996). The amino acid sequences for human PepT1 and PepT2 share 50% identity, with the majority of the homology existing in the membrane-spanning regions.

When the putative basolateral peptide transporter (Thwaites *et al.*, 1993) is cloned, of particular interest will be whether the transporter functions to couple H^+ to pump peptides out of the cell or as a facilitative transporter, whereby substrate concentration gradients will drive transport. In accordance with the biochemically defined H^+/peptide cotransport activity, functional expression of PepT1 or PepT2 in various experimental models has shown that maximal peptide uptake occurs in the presence of an extracellular pH of 5.5 to 6.0. However, significant (25 to 50%) peptide uptake does occur from pH 6.0 to 7.0. With regard to the stoichiometry of H^+/peptide cotransport, expression studies have shown that the number of H^+ required for peptide transport across the apical membrane of enterocytes depends on the charge of the substrate. For example, PepT1 displays H^+:substrate ratios of 1:1, 2:1, and 1:1 for neutral, acidic and basic dipeptides, respectively (Steel *et al.*, 1997), whereas PepT2 displays H^+:substrate ratios of 2:1 and 3:1 for neutral and basic substrates (Chen *et al.*, 1999b). Whether acidic peptides are relatively less well recognized in the presence of a lower pH than are neutral or basic dipeptides, has not been definitively established, as evidenced by the contradictory data from whole tissue (Lister *et al.*, 1997) versus *in vitro* (Brandsch *et al.*, 1997) studies.

A salient, and potentially useful feature of peptide transporters to nutritionists and pharmacologists alike, is the ability of PepT1 and PepT2 to recognize a wide variety of substrates. This relatively high degree of transport 'promiscuity' is thought to result from the need to potentially recognize over four hundred dipeptides and 8000 tripeptides that result from the digestion of 'typical' proteins (Ganapathy *et al.*, 1994). Consistent with the relatively few transport systems that have been identified for peptide transport, recognition by these 'promiscuous' transporters has been proposed to be achieved with an oligopeptide of four or less amino acids that contains at least one peptide bond, a carboxy- terminal 'L' conformer amino acid, and an overall net positive charge of less than two (Boyd, 1995). Accordingly, ß-lactam and cephalosporin antibiotics are substrates for peptide transport systems. Recently, however, even the requirement for a peptide bond has been questioned (Ganapathy *et al.*, 1998). Despite these relatively flexible requirements for recognition, substantial differences exist in substrate binding affinities among peptide transporters (Brandsch *et al.*, 1998; for a summary of K_m values see Matthews, 2000).

Expression of peptide transporter activity and mRNA

As noted earlier, the seminal research by Matthews and Adibi has resulted in the acceptance that a substantial portion, and likely the majority, of amino acids are absorbed from intestinal digesta in the form of oligopeptides, rather than as free amino acids. Given what we know about the biochemical and molecular characterization of cloned peptide transporters, it is also accepted that the mechanism of peptide absorption primarily is by PepT1, with, perhaps, some contribution by PepT2. Consistent with this understanding, rabbit PepT1 mRNA expression is greatest by epithelial cells of the small intestine, especially the jejunum, less by the liver and kidney tissue, and least by several brain tissues (Fei *et al.*, 1994). In rats, PepT1 mRNA expression by duodenal, jejunal, and ileal epithelia is reported to be equal (Erickson *et al.*, 1995). However, immunohistochemical analysis indicates that whereas PepT1 is expressed in all small intestinal epithelia, it is most abundant in the jejunum of rats (Ogihara *et al.*, 1999). Similar to the localization of SGLT1 (Na$^+$-dependent) and GLUT2 (Na$^+$-independent) glucose transporters, PepT1 protein is most abundant in the villus tip, decreasing in concentration into the crypt, but absent from goblet cells and undifferentiated basal cells (Ogihara *et al.*, 1999). This localization of greatest PepT1 mRNA content in the villus tip is consistent with the identification of the villus tip as being the site of greatest PepT1 activity in rabbits (Tomita *et al.*, 1995).

In contrast to the pattern for PepT1 expression, rabbit PepT2 mRNA expression was greatest by the kidney, and weaker by brain, lung, liver, heart and spleen tissues (Boll *et al.*, 1996). The dual expression of PepT1 and PepT2 in the kidney is consistent with the biochemically defined high- and low-affinity peptide transport systems (Daniel *et al.*, 1992). The concentration of peptides is thought to increase from the proximal to distal nephron as a result of the high apical membrane-bound peptidase activity of renal absorptive cells (Adibi, 1997). Accordingly, future immunohistochemical research is expected to reveal that PepT1 is expressed predominately in the distal region of nephrons while PepT2 will be primarily expressed in the proximal nephron region (Leibach and Ganapathy, 1996).

There is little biochemical evidence to indicate that muscle tissue possesses the capacity for H$^+$/peptide cotransport (Ganapathy *et al.*, 1994; Adibi, 1997). A recent negative examination (Chen *et al.*, 1999a) of skeletal muscle for PepT1 mRNA expression in pig, chicken, sheep and cattle supports this concept. In the liver, the ability and degree to which peptides are absorbed is controversial. Despite the detection of PepT1 mRNA in rabbit liver, and the demonstration of mediated uptake of carnosine and glycylsarcosine in hamster liver slices (Matthews, 1991), the quantitative importance of hepatic peptide absorption is challenged by the observation that rat hepatocytes were incapable of absorbing dipeptides that are less resistant to hydrolysis than glycylsarcosine and carnosine (Lochs *et al.*, 1986). Instead, it is proposed that the absorption of peptide-bound amino acids occurs only after hydrolysis to their constituent amino acids. These discrepancies could be the result of species-specific differences or, alternatively, the expression of transporter protein may be limited to membranes other than the plasma membrane. In support of this hypothesis, low-affinity peptide transport activity has been demonstrated in the lysosomal membranes of rat hepatocytes using glycylglutamine (Thamotharan *et al.*, 1996).

360

Compared to humans and laboratory species, little is known about the specific biochemical activities and mechanisms responsible for the absorption of peptides by farm animal species. However, it has been known for a number of years that peptide absorption accounts for a substantial component of the total amino acid absorption by the gastrointestinal tract of chickens (Duke, 1984). H^+/peptide cotransport activity has been measured in brush border membranes of the small intestine, ceca, and rectum of chicks (Calonge *et al.*, 1990). Consistent with the identification of H^+/peptide transport activity in the small intestine, but not with that of the ceca and colon, Northern blot analysis has identified the presence of PepT1 mRNA in duodenal (primarily), jejunal, and ileal epithelia, but not in other gastrointestinal tissue of White leghorns and broilers (Chen *et al.*, 1999a). For pigs, *in vivo* research suggests that amino acids are more readily absorbed as oligopeptides than as free amino acids (Rerat *et al.*, 1992). The dual expression of PepT1 mRNA and H^+-dependent peptide uptake capacity by jejunal tissue of growing (27 to 100 kg) pigs (Winckler *et al.*, 1999) suggests that the capacity for porcine small intestinal uptake of oligopeptides is through the functioning of PepT1.

As a corollary to arterial-venous flux studies that indicate nutritionally significant amounts of oligopeptides are absorbed across the gastrointestinal tract of sheep and cattle (Seal and Parker, 1991; Webb *et al*, 1992, Koeln *et al.*, 1993; Webb and Matthews, 1998), ruminants should possess H^+/peptide cotransport activities and proteins in mesenteric- and non-mesenteric-drained epithelia. With regard to the potential mechanism of intestinal absorption, preliminary reports indicated that epithelia of the ruminant small intestine express both PepT1- and PepT2-like functional activity. Using brush border membranes isolated from duodenal epithelium of sheep, a K_m value of 0.005 mM for Gly-Pro was observed (Backwell *et al.*, 1995), consistent with substrate affinity constants typically reported for high-affinity/low-capacity transport by PepT2. Uptake velocities measured for peptide transport by proximal intestinal tissue of sheep and cattle (Dyer *et al.*, 1996), however, are consistent with those reported for low-affinity, high capacity PepT1 transport activity. The findings that jejunal and ileal brush border membranes of cattle express glycylsarcosine affinity constants of 1.3 and .93 mM (Wolffram *et al.*, 1998), and that cattle duodenal, jejunal, and ileal epithelial tissues express PepT1 mRNA (Chen *et al.*, 1999a), provide strong corroborating evidence that bovine small intestinal epithelium possesses PepT1 transport activity.

The study of the capacity of forestomach tissues (rumen, reticulum, omasum) to absorb peptides is complicated by the structural arrangement of their keratinized, stratified squamous epithelia. However, given that 1) the typical acidity of the rumen liquor is sufficient to drive transport of peptides by PepT1 or PepT2, 2) Na^+/H^+ exchanger and Na^+/K^+ ATPase proteins essential for reestablishing H^+ gradients in epithelial cells exist and function in both ruminal and omasal epithelia, and 3) that the forestomach liquor contains significant amounts of small peptides (for a summary see Matthews *et al.*, 1996a), it is not surprising that recent research discovered that forestomach epithelia do possess the ability to absorb small peptides. That dipeptides were capable of intact passage across the complex forestomach epithelium initially was demonstrated by the transepithelial passage of intact carnosine and methionylglycine across sheep ruminal and omasal epithelial sheets mounted parabiotic chambers (Matthews and Webb, 1995). That absorption probably was the result of mediated transport is indicated by detection of mRNA capable of encoding PepT1-like activity using functional expression studies with *Xenopus laevis* oocyte studies (Matthews *et al.*, 1996b; Pan *et al.*, 1997). Subsequently, a partial-length cDNA that shared nucleic acid sequence homology to rabbit, rat, and human PepT1 cDNAs was cloned from omasal mRNA and used to detect the expression of PepT1 mRNA in both rumen and omasal epithelia (Chen *et al.*, 1999a).

Regulation of H$^+$/peptide cotransport capacity

Given the importance of H$^+$/peptide transport activity to total amino acid absorption, it is of immense interest to understand whether PepT1 transport capacity can be regulated. However, research investigating the ability of dietary substrates to alter peptide absorption capacity is limited. In mice fed a high-protein (72%) versus low-protein (18%) diet, peptide uptake capacity was increased 30 to 70% in duodenal and jejunal, but not ileal, tissue (Ferraris *et al.*, 1988). However, when equal amounts of a 54% non-hydrolyzed, partially-hydrolyzed, or completely hydrolyzed casein diet were fed, no difference in peptide uptake capacity was observed. The ability of dietary protein content to directly modulate PepT1 expression has been investigated by comparing the amount of PepT1 mRNA expressed in small intestinal epithelia collected from rats fed a diet that contained 17.5% casein (control diet) for seven days to that by rats fed an isocaloric diet that contained 50% gelatin (high protein diet) for 14 days (Erickson *et al.*, 1995). The amount of PepT1 mRNA was increased about 2-fold in the mid and proximal small intestinal epithelia of rats fed the high-protein diet. Subsequently, the potential for substrate stimulation of PepT1 that was independent of hormonal influences, and by a single substrate, was evaluated using Caco-2 cells (Walker *et al.*, 1998). The culture of cells in glutaminylglutamate media for three days resulted in a 1.6-fold increase in H$^+$-dependent peptide transport that was accompanied by a 2-fold increase in both PepT1 mRNA and protein. Overall, the study demonstrated that the increase in peptide transport capacity was the result of an increased rate of mRNA transcription and mRNA stability. Although limited, these data, generated from a variety of experimental models, suggest that peptide transport capacity is sensitive to substrate regulation.

Besides evaluating the effects of increased substrate supply on peptide transport capacity, the effect of dietary substrate deprivation (fasting) on

PepT1 expression has been investigated. In rats fasted for one day, peptide uptake capacity increased 2-fold, concomitant with a 3-fold increase in PepT1 mRNA in intestinal mucosa and PepT1 protein in its apical membranes (Thamotharan *et al.*, 1999b). Accordingly, fasting appeared to stimulate a general increase in PepT1 gene expression. These results are consistent with another study that found that the influence of a longer (4-day) fast was to increase the amount of PepT1 protein present in the villus tips of jejunal tissue of fasted rats, as compared to rats fed normal amounts of rat chow (Ogihara *et al.*, 1999). In contrast, however, when fasted rats were given a liquid free amino acid supplement, the jejunal expression of PepT1 protein was reduced. This observed ability of the presence of free amino acids to down-regulate peptide transport capacity merits further investigation to determine whether this is a general response, or one that is restricted to the employed experimental regimen.

The potential regulation of peptide transport capacity by hormones has been studied using Caco-2 cells. Physiological levels of insulin stimulated the 'recruitment' of previously synthesized PepT1 proteins from cytoplasmic stores, in a manner apparently analogous to the insulin-dependent stimulation of facilitated glucose transport activity (Thamotharan *et al.*, 1999a). Accordingly, insulin-dependent stimulation of PepT1 activity appears to be a transcription- and *de novo* protein synthesis-independent, but microtubule-dependent process. If *in vivo* studies confirm these results, then it is very likely that PepT1 activity in intestinal epithelia can be rapidly modulated in response to substrate availability. In contrast, upregulation of PepT1 activity in Caco-2 cells through stimulation of σ_1 receptors (Fujita *et al.*, 1999) is concomitant with an increase in PepT1 mRNA. Although not fully characterized, progesterone is thought to be a ligand for σ_1 receptors. Accordingly, it is speculated that toward late gestation, when nutrient demands are elevated for prolonged periods, that increased progesterone levels act to stimulate the capacity for amino acid absorption by increasing peptide transport capacity.

Conclusions

The absorption of amino acids as oligopeptides constitutes the greatest form of amino acid absorption by gastrointestinal tissues. PepT1 is the primary transporter responsible for this H^+-coupled activity and is predominately expressed in the villus tips of small intestinal tissue of mammals. In addition, the evidence is strong for PepT1 expression in forestomach epithelia of ruminants. PepT2 is the principle peptide transporter expressed in the proximal tubules, where it functions to resorb peptides from the glomerular filtrate. There is little evidence to suggest that liver or skeletal muscle absorbs intact peptides. Though limited, initial studies indicate that expression of PepT1-mediated peptide absorption capacity is highly sensitive to substrate surfeit, substrate deficit, and hormonal factors. Unresolved questions regarding peptide absorption include: 1) what is the capacity for peptide-bound versus free amino acid uptake by the gastrointestinal epithelia, 2) can this capacity be regulated *in vivo* by diet and (or) feeding regimens, and, if so, 3) will increasing the amount of peptide-bound amino acids achieve greater amino acid absorption efficiencies, and 4) is the development and use of 'model' peptides and (or) protein hydrolysates to potentiate peptide absorption capacity economically feasible.

References

Adibi, S.A. 1997. Renal assimilation of oligopeptide: physiological mechanisms and metabolic importance. Am. J. Physiol. 272, E723-E736.

Backwell, F.R.C. 1998. Circulating peptides and their role in milk protein synthesis. In: Peptides in Mammalian Protein Metabolism: Tissue Utilization and Clinical Targeting. (G.K. Grimble and F.R.C. Backwell, eds.). Portland Press, London, 69-77.

Backwell, C., D. Wilson and A. Schweizer. 1995. Evidence for a glycyl-proline transport system in ovine enterocyte brush-border membrane vesicles. Biochem. Biophys. Res. Com. 215:561-565.

Boll, M., M. Herget, M. Wagener, W.M. Weber, D. Markovich, J. Biber, D.F. Clayton, H. Murer and H. Daniel. 1996. Expression cloning and functional characterization of the kidney cortex high-affinity proton-coupled peptide transporter. Proc. Nat. Acad. Sci. USA 93: 284-289.

Boyd, C.A.R. 1995. Intestinal oligopeptide transport. Proc. Nutr. Soc. 54:519-523.

Brandsch, M., C. Brandsch, M.E. Ganapathy, C.S. Chew, V. Ganapathy and F.H. Leibach. 1997. Influence of proton and essential histidyl residues on the transport kinetics of the H^+/peptide cotransport systems in intestine (PEPT1) and kidney (PEPT2). Biochim. Biophys. Acta 1324:251-262.

Brandsch, M., F. Thunecke, G. Kuller, M. Schutkowski, G. Fischer and K. Neubert. 1998. Evidence for the absolute conformational specificity of the intestinal H^+/peptide symporter, PEPT1. J. Biol. Chem. 273:3861-3864.

Calonge, M. L., A. Ilundain and J. Bolufer. 1990. Glycyl-L-sarcosine transport by ATP-depleted isolated enterocytes from chicks. Am. J. Physiol. 259:G775-G780.

Chen, H., E.A. Wong and K.E. Webb, Jr. 1999a. Tissue distribution of a peptide transporter mRNA in sheep, dairy cows, pigs, and chickens. J. Anim. Sci. 77:1277-1283.

Chen , X.-Z., T. Zhu, D.E. Smith and M.A. Hediger. 1999b. Stoichiometry and kinetics of the high-affinity H^+-coupled peptide transporter PepT2. J. Biol. Chem. 274:2773-2779.

Daniel, H., E.L. Morse and S.A. Adibi. 1992. The high and low affinity transport systems for dipeptides in kidney brush border membrane respond differently to alterations in pH gradient and membrane potential. J. Biol. Chem. 266, 19917-19924.

Dieck, S.T., H. Heurer, J. Ehrchen, C. Otto and K. Bauer. 1999. The peptide transporter PepT2 is expressed in the rat brain and mediates the accumulation of fluorescent dipeptide derivative b-Ala-Lys-N-AMCA in astrocytes. GLIA 25:10-20.

Duke, G. E. 1984. Avian Digestion. In: Dukes' Physiology of Domestic Animals. (M. J. Swenson, ed.). Cornell University Press, Ithaca, Vol.10th, 359-366.

Dyer, J., G. Allison, N.D. Scollan and S.P. Shirazi-Beechey. 1996. Mechanism of peptide transport in ruminant intestinal brush-border membrane. Biochem. Soc. Trans. 24:247S.

Erickson, R.H., J.R. Gum, M.M. Lindstrom, D. McKean and Y.S. Kim. 1995. Regional expression and dietary regulation of rat small intestinal peptide and amino acid transporter mRNAs. Biochem. Biophysi. Res. Com. 216:249-257.

Fei, Y.-J.,Y. Kanai, S. Nussberger, V. Ganapathy, F.H. Leibach, M.F. Romero, S.K. Singh, W.F. Boron and M.A. Hediger. 1994. Expression cloning of a mammalian proton-coupled oligopeptide transporter. Nature 368: 563-566.

Ferraris, R.P., J. Diamond and W.W. Kwan. 1988. Dietary regulation of intestinal transport of the dipeptide carnosine. Am. J. Physiol. 255:G143-G150.

Fujita, T., Y. Majikawa, S. Umeshisa, N. Okada, A. Yamamoto, V. Ganapathy and F.H. Leibach. 1999. σ Receptor ligand-induced up-regulation of the H^+/peptide transporter PEPT1 in the human intestinal cell line Caco-2. Biochem. Biophys. Res. Com. 261:242-246.

Ganapathy, M.E., W. Huang, V. Ganapathy and F.H. Leibach. 1998. Valacyclovir: a substrate for the intestinal and renal peptide transporters PEPT1 and PEPT2. Biochem. Biophys. Res. Com. 246:470-475.

Ganapathy, V., M. Brandsch and F.H. Leibach. 1994. Intestinal transport of amino acids and peptides. In: Physiology of the Gastrointestinal Tract. (L.R. Johnson, ed.). 3rd edn., Raven Press, New York, 1773-1794.

Gardner, M.L.G. 1994. Absorption of intact proteins and peptides. In: Physiology of the Gastrointestinal Tract. (L. R. Johnson, ed.). 3rd edn, Raven Press, New York, 1795-1820.

Kee, A.J., R.C. Smith, A.S. Gross, D.C. Madsen and B. Rowe. 1994. The effect of dipeptide structure on dipeptide and amino acid clearance in rats. Metabolism 43:1373-1378.

Koeln, L.L., T.S. Schlagheck and K.E. Webb, Jr. 1993. Amino acid flux across the gastrointestinal tract and liver of calves. J. Dairy Sci. 76:2275-2285.

Leibach, F.H. and V. Ganapathy. 1996. Peptide transporters in the intestine and the kidney. Ann. Rev. Nutr. 16:99-119.

Lister, N., P.D. Bailey, I.D. Collier, C.A.R. Boyd and J.R. Bronk. 1997. The influence of luminal pH on transport of neutral and charged dipeptides by rat small intestine, *in vitro*. Biochim. Biophys. Acta 1324:245-250.

Lochs, H., E.L. Morse and S.A. Adibi. 1986. Mechanism of hepatic assimilation of dipeptides. J. Biol. Chem. 261:14976-14981.

Lui, W., R. Liang, S. Ramamoorthy, Y.-J. Fei, M.E. Ganapathy, M.A. Hediger, V. Ganapathy and F.H. Leibach. 1995. Molecular cloning of PepT2, a new member of the H+/peptide cotransporter family, from human kidney. Biochim. Biophys. Acta 1235:461-466.

Matthews, D.E. 1991. Protein Absorption. Development and Present State of the Subject. Wiley-Liss, New York.

Matthews, J.C. 2000. Amino acid and peptide transport systems. In: Farm Animal Metabolism and Nutrition: Critical Reviews. (J.P.F. D'Mello, ed.). CABI Publishing, Wallingford, 3-23.

Matthews, D.E. and S.A. Adibi. 1976. Peptide absorption. Gastroenterology 71:151-161.

Matthews, J.C. and K.E. Webb, Jr. 1995. Absorption of L-carnosine, L-methionine, and L-methionylglycine by isolated sheep ruminal and omasal epithelial tissue. J. Anim. Sci. 73:3464-3475.

Matthews, J.C., Y.L. Pan, S. Wang, M.Q. McCollum and K.E. Webb, Jr. 1996a. Characterization of gastrointestinal amino acid and peptide transport proteins and the utilization of peptides as amino acid substrates by cultured cells (myogenic and mammary) and mammary tissue explants. In: Nutrient Management of Food Animals to Enhance and Protect the Environment. (E.T. Kornegay, ed.). CRC Press, Inc., Boca Raton, 55-72.

Matthews, J.C., E.A. Wong, P.K. Bender, J.R. Bloomquist and K.E. Webb, Jr. 1996b. Demonstration and characterization of dipeptide transport system activity in sheep omasal epithelium by expression of mRNA in *Xenopus laevis* oocytes. J. Anim. Sci. 74:1720-1727.

Ogihara, H., T. Suzuki, Y. Nagamachi, K. Inui and K. Takata. 1999. Peptide transporter in the rat small intestine: ultrastructural localization and the effect of starvation and administration of amino acids. Histochem. J. 31:169-174.

Pan, Y. X., E.A. Wong, J.R. Bloomquist and K.E. Webb, Jr. 1997. Poly(A)+ RNA from sheep omasal epithelium induces expression of a peptide transport protein(s) in *Xenopus laevis* oocytes. J. Anim. Sci. 75:3323-3330.

Power, R. and R. Murphy. 1999. Biologically active peptides: sources, production and nutritional importance. In: Biotechnology in the feed industry. Proceedings of Alltech's Fifteenth Annual Symposium. (T.P. Lyons and K.A. Jacques, eds.). Nottingham University Press, Nottingham, 435-447.

Rerat, A., C. Simoes-Nunes, F. Mendy, P. Vaissade and P. Vaugelade. 1992. Splanchnic fluxes of amino acids after duodenal infusion of carbohydrate solutions containing free amino acids or oligopeptides in the non-anaesthetized pig. Br. J. Nutr. 68:111-138.

Seal, C.J. and D.S. Parker. 1991. Isolation and characterization of low molecular weight peptides in steer, sheep and rat portal and peripheral blood. Comp. Biochem. Physiol. 99: 679-685.

Steel, A., S. Nussberger, M.F. Romero, W.F. Boron, R.C.A. Boyd and M.A. Hediger. 1997. Stoichiometry and pH dependence of the rabbit proton-dependent oligopeptide transporter PepT1. J. Physiol. 498:563-569.

Steinhardt, H.J. and S.A. Adibi. 1986. Kinetics and characterization of absorption from an equimolar mixture of 12 glycyl-dipeptides in human jejunum. Gastroenterology 90:577-582.

Terada, T., K. Sawada, H. Saito, Y. Hashimoto and K.I. Inui. 1999. Functional characterization of basolateral peptide transporter in the human intestinal cell line Caco-2. Am. J. Physiol. 276:G1435-G1441.

Thamotharan, M., Y.B. Lombardo, S.Z. Bawani and S.A. Adibi. 1996. An active mechanism for completion of the final stage of protein degradation in the liver, lysosomal transport of dipeptides. J. Biol. Chem. 272:11786-11790.

Thamotharan, M., S.Z. Bawani, X. Zhou and S.A. Adibi. 1999a. Hormonal regulation of oligopeptide transporter Pept-1 in a human intestinal cell line. Am. J. Physiol. 276:C821-C826.

Thamotharan, M., S.Z. Bawani, X. Zhou and S.A. Adibi. 1999b. Functional and molecular expression of intestinal oligopeptide transporter (Pept-1) after a brief fast. Metabolism 6:681-684.

Thwaites, D.T., C.D. Brown, B.H. Hurst and N.L. Simmons. 1993. H(+)-coupled dipeptide (glycylsarcosine) transport across apical and basal borders of human intestinal Caco-2 cell monolayers display distinctive characteristics. Biochim. Biophys. Acta 1151:237-245.

Tomita, Y., M. Takano, M. Yasuhara, R. Hori and K. Inui. 1995. Transport of oral cepholasporins by the H^+/dipeptide cotransporter and distribution of the transport activity in isolated rabbit intestinal epithelial cells. J. Pharmacol. Exp. Ther. 272:63-69.

Walker, D., D.T. Thwaites, N.L. Simmons, H.J. Gilbert and B.H. Hirst. 1998. Substrate regulation of the human small intestinal peptide transporter, hPepT1. J. Physiol. 507:697-706.

Webb, K.E., Jr. J.C. Matthews and D.B. DiRienzo. 1992. Peptide absorption: a review of current concepts and and future perspectives. J. Anim. Sci. 70:3248-3257.

Webb, K.E., Jr. and J.C. Matthews. 1998. Peptide absorption and its significance in ruminant protein metabolism. Peptides in Mammalian Protein Metabolism: Tissue Utilization and Clinical Targeting. (G. Grimbel and C. Backwell, eds). Portland Press Ltd., London, 1-10.

Winckler, C., G. Breves, M. Boll and H. Daniel. 1999. Characteristics of dipeptide transport in pig jejunum *in vitro*. J. Comp. Physiol. B 169:495-500.

Wolffram, S., B. Grenacher and E. Scharrer. 1998. H^+-coupled uphill transport of the dipeptide glycylsarcosine by bovine intestinal brush-border membrane vesicles. J. Dairy Sci. 81:2595-2603.

The biochemistry behind esterified glucomannans – titrating mycotoxins out of the diet

KYLE NEWMAN

Venture Laboratories, Inc., Lexington, Kentucky, USA

Introduction: mold growth

As we learn more about mycotoxins and make new discoveries in this area, we begin to realize that there are many unanswered questions involving these toxins. Mycotoxins are produced by molds, which are aerobic unicellular organisms. Mold growth can occur in environments that contain lower available water than would be needed to support bacterial growth. For example, bread will support mold growth but not bacterial growth under normal conditions. Just as there are beneficial bacteria and pathogenic bacteria, not all molds produce mycotoxins. Mycotoxins are produced by certain molds and are considered a secondary metabolite of mold growth. This means that mycotoxin production occurs late in the growth phase of a mold and is usually associated with some aspect of mold strain survival. Controlling mold growth is an important first step in controlling mycotoxins. This can be best accomplished by:

1)	*Low feed moisture.* Ideally moisture levels should not exceed 12%.

2)	*Keeping feed fresh.* Mold growth takes time; and storage time before mold growth occurs depends on ambient temperature and oxygen levels in feed.

3)	*Keeping equipment clean.* Hazard Analysis of Critical Control Points (HACCP) not only controls pathogenic bacteria but is a major step in reducing mold and mycotoxin growth in hard-to-reach areas of feed preparation equipment.

4)	*Keeping the grain intact until adequately dried.* Mold growth is more prevalent in damaged or processed grains.

5)	*Using mold inhibitors.* Propionic acid-based products are very effective for mold inhibition, but will do nothing to mycotoxins. Buffered propionic acid has the advantage of being less caustic to equipment and more stable and effective for a longer period of time than acid salts or free acids. The reason for this is that when properly buffered, the acid dissociates when exposed to moisture in the feed. This prevents volatilization of the propionic acid in storage before being applied. It also allows more consistent and longer lasting mold inhibition.

Moisture in feed comes from several sources; improperly dried feed ingredients, feed manufacturing processing, and environmental storage conditions. Controlling moisture in feed manufacturing is a critical step. Heat from grinding can cause the migration and external concentration of moisture. This is important since, although it does not affect the total moisture of the feed, it causes a 'dry inside and wet outside' phenomenon that can contribute to mold growth. Pelleting also involves heat and moisture addition to the feed. In the pelleting process 3-5% moisture is added to the feed. If cooling conditions are improper, moisture is not allowed to dissipate leading to favorable conditions for molds. When done properly, pelleting is effective in reducing mold concentrations in the feed. Reductions of near 10,000-fold have been observed in pelleted feed compared to the same feed in mash form.

After the feed is manufactured, it is necessary to maintain conditions antagonistic to mold growth. It is necessary to eliminate sources of moisture in the handling and storage of feed. Low moisture feed can pick up moisture in humid conditions unless stored in sealed packaging. Equipment cleanliness is paramount to controlling mold growth since contaminated surfaces can inoculate otherwise 'clean' feed.

Mycotoxins in feed

Although the global nature of the feed market limits the ability to pinpoint ingredient region of origin, mycotoxin prevalence is somewhat regional. Aflatoxin and certain ochratoxins are primarily found in tropical and subtropical regions. Zearalenone, deoxynivalenol (DON or vomitoxin), ochratoxin A, T-2, and fumonisin are most notable in temperate regions.

AFLATOXIN

Aflatoxin can cause liver damage, decreased reproductive performance, reduced milk production, embryonic death, birth defects, tumors and suppressed immune function. Most food and feedstuff are free of aflatoxin at time of harvest. The exceptions to this rule are cotton, corn, and groundnuts such as peanuts. Corn is infected in the field where ears are subjected to insect attack followed by invasion and infection with *Aspergillus flavus* and the subsequent formation of aflatoxins. Cereal grains harvested at high moisture content such as rice and corn must be dried before they can be safely stored. In climates where humidity is high and drying and storage facilities are poor, aflatoxin risk may be high. Many species of Aspergillus grow slowly at moisture contents below 18% (fresh weight basis) making it critical to protect stored products by obtaining and keeping the moisture below 15%.

Overcoming the adverse effects of aflatoxin in feed has been extensively researched and a number of compounds have been identified that aid the animal consuming unavoidably contaminated diets. Biochemically, the presence of lactone in the molecule makes it susceptible to alkaline hydrolysis (Figure 1). If the alkaline treatment is mild, acidification may retrograde to original toxicity.

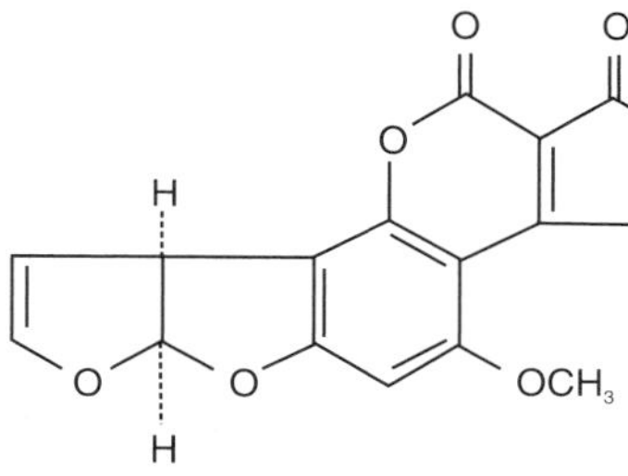

Figure 1. Structure of aflatoxin.

Activated charcoal, a porous material with a high surface area, has been used to aid in the control of aflatoxin. The efficacy of adsorbing aflatoxin with activated charcoal is unaffected by pH and retained material is usually retained throughout the gastrointestinal tract (GIT). The addition of 200 ppm activated charcoal to broiler diets containing 500 ppb aflatoxin B_1 (AFB_1) was found to be somewhat effective in reducing the adverse effects of the toxin (Jindal *et al.*, 1994). Other studies have found charcoal of minimal benefit when added to aflatoxin-containing poultry diets (Dalvi and Ademoyero, 1984). Furthermore, a management problem is encountered with the use of charcoal in the diet as it blackens the feed, feces, birds and their environment. Some manufacturers have overcome some of these problems by producing a product that contains up to 65% water (Buck and Bratich, 1986). The anti-caking agent, hydrated sodium calcium aluminosilicate (HSCAS) has also been used to adsorb aflatoxins from the diet. In poultry, 0.5% HSCAS added to diets contaminated with 7.5 mg/kg AFB_1 reduced the growth inhibitory effects and hepatic changes associated with AFB_1 (Phillips *et al.*, 1988). Other studies have examined HSCAS with combinations of aflatoxin and T-2 or ochratoxin. In trials with aflatoxin

371

and T-2, HSCAS provided almost complete protection against aflatoxin alone, limited protection against the combination and no protection against T-2 (Kubena *et al.,* 1990). Similar tests with diacetoxyscripenol (DAS) and ochratoxin A revealed limited or no improvements of HSCAS with these toxins (Kubena *et al.,* 1993; Huff *et al.,* 1992).

Sodium bentonite has been used to aid mycotoxin control with promising results. However, Schell *et al.* (1993) found that the addition of this clay had slight affects on calcium, phosphorus, iron and zinc absorption and low-ered magnesium and sodium absorption in control and contaminated feeds. Similar problems have been associated with zeolites because the adsorbent could interfere with tissue mineral distribution (Watkins and Southern, 1991) and negatively affect, for example, the utilization of dietary phosphorus by chickens (Mostaghian *et al.,* 1991).

Esterified glucomannans (Mycosorb) demonstrate a high binding affinity for aflatoxin and other toxins when compared to either activated charcoal or HSCAS. In contrast to many of the clay-based adsorbents, interference with mineral metabolism has not been noted due to more specific binding characteristics of Mycosorb. *In vitro* data have demonstrated a strong binding affinity of Mycosorb to aflatoxin. *In vivo* work in a number of species confirms these findings. Data in dairy cows indicate reductions in milk afla-toxin levels with Mycosorb added at 500 g/tonne of complete feed and sodium bentonite at 12.5 kg/tonne of feed (Figure 2, Diaz *et al.,* 1999).

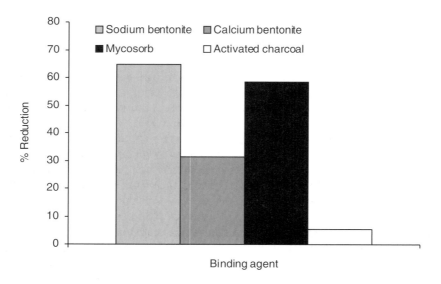

Figure 2. Effects of different binding agents on milk aflatoxin residues.

Similar results have been noted in poultry (Khararern, personal communication). *In vitro* titration data indicate that at levels of aflatoxin below 500 ppb there is no additional benefit in terms of mycotoxin binding

372

by adding more than 1 kg of Mycosorb per tonne of feed (Figure 3, Evans, personal communication).

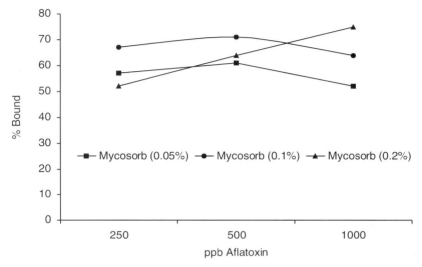

Figure 3. Titration of Mycosorb and aflatoxin levels.

OCHRATOXIN

Ochratoxin was first detected by van der Merwe *et al.* (1965) in laboratory tests to detect toxic feedstuffs in South Africa. Ochratoxin is a potent nephrotoxin and teratogen. Adverse effects have been noted in pigs and poultry at levels at or near 2 ppm. Cattle effects can include decreased performance, reduced milk production, kidney failure and death (at levels greater than 800 ppm). Studies on horses are lacking to document adverse effects. The fungus responsible for the production of ochratoxin can invade starchy cereal grains such as corn and wheat with a moisture content of 15.5-16%. Ochratoxin A is only slightly soluble in water and is absorbed in the upper sections of the GIT in a passive manner in the non-ionized form and is subjected to secretion and reabsorption via enterohepatic recycling (Leeson *et al.*, 1995). In mammals, ochratoxin A is absorbed primarily in the stomach and proximal jejunum although absorption through the lungs into the systemic circulation has also been documented (Di Paolo *et al.*, 1993). Absorption is faster in areas of the GIT where pH is low. Ochratoxin A toxicity in ruminants is thought to be relatively low due to the rumen microflora. Studies postulate that levels up to 12 mg of ochratoxin A per kg of contaminated feed are tolerated by ruminants (Hult *et al.*, 1976). However, Hohler and coworkers (1999) found that even at dosages of 2 mg/kg of concentrate feed, substantial amounts of ochratoxin A were detected in the serum of animals fed the toxin.

Ochratoxin A (Figure 4) enters circulation through the portal vein and the lymphatic vessels bound to plasma proteins, especially albumin. Due to the relatively high affinity of ochratoxin A for albumin, a number of studies have examined increasing dietary protein levels to help alleviate the deleterious effects of this toxin. Feed efficiency of broilers given 4 ppm ochratoxin A was improved at protein levels of 22 and 26% compared to broilers fed 14 and 18% protein (Bailey *et al.*, 1989; Gibson *et al.*, 1989). Vitamin C has also been shown to be beneficial in layers exposed to ochratoxin A (Haazele *et al.*, 1993). Dietary adsorbents such as charcoal and sodium calcium aluminosilicate did not alleviate ochratoxin A toxicity (Huff *et al.*, 1992; Rotter *et al.*, 1989). To date no *in vivo* data on the ability of esterified glucomannans to alleviate ochratoxin A toxicity are available. *In vitro* ochratoxin A binding by Mycosorb ranges from 8-15%. Due to the biochemical affinity of ochratoxin A for certain proteins, it is believed that improved binding to ochratoxin A could be accomplished by using cell wall extract with greater protein content.

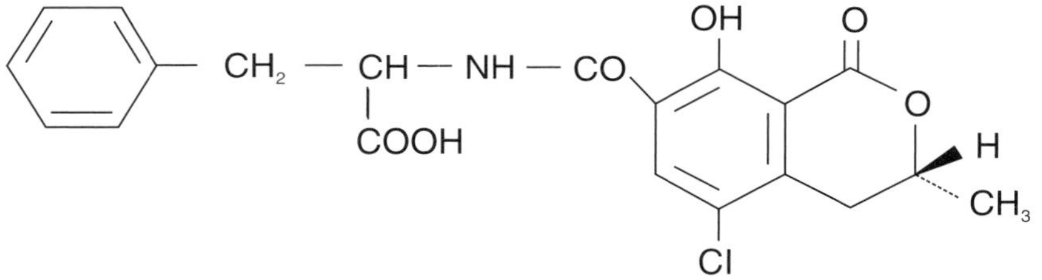

Figure 4. Structure of ochratoxin A.

FUSARIUM MYCOTOXINS

The Fusarium mycotoxins consist of over 100 fungal metabolites with the same basic structure primarily produced by *Fusarium* spp. Mycotoxins produced from Fusarium are less well-known than the Aspergillus-produced aflatoxin, but can be more detrimental to animal health. The Fusarium mycotoxins of practical concern are listed in Table 1 and illustrated in Figure 5.

Table 1. Mycotoxins from Fusarium.

Tricothecene toxins
    Deoxynivalenol (DON or vomitoxin)
    T-2 toxin
    HT-2 toxin
    Diacetoxyscirpenol (DAS)
Zearalenone
Fumonisins
Moniliformin
Fusaric acid

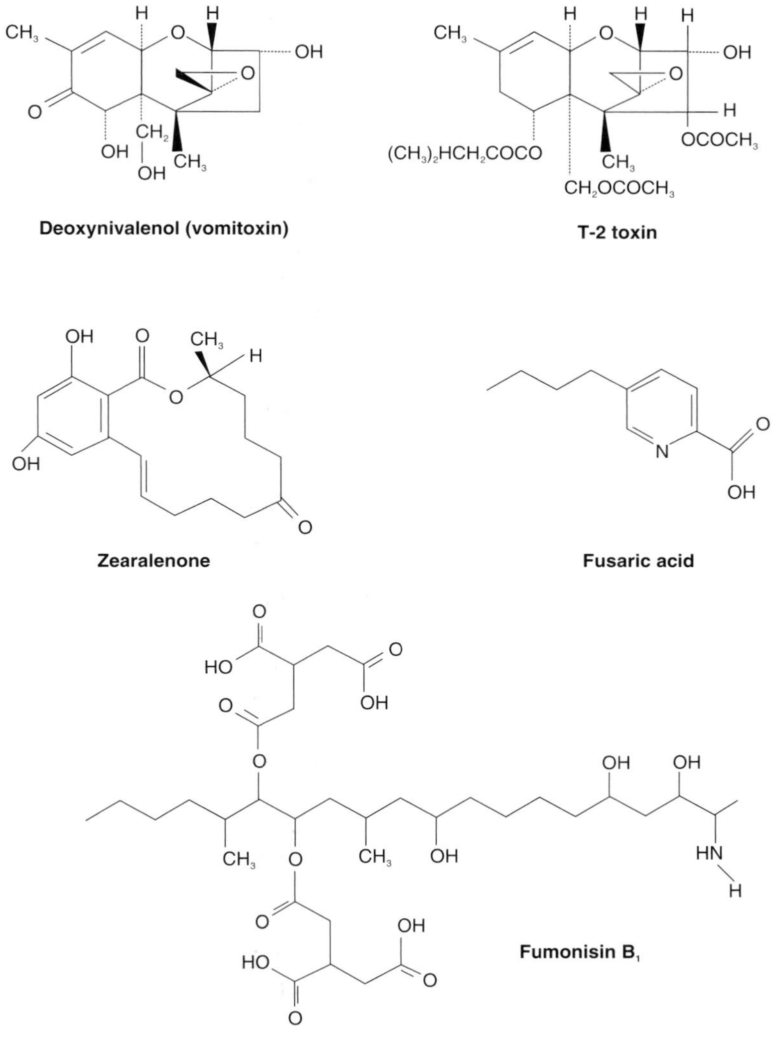

Figure 5. Fusarium mycotoxins: deoxynivalenol (vomitoxin), T-2 toxin, zearalenone, fumonisin B$_1$ and fusaric acid.

Deoxynivalenol is the most commonly detected Fusarium mycotoxin. It is a trichothecene mycotoxin, which inhibits protein synthesis. Incremental reductions in intake have been documented in pigs above 2 ppm, with vomiting at higher concentrations. Deoxynivalenol may also cause immunosuppression and affect reproduction. Similar responses have been noted in dogs and cats. In dogs feed intake was significantly reduced by DON concentrations greater than 4.5 ppm. Cat food intake was reduced at

DON levels greater than 7.7 ppm (Hughes *et al.*, 1999). Certain reports suggest that poultry and ruminants tolerate higher levels of DON than pigs and pets. However, Trenholm and coworkers (1984) indicated that DON levels above 5 ppm may be deleterious. In cattle, reduced feed intake and milk production have been noted (Whitlow and Hagler, 1999). In horses, DON-contaminated barley (40 ppm) had no effect on intake but reductions in serum levels of IgG and IgA were associated with the mycotoxin (Johnson *et al.*, 1997).

T-2 is less prevalent but more toxic than DON. Levels of 1-12 ppm can cause significant reductions in pig performance and fertility. T-2 and related toxins cause irritation, hemorrhage and necrosis throughout the digestive tract. Oral lesions have also been noted in pigs and poultry and have been suspected in horses. Zearalenone imitates the female hormone estrogen and can impair reproduction in many species. At low doses, increased mammary gland and reproductive organ size have been documented in many species. Pigs appear to be the most susceptible. Swelling of the vulva leading to rectal and vaginal prolapse is an overt symptom. In addition, uterine enlargement and ovarian atrophy is common with zearalenone.

Studies conducted in Germany demonstrated that Mycosorb bound more than twice the zearalenone after 10 minutes than other adsorbents tested at pH 4.5 and 6.0. Additionally, desorption of this toxin at pH 8 was least with Mycosorb (Volkl and Karlovsky, personal communication).

Titration of zearalenone and Mycosorb indicate reactivity similar to enzyme kinetics. Increasing concentrations of toxin yield greater binding capacity of Mycosorb up to 1000 ppb zearalenone (Evans, personal communication, Figure 6).

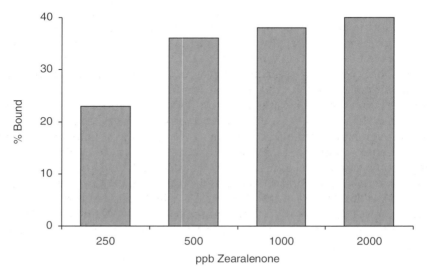

Figure 6. Effect of Mycosorb (1 kg/T) on increasing concentrations of zearalenone *in vitro*.

Fumonisin is a recently discovered mycotoxin that can impair immune function, cause kidney and liver damage, decrease animal performance and cause death. In pigs, fumonisin has been linked with porcine pulmonary edema (PPE). Fumonisin in horses can cause equine leukoencephalomalacia (ELEM), staggers, stupor, unilateral blindness, lameness, seizure (due to brain necrosis) and death. Fumonisin levels associated with PPE and ELEM contained levels of fumonisin B$_1$ ranging from 1 to 330 ppm (PPE) and 1 to 126 ppm (ELEM) (Ross *et al.*, 1991). Ross *et al.* (1992) suggested that fumonisin B$_1$ concentrations greater than 10 ppm in horse feeds were likely to be candidates for ELEM. Although naturally contaminated feeds containing fumonisin have been shown to elevate brain serotonin levels, from recent work by Trevor Smith in Canada, it seems clear that fumonisin is not responsible. Fusaric acid, also produced by Fusarium molds, has been shown to cause vomiting in pigs and elevate brain concentrations of tryptophan and serotonin. The difference in responses seen in scientific studies using purified Fusarium toxins and naturally contaminated feeds may be explained, in part, by the apparent synergism that exists between fusaric acid and other mycotoxins.

Mycotoxins in forages: fescue and ryegrass toxicities

In 1993, Hoveland estimated that approximately 688,000 horses in the US graze tall fescue. The presence of an endophytic fungus in tall fescue has been associated with lower weight gains, rough hair coats, reproductive problems and necrosis of the foot, tail and ears of horses and cattle. Increased gestation length, retained placentas, higher numbers of stillborn foals, and agalactic mares were associated with endophyte infected fescue consumption compared to mares consuming endophyte-free fescue. Although endophyte-free fescue is currently available, it is less hardy, and less resistant to overgrazing, insect damage and drought than infected grass.

Perennial ryegrass intoxication or ryegrass staggers is a neurotoxic syndrome characterized by ataxia, lack of coordination, head shaking, and collapse. Animals appear normal until disturbed. The neurological effects are temporary, but lack of coordination can lead to drowning, and running into and through barns and fences. The causative agents are compounds called tremorgens. A number of tremorgens have been identified with the most important being lolitrem B (Figure 7), which is produced by the endophytic fungus *Acremonium lolii*. Concentrations of lolitrem B are lowest in the leaf blades and highest in the leaf sheath, which tends to make ryegrass staggers most often noted in over-grazed pastures (DiMenna *et al.*, 1992). Symptoms of ryegrass staggers appear when the lolitrem B concentrations exceed 2-2.5 ppm. As is seen with fescue, the endophyte improves the vigor of the ryegrass.

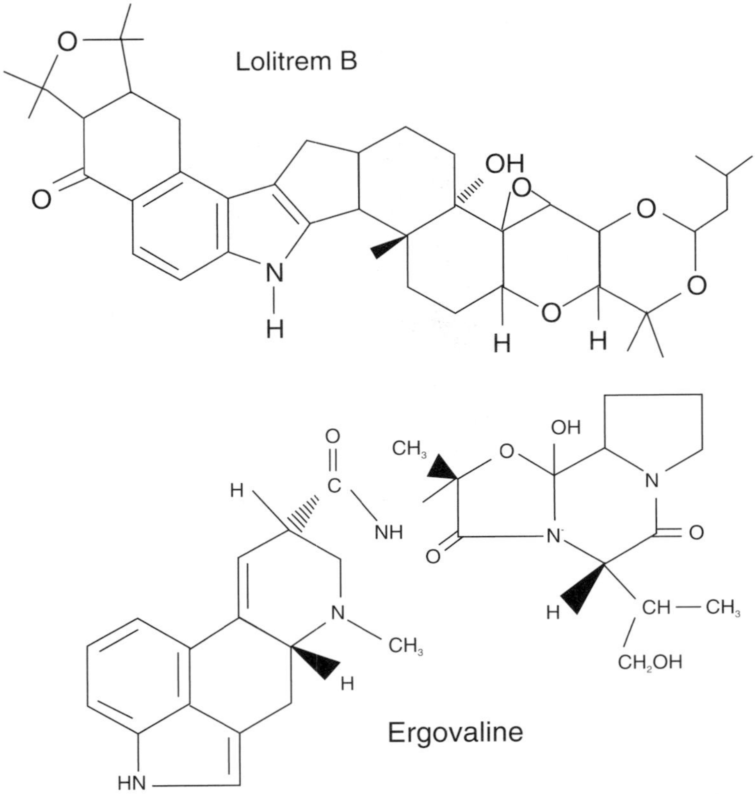

Figure 7. Lolitrem B, a tremorgen produced by *Acremonium lolii*, and ergovaline produced by *A. coenophialum*.

Ergot alkaloids have also been associated with sorghum and can have deleterious effects on poultry. Cumulative weights of broilers consuming diets containing 30 ppm sorghum ergot alkaloid with or without adsorbing agents are presented in Figure 8. Liveweight was nearly 150 g less for birds receiving sorghum ergot alkaloid compared to uncontaminated feed. In addition, these data indicate that adsorbents can help alleviate the detrimental effects of sorghum ergot alkaloid on broiler performance with the greatest numerical response seen when birds received Mycosorb (Deo *et al.*, 1999). As yet undiscovered mycotoxins may also hold the key in adding insight into mycotoxin effects on animal performance. It is well documented that the toxic effects of many mycotoxins are enhanced by the presence of more than one toxin. As more mycotoxins are discovered, it may come to pass that the above mentioned toxins only serve as markers or indicators of other unknown toxins.

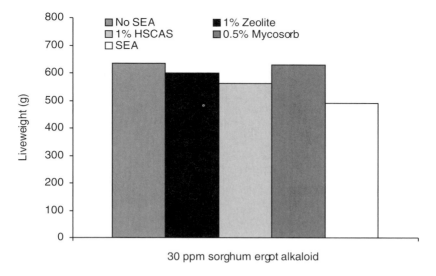

Figure 8. Effect of sorghum ergot alkaloid (SEA) and adsorbents on broiler liveweight at 23 days.

Conclusions

Mycotoxin control begins by controlling mold growth from the point of harvest and maintaining a low mold count throughout feeding. Commercial mold inhibitors can aid in reducing mold growth at the time of harvest or shortly thereafter. Not all molds produce mycotoxins; and since mycotoxins are secondary metabolites of mold growth, high or low mold counts do not necessarily mean presence or absence of mycotoxin. Molds may have already produced mycotoxin and died, leaving a low mold count and high levels of mycotoxins. Many more mycotoxins exist than are mentioned in this text as the focus has been on the more prevalent toxins. As we learn more about mycotoxins we may be better equipped to address specific problems identified with these toxins. With this, we hope to better define the mechanisms of toxicity and identify toxic levels in feed. In many species, much more data are necessary in order to understand these toxins and the interactions of multiple toxins. In certain instances, adsorbents follow characteristics similar to enzyme kinetics with binding affinity increasing as mycotoxin concentrations increase. With clays and activated charcoal certain undesirable characteristics are associated with their use such as dust problems, blackening of the feed and animal, or interference with mineral metabolism. Biochemical adsorbents such as esterified glucomannans do not display these traits and show a greater affinity for mycotoxins due to their apparent specificity for mycotoxin binding. As we advance our knowledge in this field and learn more about the widespread nature of mycotoxins and the biochemical nature of their structure, technology exists to design adsorbents for those toxins.

References

Bailey, C.A., R.M. Gibson, L.F. Kubena, W.E. Huff and R.B. Harvey. 1989. Ochratoxin A and dietary protein. 2. Effects on hematology and various clinical chemistry measurements. Poult. Sci. 68:1664-1671.

Buck, W.B. and P.M. Bratich. 1986. Activated charcoal: preventing unnecessary death by poisoning. Vet. Med. 81:73-77.

Dalvi, R.R. and A.A. Ademoyero. 1984. Toxic effects of aflatoxin B_1 in chickens given feed contaminated with *Aspergillus flavus* and reduction of the toxicity by activated charcoal and some chemical agents. Avian Dis. 28:61-69.

Diaz, D.E., W.M. Hagler, Jr., B.A. Hopkins, J.A. Eve and L.W. Whitlow. 1999. The potential for dietary sequestering agents to reduce the transmission of dietary aflatoxin to milk of dairy cows and to bind aflatoxin *in vitro*. J. Dairy Sci. (Abstract) Southern Branch, American Dairy Science Association, February 1, 1999.

Deo, P., B.J. Blaney and J.G. Dingle. 1999. Effects of mineral and organic adsorbents in meat chicken diets contaminated with sorghum ergot alkaloid. Queensland Poult. Sci. Symp. Volume 8.

DiMenna, M.E., P.H. Mortimer, R.A. Prestige, A.D. Hawkes and J.M. Sprosen. 1992. Lolitrem B concentrations, counts of *Acremonium lolii* hyphae, and the incidence of ryegrass staggers in lambs on plots of *A. lolii* infected perennial ryegrass. N.Z.J. Agric. Res. 35:211-220.

Di Paolo, N., A. Guarnieri, F. Loi, G. Sacchi, A.M. Mangiarotti and M. Di Paolo. 1993. Acute renal failure from inhalation of mycotoxins. Nephron. 64:621-625.

Gibson, R.M., C.A. Bailey, L.F. Kubena, W.E. Huff and R.B. Harvey. 1989. Ochratoxin A and dietary protein. 1. Effects on body weight, feed conversion, relative organ weight, and mortality in three-week-old broilers. Poult. Sci. 68:1658-1663.

Haazele, F.M., W. Guenter, R.R. Marquardt and A.A. Frolich. 1993. Beneficial effects of dietary ascorbic acid supplementation in hens subjected to ochratoxin A toxicosis under normal and high ambient temperatures. Can. J. Anim. Sci. 73:149-157.

Hohler, D., K.h. Sudekum, S. Wolffram, A.A. Frohlich and R.R. Marquardt. 1999. Metabolism and excretion of ochratoxin A fed to sheep. J. Anim. Sci. 77:1217-1223.

Hoveland, C.S. 1993. Importance and economic significance of the Acremonium endophytes to performance of animals and grass plants. Agric. Ecosystems Environ. 44:3-12.

Huff, W.E., L.R. Kubena, R.B. Harvey and T.D. Phillips. 1992. Efficacy of hydrated sodium calcium aluminosilicate to reduce the individual and combined toxicity of aflatoxin and ochratoxin A. Poult. Sci. 71:64-69.

Hughes, D.M., M.J. Gahl, C.H. Graham and S.L. Grieb. 1999. Overt signs of toxicity to dogs and cats of dietary deoxynivalenol. J. Anim. Sci. 77:693-700.

Hult, K., A. Teiling and S. Gatenbeck. 1976. Degradation of ochratoxin A by a ruminant. Appl. Environ. Microbiol. 32:443-444.

Jindal, N., S.K. Mahipal and N.K. Mahajan. 1994. Toxicity of aflatoxin B_1 in broiler chickens and its reduction by activated charcoal. Res. Vet. Sci. 56:37-40.

Johnson, P.J., S.W. Casteel and N.T. Messer. 1997. Effect of feeding deoxynivalennol (vomitoxin)-contaminated barley to horses. J. Vet. Diagn. Invest. 9:219-221.

Kubena, L.F., R.B. Harvey, T.D. Phillips, D.E. Corrier and W.E. Huff. 1990. Diminution of aflatoxicosis in growing chickens by the dietary addition of a hydrated sodium calcium aluminosilicate. Poult. Sci. 69:727-735.

Kubena, L.F., R.B. Harvey, W.E. Huff, M.H. Elissalde, A.G. Yersin, T.D. Phillips and G.E. Rottinghaus. 1993. Efficacy of hydrated sodium calcium aluminosilicate to reduce the toxicity of aflatoxin and diacetoxyscripenol. Poult. Sci. 72:51-59.

Leeson, S., G. Diaz and J.D. Summers. 1995. Ochratoxins. In: Poultry Metabolic Disorders and Mycotoxins. University Books. Ontario, Canada.

Mostaghian, J., C.M. Parsons, R.W. Leeper, P.C. Harrison, and H. Koelkebeck. 1991. Effect of sodium aluminosilicate on phosphorus utilization by chicks in laying hens. Poult. Sci. 70:955-962.

Philips, T.D., L.F. Kubena, R.B. Harvey, D.R. Taylor, and N.D. Heidelbaugh. 1988. Hydrated sodium calcium aluminosilicate: a high affinity sorbent for aflatoxin. Poult. Sci. 67:243-247.

Ross, P.F., L.G. Rice, R.D. Plattner, G.D. Osweiller, T.M. Wilson, D.L. Owens, H.A. Nelson, and J.L. Richard. 1991. Concentration of fumonisin B_1 associated with animal health problems. Mycopathologia. 114:129-135.

Ross, P.F., L.G. Rice, G.D. Osweiller, P.E. Nelson, J.L. Richard, and T.M. Wilson. 1992. A review and update of animal toxicosis associated with fumonisin-contaminated feeds and production of fumonisins by *Fusarium* isolates. Mycopathologia. 117:109-114.

Rotter, R.G., A.A. Frolich, and R.R. Marquardt. 1989. Influence of dietary charcoal on ochratoxin A toxicity in Leghorn chickens. Can. J. Vet. Res. 53:449-453.

Schell, T.C., M.D. Lindemann, E.T. Kornegay and D.J. Blodgett. 1993. Effect of feeding aflatoxin-contaminated diets with and without clays to weanling and growing pigs on performance, liver function, and mineral metabolism. J. Anim. Sci. 71:1209-1218.

Trenholm, H.L., R.M.G. Hamilton, D.W. Friend, B.K. Thompson and K.E. Hartin. 1984. Feeding trials with vomitoxin (deoxynivalenol)-contaminated wheat: effects on swine, poultry and dairy cattle. J. Amer. Vet. Med. Assoc. 185:527-531.

Van der Merwe, K.J., P.S. Steyn and L. Fourie. 1965. Mycotoxins. Part II. The constitutions of ochratoxins A, B and C metabolites of Aspergillus ochraceus. Wilh. J. Chem. Soc. pp. 7083-7088.

Watkins, K.L. and L.E. Southern. 1991. Effect of dietary sodium zeolite A and graded levels of calcium on growth, plasma, and tibia characteristic of chicks. Poult. Sci. 70:2295-2303.

Whitlow, L.W. and W.M. Hagler, Jr. 1999. An association of mycotoxins with production, health and reproduction in dairy cattle and guidelines for prevention and treatment. In: Biotechnology in the feed Industry, Proceedings of Alltech's 15th Annual symposium (T.P. Lyons and K.A. Jacques, eds). Nottingham University Press, UK, p. 401.

The use of binding agents and amino acid supplements for dietary treatment of Fusarium mycotoxicoses

TREVOR K. SMITH[1], MEHRDAD MODIRSANEI[2] AND EWEN J. MACDONALD[3]

[1]Department of Animal and Poultry Science, University of Guelph, Guelph, Ontario, Canada
[2]Department of Breeding and Animal Nutrition, University of Tehran, Tehran, Iran
[3]Department of Pharmacology and Toxicology, University of Kuopio, Kuopio, Finland

Introduction

Mycotoxins are metabolites produced by fungi which are toxic to livestock when consumed in biologically significant amounts. The resulting diseases are referred to as mycotoxicoses. Mold growth and mycotoxin production on feed grains are influenced by many factors but the most important of these is moisture. Stored grains should contain less than 15% moisture to minimize mold growth. Fusarium fungi are commonly found in temperate climates; and Fusarium mycotoxins are likely the most economically significant grain mycotoxins on a global basis (Wood, 1992). The numerous Fusarium mycotoxins are very diverse in chemical structure and in the characteristics of the mycotoxicoses they produce. These toxins include the trichothecenes, the fumonisins, zearalenone, moniliformin and fusaric acid. Fusarium mycotoxins differ from aflatoxin in significant ways. The feeding of blends of grains and soybean meal, however, increases the chances of aflatoxin and Fusarium mycotoxins being present in the same diet.

About 150 chemically distinct Fusarium trichothecenes have been characterized. The major effect of these toxins on livestock and poultry is a loss of appetite, and therefore these are considered to be feed refusal toxins. The most commonly reported trichothecene is deoxynivalenol (vomitoxin, DON), although others are also sometimes found. Consumption of deoxynivalenol-contaminated feeds can result in reduced feed consumption, vomiting, immunosuppression and loss of muscle coordination. Swine are the species most sensitive to dietary deoxynivalenol. Poultry are less sensitive and ruminants are the most resistant due to the action of the rumen microflora.

383

How hazardous are feeds contaminated with Fusarium mycotoxins?

The non-specific nature of the symptoms of trichothecene toxicoses, including reduced feed consumption, reduced growth and immunosuppression, make it difficult to confirm trichothecenes as the cause of lost performance. The cause could also be improper management practices or a wide range of health factors. It is common to observe symptoms of trichothecene toxicity in the field, but the contaminated feed is often determined to have negligible concentrations of trichothecenes (Trenholm *et al.*, 1983). This situation has usually been attributed to inadequate sampling of feed, errors in analysis or the presence of unknown mycotoxins. The result is lost revenue and frustration for producers.

Studies in our laboratory have indicated that the presence of fusaric (5-butylpicolinic) acid, a compound synthesized from tryptophan by Fusarium molds, will increase the growth depression seen when low levels of deoxynivalenol are fed to starter pigs (Smith *et al.*, 1997). Although fusaric acid was chemically characterized many years ago, it has not been considered to be a significant factor in Fusarium mycotoxicoses because of its relatively low toxicity. Fusaric acid is pharmacologically active, however, and alters brain neurochemistry in a wide range of animal species (Nagatsu *et al.*, 1970) including starter pigs (Smith and MacDonald, 1991). The compound is also considered to be a phytotoxin and can cause pathology in soybean and tomato plants (Matsui and Watanabe, 1988). Bacon *et al.* (1996) cultured 78 different strains of Fusarium fungi and observed that all the strains produced some amount of fusaric acid. It was suggested that since the production of this compound was so common, it should be used as a marker for Fusarium contamination of feeds.

In a survey of swine producers in Ontario, Canada, who thought their reduced performance was due to mycotoxin contamination, it was found that feed grains and complete feeds contained about 10 times as much fusaric acid as deoxynivalenol (Table 1, Smith and Sousadias, 1993). The average concentrations seen in complete feeds, however, were higher than those seen in individual grains, thereby implicating soybean meal as a potential source of fusaric acid. It is very important, therefore, to determine the mycotoxin content of the entire diet, not simply suspect grains, when estimating the potential hazard posed to livestock and poultry.

Table 1. Fusaric acid content of cereal grains and whole swine feeds.

Feedstuff	n	Fusaric acid (mg/kg)
Whole feeds	8	35.8
Dry corn	16	11.8
High moisture corn	4	26.4
Wheat	8	11.6
Barley	2	12.2

From Smith and Sousadias, 1993.

Toxicological interactions between Fusarium mycotoxins

It has often been observed that the feeding of grains naturally-contaminated with mycotoxins results in a greater toxicity than the feeding of diets containing an equivalent amount of purified mycotoxin (Trenholm *et al.*, 1994). This can be attributed to toxicological synergy among mycotoxins such as that previously described for fusaric acid and deoxynivalenol (Smith *et al.*, 1997). Excess brain serotonin, a neurotransmitter synthesized from tryptophan, can cause loss of appetite, lethargy, sleepiness and loss of muscle coordination (Leathwood, 1987). Trichothecene mycotoxins can inhibit hepatic protein synthesis (Meloche and Smith, 1995), resulting in hyperaminoacidemia (Wannermacher and Dinterman, 1983), elevation of brain tryptophan (MacDonald *et al.*, 1988) and increased brain concentrations of serotonin (Prelusky, 1993). Fusaric acid also increases brain serotonin concentrations, but this occurs through a different metabolic mechanism. Fusaric acid, a tryptophan analogue, competes with tryptophan for binding to blood albumin and thereby elevates blood free tryptophan (Chaouloff *et al.*, 1986). This results in increased brain uptake of free tryptophan across the blood-brain barrier and, once again, elevated brain serotonin concentrations.

Toward a solution: development of mycotoxin binders

A useful strategy for dietary treatment of Fusarium mycotoxicoses has been the development of specialty feed additives that can be added to feeds at low levels of inclusion to bind mycotoxins in the intestinal lumen. This effectively reduces the toxicity of a given level of contamination in feeds and allows toxic grain to be fed with minimal losses of performance. The challenge is to find binding agents with a high degree of specificity for the commonly-occurring mycotoxins. A lack of specificity may result in reduction in the availability of trace nutrients and medications. It is equally important that the binding capacity be high enough that a minimal level of dietary inclusion can be achieved. Binding agents are usually non-nutritive and are considered to be diluents, thereby reducing nutrient density. Early studies in our laboratory demonstrated that non-specific mineral additives such as bentonite (Carson and Smith, 1983a) and spent bleaching clays (Smith, 1984) could reduce T-2 toxicity. Organic fibres such as those derived from alfalfa were shown to be effective both against T-2 toxin (Carson and Smith, 1983b) and zearalenone (James and Smith, 1982; Stangroom and Smith, 1984). The lack of specificity and high levels of inclusion, however, made these treatments unpractical.

Approaches to *in vitro* and *in vivo* testing of dietary binding agents have recently been reviewed (Ledoux and Rottinghaus, 1999). Although a useful guide when conducted appropriately, *in vitro* binding studies must be accompanied by *in vivo* experiments to determine the biological significance of mycotoxin binding. An example of the more sophisticated organic polymers used as an anti-mycotoxin agent is esterified glucomannan enzymatically extracted from the cell wall of *Saccharomyces cereviciae*[1026]. This material is one of the active agents in Mycosorb, produced by Alltech, Inc.

EFFECTS OF MYCOSORB IN MYCOTOXIN-CONTAMINATED DIETS FED TO TURKEY POULTS

A 21 day experiment was conducted with day-old male poults fed blends of naturally-contaminated grains with and without supplemental fusaric acid. The most highly contaminated diet was also fed supplemented with 0.2% Mycosorb. The objective of this study was to determine the effect of feeding diets contaminated with deoxynivalenol and fusaric acid to turkey poults and to observe the potential for Mycosorb to overcome these effects. Deoxynivalenol was provided by naturally-contaminated wheat and barley. The diets fed included: 1) control, 2) contaminated grains, 3) contaminated grains + 15 mg/kg fusaric acid, 4) contaminated grains + 25 mg/kg fusaric acid, and 5) diet 4 + 0.2% Mycosorb. Diets containing contaminated grains were determined to have a deoxynivalenol concentration of about 2.4 mg/kg. The control diet was analyzed to contain 20.6 mg/kg fusaric acid. No other mycotoxins were found to be present.

Results of the trial are given in Table 2. Weight gain of poults fed contaminated grains did not significantly differ from controls. Poults fed contaminated grains + Mycosorb, however, grew significantly faster than birds fed unsupplemented contaminated grains. Feed consumption and feed efficiency were unaffected by diet. There was a trend toward increased relative gizzard weights with the feeding of contaminated grains. A clinical screen of serum metabolites was conducted at the end of the experiment. There was a significant reduction in serum cholesterol concentration in poults fed Mycosorb compared to controls.

Table 2. Effect of feeding blends of Fusarium mycotoxin-contaminated grains on growth performance and metabolism of turkey poults.

DON (mg/kg)	Fusaric acid (mg/kg)	Mycosorb (mg/kg)	Gain (g/bird)	Feed intake (g/bird)	Gain:feed	Gizzard weight (% of BW)	Serum cholesterol (mg/l)
0.3	20.6	0	650[h]	818	0.79	3.08	154.7[h]
2.1	23.3	0	651[h]	815	0.80	3.44	143.5[hi]
2.2	21.3	0	674[hi]	826	0.82	3.44	139.2[hi]
2.4	24.2	0	662[h]	832	0.79	3.61	145.0[hi]
2.4	44.7	2.0	696[i]	848	0.81	3.39	136.1[i]

[h]Means within a column with different superscripts differ significantly (P<0.05).

It was concluded that there was no toxicological synergy between deoxynivalenol and fusaric acid when fed at these concentrations. Turkey poults have been shown to be quite resistant to feedborne deoxynivalenol (Morris *et al.*, 1999). It is of interest, however, that the feeding of Mycosorb together with contaminated grains significantly increased growth rate compared to controls. It is possible that this results from the binding of fusaric acid, which was present in both the control and contaminated diets. The lowering of serum cholesterol concentrations with the feeding of Mycosorb may indicate the difficulty of providing absolute specificity in the binding of metabolites. The drop in blood cholesterol concentration is likely due to binding of bile salts in the lumen of the small intestine. This would reduce circulating levels of cholesterol that would be used for *de novo* synthesis of bile salts. Such synthesis would be required due to impaired recycling of bile salts through the enterohepatic circulation, since the salts were bound by Mycosorb and excreted in the feces.

It can be concluded that Mycosorb shows promise in promoting growth when turkey poults are fed diets containing Fusarium mycotoxins.

Toward a solution:expanding on the binder concept

Considering the challenge in developing very specific mycotoxin binders, some additional strategies may be employed. It is possible to reduce the Fusarium mycotoxin-induced brain uptake of tryptophan by feeding protein supplements rich in large neutral amino acids (Cavan *et al.*, 1988). These amino acids can compete with tryptophan for active transport across the blood-brain barrier and reduce the availability of tryptophan for brain serotonin synthesis. Examples of such protein sources are corn gluten meal and blood protein supplements.

STARTER PIG TRIALS WITH PROTEIN SUPPLEMENTS

In the summer of 1999, an experiment was conducted at the University of Guelph to determine the potential for various dietary treatments to overcome the toxicity of diets containing blends of grains naturally-contaminated with deoxynivalenol and fusaric acid. Purebred Yorkshire pigs (average initial weight 8.1 kg) were fed diets formulated to contain 4.0 mg/kg deoxynivalenol and 20.0 mg/kg fusaric acid for 21 days. Diets included 1) control, 2) contaminated grains and 3) contaminated grains + 6% red blood cell protein. There was a significant reduction in weight gain of pigs fed contaminated grains compared to controls (Table 3). The difference was largely eliminated through the feeding of red blood cell protein.

At the end of the study, a subgroup of 12 pigs fed each diet was euthanized and brains were excised and dissected into frontal cortex, pons-medulla and hypothalamus. Brain regional neurochemistry was determined by high performance liquid chromatography with electrochemical detection. The largest effects of diet were seen in the pons-medulla. The feeding of

Table 3. Effect of feeding blends of Fusarium mycotoxin-contaminated grains on growth performance and brain neurochemistry of starter pigs.

Diet	Body weight gain (kg/days 1-7)	Tryptophan	Serotonin (nmol/g pons-medulla)	5-HIAA
Control	0.5[c]	0.42[cd]	4.42[c]	0.90[c]
Contaminated[f]	0.1[d]	0.57[c]	5.85[d]	2.62[d]
6.0% RBC protein[g]	0.8[cd]	10.40[d]	5.46[d]	2.52[d]

[cde]Means in a column with different superscripts differ significantly (P<0.05).
[f]Contaminated grains.
[g]Contaminated grains + 6.0% red blood cell protein.

contaminated grains reduced brain tryptophan concentrations. The feeding of red blood cell protein, however, significantly increased brain tryptophan compared to controls. While brain serotonin levels were significantly elevated by the feeding of contaminated grains, this was numerically reduced by the feeding of red blood cell protein. Concentrations of 5-hydroxyindoleacetic acid, a metabolite of serotonin which can be used, with caution, as an index of serotonergic neuronal activity, increased significantly with the feeding of contaminated grains. There was a numerical decline with the feeding of red blood cell protein. It was concluded that the growth depression seen when pigs were fed contaminated grains was due to neurochemical changes that could be largely overcome by the feeding of red blood cell protein.

Summary

The active component of choice in commercial preparations for overcoming mycotoxin contamination of feeds is a mycotoxin binding agent. It has been demonstrated, however, that the Fusarium mycotoxin-induced brain neurochemical changes can be largely overcome by dietary supplements of large neutral amino acids. Such supplements minimize brain uptake of tryptophan, which prevents increased behaviors such as loss of appetite. These are characteristic of stimulation of the serotonergic nervous system. The evolution of commercial anti-mycotoxin products should include combining mycotoxin binding capacity with the ability to favorably alter brain neurochemistry.

References

Bacon, C.W., J.K. Porter, W.P. Norred and J.F. Leslie. 1996. Production of fusaric acid by Fusarium species. Appl. Environ. Microbiol. 62:4039.

Carson, M.S. and T.K. Smith. 1983a. Role of bentonite in the prevention of T-2 toxicosis in rats. J. Anim. Sci. 57:1498.

Carson, M.S. and T.K. Smith. 1983b. Effect of feeding alfalfa and refined plant fibres on the toxicity and metabolism of T-2 toxin in rats. J. Nutr. 113:304.

Cavan, K.R., E.J. MacDonald and T.K. Smith. 1988. Potential for dietary amino acid precursors of neurotransmitters to overcome neurochemical changes in acute T-2 toxicosis in rats. J. Nutr. 118:901.

Chaouloff, F., D. Laude, D. Merino, B. Serrurier and F.L. Elghozi. 1986. Peripheral and central short-term effects of fusaric acid, a DBH inhibitor, on tryptophan and serotonin metabolism in the rat. J. Neural Transm. 65:219.

James, L.J. and T.K. Smith. 1982. Effect of dietary alfalfa on zearalenone toxicity and metabolism in rats and swine. J. Anim. Sci. 55:110.

Leathwood, P.D. 1987. Tryptophan availability and serotonin synthesis. Proc. Nutr. Soc. 46:143.

Ledoux, D.R., and G.E. Rottinghaus. 1999. *In vitro* and *in vivo* testing of adsorbents for detoxifying mycotoxins in contaminated feedstuffs. In: Biotechnology in the Feed Industry. Proc. of the 15th Annual Symposium. (T.P. Lyons and K.A. Jacques, eds). Nottingham University Press, Nottingham, UK, pp. 369-379.

MacDonald, E.J., K.R. Cavan and T.K. Smith. 1988. Effect of acute oral doses of T-2 toxin on tissue concentrations of biogenic amines in the rat. J. Anim. Sci. 66:434.

Matsui, Y. and M. Watanabe. 1988. Quantitative analysis of fusaric acid in the cultural filtrate and soybean plants innoculated with *Fusarium oxysporum* var. *redolens*. J. Rakuno Gakuen Univ. Nat. Sci. 13:159.

Meloche, J.L. and T.K. Smith. 1995. Altered tissue amino acid metabolism in acute T-2 toxicosis. Proc. Soc. Exper. Biol. Med. 210:260.

Morris, C.M., Y.C. Li, D.R. Ledoux, A.J. Bermudez and G.E. Rottinghaus. 1999. The individual and combined effects of feeding moniliformin, supplied by *Fusarium fujikuroi* cultural material and deoxynivalenol in young turkey poults. Poultry Sci. 78:1110.

Nagatsu, T., H. Hidaka, H. Kuzuya, K. Takeya, H. Umezawa, T. Takeuchi and H. Suda. 1970. Inhibition of dopamine beta-hydroxylase by fusaric acid (5-butypicolinic acid) *in vitro* and *in vivo*. Biochem. Pharmacol. 19:35.

Prelusky, D.B. 1993. The effect of low-level deoxynivalenol on neurotransmitter levels measured in pig cerebral spinal fluid. J. Environ. Sci. Health B28:731.

Smith, T.K. 1984. Spent canola oil bleaching clays: potential for treatment of T-2 toxicosis in rats and short-term inclusion in diets for immature swine. Can. J. Anim. Sci. 64:725.

Smith, T.K. and E.J. MacDonald. 1991. Effect of fusaric acid on brain regional neurochemistry and vomiting behavior in swine. J. Anim. Sci. 69:2044.

Smith, T.K. and M.G. Sousadias. 1993. Fusaric acid content of swine feedstuffs. J. Agr. Food Chem. 41:2296.

Smith, T.K., E.G. McMillan and J.B. Castillo. 1997. Effect of feeding blends of Fusarium mycotoxin-contaminated grains containing deoxynivalenol and fusaric acid on growth and feed consumption of immature swine. J. Anim. Sci. 69:2044.

Stangroom, K.E. and T.K. Smith. 1984. Effect of whole and fractionated dietary alfalfa meal on zearalenone toxicosis in rats and swine. Can. J. Physiol. Pharmacol. 62:1219.

Trenholm, H.L., W.P. Cochrane, H. Cohen, J.I. Elliott, E.R. Farnworth, D.W. Friend, R.M.G. Hamilton, J.R. Standish and B.K. Thompson. 1983. Survey of vomitoxin contamination of 1980 Ontario winter wheat crop: Results of survey and feeding trials. J. Assoc. Off. Anal. Chem. 66:92.

Trenholm, H.L., B.C. Foster, L.L. Charmley, B.K. Thompson, K.E. Hartin, R.W. Coppock and M.A. Albassam. 1994. Effects of feeding diets containing Fusarium (naturally) contaminated wheat or pure deoxynivalenol (DON) in growing pigs. Can. J. Anim. Sci. 74:361.

Wannermacher, R.W. and R.E. Dinterman. 1983. Plasma amino acid changes in guinea pigs injected with T-2 toxin. Fed. Proc. 42:625 (abstract).

Wood, G.E. 1992. Mycotoxins in foods and feeds in the United States. J. Anim. Sci. 70:3941.

Mycotoxins and milk safety: the potential to block transfer to milk

L.W. WHITLOW, D.E. DIAZ, B.A. HOPKINS AND W.M. HAGLER, JR.

North Carolina State University, Raleigh, North Carolina, USA

Introduction: evaluating the human risks of mycotoxin contamination

Mycotoxins occur worldwide. They occur frequently in a variety of feedstuffs (Gareis *et al.*, 1989; Sharma and Salunkhe, 1991; Wood, 1992) and are therefore routinely consumed by dairy cattle. These typically low levels of mycotoxins are associated with subclinical losses in milk production, increases in disease and reduced reproductive performance. In some cases, mycotoxin concentrations in feedstuffs are high enough to be associated with severe problems including death. Diagnosis of a mycotoxicosis is difficult because of nonspecific symptoms, difficulties in feed sampling and analysis, and interactions with other stress factors. However, mycotoxins should be considered as a causative factor when unidentified problems exist.

Moy (1998) reviewed the international efforts to evaluate and reduce the human risks of mycotoxins. He stated that "human health problems caused by the consumption of most mycotoxins are complex and poorly understood", but that they may be responsible for a range of diseases.

The majority of human health risk from mycotoxins is from consumption of contaminated grains and nuts. Several mycotoxins have been shown to occur in the milk of dairy cattle. Concentrations are extremely low because only a small fraction of the amount consumed by a cow is transferred to milk in the parent form or as a derivative. The US Food and Drug Administration (FDA) has indicated that aflatoxin is the only mycotoxin that currently warrants regulation in milk (Wood and Trucksess, 1998).

Aflatoxin

Interest in mycotoxin research was renewed in the early 1960s with the discovery that aflatoxin was responsible for the outbreak of Turkey X Disease in England (Sargeant *et al.*, 1961). It was soon discovered that aflatoxin consumed by dairy cattle resulted in a toxic metabolite in milk (Allcroft and Carnaghan, 1962; 1963).

Aflatoxin is produced primarily by *Aspergillus flavus*. It is of major concern because it is carcinogenic and is found worldwide, especially in warm and humid climates including a routine occurrence in the southern US. Aflatoxin occurs in several forms of which the most common are aflatoxins B_1, B_2, G_1 and G_2. Reference is most frequently made to aflatoxin B_1 which is the most prevalent and the most toxic form.

Aflatoxin is expected to occur in about 20% of the corn grain grown in the southern US even in non-crisis years (Shotwell, 1991). In the midwestern region of the US, aflatoxin is not expected except in years with extreme weather conditions. In 1988-89 the midwest experienced a drought; and 8% of corn samples from seven midwestern states contained aflatoxin (Russel *et al.*, 1991). Aflatoxin occurrence is of concern in corn, peanuts, cottonseed and sometimes soybeans but may also occur in other feed products (Wood, 1992).

Aflatoxin can reduce performance and impair health of dairy cattle, but significant toxicity is thought to occur at dietary concentrations much greater than those which can result in illegal milk residues. Although no level of aflatoxin should be considered safe, the degree of toxicity is related to dietary level of the toxin, duration of exposure, and the amount of other stresses affecting the animal. Levels of 300 to 700 ppb are considered toxic for beef cattle depending on criteria for toxicity, and other factors affecting toxicity (CAST, 1989). Garrett *et al.* (1968) showed gain and intake in beef cattle were affected at 700 ppb, but not at 300 ppb aflatoxin. However, levels of 'no effect' cannot be determined from data with such few animals. Trends in the data, especially for increased liver weights, would indicate potential toxicity at levels as low as 100 ppb. Guthrie (1979) showed a decline in reproductive efficiency in a field case where lactating dairy cattle were consuming 120 ppb aflatoxin. When cows were changed to an aflatoxin-free diet, milk production increased over 25%. Patterson and Anderson (1982) and Marsi *et al.* (1969) also suggest that 100 ppb may reduce milk production. Applebaum *et al.* (1982) showed that impure aflatoxin produced by culture reduced production, while equal amounts of pure aflatoxin did not. Several studies suggest that naturally contaminated feeds are more toxic than would be expected from the concentrations of assayed mycotoxins. This suggests the presence of both known and unidentified mycotoxins in naturally contaminated feeds.

Milk aflatoxin residues are the result of transformation of the parent compound in the liver and its subsequent secretion into milk. Aflatoxin B_1 results in milk residues of aflatoxin M_1, while aflatoxin B_2 results in milk residues of aflatoxin M_2. Small amounts of other derivatives such as aflatoxin M_4, Q_1 and aflatoxicol can also be found in milk, however aflatoxin M_1 is the primary residue (Wood, 1991). Van Egmond (1989) concluded that aflatoxin carry-over from feed to milk is approximately 1-2 %. Frobish *et al.* (1986) found greater aflatoxin transfer to milk when the toxin was supplied by contaminated cottonseed meal than when it was supplied by contaminated corn. Aflatoxin transfer to milk was not affected by concentration in the feed or by milk production level of the cow. They concluded that concentration of aflatoxin M_1 in milk was approximately equal to 1.51% of the concentration of aflatoxin B_1 in the diet. Therefore a concentration of 33 ppb in the total diet would result in a 0.5 ppb concentration in milk (3.9 ppb in the milk dry matter, assuming 12.8% milk solids). Figure 1 shows the decline and increase in milk aflatoxin concentrations associated with the consumption of approximately 0 or 100 ppb aflatoxin and with or without binders in the diet (Diaz *et al.*, 1997).

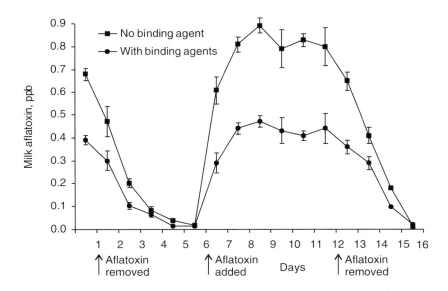

Figure 1. Clearance and appearance of aflatoxin in milk of dairy cows associated with consumption of aflatoxin contaminated corn in diets with or without the addition of clay products.

The FDA sets limits on aflatoxin in corn grain according to intended use of the grain. These values are: 200 ppb or less for breeding cattle, 300 ppb or less for finishing beef cattle, and 20 ppb or less for lactating dairy cattle. The FDA has set an action level for aflatoxin M_1 at no more than 0.5 ppb in milk. The limit on milk aflatoxin M_1 was set without going through the formal rule-making process and thus it is not binding on the courts, the public or the agency. However, the action level provides a guideline for regulatory action (Wood, 1998). Van Egmond (1989) conducted a survey during 1987 indicating that approximately 34 countries had actual or proposed regulations on aflatoxin B_1 concentrations in feedstuffs and that approximately 14 countries had actual or proposed limits on aflatoxin M_1 concentrations in milk.

Regulatory pressures and a widespread awareness have helped minimize aflatoxin problems. Surveys of aflatoxin B_1 concentrations in feedstuffs conducted during the 1980s resulted in lower levels than for surveys conducted in the 1970s (Van Egmond, 1989). The United States General Accounting Office (GAO, 1991) concluded that industry, federal and state programs are effective in detecting and controlling aflatoxin and that it is doubtful that additional programs or limits would reduce the risk of aflatoxin in the food supply. The GAO specifically examined the state-administered program in the state of Georgia as a part of its report. In 1989, 13% of corn samples tested by the Georgia Department of Agriculture exceeded 20 ppb. On farms, 3.9% of tested milk exceeded limits while at the retail level only 0.4% of milk was in violation. Current surveillance programs in the US aimed at reducing food residues make it very unlikely that aflatoxin will be fed at high enough levels and for sufficient duration to have significant production or health effects on dairy herds in those regions that have an active program.

Dairy cattle feeds should contain less than 20 ppb aflatoxin to prevent milk residues above 0.5 ppb. Concentrations of aflatoxin should be conservatively low because of uncertainties in sampling and analysis, nonuniform distribution of aflatoxin, and potential for more than one source of aflatoxin in the diet.

T-2 toxin

T-2 toxin, a Fusarium-produced toxin, has been associated with gastroenteritis, intestinal hemorrhages (Petrie *et al.*, 1977) and death in cattle (Hsu *et al.*, 1972). Serum immunoglobulins and certain complement proteins were lowered in calves receiving T-2 toxin. T-2 has been shown to reduce white cell and neutrophil count in 50 kg calves (Gentry *et al.*, 1984) as well as immunoglobulin levels in 190 kg calves (Mann *et al.*, 1983). Administration of pure T-2 toxin failed to produce hemorrhagic bowel syndrome in a cow although it did produce a rumen ulcer and edema of the submucosa of the reticulum, cecum and colon (Weaver *et al.*, 1980). Patterson *et al.* (1979) had previously failed to produce hemorrhagic symptoms in calves with either T-2 toxin or diacetoxyscirpenol. Together, these studies suggest that other unidentified toxins are present or that interactions with conditions in the field are somehow different than those encountered in the laboratory.

Analysis of corn grain samples from the 1988-89 drought year in the midwestern US showed a 13% incidence of T-2 toxin. T-2 toxin has been detected in 7% of over 2000 non-random samples submitted by farmers to the North Carolina mycotoxin testing program over a nine year period (Whitlow *et al.*, 1998). In a review of mycotoxin incidence in European countries, Gareis *et al.* (1989) indicated that T-2 had been found to occur in over 20% of oats samples and between 3% and 5% of other grains and mixed feeds.

T-2 is metabolized in the rumen to HT-2 and acetyl HT-2 (Munger *et al.*,

1987). These derivatives are less toxic than T-2, but are still potent toxins.

Residues of T-2 and its derivatives have been found in milk, but have a low transfer rate from feed to milk. After 72 hrs, an orally administered dose of T-2 at 0.42 mg/kg of body weight (approximately 36 ppm) was almost completely excreted in the feces and urine (Yoshizawa *et al.*, 1981; 1982). Milk residues, which reached a maximum of about 35 ppb, suggest that about 0.2% of T-2 and its metabolites are excreted into milk. In the lactating cow administered radioactive labeled T-2 toxin, three metabolites (3'-hydroxy-T-2 toxin, 3'-hydroxy-HT-2 toxin and 3'-hydroxy-7-hydroxy-HT-2 toxin) accounted for 30-40% of the radioactivity in urine, 60-70% of radioactivity in milk and 50-60% of the radioactivity in blood plasma. Other metabolites included HT-2 toxin, neosolaniol and 4-deacetylneosolaniol. Other investigators (Robinson *et al.*, 1979) have measured T-2 up to a peak of 160 ppb in milk on the fifth day after starting oral intubation with daily doses of 182 mg of T-2 toxin for 15 consecutive days (equivalent to about 9 ppm in the diet, assuming a daily consumption of 20 kg).

There are currently no regulations on T-2 toxin in the US.

Deoxynivalenol

In 1982 the FDA issued an advisory which recommended a level of concern for deoxynivalenol (DON) at 1 ppm in finished wheat products for human consumption, 2 ppm for wheat entering the milling process and 4 ppm for wheat by-products used in animal feeds. This advisory was updated in 1993 to 1 ppm in finished wheat products for human consumption. Advisory levels for animal feeds were changed to 5 ppm in grains and grain products (not to exceed 20% of the diet) fed to swine; 10 ppm in feeds for poultry and ruminating beef and feedlot cattle older than four months (not to exceed 50% of their diets); and 5 ppm in feed for all other animals (not to exceed 40% of their diets) (Wood and Trucksess, 1998).

Deoxynivalenol has been associated with reduced feed intake (Trenholm *et al.*, 1985) in ruminants. Symptoms of unthriftiness, low weight gain and a trend toward reduced performance have been associated with both DON and zearalenone (e.g. Noller *et al.*, 1979). Whitlow *et al.* (1991) suggested an association of DON with milk production loss. Charmley *et al.* (1993) demonstrated a 13% (2.85 kg) numerical decrease in 4% fat corrected milk production (statistics not available) utilizing 18 mid-lactation dairy cows (average 19.5 kg milk/day) consuming diets shown to contain no common mycotoxins other than DON, which was at levels of 2.7 to 6.4 ppm in treatment diets. While the decrease in actual milk production (1.35 kg) was not statistically significant, the decrease in fat test (3.92 *vs.* 3.04%) was significant. DiCostanzo *et al.* (1995a) cite results by Ingalls (1994) where lactating dairy cows were fed 0, 3.6, 10.9 and 14.6 ppm DON for 21 days without an apparent effect on feed intake or milk production, which averaged about 30 kg daily. Foster *et al.* (1986) showed that DON is associated with as yet unknown factors causing productivity losses in swine. Pure DON added to swine diets did not result in effects as severe as did similar levels of DON provided by naturally contaminated grains. Presence of DON in feed apparently indicates that the feed is moldy. In this way, DON serves as an indicator of spoilage, and the probable presence of other mycotoxins or factors more toxic than DON itself. Smith and MacDonald (1991) have suggested that fusaric acid produced by *Fusarium moniliforme* may be interacting with mycotoxins such as DON to produce more severe effects. It is well documented that multiple mycotoxins often occur in the same feed sample (Abbas *et al.*, 1989; Hagler *et al.*, 1984), and thus several interactions are possible.

Wood and Trucksess (1998) suggest that DON may be the most widely distributed of the Fusarium mycotoxins. An Ohio study of 52 preharvest corn samples from 26 farms showed 46% of samples to contain DON (Vesonder *et al.*, 1978). An Illinois survey of feeds from swine problem herds found 80% of samples contained DON and 12% zearalenone (Côté *et al.*, 1984). A 1982 survey of hard, red winter wheat in Kansas and Nebraska found a mean 1.71 ppm DON in 157 samples (Shotwell *et al.*, 1985). Fifty-eight percent of the samples contained greater than 1 ppm DON and only 8% less than 0.1 ppm. In 1993, adverse weather conditions prompted a survey of wheat and barley samples from 25 states that revealed that about 40% of samples contained more than 2 ppm DON (Trucksess *et al.*, 1995). Analysis of corn grain samples from 1993 collected from the midwestern US showed that 70% contained DON with 19% above 1 ppm and 6% greater than 2 ppm (Wood and Trucksess, 1998). Of over 2400 samples non-randomly submitted during a nine year period by North Carolina farmers, 58% contained detectable levels of DON with positive samples averaging 1.7 ppm (Whitlow *et al.*, 1998).

Deoxynivalenol is transformed to DOM-1 in the rumen with estimates of 24 hr degradation of about 50% (King *et al.*, 1984). Deoxynivalenol and metabolites are rapidly excreted, primarily through urine (Côté *et al.*, 1986a; Prelusky *et al.*, 1984; 1987). Prelusky *et al.* (1984) administered DON in an oral dose of 920 mg and found less than 4 ng/ml of free and conjugated DON in the milk. DON was excreted in milk primarily as DOM-1, but excretion rate is extremely low at 0.0001% of the dose. Côté *et al.* (1986a) found no DON, but up to 30 ppb of DOM-1 in milk of cows fed DON at about 300 mg/day (66 ppm) for five days.

Zearalenone

Zearalenone is a Fusarium produced mycotoxin that elicits an estrogenic response in monogastrics (Sundlof and Strickland, 1986), but is of less toxicity to ruminants. A controlled study with cows fed up to 22 ppm zearalenone resulted in no obvious effects except that corpora lutea were smaller in treated cows (Weaver *et al.*, 1986b). In a similar study with heifers receiving about 13 ppm zearalenone, conception rate was depressed about 25%; otherwise, no obvious effects were noted (Weaver *et al.*, 1986a). A few case reports have related zearalenone to an estrogenic response in ruminants (Khamis *et al.*, 1986; Mirocha *et al.*, 1968; Roine *et al.*, 1971). Large doses were associated with abortions in cattle (Kellela and Ettala, 1984, Mirocha *et al.*, 1974). Mirocha *et al.* (1968) isolated zearalenone from hay associated with infertility in dairy cattle. Other cattle responses may include vaginitis, vaginal secretions, poor reproductive performance and mammary gland enlargement in virgin heifers. In a field study by Coppock and Mostrom (1990), diets containing about 750 ppb zearalenone and 500 ppb DON resulted in poor feed consumption, depressed milk production, diarrhea and total reproductive failure. New Zealand workers (Towers *et al.*, 1995a, 1995b; Sprosen and Towers, 1995; Smith *et al.*, 1995) have related urinary zearalenone and zearalenone metabolites (zearalenone, zearalanone, α- and ß-zearalenol and α- and ß-zearalanol), which they refer to as 'zearalenone', to intake of 'zearalenone' and to reproductive disorders in sheep and dairy cattle. In sheep, 'zearalenone' was related to lower conception, reduced ovulation, and increased twinning rates. With dairy cattle, herds with low fertility were found to have higher levels of blood and urinary 'zearalenone' and consume pastures containing higher levels of 'zearalenone'. In addition, within herds, individual cows were examined by palpation and those that were determined to be cycling had lower blood 'zearalenone' levels than did cows that were not cycling. Differences in 'zearalenone' levels were attributed to selective grazing behavior. The reproductive problems in dairy cattle were associated with 'zearalenone' concentrations of about 400 ppb in the pasture samples.

Grain sorghum samples from 10 states harvested in 1975 and 1976 were analyzed for zearalenone with a detection limit of 100-200 ppb (Shotwell *et al.*, 1980). Twenty-eight percent were positive, with 18% above 1 ppm. In two Virginia surveys, zearalenone was found in 19 of 42 wheat samples in 1975; but none was found in samples collected from 1976-1980 (Shotwell *et al.*, 1977; Shotwell and Hesseltine, 1983). Eppley *et al.* (1974) reported that 17% of corn samples collected from Corn Belt areas from the 1972 crop where Fusarium damage was reported in association with excessive moisture contained zearalenone at levels of 0.4 to 5.0 ppm. Stoloff *et al.* (1976) surveyed the 1973 crop corn and found the incidence of zearalenone to be 10% in corn from the midwestern US and 1% in other regions of the US, with a maximum value of 0.4 ppm. Of over 1700 samples non-randomly submitted during a nine year period by North Carolina farmers, 17.5% contained detectable levels of zearalenone with positive samples averaging 0.7 ppm (Whitlow *et al.*, 1998).

Shreeve *et al.* (1979) fed dairy cows about 1 ppm zearalenone for 11 weeks without detecting a milk residue. Prelusky *et al.* (1990) administered up to 6 g of zearalenone per cow daily and found a total milk residue of up to 16 ppb, which represented about 0.01% of the dose. Hagler *et al.* (1980) administered 5 g zearalenone in ground feed to a lactating dairy cow that was milked twice daily with samples collected until 120 hr after dosing. Only trace levels of zearalenone were found in the milk obtained at 96, 108 and 120 hr after dosing and trace levels of zearalenol were also found in the milk at 108 and 120 hr after dosing. Mirocha *et al.* (1981) found that zearalenone and its metabolites reached levels above 1 ppm in milk representing about 0.7% of the zearalenone dosage, which was 25 ppm for eight days.

Zearalenone is rapidly converted to α- and ß-zearalenol in rumen cultures (Kiessling *et al.*, 1984). Ruminal degradation of zearalenone was found to be about 30% complete in 48 hrs (Kellela and Vasenius, 1982).

There are no regulations for zearalenone in feed, food or milk in the US.

Fumonisin

Fumonisin B_1 was isolated by Gelderblom *et al.* (1988) and shown to be a cancer promoter. Fumonisin B_1 has been shown to cause leukoencephalomalacia in horses (Marasas *et al.*, 1988), pulmonary edema in swine (Harrison *et al.*, 1990), and hepatoxicity in rats (Gelderblom *et al.*, 1991). While fumonisin B_1 is thought to be much less potent in ruminants than in monogastrics, work by Krick *et al.* (1981) suggested that fumonisin was toxic to sheep. Osweiler *et al.* (1993) demonstrated that fumonisin B_1 in large amounts (148 ppm) can cause mild liver damage in cattle even when fed for a short term (31 days), but without an effect on feed intake or weight gain. Whitlow (unpublished) has demonstrated that fumonisin B_1 is toxic to dairy cattle. Fed for approximately seven days prior to freshening and for 70 days thereafter, dietary fumonisin B_1 at 100 ppm significantly and dramatically reduced milk production (6 kg/cow/day) and increased serum enzymes levels indicative of liver disease.

A USDA/APHIS (Anon., 1995) survey found an average of 6.9% of 1995 corn samples from Missouri, Iowa and Illinois to contain more than 5 ppm fumonisin B_1. Over 60% of corn samples collected from 1988 to 1991 from the midwest contained fumonisin B_1 (Murphy *et al.*, 1993). FDA surveys from 1994 and 1995 show that while over 45% of shelled corn samples from both years contained detectable levels of fumonisin B_1, the percentages of samples which contained more than 1 ppm were 2.4% of the 1994 samples and 10.2% of the 1995 samples (Wood and Trucksess, 1998).

Fumonisin B_1 carryover from feed to milk is thought to be negligible (Richard *et al.*, 1996; Scott *et al.*, 1994). Prelusky *et al.* (1996) reported studies where dairy cattle were administered fumonisin B_1 either orally or intravenously. The oral dosages were approximately equal to dietary concentrations of 60 to 300 ppm. The intravenous dosages were stated to be similar to dietary concentrations of 125 to 500 ppm. No fumonisin B_1 or its metabolites were detected in milk (detection limit of 0.5 ng/ml for fumonisin B_1).

Maragos and Richard (1994) analyzed 155 milk samples collected in Wisconsin during a period when feeds were reported to be severely affected by mold. Additionally, 10 samples were collected in Illinois. Feed samples associated with these milk samples were not collected and thus fumonisin B_1 concentrations in feed were unknown. Only one of the 165 milk samples tested positive for fumonisin B_1, which was determined to be 1.29 ng/ml. This suggests that fumonisin can occur in milk, but is likely to be at very low levels.

There are no current regulations for fumonisin B_1 in feed, food or milk in the US.

Ochratoxin

Ochratoxin A is produced primarily by penicillium molds and tends to be more prevalent in cooler climates (Pohland *et al.*, 1992). Although as much as 50% of the dietary ochratoxin is destroyed within 15 minutes in the rumen (Kiessling *et al.*, 1984), there are reports of ochratoxin toxicity in dairy cattle indicating symptoms of diarrhea, kidney damage and reduced milk production (Ribelin, 1978; Vough and Glick, 1993). Sreemannorayoma *et al.* (1988) showed that calves with a functioning rumen survived ochratoxin in oral doses of 2.0 mg/kg bodyweight, while preruminant calves died when administered ochratoxin at doses of as little as 0.25 mg/kg bodyweight.

Goats were administered a single dose of radiolabeled ochratoxin A at 0.5 mg/kg (Nip and Chu, 1979). Cumulative excretion of radioactivity over seven days indicated that 53% was excreted in the feces, 38% in the urine and 6% in milk. Of the radioactivity in milk, only a small amount was in the form of ochratoxin A, representing 0.026% of the dosage administered. In a study with lactating cows, where ochratoxin A was fed at 317 to 1,125 ppb for 11 weeks, neither ochratoxin A nor its metabolite ochratoxin α were detected in milk (Shreeve *et al.*, 1979).

There are no regulations on ochratoxin in feed, food or milk in the US.

Treatments for mycotoxin contamination

Adsorbent materials such as clays (bentonite, zeolite) added to contaminated diets fed to rats, poultry, swine and cattle have helped reduce the effects of mycotoxins (Diaz *et al.*, 1997; Galey *et al.*, 1987; Harvey, 1988; Lindemann and Blodgett, 1991; Scheideler, 1990; Hayes, 1990; Smith, 1980; 1984). In most cases, clay was added to the diet at about 1%. Other absorbent materials such as activated carbon at 1% of the diet (Galvano *et al.*, 1996), and glucomannans at 0.05% of diet dry matter (Diaz *et al.*, 1999) have been shown effective in reducing aflatoxin in milk. Figure 2 shows the percentage reduction in milk aflatoxin associated with inclusion of various aflatoxin binders in the diet (Diaz *et al.*, 1999). In this study inclusion of an esterified glucomannan product (Mycosorb, Alltech, Inc.) was shown to reduce milk aflatoxin concentrations by 58% in dairy cows consuming aflatoxin-contaminated diets when included at 0.05% of the diet dry matter. The reduction of milk aflatoxin was similar to that seen for a sodium bentonite product included in the diet at 1.1% of the dry matter.

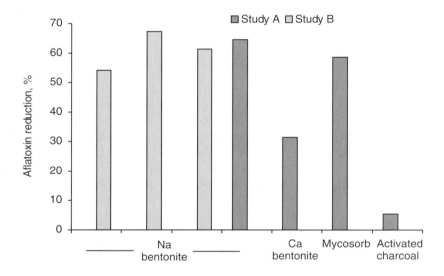

Figure 2. Effect of feed additives on reduction of milk aflatoxin residues from independent studies with lactating dairy cows (bentonites added at 1% of DM, Mycosorb added at 0.05% of DM, activated charcoal added at 0.25% of DM).

Limited studies on binding of mycotoxins other than aflatoxin are also available, but such studies are difficult to conduct *in vivo* because of the lack of a simple biological marker to estimate binding. While there are estimates for mycotoxin binding with feed additives *in vitro*, such values may not reflect binding *in vivo* (Diaz *et al.*, 1997) and are not the same for all mycotoxins (Devegowda *et al.*, 1998).

Summary

While many mycotoxins are common contaminants of feedstuffs, aflatoxin is the only mycotoxin that has received regulatory action in the US as a possible contaminant in milk. This is because aflatoxin is carcinogenic and highly toxic to humans, and because milk is a primary component of the diet of infants. Several other mycotoxins or their derivatives may be found in extremely small amounts in milk. It is thought that significant residues of these other mycotoxins occur in milk only when very high, nonclinical levels are administered to cows. Additionally the derivatives are generally less toxic than the parent compound. Therefore, mycotoxins other than aflatoxin are not considered as likely human health hazards in milk.

Regulatory efforts have successfully reduced the risk of aflatoxin in the food supply in the US (GAO, 1991). Efforts to prevent aflatoxin formation, to divert contaminated ingredients away from usage in dairy feeds, and to use feed additives that reduce aflatoxin absorption by the animal have contributed to fewer milk contamination problems.

References

Abbas, H.K., C.J. Mirocha, T. Kommedahl, R.F. Vesonder and P. Golinski. 1989. Production of trichothecenes and non-trichothecene mycotoxins by fusarium species isolated from maize in Minnesota. Mycopathologia 108:55.

Allcroft, R. and R.B.A. Carnaghan. 1962. Groundnut toxicity: *Aspergillus flavus* toxin (aflatoxin) in animal products. Vet. Rec. 74:863.

Allcroft, R. and R.B.A. Carnaghan. 1963. Groundnut toxicity: an examination for toxin in human products from animals fed toxic groundnut meal. Vet. Rec. 75:259.

Anonymous. 1995. Mycotoxin levels in the 1995 Midwest preharvest corn crop. USDA, APHIS. N195.1295.

Applebaum, R.S., R.E. Brackett, D.W. Wiseman and E.L. Marth. 1982. Responses of dairy cows to dietary aflatoxin: feed intake and yield, toxin content, and quality of milk of cows treated with pure and impure aflatoxin. J. Dairy Sci. 65:1503.

Charmley, E., H.L. Trenholm, B.K. Thompson, D. Vudathala, J.W.G. Nicholson, D.B. Prelusky and L.L. Charmley. 1993. Influence of level of deoxynivalenol in the diet of dairy cows on feed intake, milk production and its composition. J. Dairy Sci. 76:3580.

Coppock, R.W. and M.S. Mostrom. 1990. Apparent zearalenone intoxication in a dairy herd from feeding spoiled acid-treated corn. Vet. Hum. Toxicol. 32:246.

Côté, L.M., A.M. Dahlem, T. Yoshizama and W.B. Buck. 1986a. Excretion of deoxynivalenol and its metabolite in milk, urine and feces of lactating dairy cows. J. Dairy Sci. 69:2416.

Côté, L.M., J.D. Reynolds, R.F. Vesonder, W.B. Buck, S.P. Swanson, R.T. Coffey and D.C. Brown. 1984. Survey of vomitoxin-contaminated feed grains in Midwestern United States and associated health problems in swine. J. Am. Vet. Med. Assoc. 184:189.

CAST. Council for Agricultural Science and Technology. 1989. Mycotoxins: Economic and Health Risks. Task Force Report No. 116. Ames, Iowa.

Devegowda, G., M.V.L.N. Raju, N. Afzali and H.V.L.N. Swamy. 1998. Mycotoxin picture worldwide: novel solutions for their counteraction. In: Biotechnology in the Feed Industry, Proceedings of Alltech's 14th Annual Symposium (T.P. Lyons and K.A. Jacques, eds.). Nottingham University Press, Nottingham, UK, p. 241.

Diaz, D.E., J.T. Blackwelder, W.M. Hagler, Jr., B.A. Hopkins, F.T. Jones, K.L. Anderson and L.W. Whitlow. 1997. The potential of dietary clay products to reduce aflatoxin transmission to milk of dairy cows. J. Dairy Sci. 80(Suppl. 1):261.

Diaz, D.E., W.M. Hagler, Jr., B.A. Hopkins, J.A. Eve and L.W. Whitlow. 1999. The potential for dietary sequestering agents to reduce the transmission of dietary aflatoxin to milk of dairy cows and to bind aflatoxin *in vitro*. J. Dairy Sci. 82(Suppl. 1):838.

DiCostanzo, A., L. Johnston, H. Windels and M. Murphy. 1995a. A review of the effects of molds and mycotoxins in ruminants. Prof. Anim. Sci. 12:138.

Eppley, R.M., L. Stoloff, M.W. Trucksess and C.W. Chung. 1974. Survey of corn for fusarium toxins. J. AOAC 57:632.

Foster, B.C., H.L. Trenholm, D.W. Friend, B.K. Thompson and K.E. Hartin. 1986. Evaluation of different sources of deoxynivalenol (vomitoxin) fed to swine. Can. J. Anim. Sci. 66:1149.

Frobish, R.A., D.B. Bradley, D.D. Wagner, P.E. Long-Bradley and H. Hairston. 1986. Aflatoxin residues in milk of dairy cows after ingestion of naturally contaminated grain. J. Food. Prot. 49:781.

Galey, F.D., R.J. Lambert, M. Busse and W.B. Buck. 1987. Therapeutic efficacy of superactive charcoal in rats exposed to oral lethal doses of T-2 toxin. Toxicon 25:493.

Galvano, F., A. Pietri, T. Bertuzzi, G. Fusconi, M. Galvano, A. Piva and G. Piva. 1996. Reduction of carryover of aflatoxin from cow feed to milk by addition of activated carbons. J. Food Prot. 59:551.

GAO. 1991. Food safety and quality. Existing detection and control programs minimize aflatoxin. Report RCED-91-109.

Gareis, M., J. Bauer, C. Enders and B. Gedek. 1989. Contamination of cereals and feeds with fusarium mycotoxins in European countries. In: fusarium Mycotoxins, Taxonomy and Pathogenicity (J. Chelkowski, ed.). Elsevier, Amsterdam, p. 441.

Garrett, W.N., H. Heitman, Jr. and A.N. Booth. 1968. Aflatoxin toxicity in beef cattle. Proc. Soc. Exp. Biol. Med., pp. 127:188.

Gelderblom, W.C.A., K. Jaskiewicz, W.F.O. Marasas, P.G. Thiel, R.M. Horak, R. Vleggaar and N.P.J. Kriek. 1988. Fumonisins: Novel mycotoxins with cancer-promoting activity produced by *Fusarium moniliforme*. Appl. Environ. Microbiol. 54:1806.

Gelderblom, W.C.A., N.P.J. Kreik, W.F.O. Marasas and P.G. Thiel. 1991. Toxicity and carcinogenicity of the *Fusarium moniliforme* metabolite, fumonisin B_1, in rats. Carcinogenesis 12:1247.

Gentry, P.A., M.L. Ross and P.K-C Chan. 1984. Effect of T-2 toxin on bovine hematological and serum enzyme parameters. Vet. Hum. Toxicol. 26:24.

Guthrie, L.D. 1979. Effects of aflatoxin in corn on production and reproduction in dairy cattle. J. Dairy Sci. 62 (Suppl. 1):134.

Hagler, W.M., Gy. Dankó, L. Horváth, M. Palyusik and C.J. Mirocha. 1980. Transmission of zearalenone and its metabolite into ruminant milk. Acta Vet. Hung. 28:209.

Hagler, W.M., K. Tyczkowska and P.B. Hamilton. 1984. Simultaneous occurrence of deoxynivalenol, zearalenone and aflatoxin in 1982 scabby wheat from the Midwestern United States. Appl. Environ. Microbiol. 47:151.

Harrison, L.R., B.M. Colvin, J.T. Greene, L.E. Newman, and R.J. Cole. 1990. Pulmonary edema and hydrothorax in swine produced by fumonisin B_1, a toxic metabolite of *Fusarium moniliforme*. J Vet. Diagn. Invest. 2:21.

Harvey, R. B., L. F. Kubena, T. D. Phillips, W. E. Huff, and D. E. Corrier. 1988. Approaches to the prevention of aflatoxicosis. pp. 102. Proc. Maryland Nutr. Conf.

Hayes, S.M. 1990. Counteracting aflatoxin in livestock feed. In: Agricultural Research, USDA, ARS, Washington, D.C. 38(2):18.

Hsu, I.C., C.B. Smalley, F.M. Strong and W.E. Ribelin. 1972. Identification of T-2 toxin in moldy corn associated with a lethal toxicosis in dairy cattle. Appl. Microbiol. 24:684.

Ingalls, J. R. 1994. Influence of DON on feed consumption by dairy cows. pp. 129. In Proc. Western Nutr. Conf. Winnipeg, MB, Canada.

Kellela, K. and E. Ettala. 1984. The oestrogenic fusarium toxin (zearalenone) in hay as a cause of early abortions in the cow. Nord. Vet.-Med. 36:305.

Kellela, K. and L. Vasenius. 1982. The effects of rumen fluid on the content of zearalenone in animal fodder. Nord. Vet.Med. 34:336.

Khamis, Y., H.A. Hammad and N.A. Hemeida. 1986. Mycotoxicosis with oestrogenic effect in cattle. Zuchthyg. 21:233.

Kiessling, K., H. Pettersson, K. Sandholm and M. Olsen. 1984. Metabolism of aflatoxin, ochratoxin, zearalenone and three trichothecenes by intact rumen fluid, rumen protozoa and rumen bacteria. Appl. Environ. Microbiol. 47:1070.

King, R.R., R.E. McQueen, D. Levesque and R. Greenhalgh. 1984. Transformation of deoxynivalenol (vomitoxin) by rumen microorganisms. J. Agric. Food Chem. 32:1181.

Krick, N.P.T., R.S. Kellerman and W.F.O. Marasas. 1981. A comparative study of the toxicity of *Fusarium verticillioides* (= *F. moniforme*) to horses, primates, pigs, sheep and rats. Onderstepoort J. Vet. Res. 48:129.

Lindemann, M.D. and D.J. Blodgett. 1991. Various clays provide alternative for dealing with aflatoxin. Feedstuffs 63:15.

Mann, D.D., G.M. Buening, B. Hook and G.D. Osweiler. 1983. Effects of T-2 mycotoxin on bovine serum proteins. J. Am Vet. Med. Assoc. 44:1757.

Maragos, C.M. and J.L. Richard. 1994. Quantitation and stability of fumonisins B_1 and B_2 in milk. JAOAC 77:1162-1167.

Marasas, W.F.O., T.S. Kellerman, W.C.A. Gelderblom, J.A.W. Coetzer, P.G. Thiel, and J.J. van der Lugt. 1988. Leukoencephalomalacia in a horse induced by fumonisin B_1 isolated from *Fusarium moniliforme*. Onderstepoort J. Vet. Res. 55:197.

Marsi, M.S., V.C. Garcia and J.R. Page. 1969. The aflatoxin M_1 content of milk from cows fed known amounts of aflatoxin. Vet. Rec. 84:146.

Mirocha, C.J., J. Harrison, A.A. Nichols and M. McClintock. 1968. Detection of fungal estrogen (ZEN) in hay associated with infertility in dairy cattle. Appl. Microbiol. 16:797.

Mirocha, C.J., S.V. Pathre and T. S. Robinson. 1981. Comparative metabolism of zearalenone and transmission into bovine milk. Food Cosmet. Toxicol. 19:25.

Mirocha, C.J., B. Schauerhomer and S.V. Pathre. 1974. Isolation, detection and quantitation of zearalenone in maize and barley. J. Assoc. Off. Anal. Chem. 57:1004.

Moy, G.G. 1998. Roles of national governments and international agencies in the risk analysis of mycotoxins. In: Mycotoxins in Agriculture and Food Safety (K. K. Sinha and D. Bhatnagar, eds.). Markel Dekker, Inc., New York, pp. 483-496.

Munger, C.E., G.W. Ivie, R.J. Christopher, B.D. Hammock and T.D. Phillips. 1987. Acetylation/deacetylation reactions of T-2, acetyl T-2, HT-2 and acetyl HT-2 toxins in bovine rumen fluid *in vitro*. J. Agric. Food Chem. 35:354.

Murphy, P.A., L.G. Rice and P.F. Ross. 1993. Fumonisin B_1, B_2, and B_3 content of Iowa, Wisconsin and Illinois corn and corn screenings. J. Agric. Food Chem. 41:263.

Nip, W.K. and F.S. Chu. 1979. Fate of ochratoxin A in goats. J. Environ. Sci. Health B14:319.

Noller, C.H., M. Stob and J. Tuite. 1979. Effects of feeding *Gibberella zeae*-infected corn on feed intakes, body weight gain and milk production of dairy cows. J. Dairy Sci. 62:1003.

Osweiler, G.D., M.E. Kehrli, J.R. Stabel, J.R. Thurston, P.F. Ross and T.M. Wilson. 1993. Effects of fumonisin-contaminated corn screenings on growth and health of feeder calves. J. Anim. Sci. 71:459.

Patterson, D.S.P. and P.H. Anderson. 1982. Recent aflatoxin feeding experiments in cattle. Vet. Rec. 110:60.

Patterson, D.S.P., J.G. Matthews, B.J. Scheeve, B.A. Roberts, S.M. McDonald and A.W. Hayes. 1979. The failure of tricothecene mycotoxins and whole cultures of *Fusarium tricinctum* to cause experimental haemorrhagic syndromes in calves and pigs. Vet. Rec. 105:252.

Petrie, L., J. Robb and A.F. Stewart. 1977. The identification of T-2 toxin and its association with a hemorrhagic syndrome in cattle. Vet. Rec. 101:326.

Pohland, A.E., S. Nesheim and L. Friedman. 1992. Ochratoxin A: A Review. Pure J. Appl. Chem. 64:1029.

Prelusky, D.B., P.M. Scott, H.L. Trenholm and G.A. Lawrence. 1990. Minimal transmission of zearalenone to milk of dairy cows. J. Environ. Sci. Health B25:87.

Prelusky, D.B., H.L. Trenholm, G.A. Lawrence and P.M. Scott. 1984. Nontransmission of deoxynivalenol (vomitoxin) to milk following oral administration to dairy cows. J. Environ. Sci. Health. B19:593.

Prelusky, D.B., H.L. Trenholm, B.A. Rotter, J.D. Miller, M.E. Savard, J.M. Yeung, and P.M. Scott. 1996. Biological fate of fumonisin B_1 in food producing animals. In: Fumonisins in Food, Vol. 392 of Advances in Experimental Medicine and Biology (L.S. Jackson, J.W. DeVries and L.B. Bullerman, eds.). Plenum Press, New York, pp. 265-278.

Prelusky, D.B., D.M. Veira, H.L. Trenholm and B.C. Foster. 1987. Metabolic fate and elimination in milk, urine and bile of deoxynivalenol following administration to lactating sheep. J. Environ. Sci. Health. B22:125.

Ribelin, W.E., K. Fukushima and P.E. Still. 1978. The toxicity of ochratoxin to ruminants. Can. J. Comp. Med. 48:172.

Richard, J.L., G. Meerdink, C.M. Maragos, M. Tumbleson, G. Bordson, L.G. Rice, and P.F. Ross. 1996. Absence of detectable fumonisins in the milk of cows fed *Fusarium proliferatum (Matsushima) Nirenberg* culture material. Mycopathologia 133:123.

Robinson, T.S., C.J. Mirocha, H.J. Kurts, J.C. Behrens, M.S. Chi, G.A. Weaver and S.D. Nystrom. 1979. Transmission of T-2 toxin into bovine and porcine milk. J. Dairy Sci. 62:637.

Roine, K., E.L. Korpinen and K. Kallela. 1971. Mycotoxins as a probable cause of infertility in dairy cows. Nord. Vet. Med. 23:628.

Russel, L., D.F. Cox, G. Larsen, K. Bodwell and C.E. Nelson. 1991. Incidence of molds and mycotoxins in commercial animal feed mills in seven Midwestern states, 1988-89. J. Anim. Sci. 69:5.

Sargeant, K.A. Sheridan, J. O'Kelly and R.B.A. Carnaghan. 1961. Toxicity associated with certain samples of groundnuts. Nature 192:1096.

Scheideler, S.E. 1990. Aluminosilicates in poultry rations. Feed Management 41(1):22.

Scott, P.M., T. Delgado, D.B. Prelusky, H.L. Trenholm, J.D. Miller. 1994. Determination of fumonisin in milk. J. Environ. Sci. Health. B29:989.

Sharma, R.P. and D.K. Salunkhe. 1991. Occurrence of mycotoxins in foods and feeds. In: Mycotoxins and Phytoalexins (R.P. Sharma and D.K. Salunkhe eds.). CRC Press, Inc., Boca Raton, Florida, p. 13.

Shotwell, O.L. 1991. Natural occurrence of aflatoxins in corn. In: Mycotoxins and Animal Foods (J.E. Smith and R.S. Henderson eds.). CRC Press, Inc., Boca Raton, Florida, pp. 325.

Shotwell, O.L., G.A. Bennett, M.L. Gaulden, R.D. Plattner and C.W. Hesseltine. 1980. Survey for zearalenone, aflatoxin and ochratoxin in U.S. grain sorghum from 1975 and 1976 crops. J. Assoc. Off. Anal. Chem. 63:922.

Shotwell, O.L., G.A. Bennett, R.D. Stubblefield, G.M. Shannon, W.F. Kwolek and R.D. Plattner. 1985. Deoxynivalenol in hard red winter wheat: Relationship between toxin levels and factors that could be used in grading. J. Assoc. Off. Anal. Chem. 68:954.

Shotwell, O.L., M.L. Gaulden, G.A. Bennett, R.D. Plattner and C.W. Hesseltine. 1977. Survey of 1975 wheat and soybeans for aflatoxin, zearalenone and ochratoxin submitted for grading, 1975. J. Assoc. Off. Anal. Chem. 60:778.

Shotwell, O.L. and C.W. Hesseltine. 1983. Five-year study of mycotoxins in Virginia wheat and dent corn. J. Assoc. Off. Anal. Chem. 66:1466.

Shreeve, B.J., D.S.P. Patterson and B.A. Roberts. 1979. The 'carry-over' of aflatoxin, ochratoxin and zearalenone from naturally contaminated feed to tissues, urine and milk of dairy cows. Fd. Cosmet. Toxicol. 17:151.

Smith, J., C. Wesselink, J. Parr, J.M. Sprosen, E.A. Fowke, N.R. Towers and D. Laboyrie. 1995. Effect of zearalenone on ewe pregnancy rates. In: A Toxinology and Food Safety. Toxinology and Food Safety Research Group, Ruakura Research Centre, Hamilton, New Zealand.

Smith, T.K. 1980. Influence of dietary fiber, protein and zeolite on zearalenone toxicosis in rats and swine. J. Anim. Sci. 50:278.

Smith, T.K. 1984. Spent canola oil bleaching clays: potential for treatment of T-2 toxicosis in rats and short term inclusion in diets for immature swine. Can. J. Anim. Sci. 64:725.

Smith, T.K. and E. J. MacDonald. 1991. Effect of fusaric acid on brain regional neurochemistry and vomiting behavior in swine. J. Anim. Sci. 69:2044.

Sprosen, J.M. and N.R. Towers. 1995. Urinary zearalenone metabolite concentrations in herds with fertility problems. In: A Toxinology and Food Safety. Toxinology and Food Safety Research Group, Ruakura Research Centre, Hamilton, New Zealand.

Sreemannarayoma, O., A.A. Frohlich, T.G. Vitti, R.R. Marquart and D. Abramson. 1988. Studies of the tolerance and disposition of ochratoxin A in young calves. J. Animal Sci. 66:1703.

Stoloff, L., S. Henry and O.J. Francis, Jr. 1976. Survey for aflatoxins in 1973 crop corn stored on farms and in county elevators. J. AOAC 59:118.

Sundlof, S.F. and C. Strickland. 1986. Zearalenone and zearalenol: Potential residue problems in livestock. Vet. Hum. Toxicol. 28:242.

Towers, N.R., J.M. Sprosen and W. Webber. 1995a. Zearalenone metabolites in cycling and non-cycling cows: In: A Toxinology and Food Safety. Toxinology and Food Safety Research Group, Ruakura Research Centre, Hamilton, New Zealand.

Towers, N.R., C. Wesselink, E.A. Fowke and J.M. Sprosen. 1995b. Plasma *vs* urinary Azearalenone concentrations as indicators of Azearalenone intake. In: A Toxinology and Food Safety. Toxinology and Food Safety Research Group, Ruakura Research Centre, Hamilton, New Zealand.

Trenholm, H. L, B.K. Thompson, K.E. Hartin, R. Greenhalgh and A.J. McAllister. 1985. Ingestion of vomitoxin (deoxynivalenol)-contaminated wheat by nonlactating dairy cows. J. Dairy Sci. 68:1000.

Trucksess, M.W., F. Thomas, K. Young, M.E. Stack, W.J. Fulgueras and S.W. Page. 1995. Survey of deoxynivalenol in U.S. 1993 wheat and barley crops by enzyme-linked immunosorbent assay. J AOAC Int. 78:631.

Van Egmond, H.P. 1989. Mycotoxins in Dairy Products. Elsevier Science Pub. Co., Ltd. New York.

Vesonder, R.F., A. Ciegler, R.F. Rogers, K.A. Burbridge, R.J. Bothast and A. H. Jensen. 1978. Survey of 1977 crop year preharvest corn for vomitoxin. Appl. Environ. Microbiol. 36:885.

Vough, L.R. and I. Glick. 1993. Round bale silage. In: A Silage Production from Seed to Animal, NARES-67, Northeast Regional Agricultural Engineering Service, Ithaca, New York, pp. 117.

Weaver, G.A., H.J. Kurtz, C.J. Mirocha, F.Y. Bates, J.C. Behrens, T.S. Robison and S.P. Swanson. 1980. Can. Vet. J. 21:210-213.

Weaver, G.A., H.J. Kurtz, J.C. Behrens, T.S. Robison, B.E. Seguin, F.Y. Bates and C.J. Mirocha. 1986a. Effect of zearalenone on the fertility of virgin dairy heifers. Am. J. Vet. Res. 47:1395.

Weaver, G.A., H.J. Kurtz, J.C. Behrens, T.S. Robison, B.E. Seguin, F.Y. Bates and C.J. Mirocha. 1986b. Effect of zearalenone on dairy cows. Am. J. Vet. Res. 47:1826.

Whitlow, L.W., W.M. Hagler, Jr. and B.A. Hopkins. 1998. Mycotoxin occurrence in farmer submitted samples of North Carolina feedstuffs: 1989-1997. J. Dairy Sci. 81:(Abstr.)1189.

Whitlow, L.W., R. L. Nebel and W.M. Hagler, Jr. 1991. The association of deoxynivalenol in grain with milk production loss in dairy cows. In: G.C. Llewellyn, W.V. Dashek and C.E.O. Rear. 1994. Biodeterioration research 4. Plenum Press, New York, p. 131.

Wood, G.E. 1991. Aflatoxin M_1. In: Mycotoxins and Phytoalexins (R.P. Sharma and D.K. Salunkhe, eds.). CRC Press, Inc., Boca Raton, Florida, pp. 145-164.

Wood, G.E. 1992. Mycotoxins in foods and feeds in the United States. J. Anim. Sci. 70:3941.

Wood, G.E. and M.W. Trucksess. 1998. Regulatory control programs for mycotoxin-contaminated feed. In: Mycotoxins in Agriculture and Food Safety (K.K. Sinha and D. Bhatnagar, eds.). Markel Dekker, Inc., New York, pp. 459-481.

Yoshizawa, T., C.J. Mirocha, J.C. Behrens and S.P. Swanson. 1981. Metabolic fate of T-2 toxin in a lactating cow. Fd. Cosmet. Toxicol. 19:31.

Yoshizawa, T., T. Sakamoto, Y. Ayano and C.J. Mirocha. 1982. 3'-Hydroxy T-2 and 3'-Hydroxy HT-2 toxins: New metabolites of T-2 toxin, a trichothecene mycotoxin, in animals. Agric. Biol. Chem. 46:2613.

The ability of Mycosorb to bind toxins present in endophyte-infected tall fescue

JEFF EVANS AND KARL A. DAWSON

North American Biosciences Center, Alltech, Inc., Nicholasville Kentucky, USA

Summary

Tall fescue (*Festuca arundinacea*) is the most important cool season perennial grass used as a forage throughout the southeastern United States. It is able to withstand arid conditions mainly due to the fungal endophyte *Acremonium coenophialum* that infects most tall fescue. While the endophyte is beneficial to the plant, the toxins it produces have negative effects on the health and performance of grazing animals and result in a condition known as fescue toxicosis. Current methods of dealing with fescue toxicosis include removing the infected fescue completely and replacing it with endophyte-free tall fescue, reducing toxin intake through grazing management, or treating the symptoms of fescue toxicosis through antagonist therapy. These methods have had limited success. Mycosorb, a mycotoxin binder based on yeast glucan, has been shown to be effective in binding various mycotoxins produced by storage fungi *in vitro* and to reduce toxicity symptoms when added to livestock diets. Therefore, trials were conducted to determine its ability to bind the toxins produced by *A. coenophialum*.

Introduction

Tall fescue (*F. arundinacea*) is the major forage grass in the eastern and northwestern United States, covering 10,140,000 hectares (>25 million acres) in 21 states (Hoveland, 1993). It is the most abundant and economically important cool season perennial grass grown in the US. The region of cultivation (Figure 1) is predominantly from Missouri to Virginia on the north, Oklahoma to the west, Virginia to the east, and across Mississippi, Alabama, and Georgia to the south (Rohrbach *et al.,* 1995). A survey of 21 states revealed that tall fescue is mainly used for hay and pasture and estimated that 8.5 million cattle and 688,000 horses graze fescue pastures (Hoveland, 1993).

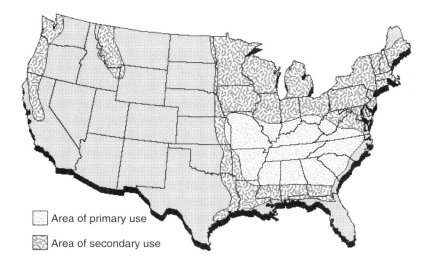

Figure 1. Range of fescue in the United States (Buckner *et al.*, 1985).

Tall fescue is desirable because of its ease of establishment, range of adaptation, and extended grazing season (Stuedemann and Hoveland, 1988). The nutritional composition compares favorably with other cool season grasses; however, performance of cattle grazing fescue during summer months is generally less than would be expected based on the nutrient composition of the grass (Joost, 1995). As tall fescue became a popular forage grass in the mid-20th century, reports of adverse effects on cattle grazing fescue began to accumulate (Bacon, 1995). It was not until 1977 that conclusive evidence of the presence of the endophytic fungus *A. coenophialum* in tall fescue and its correlation with fescue toxicosis in cattle was reported (Bacon *et al.*, 1977). The presence of endophyte was reported in 58% of forage samples submitted from 26 states (Shelby and Dalrymple, 1987). A more recent survey of 200 fields in 42 counties reported infection rates as high as 97%, and infection levels of individual fields greater than 67% for the majority of the fields (Strickland *et al.,* 1993). Problems with the endophytic fungus *A. coenophialum* are not limited to the US. Infected tall fescue has been reported in New Zealand, Italy, Wales, France, and Poland (Strickland, 1993).

Economic losses due to endophyte infections are substantial. Beef cattle grazing endophyte-infected tall fescue have been shown to have reduced weaning weights and reduced conception rates (Hoveland, 1993). Losses to the dairy industry are mainly due to reduced milk production while infected fescue is responsible for poor reproductive performance in mares. Foals born to mares grazing infected pasture are weak and frequently still-born. The endophyte reduces circulating progesterone and prolactin in mares (Porte and Thompson, 1992).

Researchers from a variety of disciplines have contributed to a better understanding of the problems involved in fescue toxicosis. Research to date has focused on four main areas: 1) identification and characterization of the toxins produced by *A. coenophialum;* 2) effects of endophyte infection on plant performance characteristics; 3) impact of fescue toxicosis on animal performance; and 4) treatment and prevention of fescue toxicosis in livestock. These studies have yielded a great deal of basic knowledge, but have failed to provide a universal technique or strategy for overcoming toxic symptoms and related performance losses.

Identification and characterization of the toxins produced by *A. coenophialum*

Much of the research since the identification of *A. coenophialum* has been dedicated to identifying the compounds responsible for toxic reactions in animals and the development of assay techniques. Fescue toxicity symptoms appear to result from the presence of a group of toxins. The two classes of compounds receiving the most attention as causative agents are the loline alkaloids and ergot alkaloids (Strickland *et al.,* 1993). N-acetyl and N-formyl loline account for the majority of the loline alkaloid content in endophyte-infected tall fescue (Yates *et al.,* 1990). The clavine alkaloids, lysergic acid amides and ergopeptines all belong to the broader group of ergot alkaloids. Several ergopeptines have been identified in endophyte-infected tall fescue including ergocornine, ergocryptine, ergocrystine, ergonine, ergosine, ergotamine and ergovaline (Yates *et al.,* 1985; Lyons *et al.,* 1986; Yates and Powell, 1988) (Figure 2). Ergopeptines account for 50% of the total ergot alkaloids, and ergovaline accounts for 80% of the total ergopeptines present (Lyons *et al.,* 1986). Clavine alkaloids and lysergic acid amide alkaloids have received less attention as causative agents for fescue toxicosis than the loline alkaloids and the ergot alkaloids (Strickland *et al.,* 1993).

A variety of procedures for the extraction, isolation, and identification of toxins produced by *A. coenophialum* have been developed. High pressure liquid chromatography (HPLC) is the preferred method of routine screening for ergopeptine alkaloids in endophyte-infected grasses (Yates and Powell, 1988). An immunological method capable of quantifying ergot alkaloids is also available (Hill *et al.,* 1994) Capillary gas chromatography is used to test for the loline alkaloids (Porter, 1995).

IMPACT ON PLANT PERFORMANCE CHARACTERISTICS

The development of endophyte-free grass cultivars began after the endophyte-associated toxins were identified as causative agents of fescue toxicosis. Comparing the new cultivars to endophyte-infected tall fescue revealed that the fungi and the host exist in symbiosis (Joost, 1995). Infected

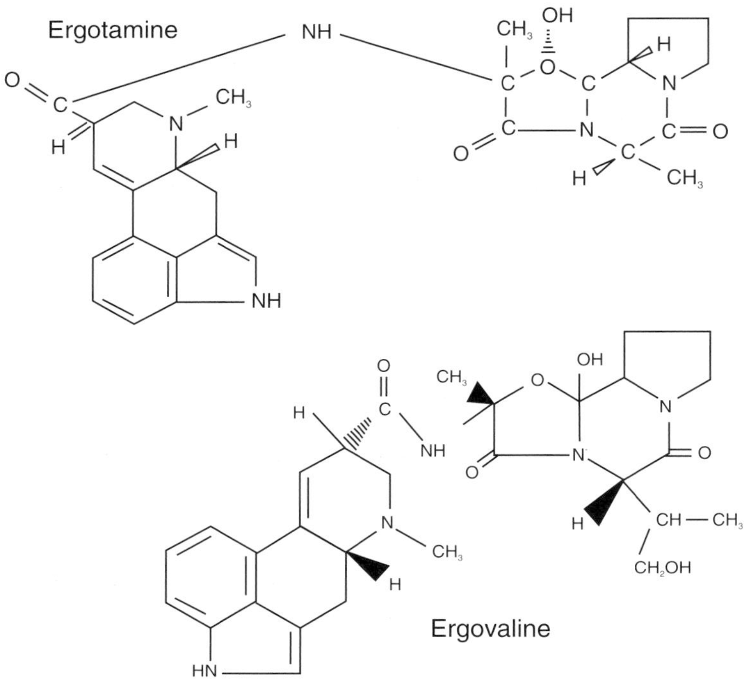

Figure 2. Important ergopeptines indentified in endophyte-infected tall fescue.

varieties show a higher germination rate, enhanced tiller formation and increased growth. Improvements in germination and tiller development promote establishment of the grass and give it a competitive advantage (Hill *et al.*, 1991). In addition, the endophyte seems to improve the ability of tall fescue to survive both biotic and abiotic stress. Endophyte-infected tall fescue has enhanced drought resistance and is a very valuable cool season grass from an agronomic perspective. The hardiness, other agronomic characteristics and high nutrient value of this grass make a strong case for finding a way to prevent its detrimental effects on animal health and performance.

IMPACT ON ANIMAL PERFORMANCE

Since the identification of a toxic endophyte in tall fescue, numerous research projects have examined effects on animals. A variety of different symptoms, including reduced body weight gain, increased body temperature, rough hair coat, reduced reproductive performance, fescue foot, excessive salivation, lower milk production and lower serum prolactin levels have been reported in animals consuming endophyte-infected tall fescue (Strickland *et al.*, 1993).

Research has been conducted on horses, sheep, cattle, quail, rabbits, and rats.

The earliest symptom recognized in cattle grazing endophyte-infected tall fescue was 'fescue foot'. Ergot alkaloids have a vasoconstrictive effect that decreases blood flow to extremities, which results in tissue death (Abney *et al.*, 1993). Vasoconstriction also reduces blood flow to the skin thereby affecting thermoregulation and can account for increased rectal temperatures in animals fed endophyte-infected tall fescue (Browning and Leite-Browning, 1997).

The two most economically significant losses associated with fescue toxicosis are reductions in feed intake and body weight gain. Reductions in weight gain have been noted in cattle, and to a lesser extent in horses (Bond *et al.*, 1986; Redmond *et al.*, 1994). Strickland et al. (1993) suggested that reduced feed intake may be due to physiological mechanisms. Increased body temperature may be the primary reason for depressed feed intake. Lower feed intake in combination with reduced digestibility could be responsible for weight gain depression (Patterson *et al.*, 1995).

Major reproductive problems in cattle and horses have been related to endophyte-infected tall fescue. Fescue toxins affect reproduction in both males and females. The majority of reproductive research in horses has focused on the pregnant mare (Porter and Thompson, 1992). Agalactia is the most commonly reported clinical sign in mares consuming infected fescue (Brendemuehl *et al.*, 1995). Other effects in mares include prolonged gestation, thickened placentas, extremely high levels of foal mortality and dystocia. The mechanisms thought to be responsible for reproductive problems are decreased concentrations of prolactin and melatonin, vasoconstriction affecting blood flow to internal organs and hyperthermia (Porter and Thompson, 1992).

The reduction in prolactin levels has been suggested to result from the interaction of endophyte toxins with the D2 dopamine receptor on the lactotroph (Aldrich *et al.*, 1993; Cross *et al.*, 1995). Decreased milk production has been reported in both cattle and horses (Strickland *et al.*, 1993). While the reduction in prolactin secretion is the most likely cause of reduced milk yields, other factors such as reduced nutrient uptake and vasoconstriction could also play a role (Strickland *et al.*, 1993).

Yeast cell wall preparations as feed additives and toxin binders

Yeasts have been used for many years as high quality protein in animal diets. High vitamin content, enzymes, and other important cofactors make yeast attractive digestive aids in ruminant and monogastric animals (Dawson, 1994). The positive effects of live yeast cultures on animal production have mainly been associated with yeast metabolites (Girard, 1996). Recent evidence suggests that other specific positive effects such as mycotoxin binding may be associated with certain fractions of the yeast cell wall. The ability of this material to bind toxins is of particular interest and was the basis for this research.

Yeast cell wall consists almost entirely of protein and carbohydrate. The carbohydrate fraction is composed primarily of glucose, mannose, and N-acetyglucosamine. Glucans and mannans, the two main sugars, are present in about equal concentrations in *Saccharomyces cerevisiae* (Figure 3). Chitin forms about 1% of the cell wall. *S. cerevisiae* contains glucans with mainly ß-1-3 linkages and some ß-1-6 linkages. Yeast mannan chains of various sizes are exposed on the external surface and are linked to cell wall proteins.

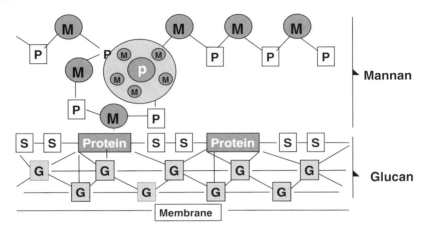

Figure 3. Structure of the cell wall of *Saccharomyces cerevisiae.*

Alltech, Inc. has been involved in the research and development of products derived from the cell wall fractions of yeast for over 10 years. Two commercial products were developed out of this work. One is a mannan oligosaccharide-based product derived from the yeast *S. cerevisiae* (Bio-Mos). It has been shown to bind enteric pathogens (Spring, 1996), enhance immune function (Savage *et al.*, 1996), and adsorb some mycotoxins present in animal feed (Trenholm *et al.*, 1994; Devegowda *et al.*, 1996). It has also been shown to improve animal health and performance in different monogastric species (Spring, 1996). A second-generation product shows great promise in mycotoxin binding ability (Table 1). It is a modified yeast cell wall preparation from *S. cerevisiae* consisting of esterified glucomannans.

During development of the commercial products, yeast cell wall preparations were screened for ability to adsorb various toxins *in vitro*. Binders were initially tested in a defined *in vitro* system; and products effective under those conditions were evaluated in a more complex system containing feed substrate and buffers to more closely simulate conditions in the gastro-intestinal tract. The *in vitro* tests demonstrated that the extent to

Table 1. Binding percentages of certain mycotoxins by modified yeast cell wall preparation and two other commercially-available binding agents.*

Binding agent	Aflatoxin	Zearalenone	Fumonisin	Deoxynivalenol
Modified yeast cell wall	95	52	45	10
Diatomaceus earth	47	12	17	–
Aluminosilicate	58	5	5	–

*Devegowda *et al.*, 1998.

which toxins were bound varied with the toxin and the cell wall preparation. The most efficient of these preparations *in vitro* was an esterified glucomannan produced from the cell wall of *S. cerevisiae*.

The yeast-derived glucomannan product (Mycosorb) has also been tested *in vivo*. Stanley *et al.* (1997) observed that layers given diets containing aflatoxin were less affected by the toxin when the diet included the glucomannan. In a study with lactating cows, Diaz *et al.* (1999) found that adding Mycosorb to feed reduced the concentration of aflatoxin B_1 in milk by more than 65%. This work suggested that such preparations are stable in ruminant feeds and can decrease absorption of certain types of fungal toxins from the gut. These observations were consistent with those from a study conducted by Chandler and Newman (1994) with yeast cell wall mannanoligosaccharides that demonstrated inability of the major rumen bacteria to utilize the cell wall preparation as a carbon source. This study showed that the cell wall preparations were fairly resistant to ruminal degradation. This suggests that the stable binding capacity of these preparations may be exploited to bind other potential toxins in the rumen. As a result of these studies, we became interested in examining the ability of the cell wall preparations to bind toxins associated with endophyte-infected fescue.

Research with modified yeast cell wall material: ability to bind endophyte toxins

In vitro toxin binding assays have been extensively used to evaluate ability of various toxin-binding agents to adsorb mycotoxins such as aflatoxin, zearalenone, T-2 toxin and vomitoxin present in stored grains. Research into the ability of a modified yeast cell wall preparation (Mycosorb) to bind toxins found in endophyte-infected was conducted in three phases:

1. Compare the ability of Mycosorb and a clay-based binder to bind toxins present in endophyte-infected fescue seed in an *in vitro* system.

2. Examine the ability of Mycosorb to bind toxins present in endophyte-infected fescue seed in an *in vitro* system containing minerals and/or organic material.

3.   Test the ability of Mycosorb to bind toxins present in endophyte-infected fescue in an *in vitro* rumen simulation system.

The phases were completed sequentially, and the results of each group of experiments are described below.

COMPARATIVE ABILITY OF MYCOSORB AND A CLAY BINDER TO BIND TOXINS PRESENT IN ENDOPHYTE-INFECTED FESCUE SEED IN AN *IN VITRO* SYSTEM

Ergotamine was chosen as a representative toxin for initial studies because it was readily available in a pure form and could be easily standardized in the analytical systems used. This toxin has been used in similar *in vitro* trials (Chestnut *et al.*, 1992) because of its structural similarity to ergovaline, the major ergopeptine alkaloid associated with endophyte infestation of tall fescue (Lyons *et al.*, 1986). The toxin binding studies were conducted in distilled water and carried out in volumes large enough to ensure a homogenous binder mixture. Initial tests demonstrated that maximum binding of ergotamine by Mycosorb was observed after a 1.5 hr incubation period (Figure 4). The amount of toxin bound was estimated by subtracting the amount of toxin measured in solution after centrifugation. This provided the basis for a rapid screening test to evaluate the relative ability of different agents to bind toxins.

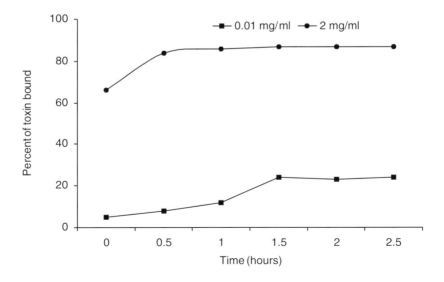

Figure 4. Effects of time and Mycosorb concentration on the percentage of ergotamine (10 ppm) bound.

A comparison of Mycosorb and a commercially available clay-based product tested ability of each binder to bind ergotamine *in vitro*. The binders were tested at 2 mg/ml with ergotamine concentrations of 0.5, 1, 2.5, 5 and 10 ppm. The lower levels of toxin represent the minimum levels that could be quantified using this assay. The upper limits are well above the ergotamine concentrations that have been shown to be toxic in animals. These upper and lower limits provide a good range in which to determine affinity of binders for the toxin. Each binder was mixed in water with the toxin and shaken for 90 minutes. Toxin levels were measured in the supernatant fluid after centrifugation.

At the concentrations tested, Mycosorb proved more effective at binding ergotamine than the clay-based material (Figure 5). At high ergotamine concentrations, it bound more than twice the amount of toxin (47 mg/g vs. 22 mg/g) under the same conditions and application rates.

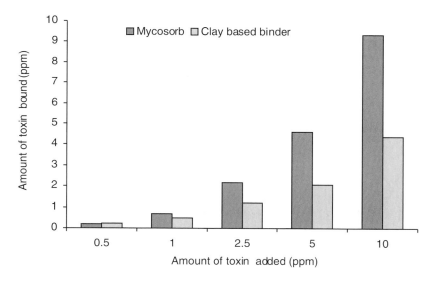

Figure 5. Comparison of the ability of Mycosorb and a clay-based binder to bind ergotamine *in vitro*. Binders were added at 2 mg/ml.

Mycosorb was then tested at rates of 0.5, 1 and 2 mg/ml with the ergotamine concentrations used in the previous test. The amount of toxin bound was clearly dependent on toxin concentration. The maximum binding equilibrium was reached at ergotamine concentrations above 2 ppm (Figure 6).

A series of extraction trials were then conducted to ensure that the binder was not simply masking or destroying the toxin during analysis. Sequential extractions with alcohol demonstrated that 60-70% of the toxin could be eluted from the toxin-binder complex. These studies demonstrated that the toxin was bound to, not destroyed by, the binder; and further that the binder

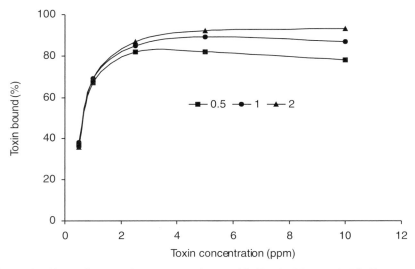

Figure 6. Effects of ergotamine concentrations on binding by Mycosorb. Binding was examined at binder concentrations of 0.5, 1.0 and 2 mg/ml.

did not interfere with the toxin assay. These observations also suggest that the binding mechanism is reversible and can be partially explained by simple saturation kinetics. As a result, the greatest degree of toxin binding can be expected at high toxin concentrations.

ABILITY OF MYCOSORB TO BIND TOXINS PRESENT IN ENDOPHYTE-INFECTED FESCUE SEED IN AN *IN VITRO* SYSTEM CONTAINING MINERALS AND/OR ORGANIC MATERIAL

The gastrointestinal environment is a very complex system containing a wide range of compounds that might be expected to affect the interaction between toxins and the binding agent. A major contributor of salts to the rumen is saliva, which contains high levels of bicarbonate and phosphate that buffer the rumen environment. To test Mycosorb in an environment similar to that found in the digestive tract, the binding assay was conducted in McDougal's artificial saliva (McDougall, 1948). Mycosorb was able to bind significant amounts of ergotamine in the artificial saliva, however there was an apparent reduction in binding capacity when this system was compared with water (Figure 7).

ABILITY OF MYCOSORB TO BIND TOXINS PRESENT IN ENDOPHYTE-INFECTED FESCUE IN RUMEN-SIMULATING BATCH CULTURES

Rumen fluid obtained from ruminally-cannulated steers was clarified for this experiment. Initial work showed interference during attempts to quantify

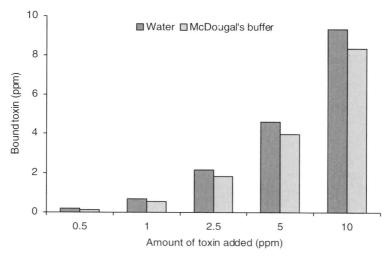

Figure 7. A comparison of the amount of toxin bound when mixed with Mycosorb at 2 mg/ml in water and in artificial saliva (McDougal's buffer).

the toxin, however, modifications to the extraction system allowed for the preparation of cleaner samples and improved toxin quantification.

The amount of toxin measured in the supernatant decreased as binder level increased, and was dramatically less than the samples containing no binder. Binding kinetics were similar to those seen in water and artificial saliva; but maximum binding and toxin affinity decreased when assays were run in rumen fluid (Figure 8).

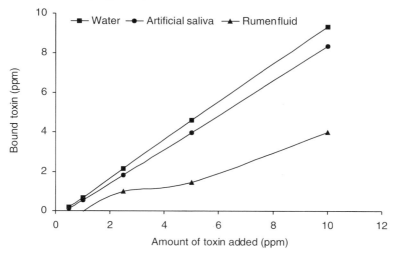

Figure 8. A comparison of amount of toxin bound when mixed with Mycosorb in the presence of five different levels of ergotamine from binding trials carried out in water, artificial saliva, and rumen fluid. The binder was added at 2 mg/ml.

419

While binding activities were decreased in the presence of the rumen fluid and artificial saliva, these preliminary experiments demonstrate the ability of Mycosorb to bind significant amounts of one of the toxins associated with fescue toxicosis in a simulated gastrointestinal environment.

Conclusions

The results of these studies indicate that Mycosorb was able to bind significant amounts of ergotamine. In addition, this modified yeast cell wall preparation bound the toxin to a much greater extent than a clay-based mycotoxin binder. Binding was dependent on mycotoxin concentration; which is consistent with a saturation model predicting a high affinity for the toxin at low toxin concentrations. Mycosorb maintained a high affinity for the ergotamine in the strong mineral environment of the artificial saliva and conditions similar to those found in rumen fluid. It appears that this binding ability could be used in strategies to decrease the bioavailability of ergotamine and similar toxins. Such strategies may be useful in preventing toxicities associated with endophyte-infected fescue.

References

Abney, L.K., J.W. Oliver and C.R. Reinemeyer. 1993. Vasoconstrictive effects of tall fescue alkaloids on equine vasculature. J. Equine Vet. Sci. 13:334-340.

Aldrich, C.G., M.T. Rhoades, J.L. Miner, M.S. Kerley and J.A. Paterson. 1993. The effects of endophyte-infected tall fescue consumption and use of a dopamine antagonist on intake, digestibility, body temperature and blood constituents in sheep. J. Anim. Sci. 71:158-163.

Bacon, C.W., J.K. Porter and J.D. Robins. 1977. *Epichloe typhina* from toxic tall fescue grasses. Appl. Environ. Micro. 34: 576-581.

Bacon, C.W. 1995. Toxic endophyte-infected tall fescue and range grasses: historic perspectives. J. Anim. Sci. 73:861-870.

Bond, J. and D.J. Bolt. 1986. Growth, plasma prolactin and ovarian activity in heifers grazing fungus-infected tall fescue. Nutr. Rep. Int. 34:93-102.

Brendemuel, J.P., T.R. Boosinger, D.I. Bransby and R.A. Shelby. 1995. The effect of short term exposure to and removal from the fescue endophyte *Acremonium coenophialum* on pregnant mares and foal viability. Biol Reproduction Monograph Series No., 1, 61-67.

Browning, R.J. and M.L. Leite-Browing. 1997. Effect of ergotamine and ergonovine on thermal regulation and cardiovascular function in cattle. J. Anim. Sci. 75:176-181.

Buckner, R.C., J.A. Boling, P.B. Burrus Jr., L.P. Bush, R.W. Hemken and M.R. Siegel. 1985. Johnstone Tall Fescue. Kentucky Agricultural Experiment Station Centennial, July.

Chandler, V.E. and K.E. Newman. 1994. Effects of mannanoligosaccharide and malto-oligosaccharide on growth of various rumen bacteria. Abstracts of Amer. Soc. for Microbiology Gen. Meeting, May, 1994. p. 266.

Chestnut, A.B., P.D. Anderson, M.A. Cochran, H.A. Fribourg and and K.D. Gwinn. 1992. Effects of hydrated sodium calcium aluminosilicate on fescue toxicosis and mineral absorption. J. Anim. Sci. 1992. 70:2838-2846.

Cross, D.L., M.L. Redmond and J.R. Strickland. 1995. Equine fescue toxicosis: signs and solutions. J. Anim. Sci. 73:899-908.

Dawson, K.A. 1994. Manipulation of microorganisms in the digestive tract: The role of oligosaccharides and diet specific yeast cultures. Proceedings of the California Animal Nutrition Conference for Feed Manufacturers.

Devegowda, G., B.I.R. Aravind and M.G. Morton. 1996. *Saccharomyces cerevisiae* and mannanoligosaccharides to counteract aflatoxicosis in broilers. Proc: Australian Poult. Sci. Symp., Sydney, Australia. 8:103-106.

Diaz, D.E., W.M. Hagler, Jr., B.A. Hopkins, J.A. Eve and L.W. Whitlow. 1999. The potential for dietary sequestering agents to reduce the transmission of dietary aflatoxin to milk of dairy cows. J. Dairy Sci. (abstract), Southern Branch, American Dairy Science Assoc., Feb. 1, 1999.

Girard, I.D., 1996. Characterization of stimulatory activities from *Saccharomyces cerevisiae* on the growth and activities of ruminal bacteria. Ph.D. Dissertation, University of Kentucky, Lexington, KY.

Hill, N.S., D.P. Belesky and W.C. Stringer. 1991. Competitiveness of tall fescue as influenced by *Acremonium coenophialum*. Crop Sci. 31:185-190.

Hill, N.S., F.N. Thompson, D.L. Dawe and J.A. Stuedemann. 1994. Antibody binding of circulating ergopeptine alkaloids in cattle grazing tall fescue. Am. J. Vet. Res. 55:419-424.

Hoveland, C.S. 1993. Importance and economic significance of the *Acremonium* endophytes to performance of animals and grass plant. Agric. Ecosystems Environ. 44: 3-12.

Joost, R.E. 1995. Acremonium in fescue and ryegrass: Boon or bane? A review. J. Anim. Sci. 73:881-888.

Lyons, P.C., R.D. Plattner and C.W. Bacon. 1986. Occurrence of peptide and clavine ergot alkaloids in tall fescue grass. Science 232:487-489.

McDougall, D.I. 1948. Studies on ruminant saliva. The composition and output of sheep's saliva. Biochem. J. Vol. 43, pp. 99-109.

Patterson, J.A., C. Forcherio, B.T. Larson, M.D. Samford and M.S. Kerley. 1995. The effects of fescue toxicosis on beef cattle productivity. J. Anim. Sci. 73:889-898.

Porter, J.K. 1995. Analysis of endophyte toxins: fescue and other grasses toxic to livestock. J. Anim. Sci. 73:871-880.

Porter, J.K. and F.N. Thompson, Jr. 1992. Effects of fescue toxicosis on reproduction in livestock. J. Anim. Sci. 70:1594-1603.

Redmond, L.M., D.L. Cross, J.R. Strickland and S.W. Kennedy. 1994. Efficacy of domperidone and sulpiride as treatments for fescue toxicosis in horses. Am. J. Vet. Res. 55:722-729.

Rohrbach, B.W., E.M. Green, J.W. Oliver and J.F. Schneider. 1995. Aggregate risk study of exposure to endophyte-infected (*Acremonium coenophialum*) tall fescue as a risk factor for laminitis in horses. Am. J. Vet. Res. 56:22-26.

Savage, T. F., P. F. Cotter and E. I. Zakrzewska. 1996. The effect of feeding mannanoligosaccharide on immunoglobulins, plasma IgG and bile IgA of Wrolstad MW male turkeys. Poult. Sci. 75(Suppl. 1):143.

Shelby, R.A. and L.W. Dalrymple. 1987. Incidence and distribution of the tall fescue endophyte in the United States. Plant Diseases 71:783-786.

Spring, P. 1996. Effects of mannanoligosaccharide on different cecal parameters and on cecal concentrations of enteric pathogens in poultry. Ph.D. Dissertation, University of Kentucky, Lexington, KY.

Stanley, V.G., Y.W. Park, C. Grayland and W.F. Krueger. 1997. Effects of mannanoligosaccharide (MOS) on aflatoxicosis, serum, liver and egg cholesterol, and egg production in chickens. In: International symposium on non-digestible oligosaccharides: healthy food for the colon? (R. Hartemink, ed) Wageningen, The Netherlands, Dec. 4-5, 1997. pg. 49.

Strickland, J. R., J. W. Oliver and D. L. Cross. 1993. Fescue toxicosis and its impact on animal agriculture. Vet. Human Toxicol. 35:454-464.

Stuedemann, J. A. and C. S. Hoveland. 1988. Fescue endophyte: history and impact on animal agriculture. J. Prod. Agric. 1:39.

Trenholm, L., B. Stewart, L. Underhill and D. Prelusky. 1994. Ability of Graingard to bind zearalenone and vomitoxin *in vitro*. Poster presentation, Alltech's 10th Annual Biotechnology in the Feed Industry Symposium, Lexington, KY, USA.

Yates, S.G. and R.G. Powell. 1988. Analysis of ergopeptine alkaloids in endophyte infected tall fescue. J. Agric. Food Chem. 36:337-340.

Yates, S.G., R.D. Plattner and G.B. Garner. 1985. Detection of ergopeptine alkaloids in endophyte infected, toxic KY-31 tall fescue by mass spectrometry/mass spectrometry. J. Agric. Food Chem. 33:719-722.

Yates, S.G., R.J. Petroski and R.B. Powell. 1990. Analysis of loline alkaloids in endophyte-infected tall fescue by capillary gas chromatography. J. Agric. Food Chem. 38:182–185.

Understanding the processes of protein degradation in forage crops provides opportunities for improved silage quality and enhanced animal production

RAYMOND JONES

Institute of Grassland and Environmental Research, Aberystwyth, Wales, UK

Introduction

UK silage production has increased from some 0.35 million tonnes in 1947 to 50 million tonnes in 1997. Silage now accounts for almost 80% of the total winter forage fed to ruminant livestock. In Europe, grass accounts for 54%, maize 32%, whole crop cereals 2% and legumes 1% of the crops harvested for silage. Silage making offers many advantages over conventional hay making, such as reduced dependence on weather, increased flexibility of conserving the crop at optimum quality and mechanisation from harvest to feeding. However, harvesting and storing wetter crops will necessitate more sophisticated machinery and storage facilities than for hay or other concentrate feeds. In particular, greater attention will need to be given to the process of preservation ensuring good compaction, anaerobic conditions and possibly additives to control the fermentation process so as to reduce in-silo losses.

In the UK, prohibition in the use of animal proteins subsequent to the BSE crisis has produced a gap in the supply of protein to ruminants. Concurrently, research evidence has shown that only 5-20% of the nitrogen (N) consumed by ruminants is being recovered in meat or milk. There is therefore the potential for large losses to the environment. Jarvis *et al.* (1996) calculated that the nitrate-N content in water drainage from a typical dairy farm was above the EU limit for most of the winter. The authors also drew attention to high losses to the atmosphere of ammonia and nitrous oxide, with potentially adverse environmental effects. Approaches to restrict loss of N from the animal have obvious appeal not only to limit environmental pollution but also to improve the economics of animal production.

Figure 1 indicates that more than 70% of the crude protein (CP) consumed by ruminants in Britain is from grassland feeds, with some 14% from cereals, 10% from oilseeds and only a trivial quantity from peas and beans. While the opportunity exists to increase production of CP at low cost this would not necessarily solve the problem of protein supply, because of inefficient utilisation of N by the animal. For example, increasing N fertiliser application to grassland from the current average level of 120 kg N/ha to 300 kg N/ha would double CP production from grassland (calculated from Morrison *et al.*, 1980) through increased yields of dry matter (DM) and increased CP concentration in the DM. This additional CP may not completely replace all of the other feed sources of N, because of limitations to feed intake and inefficient utilisation of CP in grassland feeds.

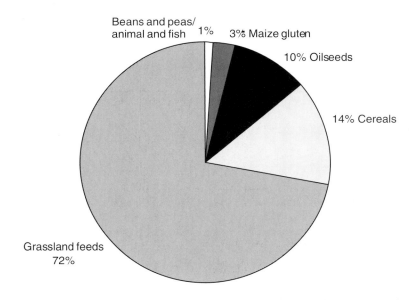

Figure 1. Supply of crude protein to ruminants in Britain in 1995 (thousand tonnes) (from Entec, 1997).

This paper will discuss opportunities for improving the efficiency of utilisation of CP in grassland feeds and the potential for use of high protein alternative forage crops.

Understanding protein degradation in forage and silage

The role of nitrogenous compounds in silage has been the subject of a review by Ohshima and McDonald (1978). Of the total nitrogen (TN) containing substances in fresh herbage, some 75-90% are in the form of protein. The remainder consists of soluble nitrogenous organic compounds including free amino acids, amides, glutamine and asparagine together with smaller quantities of amines, chlorophyll, urea products and low molecular weight peptides. Fresh forage also contains variable amounts of inorganic soluble non-protein nitrogen (NPN) present mainly as nitrate and to a much lesser extent ammonia. The concentration of the NPN products will depend on timing and extent of applied nitrogen-based fertilizers. Concentration of nitrate in fresh forage can be as high as 10% of the total N (McDonald *et al.*, 1991), while ammonia-N concentrations in fresh herbage are usually less than 1.5% (Brady, 1960). Keady (1998) concluded that while increasing N fertiliser application on grassland increased yield of DM and consequently quantity of CP, this was accompanied by a reduction in feed value as intake and performance were depressed when conserved as silage as shown in Table 1.

Table 1. Effects of fertiliser N on animal performance.*

Animal performance	Nitrogen fertiliser (kg/ha)		
	72	126	180
Silage intake, kg DM/d	12.0	11.9	11.1
Milk yield, kg/d	18.0	17.5	17.3
Milk fat, %	4.36	4.28	4.21
Milk protein, %	3.31	3.33	3.28

*Adapted from Keady (1998).

PROTEIN DEGRADATION IN SILAGE

Proteolysis during ensilage has been widely reported. Protein content can decrease from 800 g/kg to 300 g/kg during ensilage (McDonald *et al.*, 1991). Protein breakdown commences after mowing and during wilting of the plant material usually as a consequence of plant enzyme activity. Messman *et al.* (1994) studied the effect of wilting on buffer-extractable proteins from a range of species using S-dodecyl sulphate polyacrilamide gel electrophoresis (SDS-PAGE). No loss of proteins was observed following a 24 hr wilt while a reduction of 30% was detected after five days drying. The degradation of protein was also accompanied by an increase in NPN content of the extended wilted material. Other workers (Mangan *et al.*, 1991; Carpintero *et al.*, 1979) observed minimal loss of RUBISCO, the major plant leaf protein fraction in wilted silage. Studies with gamma-irradiated plant material suggest that hydrolysis (i.e. breakdown to smaller peptides and free amino acids) is largely mediated by plant enzyme proteolytic activity (Oshima and McDonald, 1978). However some strains of bacteria, *Lactobacillus plantarum* and *L. paracasei* subspecies *paracasei,* have also been demonstrated to possess some proteolytic activity (Hickey *et al.*, 1983; Sasaki *et al.*, 1995). Both plant and microbial activities contribute to further catabolism of amino acids (Oshima and McDonald, 1978). Increased concentrations of alanine are frequently observed in small scale studies; and it is postulated that this is due to decarboxylation of aspartic acid (Kemble, 1956; Oshima *et al.,* 1979; Heron *et al.,* 1986). Increases in alanine have also been observed in farm-scale ryegrass silages made at the Institute of Grassland and Environmental Research (unpublished data). Protein degradation during ensilage consistently results in decreased concentrations of glutamic acid, arginine and aspartic acid and increased concentrations of gamma amino butyric acid and ornithine (Lessard *et al.,* 1978; Oshima *et al.,* 1979; Heron *et al.,* 1986). A simplified illustration of the protein breakdown products of herbage and ensiled material is shown in Figure 2.

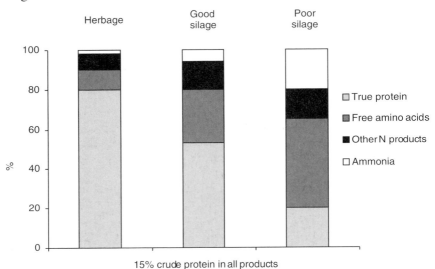

Figure 2. Protein fractions of herbage and silage.

It is clear that the most important protein fraction for efficient ruminant utilisation is the true protein (TP) component. It has also been shown (Jones, 1998) that poorly fermented silages will be associated with higher levels of free amino acids and reduced true protein. It is becoming apparent that routine silage analysis of crude protein does not provide adequate sensitivity for realistic feed formulation purposes. As shown in Figure 2, a similar crude protein value was obtained for the fresh grass herbage as for the poorly and well fermented silage. The free amino acids however, gave a better indication of the protein degradation. Unfortunately the chemical analysis procedures for the estimation of free amino acids is both laborious and expensive. Recently a new method was described by Winters *et al.* (1999a) where free amino acids from a crude extract of silage using a ninhydrin colorimetric technique was compared with conventional amino acid analysis. The new rapid technique correlated well with conventional amino acid analysis ($r^2 = 0.87$), and provides scope for further development as a routine method of predicting true protein content of silages.

IMPROVING EFFICIENCY OF UTILISATION FROM GRASSLAND FEEDS

The concentrations of CP in grazed grass, silage and grass hay are normally in the range 150-220, 100-160 and 80-120 g/kg DM, respectively, varying seasonally with N fertiliser rate, stage of maturity and the magnitude of losses during conservation. High CP levels in grassland feeds can lead to rapid breakdown in the rumen, leading to high concentrations of rumen ammonia and low levels of undegraded dietary protein (UDP). Low supply of energy to the rumen can also limit microbial protein synthesis, which can restrict the supply of essential amino acids to grass-fed animals. These effects may be even greater in silages as true protein is metabolised to free amino acids, peptides and ammonia as a consequence of proteolysis during the fermentation process.

Beever *et al.* (2000) noted that the yield of microbial protein with silages varied from 13 to 28 g microbial N/kg organic matter apparently digested in the rumen for silages compared with values of 33-58g for fresh forages. Microbial protein could be increased by improving the supply of readily available energy in feed and/or by improving the synchrony in the supply of N and energy to rumen microbes. In temperate grasses the major source of readily available energy is from water soluble carbohydrates (WSC) with concentrations in fresh grasses varying from 50-350 g/kg DM. There are characteristic differences in WSC seasonally (low in spring and autumn), with stage of growth (high during stem development) and among species (higher in ryegrass than in other sown species). Humphreys (1989) demonstrated that WSC content is heritable and varieties of perennial ryegrass have been bred with markedly higher WSC content. In a recent trial conducted at IGER where high sugar grasses were fed as zero-grazed to dairy cows, Miller *et al.* (1999) reported that milk yields were 3 kg/day higher for cows fed the experimental high sugar ryegrass (200 g WSC/kg DM) compared to the commercially available ryegrass (130 g WSC/kg DM). Differences between the varieties in dry matter intake and digestibility were also observed as shown in Table 2.

Table 2. Milk production from grazed high sugar grasses.*

	Grass species		Level of significance
	Perennial ryegrass	Hybrid ryegrass selected high sugar	
Dry matter intake, kg/d	10.8	12.5	*
Diet DM digestibility, g/g	0.64	0.71	**
Milk yield, kg/d	12.6	15.3	*

*Miller *et al.*, 1999.

OPPORTUNITIES FOR LIMITING PROTEOLYSIS IN GRASS SILAGE

Preserving grass as silage allows the possibility of changing the nature of the CP through the use of additives and crop management. Bacterial inoculants have been demonstrated to produce silages with higher proportions of true protein than silages made without additive (Jones, 1998; Merry *et al.*, 2000). It is likely that the more rapid acidification in the early phase of ensiling as a result of the dominance of homofermentative bacteria can inhibit protease activity and thereby reduce protein degradation. Jone (1998) has demonstrated improvements in animal performance with silages made with applied bacterial inoculants. This improvement in animal performance may be associated with improved efficiency of microbial protein. Sharp *et al.* (1994) reported an improvement of 33% in the efficiency of microbial protein synthesis when silages made with a biological inoculant were compared with well preserved untreated silage. Silage additives containing formaldehyde or tannins can also influence reductions in protein breakdown as discussed by Beever (1980). However, responses were dependent on the application rate used; and a risk of higher concentrations of indigestible protein led to reduced *in vivo* digestibility and enhanced faecal N loss.

While grass silage exhibits a high concentration of UDP, supplementation with high protein concentrates has shown positive benefits in milk production responses (Aston *et al.*, 1998). Such an approach will undoubtedly lead to increased losses of N to the environment (Table 3).

Table 3. Effect of increasing crude protein proportion in concentrate feed with *ad libitum* grass silage.*

	Crude protein as a proportion of total concentrate	
	0.16	0.26
N consumed	388	473
Nitrogen in:		
Urine and faeces	292	367
Milk	96	106
N in milk as proportion of N consumed	0.25	0.22

*From Aston *et al.*, 1998.

Role of alternative forage crops

In the post-BSE era alternative forage crops such as legumes, pulses, kale and lupin are assuming a much higher profile in UK agriculture as a consequence of consumer pressure to feed animals on natural, home grown forages. All of these forages are capable of giving relatively high yields of DM and of CP as indicated in Table 4. These forages are also characterised by high levels of feed intake (Beever *et al.*, 2000; Fraser *et al.*, 1999a; b).

Table 4. Protein production from forage crops in the UK.*

| | Crude protein (g/kg DM) | Yield (t/ha) | |
		Dry matter	Crude protein
White clover	220	6	1.3
Lucerne	200	10	2.0
Sainfoin	200	7	1.4
Red clover	180	9	1.6
Lotus	180	7	1.3
Kale	160	6	1.0
Grass	140	11	1.5

*Adapted from Entec, 1997.

A recent trial conducted by Dewhurst *et al.* (2000) showed higher intakes and milk yields for silages made from white clover, red clover and lucerne than from grass silage. In addition, levels of intake and production were intermediate when cows were fed mixtures of legume and grass silages as shown in Table 5.

Table 5. Effect of legume silages on feed intake and milk production with cows fed 8 kg/day of concentrates.*

	Silage dry matter intake (kg/day)	Milk yield (kg/day)
Grass	11.1	24.9
White clover	12.1	31.5
Red clover	13.5	28.1
Lucerne	13.6	27.7
Grass: white clover[†]	11.9	27.9
Grass: red clover[†]	11.0	28.6
s.e.d.	0.80	1.81

*From Dewhurst *et al.*, 2000.
[†]Cows fed 1:1 mixtures of silages on DM basis.

It must be noted that while white clover silage performed well in terms of milk production, it is unlikely that a monoculture crop would be economically viable due its low yield (2 tonnes DM/ha). Moorby *et al.* (1998) found higher levels of performance and milk production from cows fed on kale-barley silage than with grass silage alone.

In relation to protein composition and utilisation there are major differences between these forages. White clover and lucerne true protein (TP:CP) ratios (0.35-0.40) are similar to grass silage with low concentrations of WSC and extensive proteolysis resulting in high concentrations of free amino acids. However, red clover silage has a TP:CP ratio of approximately 0.6. In a comparison of lucerne and red clover silage illustrated in Figure 3 (Winters *et al.*, 1999b), the free amino acids in red clover were

markedly lower than for lucerne. Interestingly application of bacterial inoculant to these legume silages gave similar results to previous work conducted with grass silages where further reductions in free amino acids were
found.

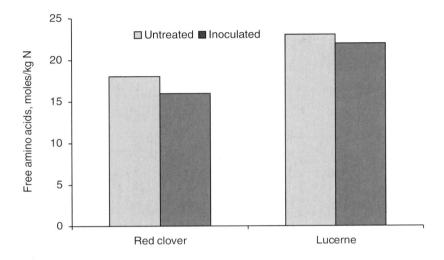

Figure 3. Free amino acids (moles/kg N) in silages made from lucerne and red clover
either untreated or treated with a biological inoculant (adapted from Winters *et al.*,
1999b).

While the above studies would indicate that using bacterial inoculant
additives provides a level of protein protection and thus higher supply of
UDP, Davies *et al.* (1999) using *in vitro* rumen simulation technology,
concluded that efficiency of microbial N synthesis was 34% higher in
untreated red clover silage compared to untreated lucerne silage.
Furthermore, when the red clover silage was treated with a biological
inoculant, a further 13% improvement in microbial protein was observed.
Beever and Thorp (1996) concluded that microbial protein yields were
higher for silages made from white clover and lucerne than for grass silages,
but this arose largely from high CP contents and high levels of feed intake.

High levels of true protein in red clover silages were first noted by Albrecht
and Muck (1991) and Jones (1993). The protection of the protein during
the fermentation process in the silo is attributed to the high content of
polyphenol oxidase (PPO) in red clover. The underlying principles of protein protection have been associated with a reaction of the PPO-generating
caffeoquinones with specific proteases (Hatfield and Muck, 1999).

Lotus and sainfoin contain condensed polyphenols (tannins), which may
restrict protein breakdown in the silo and in the rumen. Waghorn and Shelton
(1997) have provided clear evidence that tannins in *Lotus corniculatus*

grown in New Zealand improve protein utilisation, with reductions in rumen ammonia concentrations by 27%. Associated was an increase in absorption of essential amino acids from the small intestine of 50%, mainly through increased UDP, for which there is a particular requirement with grass-based diets fed to high yielding animals.

In a recent trial conducted in New Zealand (Woodward *et al.*, 1999) with dairy cows in late lactation grazing *Lotus corniculatus*, significant increases in dry matter intake (14%) and milk production (40%) were observed compared to cows on grazed grass. In order to identify the factors associated with the improvements obtained in the grazing trial, another indoor trial was conducted under a zero-grazing regime where polyethylene glycol (PEG) was dosed daily to half of the cows. The effect of the PEG was to block the proteins from binding to the condensed tannins and effectively forming a by-pass protein. The resulting 43% increase in milk yield by cows fed lotus with no PEG supplement compared to the lotus with PEG supplement indicates that the major effect on improved milk yield was due to the condensed tannin in the lotus rather than total CP supply (Table 6).

Table 6. **Milk yield and composition from Friesian cows fed ryegrass or** *Lotus corniculatus.**

	Grass	Grass + PEG	Lotus	Lotus + PEG
DM intake, kg/d	14.7	13.7	16.8	16.7
Milk yield, kg/d	10.2	9.9	16.5	13.8
Milk protein, %	3.31	3.30	3.61	3.44
Milk fat, %	5.05	5.04	4.86	4.72

*Adapted from Woodward *et al.*, 1999.
PEG dosed 3 times per day (total 3.6 l/d).

Thomson *et al.* (1971) demonstrated improved utilisation of protein in dehydrated sainfoin compared to that in dehydrated lucerne and associated this with the condensed tannins in the sainfoin. However, Fraser *et al.* (1999b) demonstrated that N utilisation of sainfoin silage when fed to growing lambs was low with a negative N balance and more than 80% of the ingested nitrogen was released in faeces. This observation would indicate that a degree of 'over protection' of protein was evident and that energy supplementation would not improve utilisation of the sainfoin silage feed.

Red clover offers more opportunities as a high protein crop on UK farms due to its improved agronomic characteristics compared to lotus or sainfoin. The crop is widely adapted to the soils and climates of northern and western Europe; and in a recent experiment DM yields were higher for red clover than grass with 200 kg N fertiliser/ha at seven out of nine sites in UK, Germany, Sweden and Finland (Halling *et al.*, 2000). The species has limited persistence, but is particularly suited to mixed and organic farming systems. Although of high moisture content and low WSC content, recent research has demonstrated successful ensilage through combination of wilting and use of either biological or chemical additives (Winters *et al*, 1999b; Pahlow *et al.*, 2000). The CP concentration from forage legumes will have major significance in the diet of animals where predominantly high energy crops such as maize form the basal diet. Increasing efficiency of microbial protein synthesis and UDP in grassland based forages are particularly important in order to maintain competitiveness of the enterprise.

Alternative grain crops

The use of home-produced rapeseed meal is a well-established practice in UK agriculture. The most interesting protein concentrate crops are probably beans, peas and lupins. Beans and peas are traditional crops for much of Britain, with important progress having been made by plant breeders in improving seed yields and harvest index by producing determinant types and, in peas, leafless and semi-leafless varieties. The protein in peas and beans is however readily degraded in the rumen with low levels of UDP (Agricultural and Food Research Council, 1983). It is unlikely therefore, that these crops would contribute to improved utilisation of protein when used in a mixed diet with grass silage, but could make a major contribution to maize silage-based diets.

Lupins are not traditionally grown as a field crop in Britain; and most of the research work carried out to improve varieties has concentrated on autumn sown varieties. However, maintaining persistency of the lupin crop over winter has been variable. New spring sown varieties of lupins offer greater flexibility of being harvested as an early season crop or allowed to mature as a grain crop.

Jones *et al.* (1999) showed benefits in wilting and application of biological inoculant on the fermentation characteristics of an autumn variety of lupin *cv* Amiga as shown in Table 7. The relatively high WSC content and low buffering capacity of a lupin forage crop at growth stage 4.7 provided sufficient substrate supply to ensure good preservation. Application of a bacterial inoculant to lupin silage gave significant benefits in reducing pH from 4.42 to 3.96 and 4.45 to 3.87 and ammonia N from 177 to 130.5 and 131 to 73 g/kg N, in both unwilted and wilted crops either untreated or treated, respectively.

The grain in lupin silage has a CP content of ~440 g/kg DM; and Moss and Grundy (1996) found some 0.4 of this to be UDP, approaching the value for soybean meal. The content of antinutritional metabolites is low. There is a need for more direct information on the nutritive value of lupins grown in the UK; but interim results indicate possibilities for substantial replacement of fishmeal and soybean meal in the diets of high yielding cows (Mansbridge and Blake, 1998). With prospects for further improvement through breeding and better agronomy, there is potential for this crop to make a major contribution to ruminant feeding in Britain.

Table 7. Mean composition of lupin silage after 90 days ensiling (all values g/kg DM unless otherwise stated).

	Unwilted		Wilted			Significance[†]	
	Control	Inoculated	Control	Inoculated	SE	DM	Additive
DM, g/kg	150.1	147.9	183.3	173.2	4.64	***	NS
pH	4.42	3.96	4.45	3.87	0.071	NS	***
Crude protein	208.6	198.8	234.3	218.8	4.21	***	**
NH$_3$-N, g/kg N	177.0	130.5	131.0	73.0	9.59	***	***
ADF	459.8	442.6	443.5	433.4	14.18	NS	NS
NDF	544.2	528.8	500.1	482.3	20.11	**	NS
WSC	7.8	10.3	7.8	13.0	0.96	NS	***

[†]NS, non-significant, **P<0.01, ***P<0.001.

Conclusions

The supply of CP to ruminants in the UK is dominated by grassland feeds, for which protein is often used inefficiently resulting in large losses to the environment. There are opportunities for improving protein supply from grazed grass herbage by either increasing crop WSC content or reducing rate of protein degradation in the rumen. The new varieties of high sugar grasses are now available commercially in the UK. In conserved grassland crops the use of biological inoculants to enhance acidification resulting in lower protein degradation offers a realistic and economic return to maximise supply of UDP in ruminants. Red clover, which is well adapted to UK conditions and has attributes that reduce protein degradation both in the silo and the rumen, has potential to complement grass swards. For grass silage-based rations, the pulse crops, beans and peas, have limitations because of low contents of UDP, but there is high potential for lupins as a seed crop with protein quality and quantity similar in characteristics to soybeans.

Approaches to improve the utilisation of CP in forages and obtaining a good balance between the supplies of N and readily available energy in the rumen are particularly important to reduce input feed costs and minimise losses to the environment.

Acknowledgements

Data supplied from the IGER trials in this paper were commissioned by the Ministry of Agriculture, Fisheries and Food, the Milk Development Council and the European Union. The Institute of Grassland and Environment Research is funded through the Biotechnology and Biological Sciences Research Council. I am indebted to Prof. R.J.Wilkins for his contribution in sourcing some of the more recent research data presented in this paper.

References

Agricultural and Food Research Council. 1983. Energy and Protein Requirements of Ruminants. Wallingford: CAB International.

Albrecht, K.A. and R.E. Muck. 1991. Crop quality and utilisation: proteolysis in ensiled forage legumes that vary in tannin concentration. Crop Sci. 31:464-469.

Aston, K., W.J. Fisher, A.B. McAllan, M.S. Dhanoa and R.J. Dewhurst. 1998. Supplementation of grass silage-based diets with small quantities of concentrates: strategies for allocating concentrate crude protein. Anim. Sci. 67:17-26.

Beever, D.E. 1980. The utilisation of protein in conserved forage. Occ. Symp. 11, Br. Grassld Soc., pp. 131-143.

Beever, D.E. and C. Thorp. 1996. Advances in the understanding of factors influencing the nutritive value of legumes. Occ. Symp. 30, Br. Grassld Soc., pp. 194-207.

Beever, D.E., N. Offer and E.M. Gill. 2000. Feeding value of grass and grass products. In: Grass, Its Production and Utilization (A. Hopkins, ed.), Blackwell Science, Oxford, pp. 140-195.

Brady, C.J. 1960. Redistribution of nitrogen in grass and leguminous fodder plants during wilting and ensilage. J. Sci. Food Agric. 11:276-284.

Carpintero, C.M., A.R Henderson and P. McDonald. 1979. Effect of wilting on ensiling characteristics. Grass Forage Sci. 34:311-315.

Davies, D.R., A.L. Winters, D.K. Leemans, M.S. Dhanoa and R.J. Merry. 1999. The effect of inoculant treatment of alternative crop forages on silage quality and *in vitro* rumen function. In: Proceedings of the X11 International Silage Conference (T. Pauly, ed), Uppsala, Sweden, pp. 131-132.

Dewhurst, R.J., D.W.R. Davies, W.J. Fisher, J. Bertilsson and R.J. Wilkins. 2000. Intake and milk production responses to legume silages offered to Holstein-Friesian cows. Proc. Br. Soc. Anim. Sci. (in press).

Entec, 1997. Home grown protein sources for animal feeds. Technical Report to Ministry of Agriculture, Fisheries and Food, Scottish Office Agriculture, Environment and Fisheries Department, Milk Development Council, Meat and Livestock Commission.

Fraser, M.D., R. Fychan, S.T. Evans, M.H.M. Speijers and R. Jones. 1999a. The effect of harvest date and inoculation on the voluntary intake and *in vivo* digestibility of kale silage by sheep. Proc. Br. Soc. Anim. Sci. p. 96.

Fraser, M.D., M.H.M. Speijers, S.T. Evans and R. Jones. 1999b. Nitrogen utilisation by lambs offered red clover and lucerne silages harvested at two different stages of growth. Proc. Br. Soc. Anim. Sci. p. 95.

Halling, M.A., A. Hopkins, O. Nissinen and U. Sölter. 2000. Production of five forage legumes for silage in northern Europe. Grassld Sci. in Europe 5(in press).

Hatfield, R. and R. Muck. 1999. Characterising proteolytic inhibition in red clover silage. In: Proceedings of the X11 International Silage Conference (T. Pauly, ed), Uppsala, Sweden, pp. 147-148.

Heron, S.J.E., R.A. Edwards and P. McDonald. 1986. Changes in the nitrogenous components of gamma-irradiated and inoculated ensiled grass. J. Sci. Food Agric., 37:979-985.

Hickey, M.W., A.J. Hillier and G.R. Jago. 1983. Peptidase activities in *Lactobacilli.* Aust. J. Dairy Technol. 38:118-123.

Humphreys, M.O. 1989. Water-soluble carbohydrates in perennial ryegrass breeding. I. Genetic differences among cultivars and hybrid progeny grown as spaced plants. Grass For. Sci. 44:231-236.

Jarvis, S.C., R.J. Wilkins and B.F. Pain. 1996. Opportunities for reducing the environmental impact of dairy farming management: a systems approach. Grass For. Sci. 51:21-31.

Jones, B.A. 1993. Inhibition of proteolysis by red clover. Proc. X Int. Silage Conf., Dublin, pp. 106-107.

Jones, R. 1998. Bridging the protein gap: potential of forage crops for UK livestock production. In: Biotechnology in the Feed Industry, Proc. of Alltech's 14th Annual Symposium (T.P. Lyons and K.A. Jacques, eds). pp 119-135.

Jones, R., R. Fychan, S. Evans and J. Roberts. 1999. Effects of wilting and application of a bacterial inoculant on the fermentation characteristics of lupin silage. In: Proceedings of the X11 International Silage Conference (T. Pauly, ed), Uppsala, Sweden, pp. 98-99.

Keady, T.W.J. 1998. The production of high feed value grass silage and the choice of compound feed type to maximise animal performance. In: Biotechnology in the Feed Industry, Proc. of Alltech's 14th Annual Symposium (T.P. Lyons and K.A. Jacques, eds). pp 157-179.

Kemble, A.R. 1956. Studies on the nitrogen metabolism of the ensilage process. J. Sci. Food Agric. 7:125-130.

Lessard, J.L, J.D. Erfle, E.D. Sauer and S. Mahadevan. 1978. Protein and free amino acid patterns in maize ensiled with and without urea. J. Sci. Food Agric. 29:506-5 12.

Mangan J.L., E.A. Harrison and R.L. Vetter. 1991. Immuno-reactive fraction I leaf protein and dry matter content during wilting and ensiling of ryegrass and alfalfa. J. Dairy Sci. 74:2186-2199.

Mansbridge, R.J. and J.S. Blake. 1998. The effect of feeding different protein sources on intake, milk yield, milk composition and liveweight in high yielding Holstein cows. Proc. Br. Soc. Anim. Prod. p. 202.

McDonald, P., A.R. Henderson and S.J.E. Heron. 1991. The Biochemistry of Silage. Second Edn. Chalcombe Publications, Marlow, UK.

Merry, R.J., R. Jones and M.K. Theodorou. 2000. The conservation of grass. In: Grass, Its Production and Utilization (A. Hopkins, ed.), Blackwell Science, Oxford, pp. 196-228.

Messman, M.A., W.P. Weiss and M.E. Koch. 1994. Changes in total and individual proteins during drying, ensiling, and ruminal fermentation of forages. J. Dairy Sci. 77:492-500.

Miller, L.A., M.A. Neville, D.H. Baker, R.T. Evans, M.K. Theodorou, J.C. MacRae, M.O. Humphrys and J.M. Moorby. 1999. Milk production from dairy cows offered perennial ryegrass selected for high water soluble carbohydrate concentrations compared to a control grass. Proc. Br. Soc. Anim. Sci. p. 208.

Moorby, J.M., P.R. Evans and N.E. Young. 1998. Milk production from dairy cows offered a conserved barley/kale bicrop compared to grass silage. Proc. Br. Soc. Anim. Prod. p. 24.

Morrison, J., M.V. Jackson and P.E. Sparrow. 1980. The response of perennial ryegrass to fertiliser nitrogen in relation to climate and soil. Tech. Rep. 27, Grassld Res. Inst., Hurley.

Moss, A.R. and H.F. Grundy. 1996. Lupins: the energy and protein value for ruminants and an evaluation as a protein source for young beef cattle. Occ. Symp. 30, Br. Grassld Soc., pp. 217-220.

Ohshima, M, P. McDonald and T. Acamovic. 1979. Changes during ensilage in the nitrogenous components of fresh and additive-treated ryegrass and lucerne. J. Sci. Food Agric. 30:97-106.

Ohshima, M. and P. McDonald. 1978. A review of the changes in nitrogenous compounds of herbage during ensilage. J. Sci. Food Agric. 29:497-505.

Pahlow, G., C. Rammer, M. Tuori, and R. Wilkins, 2000. Ensiling of established and novel legumes in Germany, Sweden and Finland. Grassld Sci. in Europe 5 (in press).

Sasaki, M., B.W. Bosman and P.S.T. Tan. 1995. Comparison of proteolytic activities in various Lactobacilli. J. Dairy Res. 62:601-610.

Sharp, R., P.G. Hooper and D.G. Armstrong. 1994. The digestion of grass silages produced using inoculants of lactic acid bacteria. Grass For. Sci. 49:42-53.

Thomson, D.J., D.E. Beever, D.G. Harrison, I.W. Hill and D.F. Osbourn. 1971. The digestion of dried sainfoin and dried lucerne by sheep. Proc. Nutr. Soc. 30, 14A.

Waghorn, G.C. and I.D. Shelton. 1997. Effect of condensed tannins in *Lotus corniculatus* on the nutritive value of pasture for sheep. J. Agric. Sci. Camb 128:365-372.

Winters, A., J. Lloyd, K. Lowes, R. Jones and R.J. Merry. 1999a. A rapid and economical technique for predicting free amino acid content in legume silage. In: Proceedings of the X11 International Silage Conference (T. Pauly, ed), Uppsala, Sweden, pp. 168-169.

Winters, A., R. Fychan, D.R. Davies, J. Lloyd, R.J. Merry and R. Jones. 1999b. Protein content of a range of ensiled legumes. In: Proceedings of the X11 International Silage Conference (T. Pauly, ed), Uppsala, Sweden, pp. 131-132.

Woodward, S.L., D.A. Clark, P.J. Laboyrie and E.B.L. Jansen. 1999. Effect of *Lotus corniculatus* and condensed tannins on milk yield and composition of dairy cows. Proc. of the New Zealand Society of Animal Production 59:152-155.

Beyond the science: what the farmer looks for in the production of silage

TIM W. J. KEADY

Agricultural Research Institute of Northern Ireland, Hillsborough, Co. Down, Northern Ireland

Introduction

Grass silage is, and will remain, the basal forage for the majority of beef and dairy cattle in Ireland, the United Kingdom, Northwestern Europe and the Nordic countries during the winter indoor feeding period. Currently in Ireland and the UK 22 and 50 million tonnes, respectively, are ensiled annually (Wilkinson and Stark, 1992), half of which are treated with an additive. Most silage in Ireland and the UK is harvested by contractor using self-propelled precision-chop forage harvesters and ensiled in bunk silos. Recently the use of big bales as a method of storage has increased in popularity, now accounting for approximately 30-35% of all silages ensiled in Ireland and the UK.

The lower prices farmers receive in the European Union for milk and beef due to recent changes in the Common Agricultural Policy clearly illustrate the need to reduce costs and produce animal products as cheaply as possible. In the production of silage, the producer aims for a product with the required intake and digestibility characteristics to support levels of performance required from the class of livestock given the forage. The aims of this paper are to highlight what the farmer requires from silage production and also to present recent research data on the prediction of silage intake.

Variation in silage quality

The quality of silage produced on-farm varies dramatically both within and between years due mainly to differences in composition of material harvested, sward type, harvest date, regrowth interval, ensiling management and additive treatment. The chemical composition and feeding value of silages from all over Ireland analysed by the Hillsborough Feeding Information System since September 1999 are presented in Table 1. Silage composition is extremely variable. Dry matter (DM) concentrations range from 12.5 to

439

43%, ammonia nitrogen (N) concentrations vary from less than 7 to 29% of total nitrogen and predicted silage intakes for a 500 kg steer vary from 5.3 to 11.4 kg/day DM. Dry matter digestibility values range from 54 to 83%. Silages with low digestibility are also characterised by low intake potential. Many of these silages would not even support maintenance of lactating dairy cows or finishing beef cattle while the best silages, offered as the sole diet, would sustain 23 litres of milk per cow per day or 1.1 kg liveweight gain in finishing beef cattle. The data presented in Table 1 clearly indicate the importance of producing high quality grass silage to support high levels of animal performance.

Table 1. Chemical analysis of silages ensiled in 1999.*

	Minimum	Maximum	Mean
Predicted silage intake[1], kg DM/day	5.3	11.4	7.7
pH	<3.4	5.6	4.1
Dry matter, %	12.5	43	23
Ammonia N, % of total N	<7	29	12
Crude protein, % DM	6.5	19.1	12.7
Dry matter digestibility, % DM	54	83	70
ME, MJ/kg DM	8.0	12.7	10.5
Potential animal performance supported under *ad libitum* feeding			
Milk yield, kg/day	0	23	8
Liveweight gain,[1] kg/day	0	1.1	0.5

*Hillsborough, 1999.
[1]for a 500 kg steer.

SILAGE FEED VALUE

To accurately supplement beef and dairy cattle with the level of concentrates needed to obtain optimal animal performance from silage-based diets, it is essential to know both the nutritive value and intake potential of the forage component of the diet. The nutritive value of silage is determined primarily by digestibility.

Silage digestibility: its importance

Digestibility is the most important factor influencing feeding value and consequently performance of animals offered silage-based diets. The effects of digestibility on animal performance have been well documented. Gordon (1989c) concluded that a 10 g/kg increase in digestible organic matter in silage DM (D-value) resulted in increases in silage DM intake and milk yield of lactating dairy cattle of 0.16 and 0.37 kg/cow/day, respectively. Similarly milk protein, which is an important component in milk pricing schemes in many countries, is influenced by silage digestibility. Keady and

Mayne (1998) concluded from a review of studies undertaken at the Agricultural Research Institute of Northern Ireland that milk protein content is increased by 0.16 g/kg for each 10 g/kg increase in silage D-value. The performance of beef cattle is also highly influenced by silage digestibility. Steen (1987) concluded that a 10 g/kg increase in D-value resulted in an increase in carcass gain of beef cattle of 33 g/day when silage was offered as the entire diet and by 28 g/day when concentrates constituted proportionally 0.20 to 0.37 of total DM intake.

Digestibility is one of the major factors affecting silage intake. Steen *et al*. (1998) concluded from a major study in which 136 silages were offered to beef cattle, that each 10 g/kg increase in silage D-value resulted in an increase in intake of 1.5%.

MAJOR FACTORS AFFECTING DIGESTIBILITY OF SILAGE

Date of harvest

Date of harvest is the most important factor affecting digestibility. Digestibility of herbage harvested between 10 May and 7 June declines linearly by 3.6 percentage units each week harvest is delayed (Keady *et al*., 2000). Similarly, the rate of decline in herbage digestibility from the primary regrowth is similar to that of the primary growth. For example, Gordon (1980) and Keady *et al*. (1999) reported declines in D-value of 3.4 and 3.5 percentage units D-value per week delay in harvesting the primary regrowth between weeks 5 and 10 of growth. Consequently, for each week delay in harvesting grass silage to sustain milk yield or carcass gain, 1.5 and 1.2 kg additional concentrate must be fed daily to lactating dairy and finishing beef cattle, respectively.

Crop lodging

Lodging or flattening of the grass crop before harvest accelerates the rate of decline in grass digestibility. In severely lodged crops digestibility may decline by as much as nine percentage units per week (O'Kiely *et al*., 1987).

Sward type

Normally silage produced from old permanent pastures has a lower digestibility than silage produced from perennial ryegrass swards. Also, it is generally assumed that the optimum time to harvest grass is when the sward reaches 50% ear emergence. However, recent studies (Steen, 1992) indicate that in order to obtain silages with similar digestibility from early and late heading varieties of perennial ryegrass, they must be harvested within 7-8 days of each other even though differences in growth stages would be 24 days (Table 2). Delaying harvest until the late varieties reach 50% ear emergence would result in a reduction in D-value of 8 percentage units relative to the early heading varieties, consequently reducing silage intake and animal performance as measured by carcass gain from 0.63 to 0.40 kg/day.

Table 2. Effect of grass variety heading date and harvest date on animal performance.*

| | Variety heading date | | | | | |
| | Early (19 May) | | | Late (12 June) | | |
Harvest date	20 May	28 May	5 June	28 May	5 June	13 June
Silage D-value, g/kg DM	73	69	64	72	68	65
Silage intake, kg/day DM	6.8	6.2	6.3	6.6	6.4	5.9
Carcass gain, kg/day	0.63	0.51	0.46	0.61	0.55	0.40

*Steen, 1992.

Silage fermentation

Relative to well-preserved silages, poorly preserved silages with low lactic acid and high ammonia nitrogen contents normally have lower digestibility. The decline in digestibility due to deterioration in silage fermentation may be as high as 5 to 6 units of D-value.

Nitrogen fertiliser application

Increasing nitrogen fertiliser application alters silage digestibility. Keady *et al.* (2000) reported a decrease in silage D-value from 71.8 to 70.5% when nitrogen fertiliser application was increased from 72 to 168 kg/ha N for first-cut silage.

Prediction of silage intake

In the past thirty years many studies (Wilkins *et al.*, 1978; Rook and Gill, 1990) have been undertaken to determine the factors influencing silage intake. The initial studies produced multi-factor relationships to predict intake. However, the accuracy of these relationships was limited due to the fact that they were based on data obtained from a number of studies and were confounded by factors such as breed of animal, previous nutritional history, physiological state, length of feeding period, concentrate feed level and composition. More recently, a major study (Steen *et al.*, 1998) was undertaken at our institute to determine the factors affecting silage intake when offered to beef cattle. One hundred and thirty-six silages were selected to be representative of the broad range of silages produced annually across Northern Ireland. These silages were purchased from commercial farms in Northern Ireland and had been produced from different sward types using different management strategies at ensiling and a range of additive treatments. The 136 silages were offered as the entire diet to 192 steers (initial live weight 415 kg) in a partially balanced changeover design experiment. The changeover design enabled the variations in intake due to animal effects to be removed statistically. During the feeding study detailed measurements of intake, chemical composition, *in vivo* digestibility and use of near infrared reflectance spectroscopy (NIRS) and electrometric titration were undertaken.

The chemical composition of the silages varied dramatically. For example, the concentrations of dry matter varied from 155 to 413 g/kg, ammonia nitrogen from 45 to 385 g/kg total N, dry matter digestibility from 53 to 80% and silage intake when offered as the sole feed from 4.3 to 10.9 kg/day DM.

Relationships between individual silage constituents and silage intake have been developed (Table 3) to provide an overview of the extent to which intake is related to, or determined by, concentrations of different silage chemical constituents. The results of this analysis clearly indicated that intake was poorly related to some chemical factors such as pH, buffering capacity and lactic, acetic and butyric acids, which previously were considered to have a major effect on silage intake. Factors of moderate importance included dry matter and ammonia nitrogen concentrations. Silage intake increased by 13 g DM for each 10 g/kg increase in silage DM content. The key factors influencing silage intake were the protein and fibre fractions and the rate and extent of digestion of these components. There were quadratic relationships between silage intake and many of the protein fractions. For example, as silage crude protein content increased from 80 to 130 g/kg DM, silage intake increased. However when silage crude protein content increased from 140 to 160 g/kg DM, silage intake remained static while silage intake tended to decrease as silage crude protein concentration increased above 160 g/kg DM. The positive linear relationship between silage digestibility and intake identified in the present study clearly indicated an increase in silage intake of 15 g DM per 10 g/kg DM increase in silage digestibility.

One of the most interesting outcomes of this major study was the fact that NIRS, on both dried and fresh samples, provided the most accurate prediction of silage intake ($R^2 = 0.90$) (Park *et al.*, 1997). Subsequently a silage intake prediction system was developed using NIRS. The standard error of prediction is 7.6% of the mean intake of the 136 silages offered in the study, which is more accurate than using multi-factor relationships developed using wet chemistry.

Thirteen of the 136 silages described above were also offered to dairy cows in late lactation in order to develop a relationship between intakes of silage when offered as the sole feed to both beef and dairy cattle. Feeding

Table 3. Relationships between individual silage parameters and silage intake.

Parameter, g/kg DM	R^2	
	Linear	Quadratic
Dry matter	0.21	
Crude protein	0.19	0.33
Acid insoluble nitrogen, N	0.09	0.21
Protein N	0.06	0.15
Soluble N	0.20	0.29
Soluble N minus ammonia N	0.35	
Ammonia N, g/kg N	0.10	
Acid detergent fibre	0.31	
Neutral detergent fibre	0.30	
Acid detergent lignin	0.31	0.47
Water soluble carbohydrate	0.08	0.23
Ash	0.03	0.13
Ether extract	0.14	0.17
Gross energy	0.00	
Lactate	0.02	0.11
Acetate	0.05	0.09
Propionate	0.08	
Butyrate	0.04	
Ethanol	0.01	
Propanol	0.08	
Buffering capacity, meq/kg DM	0.02	
pH	0.00	0.09
Digestibility coefficients		
Dry matter digestibility	0.31	
D-value	0.27	
Dry matter degradability	0.28	
Prediction using NIRS		
Dried samples	0.90	
Wet samples	0.88	

Steen *et al.*, 1998.

models have been developed at Hillsborough for beef, dairy cattle and for sheep that use the predicted silage intakes to calculate total metabolisable energy intakes and predict performance for different inputs of concentrates. Currently a Silage Feeding Information System, which provides a comprehensive silage analysis and the potential animal performance that can be achieved from the silage supplemented with different levels of concentrates, is available commercially at Hillsborough using NIRS.

PREDICTION OF SILAGE FEEDING VALUE FROM ANALYSIS OF THE HERBAGE PRIOR TO ENSILING

Recent developments in feed characterisation of grass silage (Park *et al.*, 1997; Steen *et al.*, 1998) have facilitated considerable improvements in prediction of silage feeding value. However, this information would be of considerably greater value in practice if predictions of silage value could be determined from analysis of herbage prior to ensiling. A study has just been completed at Hillsborough (Keady *et al.*, 2000) where grass from a total of 75 treatments was ensiled in 225 small scale silos from swards that had received different management practices prior to and at ensiling. The swards had received 72, 96, 120, 144 or 168 kg N/ha and were harvested either on 10, 17, 24 or 31 May or 7 June. The herbage was ensiled either untreated, treated with formic acid at 3 ml/kg or treated with an inoculant at 3 ml/kg. Following a 176 day fermentation period the silos were opened and sampled for chemical analysis and the prediction of digestible organic matter in the DM and potential dry matter intake using NIRS as described by Park *et al.* (1997). There were large variations in the chemical composition of the herbage and in the subsequent silages. Relationships between the chemical composition of the herbage at ensiling for each additive treatment and the feeding value, i.e. intake potential, D-value and potential ME intake, have been developed to provide an overview of the extent to which intake is related to, or determined by, the chemical composition of the herbage at ensiling. The effects of herbage composition on potential ME intake of untreated (U), formic acid (F) and inoculant (I) treated silages are presented in equations 1, 2 and 3:

$$\text{MEI for U} = 78.6 - 0.0042 \text{ (yield)} - 0.076 \text{ (NDF)} + 0.349 \text{ (DM)} + 2.596 \text{ (PN)} - 0.0221 \text{ (nitrate)} \quad (R^2 = 0.94)$$

Equation 1

$$\text{MEI for F} = -4.1 + 2.557 \text{ (PN)} - 0.0036 \text{ (yield)} + 0.264 \text{ (DM)} + 7.28 \text{ (pH)} \quad (R^2 = 0.93)$$

Equation 2

$$\text{MEI for I} = 75.2 - 0.0053 \text{ (yield)} - 0.087 \text{ (Hemi)} + 2.401 \text{ (PN)} + 0.2715 \text{ (DM)} - 0.0143 \text{ nitrate} + 0.493 \text{ (EE)} \quad (R^2 = 0.94)$$

Equation 3

where: MEI = metabolisable energy intake (MJ/day); yield = DM yield at harvest (kg DM/ha); NDF = neutral detergent fibre (g/kg DM); DM = dry matter (g/kg); PN = protein N (g/kg DM); nitrate = mg/ kg DM; Hemi = hemicellulose (g/kg DM); EE = ether extract (g/ kg DM); pH = pH of grass at ensiling.

Other than digestibility, which was inversely related to herbage yield, the chemical parameters of the parent herbage which were most strongly correlated with silage intake were not the major silage parameters as identified by Steen *et al.* (1998).

Costs of silage production

Many individuals and commercial organisations quote the relative values of grazed grass:silage:concentrates as being 1:3:6. However in these costings grass utilisation rates and the costs of land charges, paddock layout and labour for droving the cows are not included for grazed grass. In contrast, when costing silage the expensive silos, land charge and feeding costs are included and in-silo losses are also considered. More recently Keady and Anderson (1999) and Keady (1999), using herbage yield and utilisation rates recorded at the Agricultural Research Institute of Northern Ireland, and including land, labour, contractor and fixed and variable costs concluded that the costs of grazed grass, silage from a three-cut silage system and concentrates are £74, £92 and £153 per tonne of dry matter as fed to the animals. Consequently the relative costs of grazed grass, silage and concentrates are closer to 1:1.3:2.0 and not the 1:3:6 as often quoted. When costed on a metabolisable energy basis the relative value of grazed grass:silage: concentrates is 1:1.3:1.8. These costings clearly illustrate that the costs of grass production are relatively similar whether it is ensiled or grazed *in situ*.

MAJOR FACTORS AFFECTING THE COSTS OF SILAGE PRODUCTION

Yield

The major management factors affecting herbage yield in silage production are the level of nitrogen application and harvest date. When harvest date is delayed, herbage yield increases but digestibility declines as harvest date is one of the most important factors affecting digestibility. Keady and O'Kiely (1998) and Keady *et al.* (2000) concluded that herbage yield of the primary growth increased by 135 and 151 kg DM per day delay in harvest while digestibility declined by 3.9 and 4.2 g/kg per day delay in harvest, respectively. Consequently, delaying the first harvest by one week increases yield by approximately 1 tonne DM/ha and decreases silage costs (assuming a land charge) by £11/tonne utilisable DM to £74 for silage from the first cut, but at a cost of reducing digestibility and ME by 0.5 MJ/kg DM. Digestibility is the most important factor affecting animal performance from grass silage. As outlined earlier, to produce a similar milk yield from grass harvested one week later than intended, an additional 1.5 kg concentrates per cow per day would be required. Consequently, savings on silage cost could be eroded by the additional level of concentrates required to maintain animal performance.

Keady *et al.* (2000) concluded that as nitrogen application increased from 72 to 168 kg/ha N for first cut silage, herbage yield increased by 7.8 kg DM/kg N on average. Meanwhile Keady and O'Kiely (1998) concluded that herbage yield increased by 5.2 kg DM/kg N when nitrogen fertilisation rate increased from 120 to 168 kg DM/ha for first cut silage. However care must be taken not to apply excessive nitrogen fertiliser otherwise the feeding value of the silage will be reduced.

Wilting

There has been renewed interest in pre-wilting of grass prior to ensiling, given the development of sophisticated conditioning and tedding equipment and the desire to reduce effluent output from an environmental point of view. Detailed studies undertaken at this institute (Wright, 1997) examining factors affecting the speed of wilting indicate that the most important weather factor is the duration and intensity of sunshine and the most important management factor is the density of the swath, i.e. the lower the density the greater the drying rate. In a three-cut system, wilting does not alter the cost of silage production even though wilting increases machinery costs due to tedding and rowing up prior to harvest, but reduces silo costs and additive costs.

A total of eleven recent studies have been undertaken at this Institute (Patterson *et al.*, 1996; 1998) to evaluate the effects of rapid wilting of herbage on subsequent dairy cow performance (Table 4). These studies indicate that when herbage dry matter was increased from 160 to 320 g/kg at ensiling, rapid wilting dramatically increased intake by 17% and slightly improved milk yield by 2.4% and the concentrations of fat and protein. However rapid wilting reduces output of utilised silage/ha. In a three-cut system, wilting increased the value of milk output/cow/day but reduced cow feeding days by 174/ha of herbage ensiled and milk volume output by 3074 l/ha, consequently decreasing the value of animal product.

Table 4. The effects of wilting on animal performance.

	Unwilted	Wilted
Food intake and performance		
Silage DM intake, kg DM/day	10.2	11.9
Milk yield, kg/day	20.7	21.2
Fat, %	4.52	4.66
Protein, %	3.27	3.38
Financial analysis		
Silage costs, £/d	0.94	1.09
Milk value, £/day	4.19	4.42
Milk output, l/ha	25164	22090
Milk output/ha silage, £	5089	4601

Milk price is based at 19 p/l at 4% fat and 3.18% protein. Each 0.01% change in fat and protein concentration alters milk price by 0.018 and 0.032 p/litre, respectively. (Patterson *et al.*, 1996; 1998).

Additive treatment

Until recently, the principle objective in applying a silage additive was to improve silage fermentation under difficult ensiling conditions. This was achieved by applying either acid or sugar based additives. However, more recent research has shown that the use of effective inoculants can substantially improve animal performance without necessarily altering the fermentation quality of the silage at the time of feeding.

Animal performance is the most important measure of the efficacy of a silage additive, as producers are paid for animal product and not for the preservation quality of silages as measured by conventional laboratory analysis. When applying additives it is important to apply them at the correct rate, taking account of changes in the moisture content of the grass being ensiled. For example, if the dry matter of the herbage is increased from 180 to 250 g/kg, the fresh weight of grass would be reduced from 29.5 to 21 t/ha, consequently reducing additive requirement by 40%/ha. Silage costs are decreased by £7.5 per tonne of utilisable dry matter if an additive is not applied at ensiling. Consequently it is essential to make the correct decision when choosing an additive.

Keady (1998) reviewed the effects of silage additives on silage fermentation and animal performance. It was concluded from the mean of 11 comparisons for each additive based on either sulphuric acid, molasses or enzymes as the main active ingredient that these additives will improve silage fermentation but will not significantly improve animal performance. Consequently, the return on investment is zero, yet the costs of silage production are increased. Therefore, use of these additives must be questioned. Furthermore, formic acid under difficult ensiling conditions will increase animal performance; but under moderate to easy ensiling conditions formic acid will not give an economic response. Finally, Keady (1998) concluded that inoculant treatment increased animal performance across a wide range of conditions, regardless of whether the untreated silage was well or poorly preserved. From the mean of 11 studies undertaken at Hillsborough, inoculant treatment increased fat and protein corrected milk yield by 1.3 l/cow/day, consequently increasing milk value by 25 p/cow/day, assuming a milk price of 19 p/l. In these studies some products did not alter animal performance whereas others had major beneficial effects. The effects of an inoculant based on a single strain of *Lactobacillus plantarum* which supplied 1 million CFU/g of grass at ensiling are presented in Table 5 (adopted from the studies of Gordon (1989a; 1989b) and Mayne (1990)). The use of that particular inoculant increased milk output resulting in a return on investment of 2:1. These costings do not take into account any reduction in in-silo losses due to inoculant treatment.

Within the industry there is a popular misconception that inoculant treatment will not improve animal performance under conditions in which untreated silage would be poorly preserved. Keady (1998) concluded from a review of nine comparisons in which the untreated silages were poorly preserved, that inoculant treatment increased performance of beef and dairy cattle. More recently Patterson (1999, unpublished data) evaluated three inoculant-based products under difficult ensiling conditions (Table 6). Even though treatment with the inoculant did not improve fermentation, inoculant treatment increased animal performance, improving milk yield by 1.5 kg/day

Table 5. The effects of an inoculant based on *L. plantarum* on animal performance from the mean of three studies.

	Untreated	Inoculant
Food intake and performance		
Silage intake, kg DM/day	9.2	10.2
Milk yield, kg/day	22.9	24.4
Milk composition, %		
Fat	3.72	3.76
Protein	2.76	2.81
Silage costs, £/t	84.5	92
Cost of silage intake and additive, £/day	0.78	0.94
Value of milk output, £/day	3.93	4.25

Milk price is based at 19 p/l at 4% fat and 3.18% protein. Each 0.01% change in fat and protein concentration alters milk price by 0.018 and 0.032 p/litre, respectively. (Gordon, 1989a; 1989b; Mayne, 1990).

Table 6. The effects of inoculant treatment under difficult ensiling conditions on animal performance - three comparisons.*

	Untreated	Inoculant
Silage fermentation		
pH	4.7	4.6
Ammonia nitrogen, g/kg N	199	169
Animal performance		
Silage intake, kg/day DM	9.9	10.3
Milk yield, kg/day	25.9	27.4
Milk composition, %		
Fat	4.15	4.31
Protein	2.93	2.98

*Patterson, 1999 unpublished data.

and milk protein content by 0.05%. The many studies undertaken in the dairy and beef herds at Hillsborough clearly indicate that an effective inoculant will result in similar improvements in animal performance under a wide range of ensiling conditions, whether the herbage is ensiled direct cut or wilted prior to ensiling.

Harvest costs

Altering harvesting charges by £25/harvest/ha changes silage costs by £7.55/t utilisable DM in the three-cut system.

Silo costs

On many farms it could be assumed that the cost of silo construction has been fully written off. Consequently, if silage storage costs are omitted, the cost of utilised forage from a three-cut silage system would be reduced to £86/t assuming a land charge.

Big bales

If silage is ensiled in big bales, assuming a mean dry matter content of 25%, silage DM losses of 12% and the provision of a concrete base for storage, silage costs are increased by £4/t DM relative to clamp silage in a three-cut silage system. However if only the light crops of the second and third harvest are ensiled, the cost differential between big bale and clamp silage diminishes. This assumes no loss of bales due to damage by vermin.

Conclusions

Grass silage is, and will remain, the basal forage for dairy and beef cattle during the indoor feeding period in many areas in Northwestern Europe and elsewhere. The costs of silage production are relatively similar to those of grazing animals at pasture with the relative value of grass:silage:concentrate being 1:1.3:2.0, and not 1:3:6 as often quoted. Digestibility is the most important factor affecting animal performance in silage production. Silage intake is highly correlated to the protein and fibre fractions and not silage fermentation characteristics. Silage feeding value can be predicted from the chemical composition of the herbage at ensiling. The use of a well-proven effective inoculant results in an economic return of £2 for every pound invested.

References

Gordon, F.J. 1980. The effects of interval between harvest and wilting on silage for milk production. Animal Production 31:35-41.

Gordon, F.J. 1989a. An evaluation through lactating dairy cattle of a bacterial inoculant as an additive for grass silage. Grass and Forage Science 44:169-179.

Gordon, F.J. 1989b. A further study on the evaluation through lactating cattle of a bacterial inoculant as an additive for grass silage. Grass and Forage Science 44:353-367.

Gordon, F.J. 1989c. The principles of making and storing high quality, high intake silage. In: Silage for milk production (C.S. Mayne, ed.). Occasional Symposium of the British Grassland Society No. 23, pp. 3-41.

Keady, T.W.J. 1998. The production of high feed value grass silage and the choice of compound feed type to maximise animal performance. In: Biotechnology in the Feed Industry, Proceedings of Alltech's 14th Annual Symposium (T.P. Lyons and K.A. Jacques, eds.), pp. 157-180.

Keady, T.W.J. 1999. High feed value grass silage. How, why and its relative value to grazed grass. Paper presented at the Irish Grain and Feed Association Annual Conference, November 10, Dublin.

Keady, T.W.J. and D. Anderson. 1999. Good grazed grass is not free. Irish Farmers Journal, Vol. 51, No. 23, June 5, pp. 22-23.

Keady, T.W.J. and C.S. Mayne. 1998. Improving milk composition during the winter period through feeding. Applied Research and Development Council (NI), Technical Publication No. 1.

Keady, T.W.J. and P. O'Kiely. 1998. An evaluation of potassium and nitrogen fertilisation of grassland, and date of harvest, on fermentation, effluent production, dry matter recovery and predicted feeding value of silage. Grass and Forage Science 53:326-337.

Keady, T.W.J., C.S. Mayne, D.A. Fitzpatrick and M. Marsden. 1999. The effects of energy source and level of digestible undegradable protein in concentrates on silage intake and performance of lactating dairy cows offered a range of grass silages. Animal Science 68:763-778.

Keady, T.W.J., C.S. Mayne and D.A. Fitzpatrick. 2000. Prediction of silage feeding value from the analysis of the herbage at ensiling and effects of nitrogen fertiliser, date of harvest and additive treatment on grass silage composition. Journal of Agricultural Science, Cambridge (In press).

Mayne, C.S. 1990. An evaluation of an inoculant of *Lactobacillus plantarum* as an additive for grass silage for dairy cattle. Animal Production 51:1-13.

O'Kiely, P., A.V. Flynn and R. Wilson. 1987. New concepts in silage making. Irish Grassland and Animal Production Association Journal 21:38-50.

Park, R.S., F.J. Gordon, R.E. Agnew, R.J. Barnes and R.W.J. Steen. 1997. The use of near infrared reflectance spectroscopy on dried samples to predict biological parameters of grass silage. Animal Feed Science and Technology 68:235-246.

Patterson, D.C., T. Yan and F.J. Gordon. 1996. The effects of wilting of grass prior to ensiling on the response to bacterial inoculation. 2. Intake and performance by dairy cattle over three harvests. Animal Science 62:413-430.

Patterson, D.C., T. Yan and F.J. Gordon. 1998. The effects of bacterial inoculation of unwilted and wilted grass silages. 2. Intake, performance and eating behaviour by dairy cattle over eight harvests. Journal of Agricultural Science 131:113-119.

Rook, A.J. and M. Gill. 1990. Prediction of the voluntary intake of grass silages by beef cattle. 1. Linear regression analysis. Animal Production 50:425-438.

Steen, R.W.J. 1987. Factors affecting the utilisation of grass silage for beef production. In: Efficient beef production from grass (J. Frame, ed.). Occasional Symposium of the British Grassland Society No. 22, pp. 129-139.

Steen, R.W.J. 1992. The performance of beef cattle given silages made from perennial ryegrass of different maturity groups, cut on different dates. Grass and Forage Science 47:239-248.

Steen, R.W.J., F.J. Gordon, L.E.R. Dawson, R.S. Park, C.S. Mayne, R.E. Agnew, D.J. Kilpatrick and M.G. Porter. 1998. Factors affecting the intake of grass silage by cattle and prediction of silage intake. Animal Science 66:115-128.

Wilkins, R.J., J.S. Fenlon, J.E. Cook and R.F. Wilson. 1978. A further analysis of relationships between silage composition and voluntary intake by sheep. Proceedings of the 5th Silage Conference, Ayr, pp. 34-35.

Wilkinson, J.M. and B.A. Stark. 1992. Silage in Western Europe: A survey of 17 countries. Chalcombe Publications.

Wright, D.A. 1997. The influence of different factors on the drying rate of grass silage and development of prediction models. PhD Thesis, The Queen's University, Belfast.

Evolution of silage and silage inoculants

K.K. BOLSEN[1], MIKE WILKINSON[2] AND C.J. LIN[3]

[1]*Kansas State University, Manhattan, Kansas, USA*
[2]*University of Leeds, Leeds, UK*
[3]*Roanoke City Mills, Roanoke, Virginia, USA*

Silage defined

What is silage? Literally, silage is anything stored in a silo, which might be a hole in the ground, a tower, a bunker, a pile or a wrapped bale. The word silage is from the Greek '*siros*' meaning a pit or a hole in the ground for storing corn (*Zea mays* L.; McDonald *et al.*, 1991).

Woolford (1984) defines silage as "the product formed when grass or other material of sufficiently high moisture content, liable to spoilage by aerobic microorganisms, is stored anaerobically". Silage is produced by 'ensilage' – that is, the placing of crop material inside a vessel or a structure called a silo. The material might be an entire crop or only part of a crop, such as the grain portion.

The process of ensilage involves acidification of the crop by the products of the fermentation of sugars within the plant material. The fermentation products are organic acids, principally lactic acid. The fermentation process is similar to that which occurs in the production of yoghurt and cheese (Fung, 1988) and in the preservation of cabbage (*Brassica oleracea* L.) as sauerkraut (Woolford, 1984). Adequate acidification is vital to successful preservation of the crop, especially when its moisture concentration is relatively high, because the acidity prevents the development of spoilage microorganisms, which are less tolerant of acid conditions than are the lactic acid bacteria (Woolford, 1984; McDonald *et al.*, 1991).

Therefore, silage is defined as an acidic, fermented, stored product from an agricultural crop.

Origins of silage making

Silage making is probably more than 4000 years old. In the Old Testament, (Isaiah, 30:24) it was translated that "the oxen and young asses ate salted, seasoned green fodder". The ancient Egyptians and Greeks stored grain and whole forage crops in silos. Reviews of the history of silage refer to the mural in the Naples Museum, which shows whole-crop cereals being harvested and loaded into a small stone-built silo (Shukking, 1976; Woolford, 1984). Kirstein (1963) mentioned that silos were found in the ruins of Carthage, indicating that forage was ensiled there at around 1200 B.C. Cato (cited by Shukking, 1976) noted that the Teutons in the 1st century stored green fodder in pits in the ground and then covered the pits with dung.

Little is known about silage making between about 100 AD and the 18th century, although ensiling of forage crops probably continued to be practiced on a small scale throughout this period. According to Shukking (1976), grass was ensiled in Italy in the 13th century, and ensiling was practiced in the northern Alps, Sweden, and the Baltic region early in the 18th century. By the middle of the 19th century, interest in the ensiling of grass, beet tops, and other crops had spread beyond the Baltic and Germany to most other European countries. The increased movement of scientists and of scientific information around Europe and North America led to the growth of interest in ensiling in the 19th century.

In 1877, the French farmer Auguste Goffart published the results of his work on the ensiling of chopped forage corn and other crops (Goffart, 1877). Goffart's book was influential not only in Europe but also in North America, where it was published in 1879 by J.B. Brown, the president of the New York Plow Co., who sent copies to his customers as an advertisement for his company (Carrier, 1920). However, Brassley (1996) states that the first silo in the US was probably built in 1873 in Illinois by a farmer who had read an English translation of the articles in the *Journal d'Agriculture Practique* while he was a student at the University of Illinois. Influenced by the French reports, M. Miles, a farmer in Lansing, Michigan, experimented with ensilage made from whole-plant corn in 1875. In an article published in *Country Gentleman* on October 5, 1876, Miles described his own silage making experiences and those in France. Miles used the word 'silo', and he suggested the adoption of 'ensilage' in the absence of an English equivalent for the fermented product (Miles, 1910). By 1882, a report by the United States Department of Agriculture contained statements from over 90 farmers in both the US and Canada regarding their ensilage practices.

Goffart's work was taken up enthusiastically in the US. Miles published his first book entitled *Silos, Ensilage, and Silage, A Practical Treatise on the Ensilage of Fodder Corn*. By the end of the 19th century, most Land Grant universities were making silage and promoting its use on farms. Several universities were also conducting silage research (Hunter and Bushnell, 1916; Eckles *et al.*, 1919; and Hulbert and Christ, 1926). Kansas State Agriculture College published *Silos and Silage* (Bulletin No. 6) in 1889, which reported cattle performance and the sources of loss in an 80 ton-capacity tower silo. Seven percent of the weight of the whole-plant corn ensiled versus weight of silage removed could not be accounted for, so the authors explained it as a loss by 'evaporation'.

A major innovation to be introduced, probably around 1950, was plastic sheeting (Shukking, 1976). The earliest sheets were made of polyvinyl chloride and were used to protect small field clamp silos from rain ingress. By 1960, sheets were increasingly made from polyethylene and included better plasticizers and ultra-violet stabilizers to prevent the material disintegrating in sunlight. The sheeting was used to provide a way of separating the silage from the soil on top. However, research in the late 1950s demonstrated clearly that without adequate surface pressure on the top of the silo, air could penetrate the mass and severely reduce the quality of the silage, partly through increased temperature and greater oxidative losses (McDonald et al., 1960).

The development of the 'Dorset Wedge' system of filling bunker, trench and pile silos by Richard Waltham, a Dorset farmer, had a huge impact on silage making practices. Essentially, the method involved filling the silo and rolling the chopped material on an inclined rather than on a horizontal plane, which had the effect of reducing the area of crop exposed to the air and of achieving greater compaction during filling.

The great benefits of plastic sheeting were that air movement in and out of the silo could be reduced and surface waste could be minimized. Yet many years elapsed in North America before farmers began to use plastic sheets to reduce the surface wastage. Most silos, especially large bunkers, trenches, and piles were left unsealed after filling in the hope that rain or snow would provide an effective cover or protective seal for the ensiled crop. However, today a much higher percent of the silos are being sealed with plastic sheets because the magnitude of surface waste in unsealed silos was quantified in research by McLaughlin et al. (1978); McGuffey and Owens (1979); Ashbell and Weinberg (1992); Dickerson et al. (1992a;b); Bolsen et al. (1993); and Holthaus et al. (1995). Computer spreadsheets were made available that allowed farmers to estimate the value of silage saved by sealing based on the value of the crop, silo dimensions, cost of the plastic and cost of the labor needed to apply and remove the sheet and weighting material (Huck et al., 1997).

A current major interest is improving the hygienic quality of silage, especially with regard to reducing aerobic spoilage during the feedout period (see reviews by Weissbach, 1996; Gotlieb, 1997; Whitlow and Hagler, 1997; and Seglar, 1997). Work has been in progress in some countries for several years, with the greatest progress being made by German researchers (see reviews by Oldenburg, 1991; Honig, 1991; and Weissbach, 1996). This interest is stimulated in part by the relatively higher dry matter (DM) concentrations of silages in recent years, and also by an increasing concern that even well-preserved silage, if it is made from contaminated crops or allowed to deteriorate on exposure to air during the feedout period, might be responsible for problems of livestock health and loss of productivity (Dickerson et al., 1992; Bolsen et al., 1993).

Current production of silage and hay

In some countries of Western Europe, like Finland, silage probably has been the major method of forage preservation for many decades (Wilkinson and Stark, 1987). By 1994, the production of silage exceeded that of hay in all 17 countries of Western Europe except Austria, France, Greece, and Switzerland (Wilkinson *et al.*, 1996). The estimated areas of the major crops harvested for silage in Europe and North America in 1994 and estimated production of silage and hay in 1994 are shown in Tables 1 and 2, respectively. The information was gathered from official statistics, where available, or from estimates by individual experts. It must be stressed that the data are estimates, and therefore should be treated with appropriate caution. The US has experienced a similar trend for corn over the past three or four decades – fewer hectares harvested for silage but very little change in total output of silage. In fresh weight terms, the total amount of silage made in Europe and North America in 1994 was about 550 and 130 million tons, respectively.

Table 1. Estimated areas of crops harvested for silage in Europe and North America in 1994.

Area	Grass	Corn	Sorghum	Legumes[1]	Whole crop cereals[2]	Other crops[3]
			1000 ha			
Europe						
Western Europe[4]	9,646	3,890	—	182	324	641
Eastern Europe[5]	1,332	1,288	—	193	208	1,577
Russia[6]	9,736	7,500	—	375	—	2,251
Total	20,714	12,678	—	—	532	4,469
North America						
US	—	2,268	133	750	—	—
Canada	—	166	—	486	304	—
Total	—	2,434	133	304	500	—

[1]Mainly alfalfa; [2]Mainly wheat; [3]Mainly beet tops; [4]European Union (15 countries) + Norway and Switzerland; [5]15 countries; [6]Russian Federation.
Sources: Wilkinson *et al.*, 1996 and Wilkinson and Bolsen, 1996.

Geographic and climatic factors affecting production

The development of silage has been dominated by two main features: first, an unsuitable climate for the rapid field-drying of crops; and second, the availability of materials and equipment to ensure that the crop can be harvested and contained for several months in anaerobic conditions. Wet silage poses special problems of poor fermentation quality, especially clostridial activity and risks to cheese making from contamination of milk by clostridial spores. In areas such as northern Europe, high rainfall makes field wilting unpredictable. The AIV process (Virtanen, 1933) of adding

456

Table 2. Estimated quantities of silage and hay made in Europe and North America in 1994.

Area	Hay	Silage	Total
		10^6 tons of dry matter	
Europe			
Western Europe[1]	60.1	91.6	152.6
Eastern Europe[2]	32.3	15.4	47.7
Russia[3]	59.7	45.0	104.7
Total	152.1	152.0	305.0
North America			
US	123.0	39.3	162.3
Canada	40.9	7.4	48.3
Total	163.9	46.7	210.6

[1]European Union (15 countries) + Norway and Switzerland; [2]15 countries; [3]Russian Federation.
Source: Wilkinson and Bolsen, 1996.

hydrochloric and sulfuric acids to unwilted crops at harvest to achieve immediate acidification was so successful that today virtually all the silage made in Finland is made with an additive (Wilkinson *et al.*, 1996).

In other regions the risk of secondary fermentations in silages is considered too great and hay has remained the principal method of forage preservation. Silage making is prohibited by law in some areas of Switzerland and Italy (Wilkinson *et al.*, 1996). In these areas, high-value hard cheeses are produced and the secondary 'blowing' of the cheese during maturation, caused by the fermentation of the lactic acid in the cheese by clostridial spores from poorly preserved silage contaminating the milk, can lead to the total loss of the cheese and substantial loss of income to the producer.

The ensiling process

A well-preserved silage of high nutritional value is achieved by harvesting the crop at the proper stage of maturity; minimizing the activities of plant enzymes and undesirable epiphytic microorganisms (i.e., those naturally present on the plant) and encouraging the dominance of lactic acid bacteria (LAB) (McDonald, 1980). Two dominant features must be considered for every silage: 1) the crop and its stage of maturity, and 2) the management and know-how imposed by the silage-maker.

The key 'ensileability' criteria for a crop are: 1) dry matter content, 2) sugar content, and 3) buffering capacity (resistance to acidification) (Bolsen, 1985). In these respects, corn is the 'nearly perfect' crop, whereas alfalfa is at the other extreme and is the most difficult crop to preserve as silage. Grasses usually contain more water-soluble carbohydrates (WSC) and have less resistance to acidification than legumes.

When making decisions about silage management techniques, it is important to have a good understanding of the events that occur during silage preservation. The major processes involved can be divided into four phases:

1) aerobic, 2) fermentation, 3) stable, and 4) feedout. Each phase has distinctive characteristics that must be controlled in order to maintain forage (silage) quality throughout the periods of harvesting, silo filling, silage storing and feeding. Only a description of the fermentation phase is presented here, while the other three phases are detailed by Bolsen *et al.* (1998).

Once anaerobic conditions are reached in the ensiled material, anaerobic microorganisms begin to grow. The LAB are the most important mizioflora, because forages are preserved by lactic acid. The other microorganisms, primarily members of the family enterobacteriaceae, clostridial spores and yeast and molds, have a negative impact on silage. They compete with the LAB for fermentable carbohydrates; and many of their end products have no preservative action.

The enterobacteria have an optimum pH of 6-7, and most strains will not grow below pH 5.0. Consequently, the population of enterobacteria, which is usually high in the pre-ensiled forage, is active only during the first 12-36 hrs of ensiling (Lin *et al.*, 1992). Their numbers susequently decline rapidly, so they are not a factor after the first few days of the fermentation phase.

Growth of clostridial spores can have a pronounced effect on silage quality. Clostridia can cause secondary fermentation, which converts sugars and organic acids to butyric acid and results in significant losses of DM and digestible energy. Proteolytic clostridia ferment amino acids to a variety of products, including ammonia, amines and volatile organic acids. Like the enterobacteria, clostridial spores are sensitive to low pH; and clostridia require wet conditions for active development. Clostridial growth is rare in crops ensiled with less than 65% moisture, because sufficient sugars usually are present to reduce the pH quickly to a level below 4.6-4.8, at which point clostridia cannot grow. For wetter forages (70% moisture or more), reducing the pH to less than 4.6 either by the production of lactic acid or by direct acidification with the addition of acids or acid salts is the only practical means of preventing the growth of these bacteria with today's technology.

The period of active fermentation lasts from 7-21 days. Forages ensiled wetter than 65% moisture usually ferment rapidly, whereas fermentation is quite slow when the moisture content is below 50%. For forages ensiled in the normal moisture range (55-75%), active fermentation is completed in 7-14 days. At this point, fermentation of sugars by LAB has ceased, either because the low pH (below 4.0-4.2) stopped their growth or due to lack of sugars for fermentation.

The populations of epiphytic microorganisms on silage crops are quite variable and are affected by forage specie, stage of maturity, weather, mowing, field-wilting, and chopping (Fenton, 1987; Spoelstra and Hindle, 1989). Numerous studies have shown that the chopping process tends to increase the microflora numbers compared with those on the standing crops, and the LAB population is most enhanced (Muck, 1989; Lin *et al.*, 1992). This phenomenon was explained earlier as inoculation from the harvesting machine and microbial multiplication in the plant juices liberated during harvest. However, Pahlow (1990) demonstrated that these large increases in microflora numbers were impossible to achieve by microbial proliferation and growth because the time involved was too short, or by contamination from harvesting equipment, which could occur in the first load but not in later loads. A new 'somnicell' hypothesis proposes that bacteria assume a viable but unculturable stage on the surface of intact plants (Pahlow and Müller, 1990). The chopping process activates the previously dormant population by releasing plant enzymes (i.e., catalase and superoxide dismutase) and manganese compounds.

The LAB ferment WSC to primarily lactic acid, but also produce some acetic acid, ethanol, carbon dioxide and other minor products. This is a rather large group of bacteria, which includes species in six genera. They are divided into two categories; the homofermentative LAB produce only lactic acid from fermenting glucose and other six-carbon sugars, whereas heterofermentative LAB produce acetic acid, ethanol and carbon dioxide in addition to lactic acid (McDonald et al., 1991). In the fermentation phase, competition between strains of LAB determine how homofermentative the ensiling process will be.

Categories of silage additives

In the early years of silage production, the reason for applying an additive was to prevent secondary fermentation and a butyric acid silage. As a result, the efficacy of the additive usually was judged by its effect on typical fermentation criteria, i.e., pH and contents of ammonia-nitrogen and lactic, acetic and butyric acids (Spoelstra, 1991). This orientation on fermentation was reflected in the traditional division of additives into categories of fermentation inhibitors, fermentation stimulants, and substrate or nutrient sources.

In a comprehensive guide for silage additives available in the US, Bolsen and Heidker (1985) included information on over 150 products, and a more recent guide (Anonymous, 1992) contained nearly 80 bacterial inoculants and about 10 acid, enzyme, or nonprotein nitrogen (NPN) additives. A guide for silage products used in the UK contained over 100 additives, including 62 inoculants and 33 acid-based (Wilkinson, 1990). Spoelstra (1991) reported the results of a 1988 survey of silage additives marketed in the 12 countries of the European Community. Of the 203 additives identified, 87 were inoculants, and 83 were acid-based or salts of acids.

Efficacy of silage additives

BACTERIAL INOCULANTS

The first known use of LAB cultures was with ensiled sugar beet pulp in France at the beginning of this century (Watson and Nash, 1960). Kuchler

(1926) (cited by Spoelstra, 1991) described an inoculant system developed in Germany, which included the growing of bacteria on the farm. Many of these earlier attempts to inoculate silage crops were not successful because: 1) the strains of LAB were not adapted to a silage environment, or 2) the bacterial cultures were not viable at the time of use (Spoelstra, 1991).

Whittenbury (1961) defined the criteria that a LAB should satisfy for use in silage, and additional characteristics were cited by Woolford (1984) and Lindgren (1984). Woolford and Sawczyc (1984) screened 21 strains of LAB and found that none of them satisfied all criteria. *Lactobacillus plantarum* has been identified as one of the best suited LAB for inoculation of a silage crop; and single or multiple strains of this bacterium are included in virtually every commercial bacterial inoculant (Bolsen and Heidker, 1985; Wilkinson, 1990). Although *L. plantarum* satisfies most of the desired criteria, some strains are slow to produce lactic acid until the pH of the ensiled material falls below 5.0. Therefore, many commercial inoculants also contain species of pediococcus and/or enterococcus, which are active within the pH range of 5.0-6.5 and capable of dominating in the early stages of the fermentation phase (McDonald *et al.*, 1991).

Modern technology developed over the past three decades has greatly improved the commercial production of the bacterial cultures used in silage inoculants. An overview of the procedures were presented by Aimutis and Bolsen (1988), and a summary of the fermentation and stabilization techniques was reported by Risley (1992). Freeze-drying techniques made it possible for commercial inoculants to consistently provide high counts of viable LAB per gram of ensiled forage when the inoculant was used on farm. In addition, perhaps no other area of silage management received as much attention by both researchers and practitioners in the decades of the 1980s and 1990s as did bacterial silage inoculants. It is beyond the scope of this paper to cite all of the recently published scientific data. Summaries of several reviews are presented, as well as results from selected studies at Kansas State University, to document the effect of bacterial inoculants on silage fermentation, preservation, nutritive value and livestock performance.

Muck (1993) compiled data from over 250 studies conducted between 1985 and 1992; and most were with alfalfa, cool-season grasses or corn in North America and Europe. Inoculants significantly improved silage fermentation (i.e., by decreasing pH and ammonia-nitrogen and increasing lactic:acetic acid ratio) in 65% of the studies. When the results were separated by crop, pH was lowered by the inoculants in 75% of the alfalfa, 77% of the grass, but only 40% of the corn studies. In an earlier review that included studies conducted between 1985 and 1990, Muck and Bolsen (1991) reported improved fermentation efficiency in over 70% of the studies. At feedout, DM recovery was improved by the inoculants in 74% of the studies (25 out of 34), but aerobic stability was improved in only 42% of the studies (8 out of 19). The average increase in DM recovery in the studies that noted benefits from the inoculants was 2.5 percentage units. The authors stated that this was somewhat greater than would be expected from simply a more efficient fermentation phase alone; and that some improvement in aerobic stability during the feedout phase also must have occurred in many of the inoculated silages.

In the early 1980s, inoculants were being used to a limited extent in Europe, but results on farms were variable and scientific information was lacking on most aspects of bacterial inoculants (Castle, 1990). An international collaboration, EUROBAC, began in November 1983 and joint studies on inoculants were conducted throughout Europe and Scandinavia. Results were obtained from 17 research institutes or universities in 11 countries, and data were available from 86 separate trials carried out both in the laboratory and on the farm. Classification of the grass silages based on DM content was: 1) direct-cut, <18%; 2) dry harvest conditions or slightly wilted, 18-25%, 3) moderately wilted, 25-35%, and 4) extensively wilted, >35%. It was the aim in these trials to compare the inoculant treatments to controls (i.e., the negative control was no additive, and the positive control was the most widely used chemical additive, formic acid).

In a summary of the fermentation results, only the positive control was consistently effective in preserving the direct-cut silages (Zimmer, 1990). However, some results indicated that inoculants containing strains of the genera lactobacillus and pediococcus gave a more homolactic fermentation and a nearly 4 percentage unit lower DM loss compared to the negative control, provided the grass had at least 1.5% WSC on a fresh basis. In the 18-25% DM silages, inoculants containing strains of lactobacillus or lactobacillus and pediococcus were more effective than products that also contained a high proportion of *Streptococcus* (*Enterococcus*) *faecium*. Weather conditions during the wilting and harvesting periods produced a wide range in WSC content in the pre-ensiled grasses and more variable responses to the inoculants. In the moderately wilted silages (25-35% DM), inoculants that contained lactobacillus alone or in combination with pediococcus markedly improved the fermentation process compared to the negative control, and they were as effective as formic acid. For the grasses ensiled above 35% DM (mean, 42.6%), responses to the inoculants were variable. When the grass was wilted quickly, inoculants gave a superior fermentation and a lower DM loss. However, if wilting was delayed by unfavorable weather and the WSC content was below 2% in the fresh crop, neither inoculants nor formic acid stabilized the silages.

Grass suitable for inoculants contained a minimum of 1.5% WSC on a fresh basis and a DM content above 20-21%, but needed favorable wilting conditions to reach these values. Lactobacillus-based inoculants gave silages of fermentation quality equal to that of the positive control (formic acid), but with significantly more lactic acid and a 1.1 percentage unit higher DM recovery.

During the EUROBAC Conference held at Uppsala, Sweden in August of 1986, results of over 600 laboratory-scale experiments with silage inoculants were reported, and these were compiled by Spoelstra (1991). The data showed that inoculation of the majority of crops decreased pH values and ammonia-nitrogen levels and increased the lactic:acetic acid ratio by both increasing the lactic acid and decreasing the acetic acid contents of the silages. When averaged across all crops and ensiling conditions, lactobacillus-based inoculants increased DM recovery by 2-3 percentage units.

In the EUROBAC results, the population of epiphytic LAB on the chopped forages was higher than expected, with counts below 10^3 CFU per g (fresh basis) being the exception (Pahlow, 1990). About 55% of the grasses were in the range of 10^4-10^5 LAB per g of crop. When this was compared to the average inoculation rate of 10^5 LAB per g provided by the bacterial products, about one-third of the forages had a LAB count that was low enough to be increased by a factor of 10. For another 30% of the forages, the initial LAB population was doubled, but the remainder received significantly higher LAB populations only from products that provided 10^6 LAB per g of crop. Results showed that in general, an inoculation factor (IF) of 2 was the minimum to achieve a positive effect on fermentation quality.

Bolsen *et al.* (1988) and Bolsen *et al.* (1990) determined the effect of bacterial inoculants on silage fermentation in a series of over 50 studies conducted from 1987-1989. The four principal crops used and their ranges in DM content were: alfalfa (32-54%), wheat (30-42%), corn (32-38%), and forage sorghum (28-34%). A summary of the results showed that over 90% of the nearly 300 inoculated silages had lower pH, higher lactic:acetic acid ratio, and lower ethanol and ammonia-nitrogen contents compared to control silages. The IF was not a good predictor of a crop's response to an inoculant; and applying more than 300,000 CFU of LAB per g of fresh forage did not provide additional benefit to fermentation quality. The data also suggest that strain selection for a particular bacterial inoculant was as important as the number of LAB supplied per g of crop.

Pahlow (1991) indicated that a population of 10^6 LAB per g of fresh forage represents only a small fraction of the microflora that develop during the first 1-2 days of the ensiling process. Because few strains of epiphytic LAB have optimal properties for a silage environment, trying to establish a highly competitive strain or strains of silage-adapted LAB was still worthwhile. Pitt and Leibensperger (1987), in a modelling approach, found that the effectiveness of bacterial inoculants increased with the number of LAB supplied, and they concluded that an IF greater than 1 was necessary. However, this was based on the assumption that the epiphytic and inoculant LAB had equal maximum growth rates. They also reported that an increased acid tolerance of the inoculant strains was more important than a homofermentative fermentation.

As expected, the number of studies with bacterial inoculants that have measured animal performance (i.e., live weight gain, milk production, and feed efficiency) are considerably fewer than those that measured only fermentation and preservation criteria. In general, effects of inoculated silages on beef or dairy cattle performance appear to be small, but consistently positive. In a review of data collected from 1985-1992, Muck (1993) reported that DM intake, daily gain, and milk production were increased in about 25, 25, and 40%, respectively, of the studies with inoculated silages compared to control silages. Feed efficiency was improved in nearly 50% of the studies. When significant benefits from the bacterial inoculants were observed, DM intake, daily gain, milk production, and efficiency were increased by averages of 11, 11, 5, and 9%, respectively.

Harrison (1989) compiled data published primarily in North America between 1982 and 1989 on the effects of inoculants, enzymes, or their combinations on silage fermentation efficiency and dairy cattle performance. In 20 studies with predominantly alfalfa or grass silages, inoculants increased production of both actual and 4% fat-corrected milk by about 0.45 kg per cow per day. Cows fed inoculated silages also consumed more DM and had higher body weight gains. The greatest advantage for inoculated silages was obtained with wilted alfalfa and inclusion of at least 60% silage in the total ration on a DM basis.

Bolsen *et al.* (1992) summarized results from 26 studies conducted over a 14-year period at Kansas State University comparing fermentation efficiency, DM recovery, and beef cattle performance for inoculated or NPN-treated corn and forage sorghum silages. Treatment means for untreated, control silages and treated silages are shown in Table 3. The 19 inoculated corn silages had a 1.3 percentage unit higher DM recovery compared to untreated silages, and the inoculated silages supported a 1.8% more efficient gain and a 1.8 kg increase in gain per ton of crop ensiled. When the 10 untreated and inoculated sorghum silages were compared, inoculants increased DM recovery, improved feed conversion, and produced 2.3 kg more gain per tonne of crop ensiled. In both crops, inoculants significantly reduced the acetic acid content of the silages and tended to decrease the ethanol content and increase the lactic:acetic acid ratio.

Overall, the magnitudes of animal performance responses to inoculated silages are higher than what might be expected from the shifts in fermentation products and the impact of increased DM recovery. One rather surprising finding from the recent reviews of Muck and Bolsen (1991), Spoelstra (1991), and Muck (1993) was that bacterial inoculants significantly increased both DM digestibility (in over 60% of the studies) and fiber digestibility (in over 35% of the studies). Why this should occur is not completely understood, because LAB are not known to degrade the cell wall or other forage components that are believed to limit digestibility in beef and dairy cattle. Muck (1993) speculated that the lower pH of inoculated silages causes additional acid hydrolysis of hemicellulose, which opens the cell wall fraction for more rapid and extensive digestion by rumen microorganisms.

Muck (1993) reported that animal performance benefits were linked closely to increases in digestibility in the 31 studies reviewed. Animal performance was improved in nearly 60% of the studies (9 of 16) in which bacterial inoculants improved DM digestibility, but when digestibility was not affected by the inoculants, improved animal performance was observed in only 13% of the studies (2 of 15).

Table 3. Summary of treatment means for silage fermentation, DM recovery and cattle performance from bacterial inoculant and NPN additions to corn and forage sorghum silages.

Crop and silage treatment	No. of silages	DM recovery[1]	ADG (kg)	DM/kg of intake (kg)	DM/kg of gain (kg)	Gain/ ton of crop ensiled (kg)	pH	Lactic acid	Acetic acid	Ethanol[2]
								% of the silage DM		
Corn										
Control	15	90.2	1.09	7.73	7.10	49.5	3.82	5.3	2.5	0.8
Inoculant	19	91.5	1.12	7.76	6.97	51.3	3.82	5.5	2.3	0.6
Probability (P)	-	0.01	NS	NS	0.11	0.01	NS	0.12	0.03	NS
Control	3	91.5	1.04	7.80	7.52	48.1	3.81	4.7	2.0	-
Anhydrous NH$_3$	3	89.4	1.01	7.96	7.84	45.0	4.19	6.1	2.5	-
Probability (P)	-	NS	0.16	NS	NS	0.07	0.01	0.01	0.12	-
Forage sorghum										
Control	10	83.1	0.75	5.96	8.32	35.3	3.94	5.1	2.6	1.4
Inoculant	10	85.2	0.76	5.85	7.98	37.6	3.93	5.2	2.1	1.2
Probability (P)	-	0.01	NS	0.20	0.04	0.01	NS	NS	0.02	NS
Control	3	87.7	0.61	5.41	9.52	37.3	3.91	5.1	2.0	-
Anhydrous NH$_3$ or urea[3]	3	82.6	0.49	5.13	10.58	30.3	4.63	6.1	3.6	-
Probability (P)	-	0.09	NS	NS	NS	0.24	0.10	NS	0.08	-

Source: Bolsen *et al.* (1992).
[1]As a percent of the crop DM ensiled.
[2]Ethanol was not measured in studies conducted prior to 1984.
[3]One study with anhydrous NH$_3$ and two studies with urea.

The data reviewed indicate that bacterial inoculants are not always effective. The IF has been used to predict when an inoculant would be expected to give a significant improvement in animal performance for a particular silage crop. In studies at the US Dairy Forage Research Center, increases in milk production from wilted alfalfa silages occurred only when the inoculant supplied at least 10 times more LAB than the epiphytic, acid-tolerant LAB population on the forage (Satter *et al.*, 1991). Grass silage studies in Europe also confirm that an inoculant must provide a 10-fold increase in LAB to produce significant effects on animal performance (Spoelstra, 1991). Corn usually has 10^5-10^6 epiphytic LAB per g, and commercial inoculants provide an IF of only 1 or less (Pahlow, 1990). However, data from farm-scale inoculant studies often show increases in animal performance, and these benefits are not always explained by differences in fermentation efficiency (Bolsen *et al.*, 1992). Gordon (1989) reported that DM intake and milk production were higher for cows fed inoculant-treated ryegrass silage (10^6 CFU of *L. plantarum* per g of fresh crop) than for cows fed formic acid-treated (85% w/w applied at 2.7 liters per ton of fresh crop) or untreated silages. These improvements occurred despite similar fermentation characteristics for the three silages. Kung (1992) suggested that as yet unidentified constituents in the inoculated silages might be responsible for the nutritive value benefits.

NONPROTEIN NITROGEN SOURCES

Earlier research with urea and anhydrous ammonia additions to corn and sorghum silages was reviewed by Ely (1978). Urea-treated silages gave small but consistent improvements in daily gain, milk production, and feed efficiency compared to untreated silages that were supplemented with a similar amount of urea at feeding. Ammonia-treated silages provided benefits less frequently and had negative effects in several studies. The review did not include silage preservation results; however, retention of added nitrogen was 95% or higher for urea-treated silages but only 50-75% for ammonia-treated.

The addition of ammonia immediately raises the pH of the crop to 8-9; and the combined effect of the ammonia and high pH reduces the yeast and mold populations and usually increases aerobic stability of the silage. Ammonia also decreases the number of LAB, and this delays the start of the fermentation phase. However, the amount of fermentation products (i.e., lactic and acetic acids) increases because of the much higher initial forage pH. Ammonia breaks some of the linkages between hemicellulose and other cell wall components, which should increase both rate and extent of digestion. The high initial pH also inactivates plant proteases, and this reduces the extent of protein degradation in the ensiled crop.

In a series of six studies conducted in farm-scale silos, Bolsen *et al.* (1992) observed that anhydrous ammonia applied at 3.5-4.0 kg per ton or urea at 5.0 kg per ton (fresh basis) increased the pH value, lactic and acetic acid contents, and DM loss in both corn and forage sorghum silages (Table 2). Performance of growing cattle was not improved by the NPN-treatments, and gain per tonne of crop ensiled was reduced by 3.1 and 7.0 kg in the corn and sorghum silages, respectively.

In a review of 39 studies reported since 1985, Muck (1993) found that NPN additives increased fermentation acids in approximately 60% of the silages, and clostridial activity was a problem in low DM crops (less than 30%). In 12 of 21 studies, DM recovery in the NPN-treated silages was decreased and it increased in only three studies. Aerobic stability was improved consistently in the NPN silages. Digestibility of the NPN silages (i.e., DM, NDF, or ADF) was increased in 16 of 19 studies, and most treated silages had higher true protein content. However, these apparent improvements in nutritive value did not increase daily gain, milk production or feed efficiency in most studies, especially in recent research with grass and legume silages. The author noted that the paradoxes of improved bunk life with reduced DM recovery and improved digestibility with no benefit in animal performance needed further clarification.

FERMENTABLE SUBSTRATES

Molasses is the most widely used source of sugars and is particularly effective in improving the fermentation quality in low DM grasses and low WSC legumes and tropical forages. Castle and Watson (1985) compared molasses and formic acid additions to low DM ryegrass silages and concluded that at 20-30 liters per tonne, molasses was as effective as the acid. The application of moderate to high levels (i.e., 40-60 kg per ton of fresh crop) of cereal grains, wheat or rice brans, or citrus or beet pulps to low DM forages has improved the fermentation characteristics of the silages; and in some studies the amount of effluent was reduced (Jones *et al.*, 1990; Bolsen *et al.*, 1995). Thorough mixing of the substrates with the crop is particularly important, because if the absorbents are added in layers in silos fitted with internal drains, effluent production can be increased (Wilkinson, 1990).

ACIDS AND ACID SALTS

In Europe and in many other areas where low DM grasses are important silage crops, formic acid is the standard against which most other silage additives have been tested. Formic acid not only restricts the growth of bacteria through its acidifying (hydrogen ion) effect, it also has a selective antibacterial action, as does the weaker propionic acid (Woolford, 1975). In contrast, the mineral acids, sulfuric and hydrochloric, act solely by reducing pH and have no specific antimicrobial properties. Yeasts have been shown to be particularly tolerant of formic acid (McDonald *et al.*, 1991), and the aerobic stability of silages made with formic acid is often poor, partly because of the likely elevated yeast counts in the silage, and also because of the restricted fermentation, which leads to relatively higher contents of residual WSC in the silage.

Effects of formic acid on animal performance have been reviewed extensively (Thomas and Thomas, 1985; McDonald *et al.*, 1991). The magnitude of the improvement in animal performance depends on the preservation quality of the untreated forage, with large benefits recorded when the untreated silage is badly preserved.

Salts of acids are used widely in Europe as safer alternatives to the acids themselves and efficacy is similar, if the same rates of active ingredients are applied to the crop. Very recently, the combined addition of bacterial inoculants and acid salts has been evaluated with encouraging results (Kalzendorf and Weissbach, 1993). In 10 studies with a wide range of crops, a concentrated solution of sodium formate in which freeze-dried LAB was dispersed gave reduced fermentation losses, especially with forages that were difficult to ensile. Aerobic stability also was improved compared to silage with inoculant alone. The salt has little damaging effect on the LAB and develops its antibacterial action as the pH of the silage decreases. Because the LAB are relatively more acid-tolerant than the undesirable epiphytic microorganisms, they dominate the ensiling process.

References

Anonymous. 1992. Silage additives. In: 1993 Direct-fed Microbial, Enzyme, and Forage Additive Compendium. Miller Publ. Co., Minnetonka, Minnesota. pp. 217-261.

Aimutis, W.R. and K.K. Bolsen. 1988. Production of biological silage additives. In: Biological Silage Additives. Chalcombe Publ., Church Lane, Kingston, Canterbury, Kent, UK. pp 45-72.

Ashbell, G. and Z. G. Weinberg. 1992. Top silage losses in horizontal silos. Can. Agric. Engin. 34:171-175.

Bolsen, K.K. 1985. New technology in forage conservation-feeding systems. In: Proc. XV Int. Grassl. Congr. Kyoto, Japan. pp. 82-88.

Bolsen, K.K. and J.L. Heidker. 1985. Silage Additives USA. Chalcombe Publ., Church Lane, Kingston, Canterbury, Kent, UK.

Bolsen, K.K., A. Laytimi, R. Hart, L. Nuzbach, F. Niroomand and L. Leipold. 1988. Effect of commercial inoculants on fermentation of 1987 silage crops. In: Kansas Agric. Exp. Sta. Rpt. of Prog. 539:137-153.

Bolsen, K.K., J.L. Curtis, C.J. Lin and J.T. Dickerson. 1990. Silage inoculants and indigenous microflora: With emphasis on alfalfa. In: Biotechnology in the Feed Industry. (T.P. Lyons, ed.) Alltech Tech. Publ., Nicholasville, KY. pp 257-269.

Bolsen, K.K., D.G. Tiemann, R.N. Sonon, R.A. Hart, B. Dalke, J.T. Dickerson and C. Lin. 1992. Evaluation of inoculant-treated corn silages. In: Kansas Agric. Exp. Stn. Rpt. of Prog. 651:103-106.

Bolsen, K.K., J.T. Dickerson, B.E. Brent, R.N. Sonon, Jr., B.S. Dalke, C.J. Lin and J.E. Boyer, Jr. 1993. Rate and extent of top spoilage in horizontal silos. J. Dairy Sci. 76:2940-2962.

Bolsen, K.K., P.S. Faylon, U.M. Lustria, M. Loresco, N.F. Bolsen and B. Beltran. 1995. Unpublished data. Dairy Training and Research Institute. University of the Philippines, Los Baños, Laguna, Philippines.

Bolsen, K.K. 1985. New technology in forage conservation-feeding systems. In: Proc. 15th Int. Grassl. Congr. Kyoto, Japan. pp 82-88.

Bolsen, K.K., M.K. Siefers and R.V. Pope. 1998. Improving silage quality. In: Proc. Maryland Nutr. Conf. for Feed Mnft. Baltimore, Md, USA. pp 116-130.

Brassley, P. 1996. Silage in Britain, 1880-1990: The delayed adoption of an innovation. Agric. History Rev. 44:63-87.

Carrier, L. 1920. The history of the silo. J. Amer. Soc. Agron. p. 181.

Castle, M.E. 1990. Conclusions and future prospects. In: Proc. of the EUROBAC Conf. Swedish University of Agric. Sciences (S. Lindgren and K.L. Pettersson, eds.) Uppsala. pp 184-188.

Castle, M.E. and J.N. Watson. 1985. Silage and milk production: studies with molasses and formic acid as additives for grass silage. Grass and Forage Sci. 40:85-92.

Dickerson, J.T., G. Ashbell, K.K. Bolsen, B.E. Brent, L. Pfaff and Y. Niwa. 1992a. Losses from top spoilage in horizontal silos in western Kansas. Kansas Agric. Exp. Stn. Rpt. of Prog. 651:131-134.

Dickerson, J.T., G. Ashbell, K.K. Bolsen, B.E. Brent, L. Pfaff and Y. Niwa. 1992b. Losses from top spoilage in horizontal silos in western Kansas. Kansas Agric. Exp. Stn. Rpt. of Prog. 651:127-131.

Eckles, C.H., O.E. Reed and J.B. Fitch. 1919. Capacity of silos and silage weights. Kansas State Agric. College, Bull. No. 222, Manhattan, KS, USA.

Ely, L.O. 1978. The use of added feedstuffs in silage production. In: Fermentation of Silage-A Review. (M.E. McCullough, ed.). NFIA, West Des Moines, IA. pp 233-280.

Fenton, M.P. 1987. An investigation into the sources of lactic acid bacteria in grass silage. J. of Applied Bacteriology. 62:181-188.

Fung, D.Y.C. 1988. Laboratory Manual for Food Fermentation. Kansas State University, Manhattan, KS, USA.

Goffart, A. 1877. Manual of the Culture and Ensilage of Maize and other Fodder Crops. Masson, Paris, France.

Gotlieb, A. 1997. Causes of mycotoxins in silages. In: Silage: Field to Feedbunk. NRAES-99. NRAES, Ithaca, NY, USA. pp 213-221.

Gordon, F.J. 1989. An evaluation through lactating dairy cattle of a bacterial inoculant as an additive for grass silage. Grass and Forage Sci. 44:169-179.

Harrison, J.H. 1989. Use of silage additives and their effect on animal productivity. In: Proc. of the Pacific Northwest Animal Nutr. Conf. Boise, ID. pp 27-35.

Holthaus, D.L., M.A. Young, B.E. Brent and K.K. Bolsen. 1995. Losses from top spoilage in horizontal silos. In: Kansas Agric. Exp. Stn. Rpt. of Prog. 727: 59-62.

Honig, H. 1991. Reducing losses during storage and unloading of silage. In: Forage Conservation towards 2000. (G. Pahlow and H. Honig, eds.) Landbauforschung Volkenrode, Sonderheft 123, Germany. pp 116-128.

Huck, G.L., J.E. Turner, M.K. Siefers, M.A. Young, R.V. Pope, B.E. Brent and K.K. Bolsen. 1997. Kansas Agric. Exp. Stn. Rpt. of Prog. 783:83-85.

Hulbert, H. W. and J. H. Christ. 1926. Growing sunflowers for silage. Bull. No.141. Agric. Exp. Stn., University of Idaho, Moscow, ID, USA.

Hunter, O.W., and L.D. Bushnell. 1916. Some important fermentations in silage. Kansas State Agric. College, Bull. No. 2. Manhattan, KS, USA.

Jones, D.I.H., R. Jones and G. Moseley. 1990. Effect of incorporating rolled barley in autumn cut ryegrass silage on effluent production, silage fermentation and cattle performance. J. Agric. Sci. Camb. 115:399-408.

Kalzendorf, C. and F. Weissbach. 1993. Studies on the effect of a combined application of inoculants and sodium formate. In: Proc. 10th Silage Res. Conf. Dublin City University, Dublin, Ireland. pp 89-90.

Kirstein, K. 1963. Historical survey of the ensiling of green fodder. Das Wirtschaftseigene Futter. 9:54-65.

Kung, L., Jr. 1992. Use of additives in silage fermentation. In: 1993 Direct-fed Microbial, Enzyme and Forage Additive Compendium. Miller Publ. Co., Minnetonka, Minnesota. pp 31-35.

Lin, C., K.K. Bolsen, B.E. Brent, R.A. Hart, J.T. Dickerson, A.M. Feyerherm and W.R. Aimutis. 1992. Epiphytic microflora on alfalfa and whole-plant corn. J. Dairy Sci. 75:2484-2493.

Lindgren, S. 1984. Silage inoculation. In: Proc. 7th Silage Conf. Summary of Papers (F.J. Gordon and E.F. Unsworth, eds.) The Queen's University, Belfast, Northern Ireland. pp 3-4.

McDonald, P. 1980. Silage fermentation. In: Occ. Symp. No. 11. Brit. Grassl. Soc., Brighton, UK. pp 161-174.

McDonald, P., A.R. Henderson and S.J.E. Heron. 1991. The Biochemistry of Silage (2nd ed.). Chalcombe Publ., Church Lane, Kingston, Canterbury, Kent, UK.

McDonald, P., A.C. Stirling, A.R. Henderson, W.A. Dewar, G.H. Stark, W.G. Davie, H.T. Macpherson, A.M. Reid and J. Slater. 1960. Studies on Ensilage. Edinburgh School Agric. Tech. Bull. 24, Edinburgh, UK.

McGuffey, R. K. and M. J. Owens. 1979. Effect of covering and dry matter at ensiling on preservation of alfalfa in bunker silos. J. Anim. Sci. 49:298-305.

McLaughlin, N.B., D.B. Wilson and D.M. Bowden. 1978. Effect of a plastic cover on dry matter loses from a horizontal silo. Can. J. Agric. Eng. 20:1-10.

Miles, M. 1910. Silos, Ensilage and Silage - a Practical Treatise on the Ensilage of Fodder Corn. Orage Judd Co., New York, NY, USA.

Muck, R.E. 1989. Initial bacterial numbers on lucerne prior to ensiling. Grass and Forage Sci. 44:19-25.

Muck, R.E. 1993. The role of silage additives in making high quality silage. In: Proc. Nat. Silage Prod. Conf. NRAES-67, Ithaca, New York. pp 106-116.

Muck, R.E. and K.K. Bolsen. 1991. Silage preservation and silage additives. In:. Hay and Silage Management in North America. (K.K. Bolsen, J.E. Baylor and M.E. McCullough, eds) NFIA, West Des Moines, Iowa. pp. 105-125.

Oldenburg, E. 1991. Mycotoxins in conserved forage. p. 191-205. In: Forage Conservation towards 2000. (G. Pahlow and H. Honig, eds.) Landbauforschung Volkenrode, Sonderheft 123, Germany.

Pahlow, G. 1990. Microbiology of inoculants, crops, and silages. In: Proc. of the EUROBAC Conf. Swedish University of Agric. Sciences, (S. Lindgren and K.L. Pettersson, eds.) Uppsala. pp 13-22.

Pahlow, G. 1991. Role of microflora in forage conservation. In: Forage Conservation towards 2000. (G. Pahlow and H. Honig, eds) Inst. Grassl. Forage Res., Braunschweig, Germany. pp. 26-36.

Pahlow, G. and T. Müller. 1990. Determination of epiphytic microorganisms on grass as influenced by harvesting and sample preparation. In: Proc. 9th Silage Conf. Newcastle-upon-Tyne, UK. pp 23-24.

Pitt, R.E. and R.Y. Leibensperger. 1987. The effectiveness of silage inoculants: A systems approach. Agric. Syst. 25:27-49.

Risley, C. 1992. An overview of microbiology. In: 1993 Direct-fed Microbial, Enzyme and Forage Additive Compendium. Miller Publ. Co., Minnetonka, Minnesota. pp 11-13.

Satter, L.D., R.E. Muck, B.A. Jones, T.R. Ohiman, J.A. Woodford and C.M. Wacek. 1991. Efficacy of bacterial inoculants for alfalfa silage. In: Forage Conservation towards 2000. (G. Pahlow and H. Honig, eds) Inst. Grassl. Forage Res., Braunschweig, Germany. pp 342-343.

Seglar, W. 1997. Case studies that implicate silage mycotoxins as the cause of dairy herd problems. In: Silage: Field to Feedbunk. NRAES-99. NRAES, Ithaca, NY, USA. pp 242-254.

Shukking, S. 1976. The history of silage making. Stikstof 19:2-11.

Spoelstra, S.F. 1991. Chemical and biological additives in forage conservation. In: Forage Conservation towards 2000. (G. Pahlow and H. Honig, eds.) Inst. Grassl. Forage Res., Braunschweig, Germany. pp 48-70.

Spoelstra, S.F. and V.A. Hindle. 1989. Influence of wilting on chemical and microbial parameters of grass relevant to ensiling. Netherlands. J. Agric. Sci. 37:355-364.

Thomas, C. and P.C. Thomas. 1985. Factors affecting the nutritive value of grass silages. In: Recent Advances in Animal Nutrition. (W. Haresign and D.J.A. Cole, eds.) Butterworths, London. pp 223-256.

Virtanen, A.I. 1933. The AIV method of processing feeds. Empire J. Exper. Agric. 1:143-155.

Watson, S.J. and M.J. Nash. 1960. The Conservation of Grass and Forage Crops. Oliver and Boyd, Edinburgh, Scotland.

Weissbach, F. 1996. New developments in crop conservation. In: Proc. XI Int. Silage Conf., (D.I.H. Jones, R. Jones, R. Dewhurst, R. Merry and P.M. Haigh, eds.) Aberystwyth, UK.pp 11-25.

Whitlow, L.W. and W.M. Hagler. 1997. Effects of mycotoxins on the animal: the producer's perspective. In: Silage: Field to Feedbunk. NRAES-99. NRAES, Ithaca, NY, USA. pp 222-232.

Whittenbury, R. 1961. An investigation of lactic acid bacteria. Ph.D. dissertation. University of Edinburgh, Edinburgh, Scotland.

Wilkinson, J.M. 1990. Silage UK (6th ed.). Chalcombe Publ., Church Lane, Kingston, Canterbury, Kent, UK.

Wilkinson, J.M. and B.A. Stark. 1987. Silage in Western Europe: A Survey of 17 Countries. Chalcombe Publications, Marlow, UK.

Wilkinson, J.M. and K.K. Bolsen. 1996. Production of silage and hay in Europe and North America. In: Proc. XI Int. Silage Conf., (D.I.H. Jones, R. Jones, R. Dewhurst, R. Merry and P.M. Haigh, eds.) Aberystwyth, UK. pp 42-43.

Wilkinson, J.M., J. Hill and J.D. Leaver. 1996. Effect of swath treatment and period of wilting on field losses, ensiling characteristics and feeding value of grass silage. In: Proc. XI Int. Silage Conf., (D.I.H. Jones, R. Jones, R. Dewhurst, R. Merry and P.M. Haigh, eds.) Aberystwyth, UK. pp 46-47.

Woolford, M.K. 1975. Microbiological screening of the straight chain fatty acids (C_2-C_{12}) as potential silage additives. J. Sci. Food and Agric. 26:219-228.

Woolford, M.K. 1984. The Silage Fermentation. Marcel Dekker, Inc., New York, NY.

Woolford, M.K and M.K. Sawczyc. 1984. An investigation into the effect of cultures of lactic acid bacteria on fermentation in silage. 1. Strain selection. Grass and Forage Sci. 39:139-148.

Zimmer, E. 1980. Efficient silage systems. In: Forage conservation in the 80s. Proc. Occ. Symp. 11, Brit. Grassl. Soc., (C. Thomas, ed.) Reading, UK. pp 186-197.

Zimmer, E. 1990. Evaluation of fermentation parameters from the silage experiments. In: Proc of the EUROBAC Conf., (S. Lindgren and K.L. Pettersson, eds.) Swedish University of Agric. Sciences, Uppsala. pp 19-44.

Some milestones in our understanding of yeast culture supplementation in ruminants and their implications in animal production systems

KARL A. DAWSON

North American Biosciences Center, Alltech Inc., Nicholasville Kentucky

Introduction

Over the last two decades, our enhanced understanding of the role of yeast cultures in animal diets has resulted in the development of a group of scientifically proven supplements that enhance animal performance and improve animal health. Intense research efforts have attempted to understand the basic mechanisms, which account for the beneficial effects of yeast cultures in many groups of animals. However, the most successful basic research programs have examined the effects of yeast cultures in ruminant animals. The goal of these research efforts has been to define the application and production strategies that can optimize the response to these microbial supplements. This paper will examine some of the known effects of yeast culture supplements on microbial activity in the gastrointestinal tract of ruminants and will build a hypothetical model which explains those effects.

Production responses to a specific yeast culture, Yea-Sacc[1026]

The effects of specific yeast culture preparations on performance of ruminants have been well documented over the last two decades. Production responses have been measured in both dairy and meat production systems. Typically, two different approaches have been used to examine production responses to the yeast culture (Yea-Sacc) in dairy cattle. The first uses experimental designs that compare milk production in animal groups receiving the yeast culture supplement with those of control groups receiving unsupplemented diets (Table 1). These types of studies allow for careful evaluation of effects of yeast preparation under controlled conditions, but only use limited numbers of animals. Such studies clearly show responses to yeast supplementation strategies. The second experimental approach uses field studies to demonstrate the effects of yeast culture supplements by

Table 1. Milk production responses to Yea-Sacc supplementation in animals assigned to specific treatment groups.

Reference	Number of animals	Days in milk	Ration	Milk production (kg/d) Control	Milk production (kg/d) Yea-Sacc	% Increase
El-Nor and Kholif, 1998	27	14-104	Berseem hay with cotton seed/corn/wheat bran concentrate	8.32	9.57*	+15
					10.78*	+30
Piva et al., 1993	24	Mean 105	Corn silage based TMR with alfalfa hay	25.4	26.2*	+3
Skorko-Sajko et al., 1993	24	5-85	Cereal-legume silage	16.8	17.4	+4
Alonzo et al., 1993	80	60-150	Grass silage, concentrate	25.9	27.3	+5
Smith et al., 1993	36	150-240	Corn silage, alfalfa hay, tallow, SBM	22.0	23.6	+7
Erasmus et al., 1992	6	56-94	Ground corn, alfalfa hay, sorghum, fish meal, sunflower meal	18.9	20.1	+6
Williams et al., 1991	32	7-42 43-84	Ground barley, hay, SBM, fish meal, concentrate	22.0	25.5	+14
				23.3	27.4	+18
Dobos et al., 1990	32	0-305	Corn silage, grass, wheat meal, concentrate	18.7	20.5	+10
Huber et al., 1989	513	0-120	Alfalfa hay and silage, cotton seeds, concentrate	28.7	29.7*	+4
Günther, 1989	100	0-100	Corn silage, grass silage, concentrate	28.7	31.1*	+8
Hoyos et al., 1987	60	150-180	Corn silage, hay, cotton seed meal	30.9	32.8*	+6

*Significant difference (P<0.05).

comparing milk production during a supplementation period with that observed during a similar period when the animals receive an unsupplemented diet (Table 2). Such field studies often are much less controlled and require an understanding of many of the factors that influence animal production during a normal production cycle. However, they do allow for the evaluation of yeast culture preparation under conditions that reflect practical field application in large numbers of animals. In 22 studies with Yea-Sacc involving more than 9039 dairy animals, supplementation resulted in an average increase in milk production of 7.3%. Responses to supplementation were variable but ranged from a 2% increase to a 30% increase in milk production. Similarly, growth responses to yeast culture in meat-producing animals have been observed. These responses to yeast cultures in growing ruminant animals have also been variable and range from no significant increase in average daily gain to increases of more than 20%. An average increase in daily gain was 8.7%. These studies indicate that management practices, diets and overall stress influence responses to yeast culture supplementation. However, data from a wide range of both controlled studies and field trials suggest that yeast culture supplements can have a significant role in strategies for economically enhancing the performance of ruminant animals.

Effects of yeast cultures on the rumen

Many laboratories have examined the effects of yeast cultures on microbial activities in the rumen. In order to develop a model for explaining the effects of yeast on animal performance, it is important to review some the research milestones that have helped define the role of yeast in the rumen.

MILESTONE #1- YEAST SUPPLEMENTATION INFLUENCES RUMINAL DIGESTION

Most investigators agree that yeast culture supplementation strategies can have measurable effects on ruminal fermentations, and a number of beneficial changes in digestion have been noted. Studies in several laboratories have demonstrated that yeast culture supplementation can influence digestive processes in the rumen (Williams and Newbold, 1990; Dawson, 1992; Newbold *et al.*, 1996; Wallace 1996). Typically, the total extent of dry matter digestion was not drastically altered. However, the initial rate of digestion is readily influenced by the addition of live yeast preparations to the diets of ruminants (Figure 1). This is a characteristic of yeast supplementation that has been measured in both *in vitro* (Dawson and Hopkins, 1991) and *in vivo* studies (Williams and Newbold, 1990; Smith *et al.*, 1993; Kumar *et al.*, 1997). Since feed intake is often considered to be a function of the initial rates of fiber digestion, early stimulation of ruminal activity can be expected to have a major impact on feed consumption and can provide a driving

Table 2. Field trials comparing milk production before and after Yea-Sacc supplementation.

Site of study	Number of animals	Days in milk	Ration	Milk production (kg/d) Before Yea-Sacc	After Yea-Sacc	% Increase
France, 1995	80	-	Corn silage, grass silage, alfalfa hay, high-moisture corn, concentrate	24.6	25.9	+5
France, 1995	1340	-	Corn silage, grass silage, hay, concentrate	18.6	19.6	+5
New York, 1991	2655	170	Corn silage, hay cottonseed meal, concentrate	30.4	31.2	+3
		132		31.6	32.8	+4
		174		36.3	37.8	+4
		207		37.1	38.1	+3
		178		31.2	32.1	+3
California, 1990	2883	-	Corn silage, alfalfa hay, cereals, cottonseeds	29.0	30.4	+5
North Dakota, 1988	34	-	Corn silage, hay, cereals, concentrate	24.8	28.0	+13
North Dakota, 1988	65	-	Grass, concentrate	20.9	22.6	+8
California, 1987	627	-	Corn silage, alfalfa hay, corn gluten meal, bet pulp, cereals, cottonseeds, tallow	26.2	27.3	+4
Georgia, 1987	100	-	Corn silage, hay, concentrate	25.5	25.9	+2
Georgia, 1987	190	-	Corn meal, corn gluten meal, citrus pulp, alfalfa cubs, cottonseeds	23.6	27.3	+16

force for improved animal performance. Such studies suggest an important role for yeast culture supplementation in digestion of animals maintained on high forage diets.

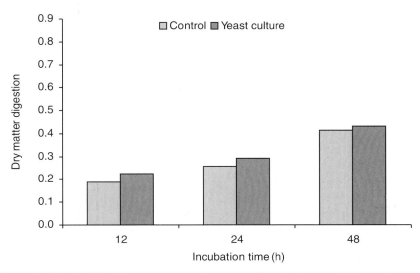

Figure 1. Effects of Yea-Sacc on *in sacco* dry matter digestion by ruminal bacteria (adapted from Kumar *et al.*, 1997).

MILESTONE #2- YEAST CULTURE SUPPLEMENTATION INFLUENCES RUMINAL LACTIC ACID METABOLISM

Other studies have demonstrated a role for yeast culture in stabilizing ruminal fermentations and in addressing ruminal disorders. Williams *et al.* (1991) demonstrated the beneficial effects of the viable yeast culture, Yea-Sacc, on lactic acid concentrations in the rumen in high concentrate diets (Figure 2). In animals fed high energy diets, decreased lactic acid concentrations are associated with higher ruminal pH and are characteristic of much more stable ruminal fermentation. These alterations in ruminal fermentation can be expected to provide for improved digestion and could also be reflected in improved intake and production. The ability of yeast to prevent the accumulation of lactic acid in the rumen suggests a role for viable yeast in overcoming ruminal dysfunctions associated with the use of high energy diets used in both high-producing dairy and fast-growing beef cattle.

MILESTONE #3- YEAST CULTURE SUPPLEMENTATION ALTERS RUMINAL NITROGEN METABOLISM

Several lines of evidence suggest that yeast culture supplementation can beneficially alter nitrogen metabolism in the rumen (Table 3). This is reflected

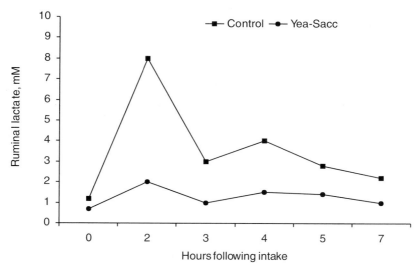

Figure 2. Effect of Yea-Sacc on the concentration of lactic acid in the rumen (adapted from Williams *et al.*, 1991).

in lower ruminal ammonia concentrations observed in animals receiving yeast supplements and is consistent with observed increases in the concentrations of bacteria in the rumen. In addition, these changes are reflected in an increased flow of bacterial nitrogen to the small intestines (Erasmus *et al.*, 1992). Altered nitrogen flow has also been associated with shifts in the basic amino acid flow out of the rumen. The beneficial increase in the flow of microbial protein from the rumen is consistent with models that suggest stimulation of microbial growth in the rumen and more efficient conversion of ammonia nitrogen into microbial protein. Since microbial protein is often used to drive protein synthesis in high-producing ruminants, these observations suggest a role for specific yeast culture supplements in stimulating protein synthesis in both beef and dairy production systems.

Table 3. Effects of Yea-Sacc on nitrogen intake and the flow of nitrogen to the small intestine of a lactating dairy cow.

Item	Dietary treatment	
	Unsupplemented	Yeast culture supplemented
Nitrogen intake, g/d	535	526
Flow to small intestines, g/N/day		
Non-ammonia nitrogen	446	488
Microbial nitrogen	255	293
Dietary nitrogen	191	195
Microbial nitrogen, % of intake	47.6	55.7

(adapted from Erasmus *et al.*, 1992).

MILESTONE #4- YEAST SUPPLEMENT ALTERS RUMINAL MICROBIAL POPULATIONS

Many investigators have attributed the beneficial effects of yeast culture directly to changes in the ruminal fermentation and to changes in the microbial population in the digestive tract (Williams and Newbold, 1990; Dawson, 1992; Newbold *et al.*, 1996; Wallace, 1996). The ability of specific yeast culture preparations to stimulate the growth of ruminal bacteria and to increase the concentrations of specific groups of beneficial bacteria in the rumen has been well documented (Table 4). Increased concentrations of the total anaerobic bacteria and of cellulolytic bacteria have been one of the most consistently measured responses to yeast culture in the rumen (Wiedmeier *et al.*, 1987; Harrison *et al.*, 1988; Dawson *et al.*, 1990; Newbold and Wallace, 1992). However, other studies have also suggested that yeast culture preparations can enhance the growth of lactic acid-utilizing bacteria (Edwards, 1990; Girard *et al.*, 1993), proteolytic bacteria (Yoon and Stern, 1996) and bacteria that convert molecular hydrogen to acetate in the rumen (Chaucheyras *et al.*, 1995b). In addition, yeast preparations have been shown to enhance the activities of fiber-digesting fungi in the rumen (Chaucheyras *et al.*, 1995a). Increased concentrations of beneficial microorganisms and enhanced microbial activities can be expected to lead to enhanced digestive processes and the destruction of metabolic intermediates that can result in ruminal dysfunction. The ability of yeast to stimulate specific groups of bacteria is consistent with many of the other physiological and metabolic effects of yeast observed in the rumen and can explain enhanced protein synthesis, improved ruminal stability and improved microbial protein synthesis.

Table 4. Effects of yeast culture supplements on the concentrations of selected bacteria in ruminal microbial populations.

Group	Increase in concentration (%)	Reference
Anaerobic bacteria	31	Wiedmeier *et al.*, 1987
	58	Harrison *et al.*, 1988
	490	Dawson *et al.*, 1990
	82 to 95	El Hassan *et al.*, 1993
	15 to 62	Newbold *et al.*, 1996
	34	Kumar *et al.*, 1997
Cellulolytic bacteria	58	Wiedmeier *et al.*, 1987
	82	Harrison *et al.*, 1988
	812	Dawson *et al.*, 1990
	113 to 246	Newbold *et al.*, 1996
	56	Kumar *et al.*, 1997
Lactic acid bacteria	0-58	Girard *et al.*, 1993

MILESTONE #5- NOT ALL YEAST STRAINS HAVE THE SAME
STIMULATORY ACTIVITIES

Several studies have demonstrated that not all yeast strains are capable of
stimulating ruminal bacteria. Evidence for strain difference has been obtained
from studies with pure cultures of ruminal bacteria and with mixed
populations. Only seven of over 50 strains tested had the ability to stimulate
the growth of fiber-digesting bacteria from the rumen (Dawson and Hopkins,
1991). In addition, other studies suggest that few strains of yeast have the
ability to stimulate both the beneficial fiber-digesting bacteria and the bacteria
associated with lactate utilization. Similarly, Newbold *et al.* (1996)
demonstrated that brewer's yeast strains and baker's yeast strains differed
in their abilities to stimulate critical groups of ruminal microorganisms (Figure
3). Baker's yeast strains had limited ability to bring about stimulation. These
studies suggest that care must be taken in selecting *Saccharomyces
cerevisiae* strains for use as feed supplements for ruminants. Such studies
also explain some of the variability in production responses since many of
the early studies relied on poorly defined yeast culture supplements.

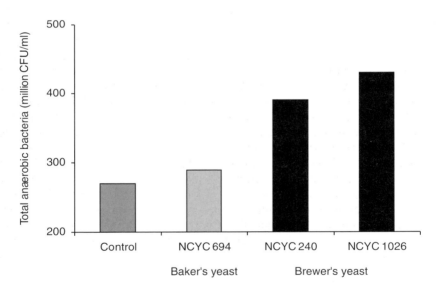

Figure 3. Effects of several yeast strains on the concentrations of bacteria in a mixed
ruminal population (adapted from Newbold and Wallace, 1992).

MILESTONE #6- METABOLICALLY ACTIVE YEAST CELLS ARE NEEDED
FOR STIMULATORY ACTIVITIES

The importance of viable or metabolically active yeast cells in a yeast culture
preparation for optimal stimulatory activity in the rumen has been established

by a number of investigators. Autoclaved yeast preparations are ineffective at increasing the numbers of viable bacteria in the rumen (Dawson *et al.*, 1990; El Hassan *et al.*, 1993). However, irradiated yeast cells that cannot reproduce but maintain their metabolic activities have been successfully used to stimulate beneficial ruminal bacteria (El Hassan *et al.*, 1993). These studies suggest that metabolic activity and not active reproduction are an integral part of the basic process leading to a maximal beneficial response to yeast culture. This requirement for metabolically active yeast cells should be considered in any model used to explain the overall effects of yeast in the rumen.

Biochemical basis explaining the stimulatory effects of yeast in the rumen

Despite the basic understanding of some of the beneficial effects of yeast cultures on the bacterial population in the rumen, the physiological basis for the enhanced microbial growth has not been completely described. A number of specific hypothetical biochemical mechanisms have been developed to explain the stimulatory effects of yeast cultures in the rumen (Dawson and Girard, 1997). Some of these have been based on the ability of yeast to provide important nutrients or nutritional cofactors that stimulate microbial activities while others suggest that the ability of yeast to control the oxygen level in the ruminal environment is important. These kinds of models have many attractive features but are individually limited in their ability to explain all of the effects associated with yeast supplementation in the rumen. However, recent studies have suggested that more basic mechanisms are involved in the overall stimulation of beneficial ruminal bacteria (Girard, 1996; Girard and Dawson, 1994; 1995). These studies have resulted in the isolation of a group of small compounds that stimulate bacteria to enter into logarithmic growth and thus stimulate microbial activities. Some of the basic characteristics of these stimulatory compounds are consistent with the basic characteristics of small biologically active peptides (Table 5). The stimulatory activities of these small peptides has been demonstrated in studies with pure cultures of ruminal bacteria (Girard, 1996). Synthetic tryptophan-containing peptides have also been shown to bring about similar stimulatory effects and have also been shown to stimulate the growth of representative fiber-digesting bacteria from the rumen. These stimulatory activities were not associated with individual amino acids (Table 6). Stimulatory activities occurred at concentrations well below those that would suggest that these compounds are limiting nutrients. Instead, they appear to serve as metabolic triggers that stimulate beneficial ruminal bacteria to enter into an exponential growth phase. This stimulatory activity toward specific strains of ruminal bacteria can explain many of the observed effects of yeast culture in the rumen. A hypothetical model explaining the action of the yeast-derived peptides in the rumen is outlined in Figure 4.

Table 5. Characteristics of low-molecular weight stimulatory factors from culture supernatants.

Item	Characteristics
Source	Isolated from supernatant from culture of *S. cerevisae* strain 1026
Effects on ruminal bacteria	30% reduction in the lag time of cultures of cellulolytic bacteria
Heat stability	Stable at 121°C for 20 min
Cold stability	Stable at -20°C for at least 6 months
Acid reactivity	Stimulatory activities destroyed following 12 N HCl-hydrolysis for 24 h at 110°C
Stability to freeze-drying	Stable
Passage through 10,000 Da filter	Yes
Passage through 1,000 Da filter	Yes
Molecular weight (estimation by gel filtration)	400 to 650 Da
Number of amino groups per molecule	at least 2
Absorbance peaks in spectral scan	280 and 210 nm

Table 6. Stimulatory effects of L-tryptophan and individual peptide preparations on the lag time of cultures of *R. albus* 7.

Preparation	Lag time (h)	Change (%)
Control (no supplement)	3.32[b]	-
Washed yeast cells	1.80[c]	-46
L-tryptophan solution	3.10[be]	-7
Ala-Pro-Gly-Trp-amide	2.17[d]	-35
Ala-Trp-Met-Asp-Phe-amide	2.77[e]	-17
Tyr-D-Trp-Gly-Phe-Met	3.15[be]	-5
Trp-Met-Asp-Phe-amide	2.13[cd]	-36
N-formyl-Met-Trp	2.78[ef]	-16
DGlu-Lys-Trp-Ala-Pro	2.48[df]	-25

[a]Cultures of *R. albus* were supplemented with each of the preparations or with water. Peptide preparations provided 40 nmoles of peptide per L. Stimulation is indicated by a reduction in the time required to initiate growth (lag time).
[b,c,d,e,f]Means (n = 3) in a column lacking a common superscript differ (P < 0.10). SEM = 0.15 h.

The stimulatory peptides are apparently not stable in the ruminal environment. Attempts to measure their presence in rumen fluid have been unsuccessful. Activities of proteolytic enzymes and rapid uptake of the peptides by microorganisms probably eliminates these compounds from the rumen very rapidly. This observation is consistent with the requirements for metabolically active yeast preparation that have been observed by a number of investigators (Dawson *et al.*, 1990; El Hassan *et al.*, 1993). It is possible that the metabolically active cells provide a continuous source of such peptides and thus can continually provide low levels of stimulation for beneficial ruminal

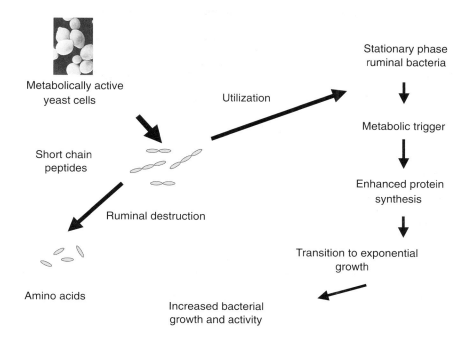

Figure 4. Model explaining the ability of specific peptides to alter microbial growth and ruminal fermentations.

bacteria. Taken together, these observations suggest that the stimulatory effects of yeast in the rumen can be at least partially explained by the presence of these biologically active compounds.

Other potential activities of yeast cultures in the rumen

It is important to recognize that stimulatory effects of viable yeast in the rumen only address some of the beneficial effects of yeast in animal production systems. Research in this area has resulted in a number of new concepts that have evolved into useful animal supplements. Currently yeast cell wall products are available that prevent colonization by pathogenic microorganisms in the gut, alter the composition of microbial populations in the intestinal tract, modulate immune function and alter the structure of the gut wall. These developments are all the result of in depth study of yeast culture supplementation and are currently used to enhance the performance of both ruminant and non-ruminant animals.

Conclusions

The research has demonstrated that viable yeast cell preparations can stimulate specific groups of beneficial bacteria in the rumen and has provided mechanistic models that can explain the effects of yeast on animal performance. Continuous research with yeast culture supplements has clearly established scientifically proven strategies for modifying microbial activities in the rumen and techniques for improving animal performance and health.

References

Alonzo, R., E. Mirales and J. Killen. 1993. Effect of viable yeast culture (Yea-Sacc[1026]) on milk yield of Holstein cows and on weight gain of calves at 90 days. J. Anim. Sci. 71(Suppl. 1):289 (Abstr.).

Chaucheyras, E, G. Fonty, G. Bertin and P. Gouet. 1995a. Effects of live *Saccharomyces cerevisiae* cells on zoospore germination, growth and cellulolytic activity of the rumen anaerobic fungus, *Neocallimasttifiontalis* MCH3. Current Microbiology. 3 1:20 1.

Chaucheyras, F., G. Fonty, G. Bertin and P. Gouet. 1995b. *In vitro* H2 utilization by a ruminal acetogenic bacterium cultivated alone or in combination with an Archaea methanogen is stimulated by a probiotic strain of *Saccharomyces cerevisiae*. Appl. Environ. Microbiology. 6 1:3466.

Dawson, K.A. 1992. Current and future role of yeast culture in animal production: A review of research over the last six years. In: Supplement to the Proceedings of Alltech's 8th Annual Symposium. Alltech Technical Publications, Nicholasville, KY.

Dawson, K.A. and I.D. Girard. 1997. Biochemical and physiological basis for the stimulatory effects of yeast preparations on ruminal bacteria. In: Proceedings of Alltech's 13th Annual Symposium on Biotechnology in the Feed Industry (T.P. Lyons and K.A. Jacques, eds.). Nottingham University Press, Nottingham, UK, pp. 293-304.

Dawson, K.A. and D.M. Hopkins. 1991. Differential effects of live yeast on the cellulolytic activities of anaerobic ruminal bacteria. J. Anim. Sci. 69(Suppl. 1):531 (Abstr.).

Dawson, K.A., K.E. Newman and J.A. Boling. 1990. Effects of microbial supplements containing yeast and lactobacilli on roughage-fed ruminal microbial activities. J. Anim. Sci. 68:3392.

Dobos, R.C., A.J. Dickens and T.J. Norris. 1990. Yea-Sacc[1026] for dairy cattle in low concentrate input systems: Effects on milk yield and composition in an Australian experiment. In: Biotechnology in the Feed Industry, Vol. VI. Alltech Technical Publications, Nicholasville, KY.

Edwards, I.E., T. Mutsvangwa, J.H. Topps, and G.F.M. Paterson. 1990. The effects of supplemental yeast culture (Yea-Sacc) on patterns of rumen fermentation and growth performance of intensively fed bulls. Anim. Prod. 55:35-40.

El-Nor, S.A. H.A., and A.M. Kholif. 1998. Effect of supplementation of live yeast culture in the diet on the productive performance of lactating buffaloes. Milchwissenschaft. 53:663.

El Hassan, S.M., C.J. Newbold and R.J. Wallace. 1993. The effect of yeast culture on rumen fermentation: growth of the yeast in the rumen and the requirement for viable yeast cells. Anim. Prod. 56:463.

Erasmus, L. J., P.M. Botha and A. Kistner. 1992. Effect of yeast culture supplement on production, rumen fermentation and duodenal nitrogen flow in dairy cows. J. Dairy Sci. 75:3056.

Girard, I.D. 1996. characterization of stimulatory activities from *Saccharomyces cerevisiae* on the growth and activities of ruminal bacteria. Ph.D. Dissertation. University of Kentucky, Lexington.

Girard, I.D. and K.A. Dawson. 1994. Effects of yeast culture on the growth of representative ruminal bacteria. J. Anim. Sci. 77(Suppl.1):300 (Abstr.).

Girard, I.D. and K.A. Dawson. 1995. Stimulatory activities from low-molecular weight fractions derived from *Saccharomyces cerevisiae* strain 1026. 23rd Biennial Conference on Rumen Function, Chicago, Illinois, p.23.

Girard, I.D., C.R. Jones, and K.A. Dawson. 1993. Lactic acid utilization rumen-simulating cultures receiving a yeast culture supplement. J. Anim. Sci. 71(Suppl. 1):288.

Günther, K.D. 1989. Yeast culture's success under German dairy conditions. In: Biotechnology in the Feed Industry, Vol V. p 38. Alltech Technical Publications, Nicholasville, KY.

Harrison, G.A., R.W. Hemkin, K.A. Dawson, R.J. Harmon and K.B. Barker. 1988. Influence of addition of yeast culture supplement to diets of lactating dairy cows on ruminal function and microbial populations. J. Dairy Sci. 71:2967.

Hoyos, G., L. Garcia and F. Medina. 1987. Effect of feeding viable microbial feed additives on performance of lactating cows in a large dairy herd. J. Dairy Sci. 70(Suppl. 1):217 (Abstr.).

Huber, J.T., J. Sullivan, B. Taylor, A. Burgos and S. Cramer. 1989. Effect of feeding Yea-Sacc on milk production and related responses in a commercial dairy herd in Arizona. In: Biotechnology in the Feed Industry, Vol V. p 35. Alltech Technical Publications, Nicholasville, KY.

Kumar, U., V.K. Sareen and S. Singh. 1997. Effect of yeast culture supplement on ruminal microbial populations and metabolism in buffalo calves fed a high roughage diet. J. Sci. Food Agric. 73:231-236.

Newbold, C.J. and R.J. Wallace. 1992. The effect of yeast and distillery by-products on the fermentation in the rumen simulation technique (Rusitec). Anim. Prod. 54:504.

Newbold, C.J., R.J. Wallace and EM. McIntosh. 1996. Mode of action of the yeast *Saccharomyces cerevisiae* as a feed additive for ruminants. Br. J. Nutr. 76:249.

Piva, G., S. Belladonna, G. Fusconi and F. Sicbaldi. 1993. Effects of yeast on dairy cow performance, ruminal fermentation, blood components and milk manufacturing properties. J. Dairy Sci. 76:2717.

Smith, W.A., B. Harris, Jr, H.H. Van Horn and C.J. Wilcox. 1993. Effects of forage type on production of dairy cows supplemented with whole cottonseed, tallow and yeast. J. Dairy Sci. 76:205.

Skorko-Sajko, H., J. Sajko and W. Zalewski. 1993. The effects of Yea-Sacc[1026] in the ration for dairy cows on production and composition of milk. J. Animal and Feed Sci. 2:159-167.

Wallace, R.J. 1996. The mode of action of yeast culture in modifying rumen fermentation. In: Proceedings of Alltech's 12th Annual Symposium on Biotechnology in the Feed Industry (T.P. Lyons and K.A. Jacques, eds.). Nottingham University Press, Nottingham, UK, pp. 217-232.

Wiedmeier, R-D., M.J. Arambel and J.L. Walters. 1987. Effects of yeast culture and *Aspergillus oryzae* fermentation extract on ruminal characteristics and nutrient digestion. J. Dairy Sci. 70:2063.

Williams, P.E.V. and J.C. Newbold. 1990. Rumen probiosis: The effects of novel microorganisms on rumen fermentation and rumen productivity. In Recent Advances in Animal Nutrition (W. Haresign and D.J.A. Cole, eds.). Butterworths, London, England, p. 211.

Williams, P.E.V., C.A.G. Tait, G.M. Innes and C.J. Newbold. 1991. Effects of the inclusion of yeast culture (*Saccharomyces cerevisiae* plus growth medium) in the diet of dairy cows on milk yield and forage degradation and fermentation patterns in the rumen of steers. J. Anim. Sci. 69:3016.

Yoon, I.K. and M.D. Stern. 1996. Effects of *Saccharomyces cerevisiae* and *Aspergillus oryzea* cultures on ruminal fermentation in dairy cows. J. Dairy Sci. 79:411.

Fibrozyme and *in vitro* NDF response: moving from theory to practical commercial reality

J.D. JOHNSTON

Ritchie Feed & Seed, Gloucester, Ontario, Canada

Introduction

Successful dairy farming in the present age is a challenge as today's dairies face the universal problems of diminishing returns on equity and ever more pressing environmental rules. Solving these problems is not a matter of finding one magical answer, as success lies in understanding and utilizing the knowledge base of multiple disciplines. Nutrition is but one of these disciplines; however as ration expense is usually the largest cost component faced by producers, consideration of any process or product that raises returns is necessary.

Improvements in the engineering of dairy feeding systems and a better understanding of ration digestibility have shown obvious promise (Schurig and Rodel, 1993), as have harvesting equipment advances such as kernel processors. Production increases of 10% (Straub *et al.*, 1996) and improvements in dry matter intake (Schurig and Rodel, 1993) have been reported when kernel processing was employed. Responses have not always been positive nor have there been consistent improvements in milk protein or fat levels (Miller *et al.*, 1969). The reasons for this variability in response are not entirely understood, but the stage of crop maturity, ruminal starch disappearance and the dynamics of fiber disappearance are reasonable guesses. It must however be remembered that kernel processors are designed primarily to affect the rate of starch availability; and their effect on fiber digestion *per se* does not appear to be large (Spain, 1998; Johnston *et al.*, 1999). As most corn silages are 40-60% grain, the implications regarding digestion of the fiber portion are significant and should not be ignored.

Exogenous fibrolytic enzymes represent one possible option for improving dietary fiber disappearance rates; and several authors have reported on their successful use (Rode *et al.*, 1999; Kung *et al.*, 2000; Zinn and Salinas, 1999). Most of the research reported to date involved the use of enzymes sprayed on the forage before its incorporation into the final diet. This paper will deal with the evaluation of a dry commercial enzyme supplement (Fibrozyme, Alltech, Inc.) intended as a feed supplement rather than a forage treatment. The product was evaluated through measurement of its effects on *in vitro* neutral detergent fiber (NDF) (IVNDF) digestion of corn silage and the production responses of a commercial dairy herd fed diets balanced to take into account the enzyme effects on silage digestion characteristics using CPM ration formulation.

Measuring NDF digestibility

Measurements of NDF digestibility rates can be achieved using *in vivo, in situ,* or *in vitro* techniques. Of the three, the *in vivo* procedure is undoubtedly the best, but is very costly and time consuming. *In situ* techniques have been shown to offer an accurate measurement of rumen degradation rates over various outflow rates (Arieli *et al.*, 1996), but the logistics of chemical analysis of the digested samples are time consuming and do not lend themselves to automation. *In vitro* analyses, on the other hand, have been greatly simplified with the development of new analytical systems such as Ankom Technologies, and their use for measuring 30 hr IVNDF digestibilities has grown. This type of analysis is not without problems, as it relies on several assumptions about pH and residency times. Time course IVNDF digestibilities are, however, a tool that can be used to screen large numbers of samples in an effective and affordable manner.

Methodology is obviously of critical importance, as the measurement technique must demonstrate accuracy without interfering in fermentation in order to describe feed ingredients in a manner that can be used in rumen models. Grant and Mertens (1992) reported that lag times were an important concern as they can be lengthened by decreased pH levels or by the inclusion of non-structural carbohydrates. Recent work (Piwonka and Firkins, 1996) has shown that neither the lag time nor the extent of NDF digestion is affected when pH is in the 6.2 to 6.8 range, although the overall rate can be diminished. Several studies (Grant and Weidner, 1992; Hiltner and Dehority, 1983) have shown that pH of 6.2-6.8 is the threshold for optimal NDF digestion; hence *in vitro* analyses should be conducted with inoculum pH in this range.

The *in vitro* measurement of digestibility has progressed from the early two-stage technique described by Tilley and Terry (1963) to the more automated systems of today. Several authors have reviewed the newer techniques (Garman *et al.*, 1997; Cohen *et al.*, 1997) and have shown that the results obtained from the new systems are reliable and repeatable. One technique reported employed the Ankom Daisy II, with which NDF digestibility can be measured for forages, grains, or total mixed rations. The system utilizes miniature filter bags immersed in filtered rumen inoculum and buffer. The fermenting chamber holds up to four jars that can contain up to 25 filter bags each. This system offers a great deal of flexibility as far as experimental design is concerned. Analysis of results using the system has shown that similar samples can be successfully fermented within one jar or mixed with other samples within the same jar. As the samples are digested in separate filter bags, sequential ADF and NDF analyses can be performed with a minimum of problems once the fermentation is complete.

Use of *in vitro* analysis to screen forages

In vitro techniques to measure 30 hr IVNDF disappearance are certainly of value and have been used as one method of ranking corn silage varieties (Thomas *et al.*, 1998). In this work, varieties from three different companies were compared. *In vitro* true dry matter disappearance (IVTDMD) was shown to differ (P<0.07), as did *in vitro* NDF disappearance. Further work conducted at the Miner Institute revealed IVNDF disappearance rates for corn silages ranging from 24.87 to 61.56% with a coefficient of variation (CV) of 19.53% for samples originating from farms throughout New England (Allshouse *et al.*, 1998). Multivariate analysis of these samples demonstrated that rainfall and temperature also contributed significantly to the variation in INTDM disappearance (Majewski *et al.*, 1998).

A similar use of *in vitro* analyses began at Ritchie Feed and Seed in the summer of 1997. The initial thought was to attempt a categorization of forage samples by variety and geographic area. This effort soon proved all but futile, as large intra- and intervarietal differences were observed both within and between regions. Some of this variability was anticipated given the soils of eastern Ontario, but the CV was unexpectedly large. Upon realizing the degree of variability (Table 1), work began to further quantify the differences among forage samples. Production differences between herds with similar average days in milk fed TMRs based on corn silages with similar 30 hr IVNDF disappearance values led us to believe that the answer perhaps lay in the degree and extent of digestion expressed at various time points. The problem then becomes one of which time point(s) to select, and whether the choice remains constant. Our experience has shown that time point selection is not constant as the effects of maturity at harvest require varied time point selection.

Table 1. *In vitro* **NDF analyses for corn silage.**

| | Sampling time (hrs) | | | | |
	0	3	6	30	48
Number of samples	100	100	100	100	100
Mean	44.598	40.489	38.415	24.526	20.249
SD	5.9941	4.6858	4.8739	4.5757	3.6616
SE mean	0.5689	0.4448	0.4626	0.4343	0.3475
Coefficient of variation	13.440	11.573	12.687	18.656	18.083
Maximum	56.800	52.400	50.800	37.900	29.800

Implications of variations in NDF digestibility

The dairy industry is very focused on dry matter intake. The more dry matter a cow consumes, the more milk and milk components the cow will produce. To maximize dry matter intake, it is important to understand the quality and digestibility of the forage component of the diet. The techniques currently used in North America to predict energy from the acid detergent fiber (ADF) or NDF content are unsatisfactory, as the values give variable production responses. The basic assumption in these approaches is that all fibers are digested at the same rate and are passed from the rumen at the same rate. These techniques worked initially, but newer data have shown that it is time to move on. Japanese workers have developed the Oa and Ob system (Sniffen and Chalupa, 1998; Zinn and Salinas, 1999), which delineates fast and slow fiber fractions. The Oa fraction is the amount of fiber that disappears in a 4 hr digestion using a fiber digesting enzyme system, while the Ob fraction represents the slower-digesting fraction.

With the release of feeding programs that include predictions of rumen microbioal protein yield, we have been able to see how alterations in the NDF disappearance rate can influence level of milk produced through changes in rumen pH and the extent of rumen microbial protein synthesis. The technique found to be most successful was use of time point analyses to estimate rapid and slow NDF digestion rates. Results from this approach are given in Table 2, which shows how a swing of 10 points in the soluble NDF fraction can have a dramatic effect on milk production and on predicted NE_L levels. The data in Table 2 were generated from *in vitro* analyses using the CPM model and corrected 48 hr NDF levels. The carbohydrate B2 (C:B2) fraction represents the rate of NDF disappearance.

Table 2. The effect of NDF digestion rate on predicted milk yield and predicted NE_L.

C:B2 rate (%/hr)	Milk yield (kg)	Predicted NE_L
2	31.8	1.43
4	34.0	1.60
6	35.6	1.70
8	36.7	1.77
10	37.6	1.82
12	38.3	1.86

Response to enzymes in ruminant diets

The inclusion of enzymes in monogastric diets is quite common. Their use in ruminant diets has not been as prevalent as the fibrolytic activity of rumen microbes is such that the inclusion of exogenous enzymes in the diet was felt to be unwarranted. Additional concerns have been that exogenous enzymes cannot survive proteolysis in the rumen and (or) that enzyme activity would be diminished by conditioning systems such as pelleting. Recent research has demonstrated that these concerns may be unwarranted, as positive effects have been noted in both dairy and beef cattle (Beauchemin *et al.*, 1995; 1999). Production responses have ranged from feed efficiency improvements of 10% in beef cattle (Beauchemin *et al.*, 1995) to milk increases of 2.5 kg when lactating cattle were fed a TMR diet treated with a fibrolytic enzyme product (Stokes and Zeng, 1995). A recent two year study examining effects of a cellulase/xylanase mixture fed to lactating Holsteins demonstrated that the productive improvements in milk yield and 3.5% fat-corrected milk yield were most likely due to improved NDF digestion. These authors reported a significant ($P<0.05$) increase in 48 hr NDF digestion, but only a numerical increase at 12 hr. Other authors have shown a significant increase in NDF digestion within six hours while the effect was lost at digestion times of 30 or 48 hrs (Johnston and Shivas, 1999) (Table 3). This time difference is important, as it would appear that productive responses do occur if NDF digestion improvements take place within the first 6 hrs after ingestion.

Table 3. The effects of Fibrozyme on the rate and extent of NDF disappearance from corn silage hybrids planted at three densities.

All hybrids	Initial rate of digestion (6 hrs)			Extended rate of digestion (30 hrs)			NDF remaining (48 hrs)	
	Control	Fibrozyme	Increase (%)	Control	Fibrozyme	Increase (%)	Control	Fibrozyme
22K	1.39	2.13	72.8	13.08	12.86	19.9	20.10	19.27
27K	2.49	3.32	69.3	14.83	12.81	11.7	19.89	19.86
32K	2.57[a]	4.66[b]	196.7[c]	14.35	15.17	13.3	21.20	20.37
Overall	2.15[a]	3.38[b]	112.9[c]	14.09	13.61	7.1	20.39	19.83

[a,b] Means with different superscripts differ ($P<0.05$).
[c] Significant increase ($P<0.05$) with Fibrozyme.

STUDIES WITH FIBROZYME

In vitro response: effects of corn silage variety and planting density

As the practical impact of the various commercial enzyme products would be expected to vary owing to differences in amounts and types of enzyme activities present, generalized conclusions cannot really be drawn. With this in mind, a field trial was undertaken to see if the product Fibrozyme (Alltech Inc., Nicholasville, KY) affected *in vitro* NDF disappearance rates, and if so in what manner. The study involved four corn silage hybrids planted at three densities of 22K, 27K, and 32K per acre. Samples were taken following a 90 day fermentation, with NDF disappearance rates being calculated from the results of *in vitro* analyses. Fibrozyme was added at a rate that would be equivalent to 15 g/head/day. The corn hybrids selected represented a reasonable cross section of those available to today's producers and included both leafy and grain-type corn plants. NDF levels were determined using equipment produced by Ankom Technologies. Rumen fluid was taken from lactating Holsteins producing in excess of 30 kg/day. The fluid was strained through four layers of cheese cloth and added to a Kansas State buffer system. The samples were fermented for 0, 3, 6, 30 and 48 hrs at a constant temperature of 39.1°C. The hybrids used in the study were grown with three replicates per hybrid for all planting densities and were analyzed with three replicates.

Fibrozyme increased disappearance of NDF (P<0.05) across corn silage hybrids and planting rates within the first 6 hrs of *in vitro* fermentation (Table 3). This effect is of particular interest as field reports on the success of enzyme supplements have been mixed. Use in the field has no doubt been based on 'one enzyme fits all corn silage varieties' strategy; and the fact that there was a significant difference in how different hybrids responded to Fibrozyme offers one reason why field responses to enzymes may vary.

Correlations between Fibrozyme response and plant characteristics or digestion rates were calculated (Table 4, Figures 1,2). Several relationships between ADF and NDF were also examined; as it has been hypothesized that the success of Fibrozyme could be predicted by the numerical difference between NDF and ADF. This hypothesis was not proven as the correlation coefficient between Fibrozyme response and NDF-ADF was very low (Table 4). The correlation analyses revealed a window of opportunity for use of Fibrozyme based on initial NDF digestion (NDF disappearance within the first 6 hrs of *in vitro* fermentation). The window lies within the 37 to 42% NDF range as may be seen in Figure 2. The practical importance of this information lies in the fact that Fibrozyme would not appear to alter the NDF disappearance of very high quality corn silage nor will it improve that of poor quality silage. It would however significantly affect the corn silages that fall in between, as shown in Table 1. This includes a wide range of corn silages. The data in Table 1 were drawn from the analyses of corn silage samples grown in similar environmental conditions during the summer of 1998 in the Ottawa Valley.

Table 4. The relationship between Fibrozyme and corn silage characteristics.

Factor	Correlation
Corn hybrid	0.077
Planting density	0.233*
NDF content	-0.259*
ADF content	-0.389*
NDF:ADF ratio	-0.024
NDF-ADF	-0.136
Initial NDF digestion	-0.406*

*P<0.05.

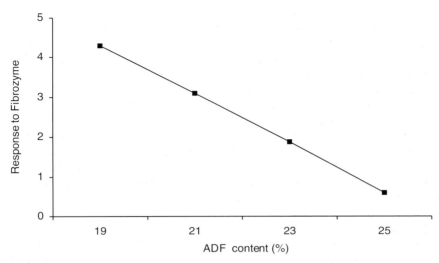

Figure 1. Effects of ADF content of corn silage on *in vitro* activity of Fibrozyme.

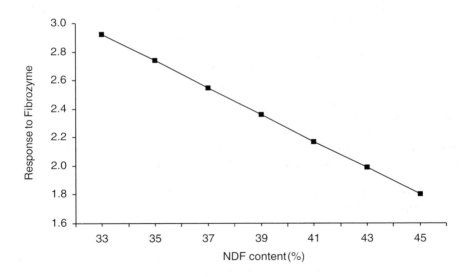

Figure 2. Effects of ADF and NDF content of corn silage on *in vitro* activity of Fibrozyme.

Application of Fibrozyme and IVDMD data at a commercial dairy

Having shown that a window of opportunity existed for the use of the Fibrozyme product, the next step was to ascertain whether this *in vitro* screening technique could be applied in ration formulation to gain a response in milk production. A farm with corn silage (1999 crop) within the correct NDF 'window of opportunity' was selected and Fibrozyme was

493

added to the diet in a commercial supplement. The silage had fermented for 80 days prior to its being fed, with pH and visual assessments indicating that the silage had fermented well. The diet was balanced using the CPM model with considerations being made for rate and extent of fiber digestion.

The DHIA results for the farm are given in Table 5, with the 1999 corn silage usage beginning two weeks prior to the October test date. Milk yield dropped 2 liters/day once the 1999 corn silage crop was fed. The response to the inclusion of the 1999 corn silage, when the other diet components were left similar, was a loss of milk within five days. The effect of inclusion of Fibrozyme was a return of milk production to previous levels. These dietary changes fell in line with monthly DHIA testing; and the milk response was recorded with similar days in milk. This was extremely encouraging, as it appeared to demonstrate that diet formulation based on the corn silage parameters determined with *in vitro* analysis did in fact work. Fortunately, few cows freshened or were dried off during this period. While this was due more to good luck than good experimental management, the production improvements indicated that it would be worthwhile to run a more controlled experiment that would allow removal of 'cow day' effects while also determining whether effect of the enzyme was due to changes in dry matter intake.

Table 5. Effect of Fibrozyme on milk production at an 81 cow dairy.

	1998 corn silage	1999 corn silage No Fibrozyme	1999 corn silage With Fibrozyme
Average days in milk	183	184	184
Average production, l/day	27	25	27
Average milk fat, %	4.1	4.1	3.9
Average milk protein, %	3.5	3.5	3.5

A second trial was run under more controlled experimental conditions. A free stall dairy with 137 cows was used in a switchback design with two week periods. The majority of the cows on test were in either their first or second lactations, but this was felt to be a positive as these animals would face the greatest challenge as far as intake was concerned (Table 6). Corn silage samples were collected prior to and during the course of the trial to identify the NDF characteristics; and the average of 10 samples is shown in Figure 3. The NDF fractions of the corn silage fell within the 37 to 42% NDF window of opportunity and the CPM model was used to design the diet used in the trial (Table 7). Fibrozyme was added to the diet at 15 g/head/day by inclusion in a protein supplement that was pelleted at 165°F and 137 kPa in order to minimize the possibility of enzyme denaturation. Once the trial began, the diet proportions remained constant save for dry matter corrections. In order to minimize any production variability arising from incompletely fermented corn silage, the diet was based on silage harvested in the fall of 1998 and stored in a sealed bunker since harvest.

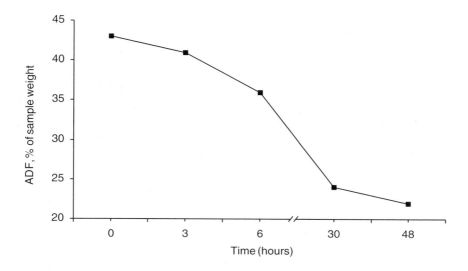

Figure 3. NDF Disappearance in corn silage (N=10).

Table 6. Lactational status of cows.

Lactation	Average days in milk at start	Range in days
1	86.1	21-171
2	133.7	13-388
3	132.0	14-262

Table 7. Ingredient and chemical composition of total mixed ration.

Composition	% of dry matter
Hay	1.74
Haylage	21.4
Corn silage	26.73
High moisture corn	31.09
Raw soybeans	9.44
Protein pellet	9.58
Chemical analysis	
Dry matter	43.1
Crude protein	16.2
NDF	32.3
Starch	34.9
Ne_l, Mcal/kg (calculated)	1.69

As previous field experience had shown that forages with constant rates of NDF disappearance yield more productive milk responses in lactating cattle, efforts were made when formulating the diet to keep the overall disappearance rate of NDF in the total mixed ration (TMR) diet as constant as possible. This was done by matching the NDF rates of the ingredients to the theoretical ideal, and the results are shown in Figure 4. Of interest is that the predicted C:B2 from the CPM model (CPM-Version 1, 1998) was 7.6%/hr while the calculated rate from our results was 7.2 %/hr; and therefore some degree of confidence can be placed in the concept of designing rations along these lines. A similar exercise was run on the protein side, with the theoretical soluble intake protein (SIP) being 41%, while the calculated amount from the lab analyses was 49%.

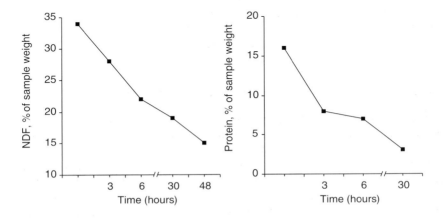

Figure 4. *In vitro* disappearance of NDF and protein from the test diet TMR.

The performance results showed that addition of Fibrozyme increased milk yield while its removal from the diet was associated with a decline in milk production (Table 8). The production data demonstrated that *in vitro* analysis of NDF disappearance rate is a valid and valuable tool when designing rations.

Table 8. Changes in milk production (%) associated with the supplementation of Fibrozyme in dairy rations.

Parity	Number of animals	Period 1 (with Fibrozyme)	Period 2 (without Fibrozyme)	Period 3 (with Fibrozyme)
1	77	+5.33[a]	-1.85[b]	+0.31[b]
2	31	+6.04[a]	-4.53[b]	+0.20[ab]
3	19	+1.48[a]	-1.18[ab]	-8.81[b]

[a,b]Means within the same row with different superscripts differ (P<0.05).

The unequal parity and wide range in days in milk of the cows in the trial made the statistical analysis a challenge. The average milk production change across parities amounted to 1.32 litre/day, with the second lactation cows rising the most with a 1.88 litre/day change. The statistically significant milk response was lost, as expected, during the Fibrozyme withdrawal portion of the trial. Questions could be raised as to the measured effect when the Fibrozyme was reintroduced during the last part of the trial; and one possible answer is that there was a refractory response. If this is the case, it would be of minimal significance on a commercial basis as producers would not add and remove the enzyme on such short notice.

Of particular interest was the numerical increase in milk protein, which approached statistical significance (P<0.06) in the first parity cows. This increase was presumably due to increased microbial protein production in the rumen. One could speculate as to whether this improvement was due to a direct enzymatic effect or changes in rumenal microbial populations, however drawing such a conclusion is far beyond the scope of this field trial.

Economic impact of changes in NDF disappearance

Reviews of the diets fed high producing dairy herds have shown that they usually have a large percentage of highly fermentable NDF, and that these types of ingredients will result in both increased rumen microbial yields (CPM-Version 1, 1998) and improved milk production. The improvements occur for many reasons, but an overall improvement in ruminal health/function would appear to be the most logical explanation. The economic potential of harnessing improvements in fiber digestion can be significant, and in today's tight market it can be a lifesaver. As an example of just how large savings in production costs can be, data were collected from a 150 cow free stall herd producing approximately 30 liters per cow per day. The farm has two silos for corn silage. One silo had corn silage stored at 36% DM with a C:B2 rate of 3.07 %/hr and the other silo had corn silage at 32% DM with a C:B2 of 7.0%/hr. Switching from one silo to the other resulted in a 0.75 liter in increase in milk and improved herd health (Dairy Farmers of Ontario, 1999). Formulating diets based on the corn silage with a 7.0% C:B2 fermentation rate allowed the option of either an increase in potential milk production or a savings in feeding costs. As may be seen from Table 9, switching between the two corn silages offered an opportunity to alter how ingredients were used in the final TMR. The economic benefits of these changes were impressive. Savings of $0.68 CDN were seen on a daily basis, while on an annualized basis for 150 milking cows, this difference could contribute $37,250 to the producer's bottom line.

Assessing the economic benefits of using Fibrozyme can be done using the same type of logic. Unlike most other feed additives, this product has a predictable effect on the disappearance of corn silage NDF. If the NDF is within the window of opportunity, theoretical improvements of 12% are possible, and depending on the formulation of the final TMR this can result in a milk production increase of 1.52 liters. The studies discussed above

Table 9. Diets used on 150 cow dairy using corn silages with different NDF digestibilities.

	C:B2 at 3.0%/hr	C:B2 at 7.0%/hr
Haylage	5.0	5.0
Corn silage	22.5	24.3
Brewers grains	7.0	11.9
Corn ground	6.3	5.2
Barley	1.0	1.0
Wheat shorts		1.5
Protein mix	2.4	2.799
Feed costs, $/cow/day	4.05	3.37
Crude protein, %	18.22	17.96

demonstrated that the theoretical and practical worlds can in fact meet as evidenced by increased average milk production of 1.5 liters/day in a diet formulated using IVNDF disappearance data to characterize silage NDF.

References

Allshouse, R.D., C.J.Majewski and C.J. Sniffen. 1998. Investigations in forage quality. 1. Variation in forage quality in the northeast. W.H. Miner Agricultural Research Institute.

Arieli, S.J., J. Mabjeesh, Z. Shabi, I. Bruckental, Y. Aharoni, S. Zamwel and H. Tagari. 1996. *In situ* assessment of degradability of organic matter in the rumen of the dairy cow. J. Dairy Sci. 81:1965-1990.

Beauchemin, K.A., L.M. Rode and V.J.H. Sewalt. 1995. Fibrolytic enzymes increase fiber digestibility and growth in steers fed dry forages. Can. J. Anim. Sci. 75:641-644.

Beauchemin, K.A., W.Z. Yang and L.M. Rode. 1999. Effect of grain source and enzyme activity on site and extent of nutrient digestion in dairy cows. J. Dairy Sci. 82:378-390.

Cohen, M.A., H.E. Maslanka and L. Kung. 1997. An evaluation of automated and manual *in vitro* methods for estimation of NDF digestion. Conference on Rumen Physiology, Chicago, IL.

CPM-Dairy version 1.0, Copyright 1998 by The Center for Animal Health and Productivity, School of Veterinary Medicine, University of Pennsylvania, Kennett Square PA; The Department of Animal Science, Cornell University, Ithaca NY; and The William H. Miner Agricultural Research Institute, Chazy NY.

Dairy Farmers of Ontario. 1999. Milk shipments, February.

Garman, C.L., L.A. Holden and H.A. Kane. 1997. Comparison of *in vitro* dry matter digestibility of nine feedstuffs using three different methods of analysis. J. Dairy Sci. 80(Suppl. 1):260.

Grant, R.J. and D.R. Mertens. 1992. Development of buffer systems for pH control and evaluations of pH effects on fibre digestion *in vitro*. J. Dairy Sci. 75:1581-1587.

Grant. R.J. and S.J. Weidner. 1992. Digestion kinetics of fibre: influence of *in vitro* buffer pH varied within observed physiological range. J. Dairy Sci. 75:1060.

Hiltner, P. and B.A. Dehority. 1983. Effect of soluble carbohydrates on digestion of cellulose by pure cultures of rumen bacteria. Appl. Environ. Microbiol. 46:642.

Johnson, L., J.H. Harrison, C. Hunt, K. Shinners, C.G. Doggett and D. Sapienza. 1999. Nutritive value of corn silage as affected by maturity and mechanical processing: a contemporary review. J. Dairy. Sci. 82:2525-2944.

Johnston, J.D. and I.C. Shivas. 1999. Formulating the fourth diet. In: Biotechnology in the Feed Industry. Proceedings of the 15th Annual Symposium (T.P. Lyons and K Jacques,eds). Nottingham University Press, UK.

Kung Jr., L., R.J. Treacher, G.A. Nauman, A.M. Smagla, K.M. Endres and M.A. Cohen. 2000. The effect of treating forage with fibrolytic enzymes on its nutritive value and lactation performance of dairy cows. J. Dairy Sci 83:115-122.

Majewski, C.J., R.D. Allshouse and C.J. Sniffen. 1998. Investigations in forage quality. II. Variability in forage quality parameters for corn hybrids. W.H. Miner Agricultural Research Institute.

Miller, C.N., C.E. Polan, R.A. Sandy and J.T. Huber. 1969. Effect of altering physical form of corn silage on utilization by dairy cattle. J. Dairy Sci. 52:1955-1960.

Piwonka, E.J. and J.L. Firkins. 1996. Effect of glucose fermentation on fibre digestion by ruminal microorganisms *in vitro*. J. Dairy Sci. 79:2196-2206.

Rode, L.M., W.Z. Yang and K.A. Beauchemin. 1999. Fibrolytic enzyme supplements for dairy cows in early lactation. J. Dairy Sci. 82:2121-2126.

Schurig, M. and G. Rodel. 1993. Power consumption and the effect of corncrakers. ASAE paper 931586. American Society of Agricultural Engineers, St Joseph, MI.

Sniffen, C.J. and W. Chalupa. 1998. Protein and amino acid nutrition of lactating cows – an update. Dairy Professional Program, Cornell 1998.

Spain, Jim. 1998. Profitable forage management strategies. Western Canadian Dairy Seminar, Advances in Dairy Technology. Red Deer, Alberta.

Stokes. M.R. and S. Zeng. 1995. The use of carbohydrate enzymes as feed additives for early lactation cows. 23rd Biennial Conf. Rumen Function, Chicago, Il., 23:35 (Abstr.).

Straub, R.J., R.G. Kroegel, L.D. Satter and T.J. Krause. 1996. Evaluation of a corn silage processor. ASAE paper no. 961033. American Society of Agricultural Engineers, St. Joseph. MI.

Thomas, E.D., C.S. Ballard, C.J.Sniffen, D.S. Tsang, R.D. Allhouse and P. Mandebvu. 1998. Effect of hybrid on corn silage yield, nutrient composition, *in vitro* digestion, intake by Holstein heifers, intake and milk production by lactating Holstein cows. W.H. Miner Agricultural Research Institute, Chazy, NY. 98-13.

Tilley, J.M.A. and R.A. Terry. 1963. A two-stage technique for the *in vitro* digestion of forage crops. Journal of British Grassland Society 18:104-111.

Zinn, R.A. and J. Salinas. 1999. Influence of Fibrozyme on digestive function and growth performance of feedlot steers fed a 78% concentrate growing ration. In: Biotechnology in the Feed Industry. Proceedings of Alltech's 15th Annual Symposium (T.P. Lyons and K.A. Jacques). Nottingham University Press, Nottingham, UK.

Index

507

ALLTECH AROUND THE WORLD

A Listing of Alltech International Offices and Distributors

ARGENTINA
ALLTECH ARGENTINA
Patricia Caporaso, Ing. Agr.
Arce 348 P.B. "B"
1426 Buenos Aires
TEL: 54-1-775-4923
FAX: 54-1-776-2129

AUSTRALIA
ALLTECH AUSTRALIA
Kim Turnley
Unit 9 No. 810 Princes Highway
Springvale, Victoria 3171
TEL: 61-3-9574-2333
FAX: 61-3-9574-2444

BOLIVIA
ALLTECH BOLIVIA Ltda.
Clodys A. Menacho R., Ing.
Tercer Anillo Externo
Esquina Av. Beni, Santa Cruz
TEL: 591-343-2422   FAX: 591-343-5482

BRAZIL
ALLTECH DO BRASIL
Marc Larousse
Caixa Postal 10808,
Cep: 81170-610, Curitiba-PR
TEL: 55-41-3479291
FAX: 55-41-3479894

CANADA
ALLTECH CANADA
Nick Smit & Pat Charlton
449 Laird Road
Guelph, Ontario, N1G 4W1
TEL: 519-763-3331
FAX: 519-763-5682

CHILE
ALLTECH CHILE
Mario Román
Luis Uribe 2720
Nuñoa, Santiago
TEL/FAX: 56-2-204-3990   56-2-204-0905

CHINA
ALLTECH ASIA PACIFIC BIOSCIENCE
CENTER
Ruojun Wang, Ph.D
No. 30 Baishiqiao Road
Beijing 100081
TEL: 86-10-6897-5844
FAX: 86-10-6897-5981

COLOMBIA
ALLTECH COLOMBIA
Luis Londoño
Carrera 38 #134-06
Santa Fé de Bogotá
TEL: 57-1-627-5484
FAX: 57-1-625-0457

COSTA RICA
NUTEC, S.A.
Carlos Lang
Apartado 392, P.O. Box 392
Tibas
TEL: 506-2-33-31-10
FAX: 506-2-33-31-10

CROATIA
ALLTECH BIOTECHNOLOGY
Nenad Fuchs
10000 Zagreb
Nodilova 17
TEL: 385-1-464-9336
FAX: 385-1-299-5599

Distributors around the world

CYPRUS
CHRONEL BIOTECHNOLOGY Ltd.
Christoforus Kyriacou
21 Gen. Timayia Avenue,
P.O. Box 2792, 6503 Larnaca
TEL: 357-4-638082
FAX: 357-4-636251

CZECH REPUBLIC
ALLTECH CZECH REPUBLIC
Valdimir Šiške, Ph.D
Mezirka 13, 60200
Brno
TEL: 42-0-541-21-57-40
FAX: 42-0-541-21-57-41

DENMARK
ALLTECH DENMARK
Peder Villadsen
2, Graabroedrestraede
DK-8900 Randers
TEL: 45-86-439700
FAX: 45-86-429300

DOMINICAN REPUBLIC
SANUT, S.A.
Miguel A Lajara P.
Km 10 1/2 Aut. Duarte
Apto Postal 30-004, Santo Domingo
TEL: 809-560-5840   FAX: 809-564-4070

ECUADOR
ALLTECH ECUADOR
Ari Fisher
Cdla. Kennedy Norte Mz 305, Calle
Francisco Rodriguez, Entre Eleodoro
Arboleda y Alberto Borgess, Guayaquil
TEL: 593-4-398606
FAX: 593-4-283286

EGYPT
INTERNATIONAL FREE TRADE Co.
Magdy Hassan
15 El Mahad El Eshtraky Street
Merryland-Heliopolis, Cairo 11341
TEL: 202-25-800-28
FAX: 202-25-827-93

FINLAND
BERNER LTD.
Antti Rinta Harri
Eteläranta 4B
SF 00130 Helsinki
TEL: 358-9-134-511
FAX: 358-9-134-51380

FRANCE
ALLTECH FRANCE
Denis Gallet
2-4, Avenue du 6 juin 1944
95190 Goussainville
TEL: 33-1-398-86351
FAX: 33-1-398-80778

GERMANY
ALLTECH DEUTSCHLAND GmbH
Ronald Kraeft
Esmarchstraße 6
23795 Bad Segeberg
TEL: 49-4551-88700
FAX: 49-4551-887099

GHANA (WEST AFRICA)
BIOTRADE LTD.
Felicio Baëta
No. 4, First Rangoon Close
P.O. Box 7383, Accra-North
TEL/FAX: 233-21-774444

HONDURAS
SBF
Sigfrido Burgos Flores
Colonia Palermo No. 1862, PO Box 4852,
Tegucigalpa
TEL/FAX: 504-230-4119

HUNGARY
ALLTECH HUNGARY
Levente Gati
H-2040 Budaörs, Gyár u. 2.
TEL: 36-23-418-939
FAX: 36-23-418-930

INDIA
VETCARE
Bharat Tandon
IS-40 KHB Industrial Area
Yelahanka New Town, Bangalore 560064
TEL : 91-80-8460060
FAX: 91-80-8461240

INDONESIA
P.T. ROMINDO PRIMAVETCOM
Dr. Lukas, Dr. Saharjo
No. 266
Jakarta 12870
TEL: 62-21-830-0300
FAX: 62-21-828-0678

IRAN
DAROU GOSTAR CO.
H. Morakabi
No. 66 Pardis Street, Shiraz Square
Vanak Avenue, Tehran 19916
TEL: 98-21-804-6163
FAX: 98-21-803-2017

IRELAND
ALLTECH IRELAND
Aidan Brophy
Sarney, Summerhill Road
Dunboyne, County Meath
TEL: 353-1-825-2244
FAX: 353-1-825-2251

ISRAEL
LUXEMBOURG PHARMACEUTICALS,
LTD.
Zvi Kaufman
P.O. Box 13, Tel Aviv 61000
TEL: 972-3-5107373
FAX: 972-3-5100882

ITALY
ASCOR CHIMICI, S.R.L.
Arnaldo Valentini
Via Piana, 265
47032 Capocolle (FO)
TEL: 39-0543-462411
FAX: 39-5043-448644

JAMAICA, W.I.
WINCORP
Leon Headley
38-39 Caracas Avenue,
Kingston Free Zone
TEL: 809-923-6880   FAX: 809-923-6856

JAPAN
BUSSAN BIOTECH CO., LTD.
Nick Koyama
3rd Fl, Shiba Daimon, Makita Bldg 5-8, 2-
Chome Shiba Daimon
Minato-Ku, Tokyo
TEL: 81 3 5470 6601
FAX: 81 3 5470 6606

KENYA
ALLTECH EASTERN AFRICA, Ltd.
Tarnya Fasol
Office 2A UNIDO Office Suite, New
Rehema Hse. Rhapta Rd.,
Westlands, Nairobi
TEL/FAX: 254-2-449-082

LEBANON
YOUSEF FREIHA & SONS
Ralph Freiha
P.O. Box 90261 Sed El Bouchrieh,
Industrial City, Freiha Bldg.,
Beirut
TEL: 961-1-499721   FAX: 961-1-497171

MALAYSIA
DIETHELM MALAYSIA SDN.BHD.
Kwang Say Yoon
74, Jalan University, 46200 Petaling Jaya,
Selangor Darul Ehsan
TEL: 603 755 2322   FAX: 603 756 5253

MEXICO
ALLTECH DE MEXICO, S.A. DE C.V.
Gladys Hoyos
Dr. Enrique Gonzalez Martinez No. 244,
Col. Sta. Maria La Ribera C.P. 06400
TEL: 52-5-547-5040 (to 44)
FAX: 52-5-547-2443

NETHERLANDS
ALLTECH NETHERLANDS
Gerdien Schuerink
Hollandsch Diep 63
2904 EP Capelle aan den IJssel
TEL:31-10-450-1038
FAX:31-10-442-3798

NEW ZEALAND
CUNDY TECHNICAL SERVICES
Mike E. Cundy
5 Seibel Road, RD1
Henderson, Auckland 8
TEL:64-9-837-3243   FAX:64-9-837-3214

PERU
ALLTECH PERU
Ricardo Sahagun, Ing.
Calle Mario Valdivia # 180
San Miguel, Lima 32, Perú
TEL: 51-1578-0003
TEL/FAX: 51-1578-2131

PHILIPPINES
ALLTECH PHILIPPINES
John Harvey
Room 301, Lalaine Bldg.,
#469 Real St., Alabang-Zapote Rd., 1750
Almanza, Las Piñas, Metro Manila
TEL: 63-2-800-9153
FAX: 63-2-800-9145

FERMENTATION INDUSTRIES CORP.
Rodney Vincent Choa Yu
Suite 1305 Far East, Bank Bldg., 550
Quintin Parades St., Binondo, Manila
TEL: 63-2-241-0846
TEL/FAX: 63-2-241-0870

POLAND
POLMARCHÉ
Wojciech Zalewski, Ph.D
ul. Szczesliwicka 29/31
02-353 Warszawa
TEL/FAX: 48-22-722-9950

PORTUGAL
ALLTECH PORTUGAL
Jorge Cardoso
Rúa Pedro Alvares Cabral 5, R/c/Leceia,
2745 Barcarena
TEL: 351-1-422-7053
FAX: 351-1-421-8100

ROMANIA
ALLTECH ROMANIA
Liviu Panta, Ph.D
Sos Panduri 25
BI P3A et. 1. , Sector 5, Ap. 5
762291 Bucuresti
TEL/FAX: 401-410-4779

RUSSIA
ALLTECH RUSSIA
Ul. Novaya Basmannaya, 12
Office 111
107078 Moscow
TEL: 7-095-265-1645
FAX: 7-095-265-4576

SAUDI ARABIA
ARASCO
A. Al-Rubaian
P.O. Box 53845
Riyadh 11593
TEL: 966-1-4191933
FAX: 966-1-419-1520

SLOVAKIA
ALLTECH SK, s.r.o.
Rastislav Bobcek, Ing.
J. Mrvu 28
949 01 Nitra
TEL: 421-87-519-358
FAX: 421-87-517-209

SOUTH AFRICA
ALLTECH BIOTECHNOLOGY (AFRICA
& MIDDLE EAST)
Nick Smit
P.O. Box 2654, Somerset West 7129
TEL: 27-21-8517-052
FAX: 27-21-8517-000

SOUTH KOREA
ALLTECH KOREA
Myun-Soo Han, Ph.D
714 Hyundai Officetal
1589-8 Seocho Dong, Seoul, 137-070,
Seocho-Ku
TEL: 82-2-584-6203
FAX: 82-2-584-6202

YOONEE CHEMICAL CO., LTD
Jung Jooe Lee, D.V.M.
ILBok Bldg 2f.
1602-4, Seocho Dong
Seocho-Ku, Seoul 137-070
TEL: 82-2-585-1801
FAX: 82-2-521-1300

SPAIN
PROBASA
Juan Rosell Lizana
Argenters 9 Nave 3, Pol Ind Satiga, Sta.
Perpetua de la Mogoda,
Barcelona 08130
TEL: 34-93718-2215
FAX: 34-93719-1307

SWEDEN
VETPHARMA AB
Thord Bengtsson
Annedalsvägen 9
SE-227 64 LUND
TEL: 46-46-128100   FAX: 46-46-146555

SWITZERLAND
INTERFERM AG
Fritz Näf
Strangenstrasse 1a
CH-8304 Wallisellen
TEL: 41-1-839-1010
FAX: 41-1-839-1019

TAIWAN
Alltech Co. Ltd.
Sirpha Chuh-Hsiang Chen
6F-3, No. 181, Dah-Yoou Road
Taoyuan City, 330, Taiwan ROC
TEL: +886-3-331-5230
FAX: +886-3-338-6140

THAILAND
ALLTECH THAILAND
David Faulkner
2533 Sukhumvit Road, Bangchack
Prakhanong, Bangkok, 10250
TEL: 66-2-742-4545
FAX: 66-2-742-4547

DIETHELM TRADING CO. LTD.
2533 Sukhumvit Road, Bangchack
Prakhanong, Bangkok, 10250
TEL: 66-2-332-7140
FAX: 66-2-332-7166

TURKEY
ARES GIDA TARIM HAYVANCILIK SAN.
TIC. LTD. STI.
Rasit Kayira and Ufuk Talay
172 Sokak No. 19/7
Izeltas Galeria 2. Kisim, Isikkent, Izmir
TEL/FAX: 90-232-472-0649

UNITED KINGDOM
ALLTECH UK
Jem Clay
Alltech House, Ryhall Road
Stamford, Lincolnshire, PE0 1TZ
TEL: 44-1780-764512
FAX: 44-1780-764506

UNITED STATES OF AMERICA
ALLTECH, INC.
CORPORATE HEADQUARTERS
3031 Catnip Hill Pike
Nicholasville, Kentucky 40356
TEL: 1-606-885-9613
FAX: 1-606-885-6736

VENEZUELA
ALLTECH VENEZUELA
Jorge Arias
Urb. Industrial Terrazas de Castillito
Calle 98, Parcela No. L-138
Valencia, Edo. Carabobo
TEL/FAX: 58-41-717595 / 58-41-717305

VIETNAM
BAYER AGRITECH SAIGON
Ehler Borgs
1/3 Xom Moi Hamlet, Phuoc Long, Thu
Duc District, Ho Chi Minh City
TEL: 84-8-960127
FAX: 84-8-961-523

YUGOSLAVIA
ALLTECH YUGOSLAVIA
M. Vukic Vranjes
Somborska 57
Yu-21000 Novi Sad
TEL/FAX: 381-21-301-083

ZIMBABWE
S.A.F.C.O.
Bruce Grant
P.O. Box ST324
Southerton, Harare
TEL: 263-4-620486/7/8
FAX: 263-4-620558/669701